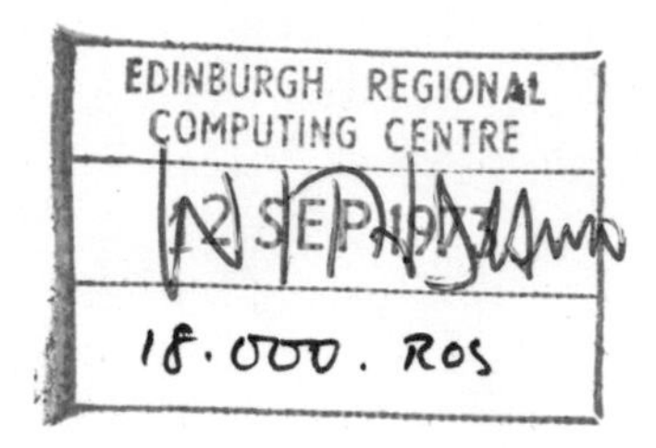
EDINBURGH REGIONAL
COMPUTING CENTRE
12 SEP 1973
18.000. ROS

EDINBURGH REGIONAL
TS7

NUMERICAL METHODS IN COMPUTER PROGRAMMING

IRWIN SERIES IN QUANTITATIVE ANALYSIS FOR BUSINESS

CONSULTING EDITOR

ROBERT B. FETTER *Yale University*

BOWMAN & FETTER *Analysis for Production Management* Revised Edition

BIERMAN, BONINI, FOURAKER, & JAEDICKE *Quantitative Analysis for Business Decisions* Revised Edition

MARTIN *Electronic Data Processing* Revised Edition

BASS, BUZZELL, GREENE, LAZER, PESSEMIER, SHAWVER, SHUCHMAN, THEODORE, & WILSON *Mathematical Models and Methods in Marketing*

MORRIS *Analysis for Materials Handling Management*

FRANK, KUEHN, & MASSY *Quantitative Techniques in Marketing Analysis: Text and Readings*

HOWELL & TEICHROEW *Mathematical Analysis for Business Decisions*

MORRIS *Management Science in Action*

BOWEN *Mathematics: With Applications in Management and Economics*

BERANEK *Analysis for Financial Decisions*

MCMILLAN & GONZALEZ *Systems Analysis: A Computer Approach to Decision Models*

THEODORE *Applied Mathematics: An Introduction: Mathematical Analysis for Management*

ELLIOTT & WASLEY *Business Information Processing Systems*

ROSENTHAL *Numerical Methods in Computer Programming*

NUMERICAL METHODS IN COMPUTER PROGRAMMING

by

MYRON R. ROSENTHAL
Illinois Institute of Technology
Chicago

1966 • RICHARD D. IRWIN, INC. • HOMEWOOD, ILLINOIS

First Printing, September, 1966

Printed in the United States of America

Library of Congress Catalog Card No. 6–24614

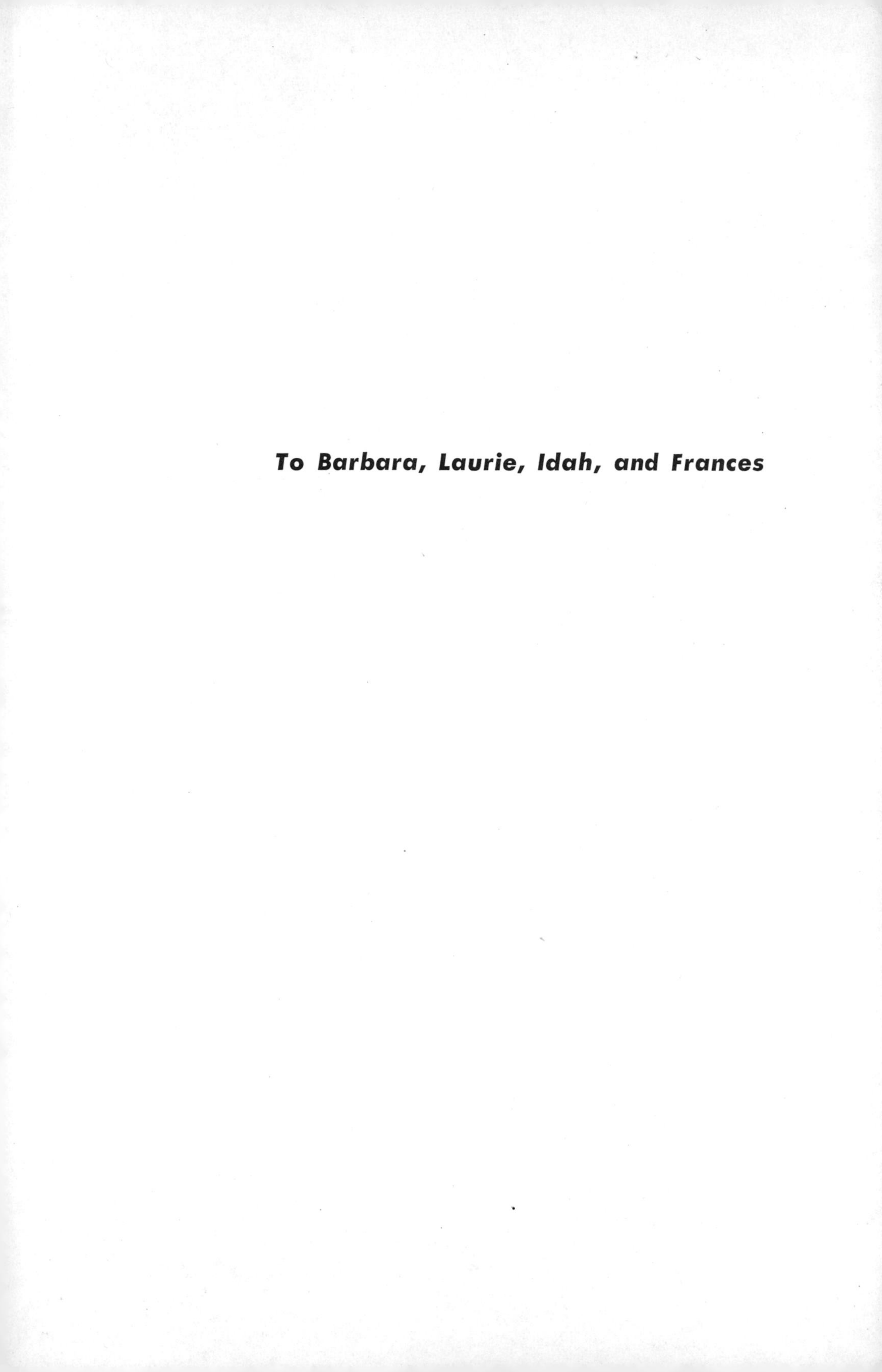

To Barbara, Laurie, Idah, and Frances

Acknowledgments

I am indebted to many of my students for their time in programming, typing, proofreading, and their general comments. It is not possible to mention all of them here, but the following were particularly helpful: Frank Oliva, Meyer Yasnoff, Walter Reising, Vernoy Johnson, and Edward Reingold.

In addition my thanks are due my colleagues at Illinois Institute of Technology for their comments on the material and scope of the manuscript. These include J. Kaplan, T. Church, S. Block, and W. Ryder. Above all, I wish to thank Dr. Haim Reingold, Chairman of the Department of Mathematics of I.I.T., for his encouragement.

I have found invaluable the many references which I have consulted in the process of writing this manuscript. These are listed in the footnotes as well as in the Table of References to credit the authors as well as to provide the reader with material to consult for further details or another view of his particular problem.

Lastly, I am indebted to my mother, Mrs. Idah Rosenthal, for doing most of the typing of the manuscript and to my wife for permitting so much of our spare time to be spent in the writing of this manuscript.

Myron R. Rosenthal

Chicago, Illinois
July, 1966

Table of Contents

Introduction

In this book the FORTRAN language is presented to the reader as a vehicle through which he can communicate with the computer. First, a basic version of the language (comprising most of which is known as FORTRAN II) available on most computers is presented along with many examples; then, the language is extended to FORTRAN IV and finally to FORMAC.

Our experience with classes of university and high school students has indicated that the greatest source of difficulty lies, not in teaching FORTRAN as a language, but in applying the FORTRAN language to problems. To help the reader make the transition from a knowledge of the language to its application, we take the approach of establishing a group of simple basic programs, which are then used as building blocks for more complicated programs. Many examples are offered which demonstrate that different mathematical or logical approaches may save a great deal of time on the computer.

For the presentation of numerical methods in this book, we assume that the reader has studied college algebra and possesses a slight knowledge of the calculus; actually, by today's standards, this amounts to only a good high school mathematics background. The book is designed for a one- or two-semester introductory course; it will profit the potential business major as much as the potential engineering or physics major because it is of such a basic nature. The work is concentrated in the area of approximate methods, iterative techniques, and other methods (including direct numerical methods) applied to the areas of determinants, matrices, statistics, and solution of equations.

Illinois Institute of Technology has conducted a program in numerical methods and FORTRAN programming through the mathematics department since 1960. For the first two years, one course was offered on the senior level; sophomores and juniors were allowed to register for the course upon the approval of their advisors. Since graduate students are allowed to take senior level courses for graduate credit, the course was also popular among these students. We envisioned this course as a prerequisite for a mathematics course covering some more advanced numerical methods and numerical analysis. However, we discovered the following problem: since the students were not introduced to the computer until their senior year, they had not taken enough mathematics courses of the applied nature, and therefore much time in the advanced course had to be spent teaching applied mathematics instead of studying ways to program the problems and handling the errors involved with these types of calculations.

For the 1964–65 academic year, the enthusiasm of the university administration toward computerized calculations was reflected in their establishing, in the mathematics department, a course in FORTRAN and numerical methods, required of all sophomore engineering students. The material covered in that course is the material offered in this book. The advantage in offering a course of this nature to freshmen and sophomores is threefold.

First—in order to program a computer, the student cannot afford to be haphazard in his presentation, because the computer will do exactly what it is told; an error due to a haphazard presentation is no different from an error due to faulty methods. In other words, the computer forces the student to express his thoughts in a precise way. A good presentation is important whether the student is studying engineering, business, or any other of many topics.

Second—for those students who have a proficiency in computer methods, this early exposure will allow them to concentrate on courses as undergraduates which will prepare them for advanced study in numerical methods.

Third—for those students who intend to use computers as a way to speed tedious calculations so that they may concentrate on other more enlightening facets of either the physical sciences, biological sciences, or business, an early exposure to introductory numerical methods will demonstrate where and in what way the computer can be of benefit to them.

Further, even if the student never uses the computer again, it will be of value to him to become acquainted with the computer terminology and applications, since these terms are beginning to appear more and more frequently in all areas of society. Although the use of the computer and associated numerical and nonnumerical techniques have made progress in industry and colleges, this progress would have been much more rapid if more people understood how to communicate with computers and how to use them to the greatest advantage. Even today, many people have a misconception of the role of the computer in industry and elsewhere. The following statement, which appeared in a national magazine,[1] reflects the attitude of some management people and scientists who have not been directly involved with computers:

> A programmer is a person who passes as an exacting expert on the basis of being able to turn out, after innumerable computer operations, an infinite series of incomprehensible answers, calculated with micrometric precision from vague assumptions, based on debatable figures taken from inconclusive documents, and carried out on instruments of problematical accuracy by persons of dubious reliability and questionable mentality for the avowed purpose of annoying and confounding a hopelessly defenseless operating organization.

An attitude of this nature can be attributed to the lack of education on the part of the individual or to an experience with a poor programmer or both. In any case, we can immediately lay to rest the part of the above statement referring to "instruments of problematical accuracy," because the accuracy of digital computers is sufficient for most problems; the possibility of actual internal errors in the computer is negligible.

---

[1] *Datamation.*

1. Basic Ideas of FORTRAN

1.1. Development of Digital Computers

1.1.1. The Early Days—Reasons for Computer Development

Development of weapons systems, strategic planning, logistics, and other problems basic to troop activities during World War II, as well as scientific developments related to the war (such as development of atomic energy), emphasized the need for high-speed computational equipment. Many of the problems arising in these areas could not be solved through manual computations or the electromechanical-type computing machines available at this time.

Experimentation on high-speed computing devices began in the early 1940's. The first computer of the time was developed at Harvard University, with the aid of related developments at the Bell Telephone Laboratories. This computer, called MARK I, was operational in early 1944. Information was transferred internally through a series of relays. Relative time for operations was in tenths of a second; for example, the time to add two numbers was about 0.2 to 0.5 second. At this speed, only a very small portion of the average scientific problems could be solved by the computer.

1.1.2. Limitations

In addition to its failure to meet the need for higher internal operating speeds, the MARK I was limited in the following areas:

1. The instructions to the computer were either wired directly into the computer or could be wired on a board external to the computer, which would be at-

tached to the computer in order to solve the problem. All possible changes in the program were necessarily wired into the board; it was not possible to make changes in the instructions based on parameters or calculations as the computer progressed toward solution of the problem. Due to the time required to wire the boards, a great deal of effort was necessary to solve even the simplest problems. Any change in the program based on prior calculations required a rewiring of the board, thus demanding additional time on the part of the analyst.

2. Limited internal storage capacity; this included the number of instructions which were wired into the program board and storage for data.

1.2. The Computer Evolution

1.2.1. Electronic Circuitry

The first major breakthrough which enabled engineers to improve the internal speeds of the computer was the introduction of electronic tubes instead of electromechanical relays for the computer circuitry. Electronic tubes were introduced to the computer field in the ENIAC, a computer completed in 1945 at the University of Pennsylvania. The ENIAC made available internal speeds of up to 1,000 times the speed of the MARK I.

1.2.2. The Stored-Program Concept

A second major breakthrough occurred in 1946; John von Neumann and Herman Goldstine proposed that the instructions to the computer, as well as the data, be stored internally by the machine instead of being wired into a board attached to the computer. The greatest advantage of storing the instructions internally is that it enables the analyst to write instructions which allow the computer to modify other instructions based upon intermediate results or parameters. Now, it became unnecessary for the analyst to change wires in the middle of the program; therefore, the overall computing speed was increased by the innovation of the stored-program (group of instructions which give the computer the steps necessary for the solution of the problem) concept.

Two additional advantages of the stored-program concept were:

1. Reduction of internal storage space needed for solution of a given problem because of the ability to use the computer to modify instructions.
2. Reduction of the analyst's time to write a given program because it is inherently less time consuming and many times easier to write a single program to solve a problem than to write several smaller programs.

From 1946 to the present, the internal speed of computers has again been increased more than 1,000 times, through better circuit design and the introduction of the transistor. These electronic developments not only have increased internal computing speeds but also have greatly reduced the size of computers and the cost per unit of computing ability. Reduction in size and increase in speed has led to greatly increased size of internal computer storage; storage capacity has been increased about 100,000 times over that available in the MARK I.

1.3. Scientific and Data Processing Problems

For the solution of scientific problems, the major factor is internal computing speed; scientific problems are characterized by little data (in relation to work necessary to compute the answer) and very little output. However, for solving data processing problems, the major factor is the speed with which the computer can handle the data and the results, because a great bulk of data characterizes such problems—for example, the processing of tax returns by the Internal Revenue Service.

As computers were developed for handling scientific problems in universities and industrial laboratories, data processing problems were assuming a greater magnitude. Commercial firms as well as the U.S. government began to look for help in the solution of data processing problems. By far the most popular early computer used to solve data processing problems was the IBM (International Business Machines) 650 computer, released to the public in the early 1950's. The IBM 650, and following computers which were designed with an eye toward data processing problems, required very fast input (methods to get data into the computer) and output (methods by which the results could be obtained from the computer); it is usually impossible, even with the computers of today, to have internal storage space for the data for large data processing problems.

The speed of input and output increased with the development of new electronic devices; therefore, the speed of data processing computers increased at about the same rate as the speed of scientific computers. We do not mean to infer that the only difference between data processing computers and scientific computers were the input-output devices. The entire representation of data and instructions were usually different in the two types of computers.

1.4. Economics—The Plight of the Analyst

Although the speed increased and cost per unit of computing capability decreased, mass use of computers to solve problems would not have taken place unless the time necessary to write the program was greatly reduced from the times required in the late 1940's and early 1950's. Today, it may appear to many people that our society could not function without electronic digital computers; however, as in the development of other items, economics determined the road for the computer manufacturers. One of the most significant costs was the time necessary to write the average program, whether it be a scientific program or a data processing program.

1.5. Computers and the Need for a Translator

1.5.1. The Computer Manufacturer and the Computer User

Imagine yourself as the manager of a company which designs, manufactures, and sells computers. In addition to building reliability into the computer, you must consider these points:

1. *Logic*—The machine should include enough instructions so that the knowledgeable user can take advantage of the computer to solve his problems.
2. *Programming ease*—Is there a great barrier between the language of the programmer (here, we refer to the English language) and the language understood by the computer?
3. *Internal storage space*—Does the computer have fast access to enough instructions and data so that the problem can be solved without taking the trouble of breaking the program into smaller parts.
4. *Economics of space*—Since the user must put the computer in his place of business, the more space the computer requires, the more costly for the user.
5. *Economics of money*—The price of the computer compared to its problem-solving ability should be competitive with that of other computers and allow a reasonable payout from reduction of costs.

Costs of renting the computer and costs of space to store the computer, considering the novelty of the item, were acceptable to the larger industrial firms in the early 1950's. We do not claim that the earliest computers justified their price through reductions in costs; but the computer was a prestige item. In addition to the rental fee, the total cost of operating computers included a staggering cost to the company of obtaining a useful program. Programming cost was affected by the following:

1. Difficulty of conversing with the computer in its own language. In order to keep the price and space at a feasible figure, the number of instructions was limited to those absolutely required to carry out the basic logic; also, to keep the amount of circuits at a minimum, numbers, to some base, were used to represent these basic instructions. For example, say there are less than 100 instructions; then the numbers 00 to 99 would require the interpretation of only two digits. The number 11 might represent the instruction, ADD some number to another number, or ADD some number to a temporary storage area where another instruction will be required to get the sum. Because the programmer is not used to talking in numbers, the use of the computer's language slows the process of writing the program.

The main difficulties, however, lie in the need for many instructions to perform most of the parts common to most programs. Basic tasks, such as preparation of a neat output for reports; ability to read the input data into the computer; choosing one set of instructions at one time and another set of instructions at some other time based on some conditions like the number of hours, the department, etc.; and the need for the common mathematical functions, sine, cosine, logarithm, tangent, exponential. In addition to these basic parts of most programs, there will, in all likelihood, be a need for groups of instructions (routines) to perform table look-up, search for certain items in a list, sort certain items, calculate the determinant of a matrix, and calculate the inverse of a matrix, to name just a few. The programmer encountered two large problems concerning the above routines. First, the programmer was required to write any of the above routines he needed for a program, since there were no routines available from other sources. In other words, the programmer was forced to write his own library of common routines. Second, even after the programmer had amassed a good number of routines, he found it difficult to use these routines in different places in different programs.

In addition to using numbers to represent instructions, writing his own routines, and devising a way to place these routines in a program, the programmer faced the problem of specifying the place in the computer where the computer could find the data and the instructions needed to execute the program and thus solve the problem. To simplify the circuitry of the computer, a numbering system is used to reference the storage area. For example, if there are 40,000 storage locations for instructions and data, a five-digit base 10 system could be used—the addresses being 00,000 to 39,999. The instructions to add the data at 10151 to the data at 30121 might take the form; 11 10151 30121. By conversing with the computer in its own language (machine language), the programmer must keep track of what data and instructions are located in what positions in the computer.

2. Lack of experienced programmers. At the time of the introduction of the first commercial computers, only a few people working at major universities had programming experience; these people could only be lured to industry for a very high price. The alternative to hiring experienced people was training the company's own people through experimentation with the computer. It is not clear from available statistics as to which of the two alternatives is more costly to industry.

3. The cost of not completing the job in the allotted time because of the difficulty inherent in programming and the use of inexperienced people.

Complaints from the computer users and potential computer users in regard to programming costs made it obvious to the computer manufactures that there was only one road to take in order to further the advance of computers on the commercial market. Computer manufacturers decided to develop a program which would utilize the computer to translate a program written in a programmer-oriented language into a program which would accomplish the same purpose, but in machine language. To do this, they decided to train their own employees, or, if necessary, to hire others in the programming field. A comparable situation would be the hiring of a translator to enable an American to speak in English and yet have his thoughts conveyed to a Russian who could speak only Russian.

The most successful translator to appear up to this date in the scientific area is FORTRAN (Formula Translator) developed by the International Business Machine Corporation. By successful we mean that the FORTRAN translator is used by more computer installations than any other language.

The popularity of the FORTRAN language has been enhanced by the fact that a FORTRAN program written for a smaller computer can immediately be run on a larger computer (compatible upwards); and with some modest modification, a program written in FORTRAN for a larger computer can be run on a smaller computer (in a somewhat less efficient manner). It is also true that almost any problem written in any other translating language can be written in FORTRAN.

Figure 1–1 shows symbolically the place of the FORTRAN translator program in the operations of placing a program on the computer. In computer terminology, the FORTRAN program is called a compiler instead of a translator because the FORTRAN program (hereafter the FORTRAN program will be referred to as the FORTRAN compiler) can produce more than one machine language instruction for every FORTRAN language instruction; a translator program is defined to be a program which produces one machine language instruction per source (instructions written in the programmer oriented language are called source instructions) language instruction. The compiled program in machine language is called the OBJECT program.

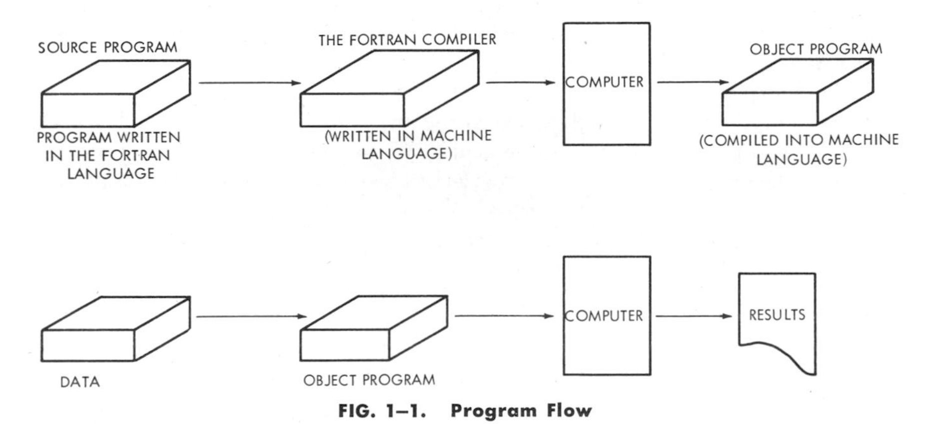

FIG. 1–1. Program Flow

The remainder of Chapter 1 and Chapter 2 through Chapter 4 will be devoted to the FORTRAN II language and the ways in which the use of the FORTRAN compiler simplifies computer programming; Chapter 5 will explain the differences between the FORTRAN II language and the FORTRAN IV language. We shall look at the internal design of the computer only in the instances where these considerations will be of help to the reader in understanding how and why the FORTRAN compiler operates in the stated manner.

1.5.2. Basic Concepts of FORTRAN as a Compiler

A computer, like a human mind, must have very fast reference to certain items if it is to operate efficiently and without a great deal of manual interference. If a person memorizes certain facts, he can recall these facts faster than if it were necessary for him to look for them in a reference book. The part of the computer which has fast recall to instructions and data is called the memory. One could imagine the memory of the computer to be a series of storage boxes, similar in some ways to the strong boxes in a bank vault. In a good-sized computer, there would be about 30,000 to 40,000 of these boxes. For the computer to reference these boxes, they must be numbered;

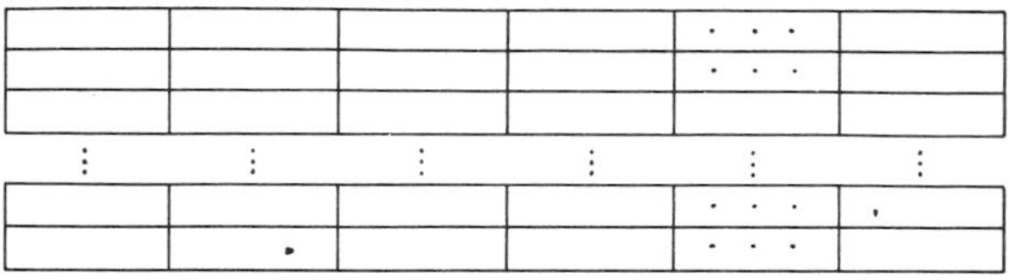

FIG. 1–2. Computer Memory

this number is then the address of the box or where it can be located in the memory.

The address of the storage location is comparable to the number on the strong box; the *contents* of the storage location are either instructions or data. The difference between the storage location and its contents cannot be too strongly emphasized. We will call the address either of the following: when the contents of the storage position is an instruction, the address will be called a statement number; if the contents of the storage location is a piece of data, then the storage location will be called a variable.

One system of addresses would be to start at 00000 and take successive integers until we get to 39999. Assuming this system is used, let us consider an example. Figure 1–3 shows the piece of data 367 in storage location

LOCATION 10151 — 367

LOCATION 21257 — 11

FIG. 1–3. Storage of Data and Instructions

10151 and the instruction word ADD in location 21257. (The instruction ADD would undoubtedly be coded into a number, such as 11. In addition to the coded instruction would be the addresses of the data to be added.) We call the data, or the contents of a location in the memory, a constant. Then, corresponding in certain respects to mathematical terminology, the storage location itself will be called a variable. With this picture of the memory, one can then understand why, not unlike mathematics, a variable can take on many values over a finite region. We will soon see that certain variables take on a range of values over the integers and other variables take on a range of values over the real numbers. To change the value of the variable, a new constant is moved into the location representing that variable; when the new constant comes into that location, the old constant is removed. By the same type of logic, a storage location for an instruction will be called a statement number (or an instruction number), and the contents of that location will be the instruction itself.

As one might imagine, it is difficult and time consuming to have to remember in which one of 40,000 locations a certain piece of data or a certain instruction is located. FORTRAN simplifies this by allowing the user to give the location (variable) a symbolic name which has significance to the user and therefore is easy to remember. FORTRAN goes one step further to simplify the work of programming the computer. Different computers may be designed differently in order to be able to perform certain tasks better than others. One result of this difference in internal design could be a different way of representing numbers in the computer. One computer might represent numbers to the base 2, another to the base 8 and yet another to the base 10. Since most people are more familiar with the base 10 system, it is easier for most people to work with this system. FORTRAN allows the user always to work in base 10 number system no matter what internal basing system the computer is designed for. It would be advantageous to be able to use integer numbers, such as, 1, -15, -327, 25, 2752, and 13121; and real numbers, such as, 21.157, -1.316×10^{-27}, 0.000375, and 31.15×10^{30}. Certain advantages lie in the use of integers as opposed to real numbers and vice versa. We will now explore these advantages and disadvantages as well as the method FORTRAN II uses to distinguish different types of variables as well as distinguishing variables from constants.

1.6. Constants, Integers, and Real Variables

1.6.1. Fixed-Point and Floating-Point Notation

An integer number is also called a fixed-point number in computer terminology because the decimal point is always assumed to be to the right of the number. That is, 627., 5782., and $-28.$, can all be regarded as integers because there is no fractional part; the decimal point is fixed at the right of the number.

Real numbers are also called floating-point numbers because the computer keeps track of the decimal point in the following way: assume that each storage cell in the memory of the computer can hold 10 decimal digits. Eight digits are used to express the number and the remaining two digits are used to keep track of the decimal point. The real number 25.267 might look like Figure 1–4 in the machine. In this exhibit, the programmer instructs the computer to assume that the decimal point lies immediately to the left of the most significant figure; i.e., $.25267000 \times 10^2$. An equally good assumption would be for the decimal point to be to the right of the number or in the middle of the number. When the decimal point is assumed to be at the left, the number is called a normalized floating-point number. The representation of a floating-point number is a good example of the way in which a programmer can direct the computer to do something for which there is no special circuit built into the computer. Since the computer recognizes only the digits 0 to 9 (here we are discussing a decimal computer; a binary computer recognizes only the digits 0 and 1) a decimal point is not a legal character; and even if the decimal point were a legal character, there are no circuits available for moving the decimal point or keeping track of the

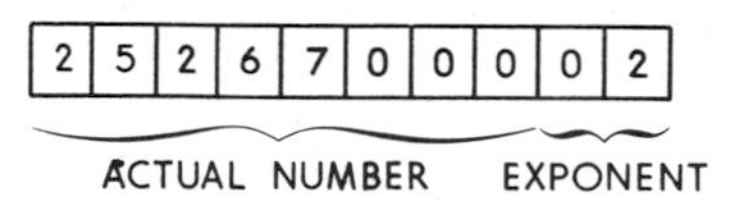

FIG. 1–4. Internal Representation of a Real Number

decimal point. Nevertheless, the people writing the FORTRAN compiler have devised a routine giving the computer a way to keep track of a decimal point, thus providing the programmer using the FORTRAN language the use of decimal numbers in the normal manner.

1.6.2. Advantages and Disadvantages of Floating-Point Numbers

One disadvantage of using floating-point numbers is that round-off error may occur even in addition and subtraction. Given that it is required to add the numbers 21,058 and $.056 \cdot 10^{-5}$. To exhibit a negative character-

FIG. 1–5. Floating-Point Numbers

istic or negative number, we put a dash over the low-order digit. Now, in order to add two floating-point numbers, the magnitude of their characteristics must be the same. Therefore, if we assume that the smaller number will be shifted so that its characteristic is also .05, it is apparent that the sum of the two numbers will be 21,058, because the addition is performed as shown in Figure 1–6. In the smaller number, one should notice that

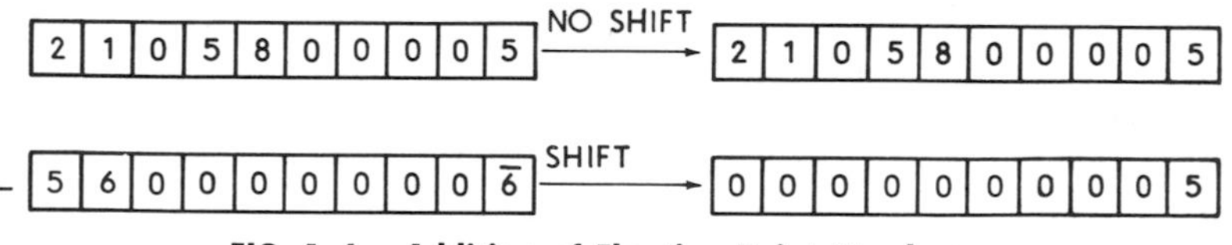

FIG. 1–6. Addition of Floating-Point Numbers

every time the characteristic is increased by 1, the number is moved one space to the right. Therefore, to move a -6 to $+5$ we need to move the numbers 5 and 6 over 11 spaces to the right. However, there are only eight spaces in the storage box, so the resulting number is zero. The crux of the above example lies in the fact that it is unwise to add numbers which have a great difference in magnitude because the number of spaces per storage box is some given number and does not vary with the problem. When multiplying two numbers, in either floating point or fixed point, the product may lose significance due to round-off error. For example, say each location has room for four digits (i.e., maximum of four significant figures); thus the product of the numbers 35.31 and 1.005 is 35.48655. Since each location has room for only four figures, some figures must be dropped. To round the number to four significant figures means to add the number 5 to the fifth most significant figure; if the result forces a carry, add 1 to the fourth most significant figure, but if the result does not force a carry, leave the fourth most significant figure alone. To multiply two normalized floating-point numbers, one multiplies the mantissas and adds the characteristics.

In commercial computer applications, such as banking, errors due to rounding numbers must be minimized; therefore, fixed-point arithmetic is used for these applications. Fixed-point arithmetic is feasible for commercial applications because of the few calculations per result inherent in these applications. For a limited number of calculations, the user can manually keep track of the decimal point. However, in the solution of most scientific problems on a computer, one must go through many routine calculations (i.e., addition, subtraction, multiplication, and division) before obtaining an answer; as the amount of calculations increase, the task of keeping track of the decimal point becomes very difficult. Therefore, floating-point arithmetic must be used for scientific applications. Of course, the user still must contend with round-off errors; this problem may cause the programmer to write many extra instructions to control the error (more will be said about round-off errors in the chapters on numerical methods.)

1.6.3. FORTRAN Notation for Fixed- and Floating-Point Variables

FORTRAN enables the programmer to give mnemonic names with a meaning for the particular problem to the storage locations of the memory of the computer; this feature eliminates the need of memorizing many numbers or having to spend a great deal of time referring to a list of numbers every time the programmer wishes to specify a memory location.

A variable (to remind the reader, variable and storage location are synonymous in FORTRAN programming) which may contain fixed-point constants can be given a name with 1 to 6 alphameric characters (an alphameric character is either a number from 0 to 9 or a letter from A to Z), the first character of which must be one of the six letters I, J, K, L, M, or N. The following are examples of fixed-point variables:

JOBNO1, KI, IPRES1, MANNO3, N5

A variable which may take on different floating-point constant values can be given a name with 1 to 6 alphameric characters, the first character of which must be a letter other than I, J, K, L, M, or N. The following are examples of floating-point variables:

X1, VELCTY, STEAM, Y, and XSQRE

1.7. Vector Notation and Subscripted Variables

Students of physics and engineering should be familiar with the representation of the magnitude and direction of force as a vector quantity. However, the representation of variables as vector quantities is not limited to the physical sciences. One might think of sales as a vector quantity in the study of business; i.e., sales certainly has direction and magnitude.

1.7.1. Vector Notation

If we assume that the tail of the vector starts at the origin of the space of two dimensions, then the head of the vector would represent a unique point. This has a component in the X_1 direction and a component in the X_2 direction:

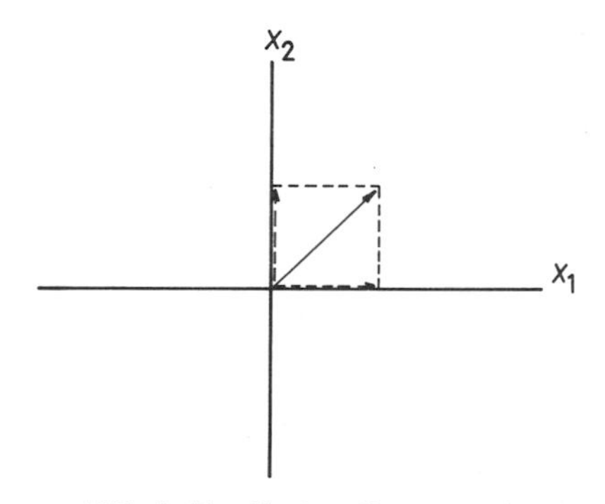

FIG. 1–7. Vector Components

A convenient way to express the location of this point is to give the number of units in both the X_1 and X_2 directions by the following couple (X_1, X_2). Although it is not possible to graphically express a point in more than three dimensions, it will be advantageous for us to extend the above notation to n-dimensional space by the following n-tuple $(X_1, X_2, \ldots .X_n)$. Vector notation will be used in both mathematical and business examples in later chapters.

1.7.2. Subscripted Variables

Previously it has been pointed out that FORTRAN simplifies programming by allowing the programmer to use mnemonic names by variables. Now by breaking variables into major classes, the programmer's task of memorizing names is further reduced by vector notation. Let us say that a certain sales analysis program makes it necessary to have one memory location for each salesman. Instead of giving the salesmen variable names such as, MAN1, MAN2, ... , MAN10, the programmer can give the class of salesmen the name MAN and then use a subscript to refer to the specific salesman. The subscript gives the location in the array; for the array called MAN.

Unsubscripted Variable Name		*Array Name*	*Location in Array*	*Subscripted Variable Name*
MAN1	▭	MAN	1	MAN (1)
MAN2	▭	. . .	2	MAN (2)
MAN3	▭	. . .	3	MAN (3)
MAN4	▭	. . .	4	MAN (4)
.	.		.	.
.	.		.	.
.	.		.	.
MAN10	▭	. . .	10	MAN (10)

FIG. 1–8. Locations as Unsubscripted and Subscripted Variables

Of course, 10 locations are needed for the subscripted variable, MAN.

To reference any storage location in an array, the programmer could write the subscript as a *variable;* the value the variable takes on at any time gives the location in the array at that time. In the above array, MAN, with variable subscript I (MAN(I)), a reference is made to the fourth location in the array, MAN, when I takes on the value 4. If the subscript I is allowed to vary from 1 to 10, we could refer to any salesman from 1 to 10 as MAN(I); this type of variable is called a subscripted variable. In other words, the variable I acts as a pointer. A subscript of the form 4.2, 6.85, or 3.281 would have no meaning since there is no 4.2 position, or no 6.85 position, or no 3.281 position; the locations in the array must be indexed or subscripted by the integers (fixed-point numbers) to have any validity. Rules concerning the nature of the subscript will be given in the next few pages.

The above nomenclature concerning subscripted variables and variable subscripts may be confusing to the reader. The array MAN consists of 10 locations; each location is a subscripted variable which may be written in either of the following forms:

A	*B*
MAN (1)	MAN (I)
MAN (2)	
.	
.	
.	
MAN (10)	

FIG. 1–9. Two Ways to Write Subscripted Variables

Each of the locations in Figure 1–9*A* or the locations MAN(I) in Figure 1–9*A* are subscripted variables. However, the subscript specifying the locations in Figure 1–9*B* are the constants, 1,2,3, . . . , 10, while the subscript specifying the location in Figure 1–9*B* is the variable I. I may therefore be called a variable subscript, meaning that a location in the computer, known as I to the FORTRAN compiler, may contain the constants 1,2,3, . . ,10.

1.7.3. Subscripted Variables—Two Dimensions

The types of subscripted variables discussed in the above paragraphs are called one-dimensional subscripted variables because one subscript can uniquely specify a point in one-dimensional space but not in a space of higher dimensions, as can be seen from the following diagrams.

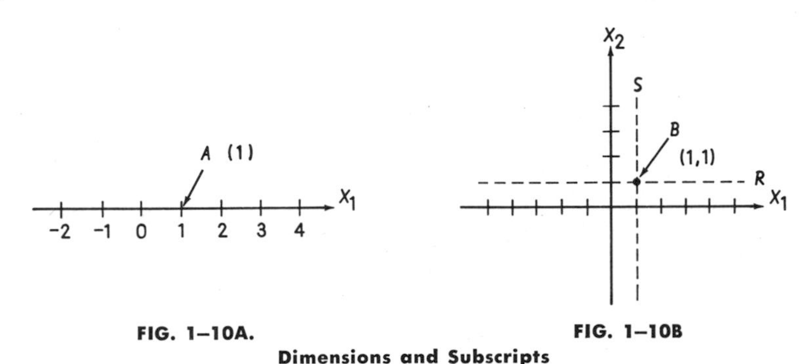

FIG. 1–10A. **FIG. 1–10B**
Dimensions and Subscripts

In Figure 1–10A, the point A can be uniquely specified by one number, i.e. the number 1, which is the index of the line X_1. However, in Figure 1–10B the point B cannot be uniquely specified by a single number, because it lies on both the lines R and S. To specify the location of the point B, we therefore must give its location on both lines. This example illustrates the need for two-dimensional subscripted variables requiring the couple of indices (I, J). A more practical example would be the two-dimensional array shown in Figure 1–11.

		Jan.	Feb.	Mar.	Apr.	MONTH . . .	Nov.	Dec.
	1							
	2							
MAN	3							
	. . .							
	200							

FIG. 1–11. Each box has the hours worked in that month for a particular man.

To locate the hours worked in March for man number 4, one might use the subscripted variable MAN(4,3), where the first subscript identifies the man and the second subscript identifies the month. In general, we could write the following array having m rows and n columns in the following way:

$$\begin{matrix} a_{11} & a_{12} & a_{13} & \cdot & \cdot & \cdot & \cdot & a_{1n} \\ a_{21} & a_{22} & a_{23} & \cdot & \cdot & \cdot & \cdot & a_{2n} \\ \cdot & \cdot & \cdot & \cdot & \cdot & \cdot & \cdot & \cdot \\ \cdot & \cdot & \cdot & \cdot & \cdot & \cdot & \cdot & \cdot \\ \cdot & \cdot & \cdot & \cdot & \cdot & \cdot & \cdot & \cdot \\ a_{m1} & a_{m2} & a_{m3} & \cdot & \cdot & \cdot & \cdot & a_{mn} \end{matrix}$$

The first subscript identifies the row and the second subscript identifies the column.

In addition to the notational advantages already mentioned, the ability to use subscripted variables also enables the programmer to write shorter programs, because he can make better use of each instruction. An instruction containing MAN(I) can be used to operate on MAN(1), MAN(2), . . . , MAN(10), as I varies from 1 to 10. A detailed discussion on multiple use of an instruction is contained in the section on control statements.

1.7.4. Subscripted Variables—Rules

Like every language, FORTRAN has rules governing the use of such basic components as constants and variables. We have already mentioned the rules on naming constants and variables. The forming of subscripted variables must adhere to these rules.

1. For FORTRAN II one cannot use a variable with more than three subscripts (i.e., no four-dimensional subscripted variables are allowed).
2. The subscripts must be put in parenthesis following the name of the variable. For example, the subscripted variable X(I). X is the variable and I is the subscript.
3. If two subscripts are used, they must be separated by a comma. For example, the subscripted variable Z(J,K).
4. The subscripts must be one of the following types:

	Example
a) A fixed-point variable	I
b) A fixed-point constant	2
c) A fixed-point variable plus a fixed-point constant	I+2
d) A fixed-point variable minus a fixed-point constant	I−2
e) A fixed-point constant multiplied by a fixed-point variable (in FORTRAN an asterisk represents the operator which carries out multiplication.)	2*I
f) A fixed-point constant multiplied by a fixed-point variable plus or minus another fixed-point constant	2*I+3 or 2*I−3

A common mistake for beginning student of FORTRAN is to use the same variable in both its unsubscripted and its subscripted form; i.e., one might try to have variables X and X(I). A storage location is assigned to the subscripted variable X(1), X(2), ... ,X(N), i.e., as I varies from 1 to N. Since no two locations may have the same variable name (this is similar to having two strong boxes with the same number; to avoid such a chaotic situation, the numbering of the vaults must be unique), there can be no meaning for both unsubscripted and subscripted versions of the same variable in the same program.

The reader should beware of another detail at this stage. Since the integer subscripts begin at 1 in FORTRAN, the use of the subscript zero is a source of error. In the memory of the computer, the storage locations allocated to a subscripted variable may be viewed as shown in Figure 1–12. The location

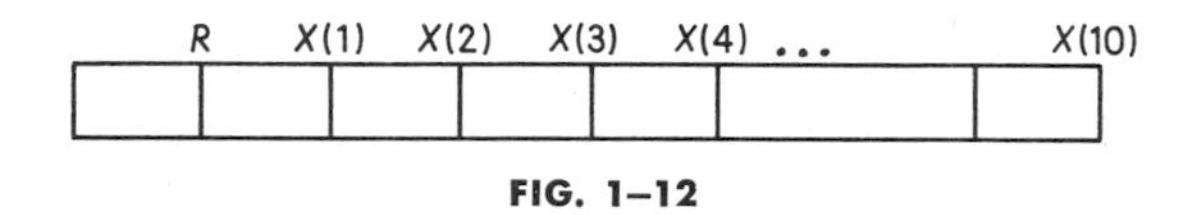

FIG. 1–12

with symbolic name R has already been allocated by the FORTRAN compiler. X(1), the first location of 10 locations in the X array, is then allocated the first location following R. Now if the programmer uses the fixed-point variable I as a subscript and either by mistake or by intent I takes on the value 0, the subscripted variable X(0) would then reference the location preceeding X(1), which is location R. No errors would be signaled by the FORTRAN compiler, but it is possible that the answer will be wrong. Instead of using a variable subscript, the programmer might use the fixed-point constant 0 as a subscript. In this instance, a message pointing out the error would be given to the programmer at compile time. In the first case, the FORTRAN compiler cannot know at compile time what values the variable I will receive; therefore, no message will be printed out. In the second case, the FORTRAN compiler will examine the subscript, and upon finding a zero subscript, a message will be typed out at compile time. Of course, if the reader follows the same line of reasoning as above, the reader can rule out negative subscripts.

1.8. Expressions

The next step in constructing the grammar of the FORTRAN language is the use of the basic elements, i.e., combining the constants and the variables to form arithmetic expressions. One can see some similarity in this construction and the formation of phrases in the English language from nouns, verbs, adjectives, adverbs, etc.

The purpose of the arithmetic expression is to perform some arithmetic operations. To this end, the following arithmetic operators are used to combine constants and variables:

Level 1	**	Exponentiation		
Level 2	*	Multiplication;	/	Division
Level 3	+	Addition ;	−	Subtraction

1.8.1. Evaluation of Arithmetic Expressions—Rules

To give a unique meaning to each arithmetic expression, it is necessary to establish two rules governing the evaluation of an arithmetic expression. The first is that preference is given to exponentiation (i.e., if the exponential operator appears in an expression, it is evaluated first—in other words, it is on the first or highest level of preference), then to either multiplication or division, and finally to addition or subtraction.

The second rule states that all arithmetic expressions should be evaluated from the left to the right. The following examples illustrate the use of the above two rules in evaluating arithmetic expressions:

1.8.2. Evaluations of Arithmetic Expressions—Examples

R*S/T**F+A*B**Z

How FORTRAN evaluates the above expression—

Step 1	T^F	T raised to the F power
Step 2	B^Z	B raised to the Z power
Step 3	$R \cdot S$	The product of R and S is formed
Step 4	$(R \cdot S)/T^F$	The above product is divided by T to the F power
Step 5	$A \cdot B^Z$	The product of A and B to the power Z is formed
Step 6		Form the total expression by taking the sum of $(R \cdot S)/T^F$ and $A \cdot B^Z$

Even if one adheres to the two rules, it is possible for an expression to have a meaning different from the desired meaning. For example, if the programmer wishes to multiply A by B, and divide this product by the product of C multiplied by D, the programmer must use parenthesis. The correct FORTRAN expression is A*B/(C*D).

The evaluation of the above expression will take place in this way:

1. A is multiplied by B.
2. The product of A and B is divided by something; to illustrate the way FORTRAN interprets the parenthesis we present the following paragraph in a manner displaying FORTRAN as a person able to speak.

   "The division operator implies that the product of A and B should be divided by something; but, the left parenthesis implies that all operations within the parenthesis must be performed before the division operation is allowed to take place."

   In other words, there exists a separate expression within the parenthesis

which must be performed before the division takes place. Therefore, the next step is to take the product of C and D.
3. Divide the product of A and B by the product of C and D.

If the parenthesis were not placed around the expression C*D, the result could be described as the product of A, B, and D, the quantity divided by C. The steps involved in evaluation of the expression A*B/C*D:

1. Form the product of A and B.
2. Divide this product by C.
3. Multiply the entire quantity by D.

Another example which illustrates the need for parenthesis is A**B**C. If the programmer desires the result to be A raised to the B power, the quantity raised to the C power, he should write (A**B)**C. If the programmer desires the result to be A raised to the power B^C, he should write A**(B**C).

These two quantities are obviously not the same. The first can be expressed as $A^{B \cdot C}$, while the second is A^{B^C}.

Besides the two rules regarding the way an expression is evaluated there are other rules which were established by the designers of the FORTRAN language to avoid confusion and to enable the computer to run the program in a shorter time.

1.8.3. Detailed Rules

Rules regarding the writing of arithmetic expressions:

1. There must be the same number of right and left parenthesis; this is obvious.

2. The mode of an expression must be either fixed point or floating point but not both. For instance, the expression (A*D) /2 is illegal because A and D are floating-point variables but 2 is a fixed-point constant. By placing a decimal point after the 2, we would correct this expression. Another example of an expression which is mixed mode would be I+J−A**2. There is one exception to the rule of mixed mode expressions. A floating-point variable or constant may be raised to either a fixed- or a floating-point power. Therefore, the expression A*B**2 is a valid one. However, a fixed-point variable or constant cannot be raised to a floating-point power. At this point, we mention that A**2 is evaluated as $A \cdot A$; but, A**2. is evaluated as $e^{2 \log A}$. The availability of these two different methods gives the programmer the flexibility needed to write an efficient program. Up to a certain power, it is quicker for the machine to multiply than to take logs. After that point, the opposite is true. Also, if the variable takes on a negative value, the computer will type out an error message if the logarithm method is used, since a negative number raised to a power is not defined for real numbers. We will say more in later chapters about efficiency in the writing of programs.

3. No two operators may appear successively without interruption by a variable or constant or parenthesis. The expression $A+-B$ is invalid; but the expression $A+(-B)$ is valid. One should note that the use of parenthesis cannot give the

wrong result; however, if they are not needed, their appearance forces the waste of computer time, since the parenthesis must be interpreted by the computer.

1.9. The Arithmetic Statement

Computers are programmed to solve problems by reading data and making calculations on that data leading to intermediate values, which are then used as the basis for further calculations—leading eventually, we hope, to an answer, which is then displayed on some output media. To store intermediate values as well as to perform arithmetic operations, the FORTRAN language contains the arithmetic statement. Like other FORTRAN statements to be covered in the following chapters, the arithmetic statement is an instruction to the computer to perform some operation; namely, to use an arithmetic expression to calculate some results using constants available in the computer at the time of execution of the statement and to store these results in some location in the memory.

1.9.1. The Arithmetic Statement—Basic Operations and Examples

The form of the arithmetic statement is

$$\left\{\begin{matrix}\text{Variable} \\ \text{or} \\ \text{subscripted} \\ \text{variable*}\end{matrix}\right\} = \left\{\begin{matrix}\text{Arithmetic expression} \\ \text{or} \\ \text{FORTRAN function}\dagger \\ \text{or both}\end{matrix}\right\}$$

*(The variable may be either of fixed-point or floating-point mode).
†FORTRAN functions will be discussed in Chapter 4.

The rules established for the subscripts and arithmetic expressions still hold in the formation of arithmetic statements. The arithmetic statement is translated by the FORTRAN compiler into a series of instructions; namely:

1. Find the mathematical value of the arithmetic expression on the right-hand side of the equal operator.
2. Take that calculated value and place it into the location specified by the variable or subscripted variable name on the left-hand side of the equal operator—the value which previously occupied that location is lost.

For example, $X = 2.5 + 3.6$

The computer takes the sum of 2.5 and 3.6, i.e., 6.1, and places this value in the location called X. If the value in location X before the execution of the above statement was −21.635, it is lost. In other words, the equal operator is a signal to the FORTRAN compiler to cause the computer to move the result of the calculation on the right side to the storage location specified by the variable on the left-hand side.

A few additional examples are now presented to illustrate the use of arithmetic statements:

Y(2)=X+2.*Z**2

The value in Z is squared, multiplied by 2, and added to X. Then this result is placed in the second position of the one-dimensional array Y; the previous value of the variable Y(2) is destroyed in the process. It should be pointed out that the values in storage locations X and Z are the same as they were before the statement was executed by the computer.

X=X+1

The value in location X is now one greater than it was before the execution of the statement. One might say the new value of X is equal to the old value of X plus 1. In this case, the value of the variable appearing on the right-hand side before the execution of the statement is changed, because the same variable also appears on the left-hand side of the statement.

K=X; Y=L

These examples illustrate the way in which to instruct the computer to give the fixed-point equivalent of a floating-point constant and vice versa. In the first of the above two examples, the floating-point constant in location X is transferred to location K; in the process the decimal part of the floating-point constant is lost. The process of cutting off the decimal part of a number is called truncation. The floating-point constant in location X remains unchanged. If the floating-point constant is 2.72, the constant placed in K is the fixed-point number 2; i.e., the decimal part has been truncated.

Assume, in the second case, that the fixed-point constant 25 is in location L, then the floating-point constant 25.0 is placed in location Y. Remember that the length of fixed point variables may be different than that of a floating-point variable (see Section 1:2):

Z=K/L+2

The fixed-point expression on the right side of the equal operator is first evaluated by the methods of fixed-point arithmetic and then the result is converted to a floating-point number and placed in location Z. If the constant in K is 7 and the constant in L is 2, the division operation, 7/2, gives a result of 3.5, which is then truncated to 3, because the division operation was performed on fixed-point numbers. The final result is 5, and this fixed-point number is placed in location Z as the floating-point number 5.0.

The above examples have demonstrated a very important use of the arithmetic statement—the execution of this arithmetic statement at run time. However, the use of the arithmetic statement by the FORTRAN compiler at *compile time* cannot be overemphasized. According to the theme established earlier in this chapter, the author feels that a knowledge of the techniques used by the FORTRAN compiler to set up the object program (remember, the object program is the translated program) is essential to people wishing to write programs in the FORTRAN language; therefore, the next few paragraphs will be devoted to the use of the arithmetic statement by the FORTRAN compiler at compile time.

1.9.2. The Use of the Arithmetic Statement for Reservation of Storage Space and Definition

The FORTRAN compiler must set aside locations and create a correspondence between the machine addresses of these locations and the symbolic variable name given to the location by the programmer. One method which the FORTRAN compiler uses to reserve a location for a symbolic variable's name is for that variable's name to appear on the left side of an arithmetic statement; upon its first appearence on the left side of an arithmetic statement, the variable is given a location in the memory.

In addition to reserving space for variables, the FORTRAN compiler contains certain routines (a group of instructions) which attempt to prevent the programmer from making errors; one such routine is written to prevent the programmer from taking a constant value from a storage location and using it in a calculation without placing a value in that location at a prior time in the program. For example, the programmer writes the statement:

$$R = X + Y \tag{1-1}$$

suppose the variable X has not appeared earlier in the program, but later appears in many statements, one of which might be:

$$X = Z ** 2.2 + S * 3.1 \tag{1-2}$$

Two separate cases can be considered; first, let us say that the present run on the computer is the first run of the program on the machine at this time. The appearance of X on the right-hand side of statement (1–1) leads one to believe that the programmer assumes storage location X to have a zero value since he has not attempted to place a value in X, either through its prior appearance on the left-hand side of an arithmetic statement, via an input statement, or by some other means. The assumption of a zero value for location X is not a good one; the operator may not have cleared the machine before entering the program or the FORTRAN compiler may have left some result in that area. In the second case, the program may be used to solve the problem for one set of data after another on a continual basis. After the problem has been solved for the first set of data, there is a nonzero value in location X due to the execution of statement (1–2). To avoid the possibility of the above error, the FORTRAN compiler will not allow the programmer to use a variable (whether it be on the right-hand side of an arithmetic statement, as a subscript or some other use) before the FORTRAN compiler becomes satisfied that the variable can take on a value. When the FORTRAN compiler becomes satisfied that the variable can take on a value, we say that the variable has been defined. The FORTRAN compiler uses the first appearance of a non-subscripted variable (single storage location) on the left-hand side of an arithmetic statement to both reserve the storage location and to define that variable. If the variable appears in other places in the program before it is defined, a message will be typed out under the instructions of the FORTRAN compiler; "Variable ______ in statement ______ has not been defined."

The tasks of the reservation of storage space and definition for the case of subscripted variables cannot be handled by the FORTRAN compiler in the same way as the nonsubscripted variables. Assume that the first appearance of the variable $X(3)$ on the left-hand side of an arithmetic statement takes place in the statement

$$X(3) = R + S + T \tag{1-3}$$

later in the program the first appearance of $X(1)$ is

$$X(1) = Z - 2.5 \tag{1-4}$$

still later on $X(6)$, $X(4)$, and $X(10)$ may appear as

$$\mathrm{X}(6) = \mathrm{X}(3) + 8.25 * \mathrm{Y} ** 2 \tag{1-5}$$
$$\mathrm{X}(4) = \mathrm{X}(6) * \mathrm{A} + 5.1 \tag{1-6}$$

and

$$\mathrm{X}(10) = 8.153 \tag{1-7}$$

Upon noticing X(3) on the left-hand side of statement (1–3), the FORTRAN compiler might instruct the computer to reserve space for X(1) and X(2) in addition to a space for X(3); and space could be reserved for X(4), X(5), and X(6) upon the appearance of X(6) in statement (1–5). The appearance of X(1) in statement (1–4) and the appearance of X(4) in statement (1–6) would cause no further reservation of space, since space has already been reserved for these variables. If space were reserved in this manner, the memory might take on the following appearance:

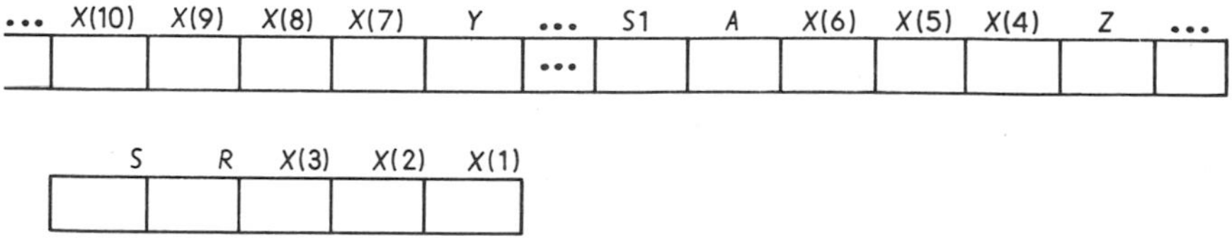

...	X(10)	X(9)	X(8)	X(7)	Y	...	S1	A	X(6)	X(5)	X(4)	Z	...
						...							

S	R	X(3)	X(2)	X(1)

The discontinuity of variables in the same array would lead to more difficult addressing problems for the FORTRAN compiler than if all the variables in the X array followed each other; however, this problem can be solved with correct programming techniques.

A much more difficult problem arises when the subscript is not a constant but a variable. For example, assume the first appearance of a variable from the X array took place in the following statement:

$$X(I) = 2.5 * Y + 8.213 \tag{1-8}$$

Since the FORTRAN compiler cannot know at compile time the range of values the subscript I will take on at run time, the compiler cannot know how many storage spaces will be needed for the X array. When I takes on values within the range 1 to 10, 10 storage locations must be reserved; when I takes values between 1 and 500, 500 storage locations are necessary. It should now be clear that the FORTRAN language needs to offer the programmer some method with which to reserve space other than the appearance of the subscripted variable on the left-hand side of an arithmetic statement; hence, the reason for including the DIMENSION statement in the FORTRAN language.

1.9.3. Subscripted Variables and the DIMENSION Statement

At compile time, an array is assigned the number of storage spaces specified in the DIMENSION statement; the appearance of the array name X in the statement

DIMENSION X(10)

allows the FORTRAN compiler to reserve ten spaces for the X array. To stipulate that 10 storage spaces are to be reserved for the X array implies that the range of the subscript, I, in the statement

$$X(I) = 2.5 * Y + 8.261 \tag{1-9}$$

is limited to the integers from 1 to 10.

When the subscripted variable is written in the DIMENSION statement, the subscript must be a fixed-point constant.

DIMENSION X(10) is correct;
DIMENSION X(N) is not correct.

The FORTRAN compiler cannot know how many locations to assign to the variable X when the subscript N is used, because at compile time it is impossible for N to have a value (a variable cannot take on a value until run time). The programmer should estimate the maximum size of the array X for any possible set of data that might be used as input to the program and he should use this number as the subscript in the DIMENSION statement.

1.9.4. Subscripts and General Programs

Throughout the book we shall stress the general program; that is, a program which will be used to solve the same problem many times, each time with a different set of data (a program which is limited to the number of times or the type of data that can be used is not general). In a general program the array X will undoubtedly vary in size. If the constant in the DIMENSION statement representing the subscript is not the maximum size possible with any proposed set of data, it is possible to be thrown into the following situation: the programmer may force the subscript I to take on the value 12, when only 10 spaces have been reserved for the subscripted variable X. The above error actually is more serious than the error created by not mentioning the subscripted variable in the DIMENSION statement —the latter error will cause an error printout; but when underestimating the space needed, no error indication will be printed by the computer. The program may or may not result in an answer (the computer may be halted by an illegal instruction code), but even if the computer gives an answer to the problem, it will be wrong. To clarify the above error, consider array X which appears in the following program:

DIMENSION X(10)

———

———

———

Perform the following operation N times,

X(I) = R + I

(Methods by which the programmer can tell the computer to perform the aforementioned operation will be explained in the next chapter.) If the variable I takes on a value greater than 10, say 12, the FORTRAN compiler will look for the value of X(12) in a location prior to the storage locations allocated to the X array. In fact, when I takes on the value 12, a reference

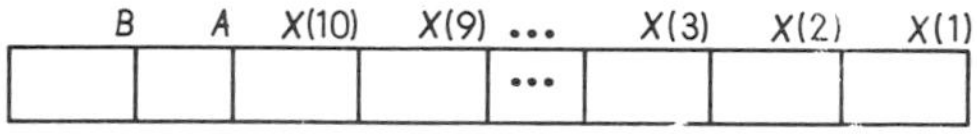

B	A	X(10)	X(9) ...		X(3)	X(2)	X(1)
				...			

to X(I) will look for the value in location B. The compiler cannot know at compile time what values the variable subscript I will take on at run time; therefore, the compiler cannot instruct the computer to print an error message when I exceeds 10.

Although the appearance of an array name in a DIMENSION statement can be used by the FORTRAN compiler to reserve storage space for that array, the same appearance of the array name in a DIMENSION statement cannot be used to define the subscripted variables in the array. It was mentioned earlier in this section that the purpose of making the programmer define his variables was to avoid the possibility of making an error in assuming the wrong value to be in a storage location just before the running of the program. Since the initial value in a storage location might be zero, one, or any one of many other numbers, the FORTRAN compiler cannot automatically assign one value, at run time, to all variables in an array appearing in a DIMENSION statement.

```
DIMENSION  X(10), Z(10)

______

Statements defining the variables R,S,T, and U.

______

X(1) = 2.5 * R
X(2) = 3.75 * R + U **2
X(3) = 2.153 * S ** 3
X(4) = R + S /(T * 3.6)

______

Repeat the following statements N times—

Z(I) = X(I) ** 2.5                                    (1–10)
```

If N takes on the value 10, the FORTRAN compiler will instruct the computer to print the error message for undefined variables because the varibles X(5), X(6), X(7), X(8), X(9), and X(10) cannot take on a value before the execution of statement (1–10), because they do not appear on the left side of an arithmetic statement or any other statement (to be discussed later) which could define a variable.

1.9.5. Arithmetic Statements—Statement Numbers

Since the FORTRAN statement is an instruction to the computer, the statement must be stored somewhere in the computer memory, so that the computer can refer to it. The symbolic address of a statement is the statement number. The similarity between variables and statement numbers as storage locations as opposed to constants and instructions which are the material in these locations was stressed early in Chapter 1. The range of statement numbers is 0000 to 9999. A set of logical questions at this point would be: Does a number need to be placed on every statement? To answer the above question, we must again resort to an examination of a small part of the internal operations in the computer.

Let us assume that the following lines represent some type of FORTRAN statements, which taken together, comprise the program:

```
      ______________________________
0010  ______________________________
      ______________________________
      ______________________________
0015  ______________________________
      ______________________________
```

The program starts with the statement before the statement number 10. Although this statement does not have a number, the FORTRAN compiler instructs the computer to put the first statement in a certain location, say 8800 (this is an actual location in the memory of the computer—there may be a total of 32,000 locations, 12,000 locations, 80,000 locations or some other number). The computer initiates the program at location 8,800 because that number is placed in a special register[1] of the computer, called the control counter. Unless the computer is specifically instructed to execute a statement other than the next sequential statement, the control counter is automatically stepped up to the number of the next sequential statement. There exists a specific control statement, the "GO TO" statement (to be discussed in the next chapter), available to the programmer if he wishes the computer to execute a statement other than the next sequential statement, in other words, the programmer has the option of branching out of the normal sequence. The GO TO statement places the address of the desired statement into the control counter so the computer can branch to that statement in the next step.

The above examination of the control counter and the process of branching throws some light on the question regarding the numbering of statements. If there is no desire to branch to statement B, except from statement A, then statement B need not be numbered.

```
______________________________
______________________________
______________________________
______________________________  A
______________________________  B
```

In other words, the only time we need to number a statement occurs when we wish to branch there out of the normal sequence of statements. It should be noted that although statement B need not be numbered, the numbering

[1] A register is a storage location with two additional properties: (1) The computer can move material in and out of the register faster than in the case of the normal storage location; and (2) The programmer usually cannot refer directly to the registers (i.e., since the programmer cannot give a symbolic name to a register, he cannot place the name of the register on the left-hand side of an arithmetic statement—some computers do have directly addressable storage registers).

of that statement will not result in an error; however, the computer will waste time and memory space by setting up the machine-language statement and storage locations necessary for a statement number. Therefore, a good rule is not to number statements unless a number is required for branching purposes. If the program contains some statement numbers which are not required for branching, the FORTRAN compiler will instruct the computer to print out the sentence; "Unreferenced Statement Numbers . . .(*list of statement numbers*). . . ." At this point in the compilation of the object deck, the programmer has the option of changing his program to eliminate the statement numbers which are not required; the program is then recompiled after the changes are made—or, the programmer can run the program without making any changes. A great many unreferenced statement numbers will create an inefficient program, so it may be to the advantage of the programmer to make the changes and recompile the program.

1.9.6. The Punched Card

One method of placing material into the computer, whether this material be instructions or data, is via the media of the punched card. Figure 1–13 illustrates that the card has 80 columns and 12 rows; the rows are

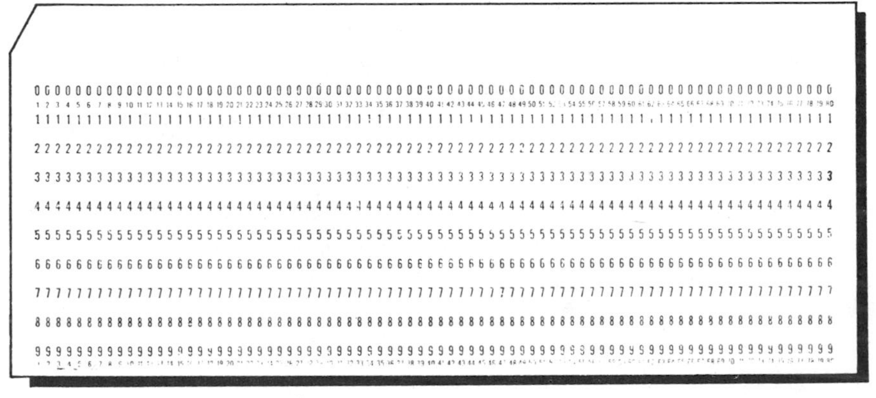

FIG. 1–13. The Punched Card

numbered(from the top of the page) 12,11,0,1,2, . . . ,7,8,9. In each column the rows 0 to 9 represent the digits 0 to 9; to enable the user to place letters and special symbols(such as, (, \$. + =)) in one column, the rows 12, 11, and 0 are combined with the other digits to form a code.

Following is an illustration of the FORTRAN coding form, which is marked to indicate the positions in the card for the elements of arithmetic statements, including statement numbers (Figure 1–14). Each arithmetic statement requires at least one line on the form. Each line on the form represents one card.

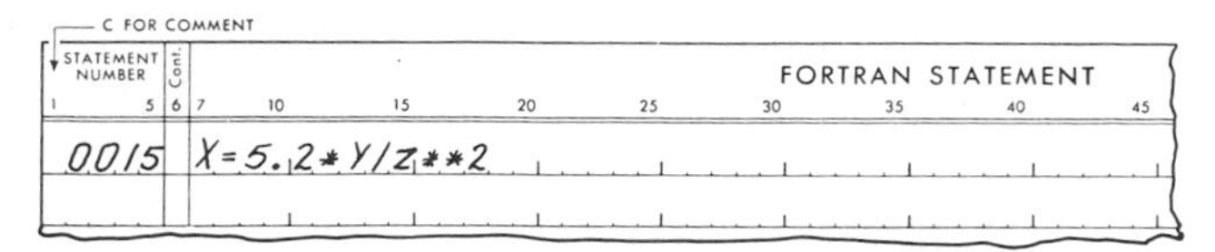

FIG. 1–14. FORTRAN Coding Form

Columns 2 through 5 are reserved for the statement number. If nothing is punched in columns 2,3,4, or 5, the number is assumed to be zero. In Figure 1–14, the statement number is 0015. The FORTRAN statement may start in column 7 and proceed through column 72. The statement on the above card would be coded into the card by a keypunch. By placing a "C" in column 1, the programmer may use the rest of the card for his own comments. These comments will not be printed or punched with the results of the problem but will be listed with the source deck cards; comment cards can be used to indicate the separate parts of the program to give other information which might help the programmer check the program. It is a wise procedure for the programmer to list the cards he has punched so that he may easily check them with the written program; many errors of the beginning programmer are keypunch errors. Comment cards are not processed by the FORTRAN compiler.

Columns 73 through 80, for FORTRAN statement cards, are not processed by the compiler; in this field the programmer may number the source deck cards consecutively so that they may be sorted into their original order if they are inadvertantly dropped on the floor (all of the above rules on the form of the card hold only for FORTRAN statement cards and not for data cards—data cards may utilize all 80 columns of the card; data cards will be discussed in greater detail in Chapter 3).

In some versions of FORTRAN, a statement may be continued from one card to the next card by placing a 0 or blank in column 6 on the first card, a 1 in column 6 of the second card; and if a third card is needed for the statement, a 2 should be punched into column 6 of the third card, etc. When continuation cards are not allowed by FORTRAN, the programmer faces a very slight inconvenience. Let us say that the programmer must write a long arithmetic statement, one longer than 65 characters, so that more than one card is needed, in order to evaluate an engineering formula. For example, X = Y + 2* R**5 + ... +Z(5)/R; if no continuation cards are permitted, it is necessary to calculate an intermediate result and then a final result.

```
X = Y + 2 * R**5 + . . . + G **2
X = X + F * S + 2.5 + . . . + Z(5)/R
```

In the above example, the storage location X is used to hold the intermediate value as well as the final value. When continuation cards are permitted.

the programmer need not write the statement number for cards after the first one. For example, Figure 1–15 shows what would occur if, say, the statement referred to in the previous example was number 0025.

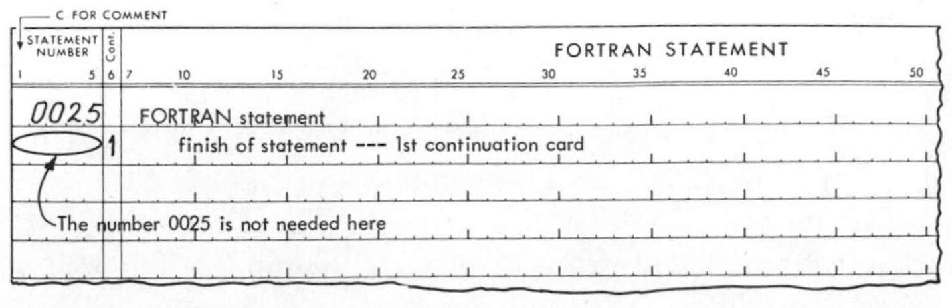

FIG. 1–15

Problems

1.1. Examine the following statements; then indicate what values are in location X(4), L, and A after the computer executes the statements.

```
DIMENSION  X (4)
X (1) = 1.25
X (2) = 2.1
X (3) = 3.2
X (4) = 3.5
L = 1.25
X(L) = X (L+1)+X (L+2)+X (L+3)
R = X (L)+2.5 / 1.2 * X (L+1)
A = R+X (L)
```

To have the computer do the calculations and print out the answers the reader should add the statements:

```
   WRITE (6,1) X (4), L, A
1  FORMAT (F15.5, 5X, 15, 8X, F15.5)
   STOP
   END
```

The last four statements will be explained in detail in later chapters.

1.2. The following statements may be utilized to sum a given number of values and then divide the sum by the total number of values.

```
DIMENSION  X (10)
X (1) = 2.31
X (2) = 3
X (3) = 2
X (4) = 1.2
X (5) = 2.1
X (6) = − 1.5
X (7) = 3.1
X (8) = 1
X (9) = 5.1
X (10) = 3.25
X (1) = X (1)+X (2)+X(3)+X(4)+X(5)+X(6)+X(7)+X(8)
```

```
1  X(9) X(10)
   REAN = X (1) / 10.
   WRITE (6,5) REAN
5  FORMAT (F 10.4)
   STOP
   END
```

If you were writing a compiler, what general types of statements would you need to reduce the total number of statements necessary for the above program. Using your hypothetical statements, do you think the program would run faster or slower than the given program? Does your program save any storage space? What advantages does your program have over the given program besides having less statements? Do you think it would be difficult to write a compiler which could translate your hypothetical statements to machine language so that the computer could understand your program?

2. Control Statements

A program which must evaluate anything other than the very simplest type of problem will need to execute statements in different orders at different times; or, the programmer will have to instruct the computer to branch to different parts of the program depending on the decision at that point. Assume that in a particular problem, a decision must be made at some point in the program as to whether the employee should be paid overtime or regular time. If management has chosen to pay regular time for the first 40 hours worked during any week and overtime for any hours above 40, the program must branch to a different part of the program when the amount of hours worked during that week has exceeded the 40-hour mark.

Question: Are the hours worked this week equal to or less than 40?

(*a*) Answer yes: continue in normal sequence.

(*b*) Answer no: use regular time rate for the first 40 hours and then use the overtime rate for the remaining hours.

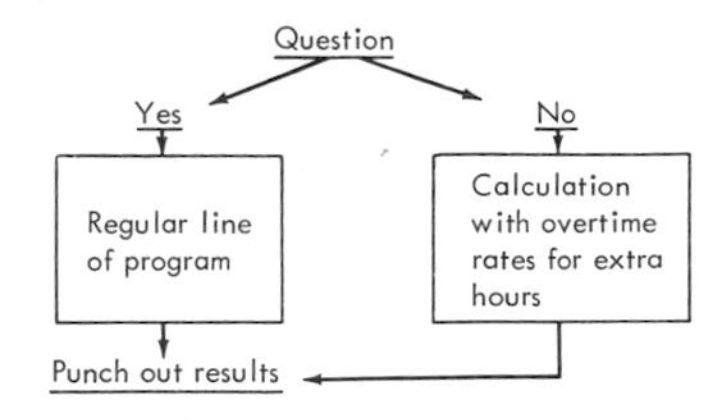

FIG. 2–1. Read in Employee's Card

Decision-type statements and their associated branch-type statements are absolutely essential to the logic involved in solving both business and scientific problems on the computers; these groups of statements with their auxiliary statements will be called control statements.

2.1. The GO TO or Unconditional Branch Statement

In an earlier section the reader was introduced to the way the FORTRAN compiler and the computer execute statements in consecutive order via the control counter. To take a statement other than next sequential statement requires some type of branching statement. The unconditional branch statement involves no logic or decision making; as its name implies, there is no condition on which it does not execute the branch. The statement has the following form:

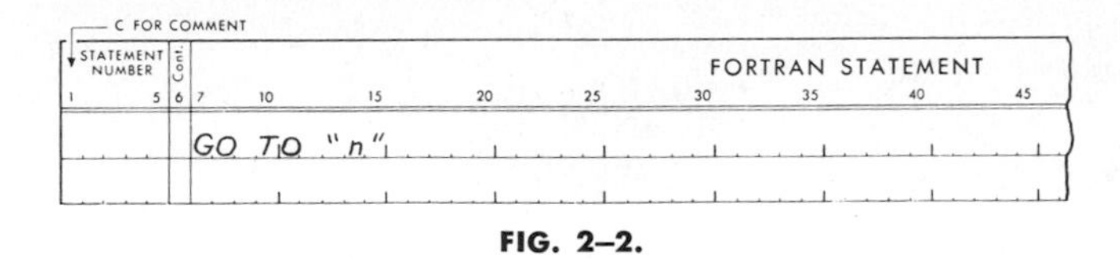

FIG. 2–2.

where n is the number (it cannot be a variable) of a statement in the program. If the statement number n does not appear elsewhere in the program, the FORTRAN compiler will instruct the computer to print out an error message emphasizing this particular type of error (this error message is typed out at compile time). Statement number n may appear before or after the unconditional branch statement in the program.

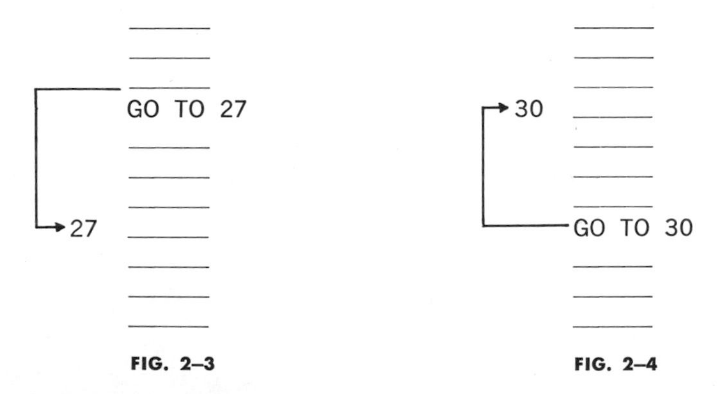

FIG. 2–3 FIG. 2–4

A look at the above figures reveals that the unconditional branch statement is worthless without the use of other conditional branch statements. In Figure 2–3, the statements between the GO TO statement and statement number 27 will never be executed and therefore need not be written down at all. Once the computer executes the statement, GO TO 30, in Figure 2–4, it will remain within the group of statements between statement number 30 and the GO TO statement until the operator stops the computer.

An example of the use of the conditional branch and the difference between it and an unconditional GO TO statement will be given in the next section.

2.2. The COMPUTED GO TO Statement

As opposed to the unconditional "GO TO" statement, the "COMPUTED GO TO" statement is conditional; the condition is the value of a variable which acts as a switch. The way the switch is set depends on some condition of the problem. In its formal form, the statement is GO TO (n_1, n_2, ... n_k), L; n_1, n_2, ... ,n_k are numbers of statements which appear in the program. The only limit on the amount of statement numbers in the parenthesis is the length of the card available for punching in FORTRAN. In those versions of FORTRAN in which continuation cards are allowed, this statement may be extended to more than one card, thereby permitting many more statement numbers within the parenthesis. For instance, let us look at a "COMPUTED GO TO" statement which has seven statement numbers; that is, there are seven choices available.

```
GO TO (202,27,13,1,132,17,7),L
```

It should be noticed that the statement numbers need not be in order. The letter L represents a fixed-point variable which must be restricted to the constant values 1 through 7 by the programmer. When storage location L has the value 6 at the time the above statement is executed, then the computer will next execute the statement numbers 17; however, if storage location L has the value 3 at the time of execution of the above statement, then the computer will next execute the statement numbered 13.

The following is implied:

```
GO  TO   (202, 27,13,1,132,17,7), L
Values of L  1   2  3 4   5  6 7
```

The number of the statement appearing over the value of L is the one that the computer will take next if L has the value when the above statement is executed by the computer.

Two types of error can occur if the programmer is not careful when he uses the above statement. The first type of error occurs at compile time and is usually much easier to correct than the second type of error, which occurs at run time. A statement number appearing in the COMPUTED GO TO statement, such as 132, for which there is no corresponding statement in the program (i.e., no statement number 132 appears in the program) creates an error of the same nature as the error mentioned in the previous section for the unconditional "GO TO" statement. Similar to the error in that statement, the FORTRAN compiler instructs the computer to print an error message at compile time; the programmer should either place a number on the desired statement or else remove that number from the "COMPUTED GO TO" statement and make the corresponding change in the variable L.

```
310  K=2*M+1
  1  ———
  5  ———
     GO  TO  (210,105,1,37,25,17,6,5);K
 25  ———
210  ———
 17  ———
 37  ———
105  ———
  6  ———
```

Statement number 310 may be only one of many arithmetic or input statements which determine the value of the variable K. For some reason, perhaps an oversight by the programmer, the value in storage location M becomes 4 or greater. Then the constant value taken on by the variable K in statement 310 is equal to or greater than 9. Since there are only eight statement numbers in the COMPUTED GO TO statement, an error is created within the program.

The FORTRAN compiler cannot know at compile time what values will be taken on by the variable K during run time; therefore, no message can be typed out to notify the programmer either at compile time or at run time. No error message is typed out at run time because this would necessitate continual testing of the value in the location called K.

Usually, the computer will stop before a result can be obtained, because this error will lead to an illegal instruction code. For the experienced programmer who knows how to operate the computer and who places his own program on the computer, the appearance of an illegal instruction code in one of the computer registers might put this programmer on the trail of this type of error. Normally, the programmer would not be in contact with the computer, but he would receive the information that the computer stopped somewhere in the program and he would be given the values in the registers. Now this error should be considered as only one of many types of errors which could cause the computer to stop on an illegal operation code before giving a result; in other words, the programmer should check the COMPUTED GO TO statement as one of the first steps in debugging the program.

The following practical example is designed to illustrate the difference between the unconditional and conditional GO TO statements.

The RST company needs a program which will process its payroll on the computer (actually we will present a very simple example giving only a very small part of the normal payroll application). Each employee is given a card with his name already punched in columns 1 through 20. In other parts of the card are punched such information as pay rate, hours worked for the week, total pay for the year, insurance, etc. For this example we are only concerned with column 40, which gives the number of the department. The five departments in the company (numbers 1,2,3,4, and 5) have many parts of their payroll figured in the same way, but certain parts must be figured differently for each department. One department may be paid straight salary while another is paid on the incentive basis; one department may have a stock plan different from that of another department. One department may receive a bonus while the other receives no bonus. In any case, one part of the program will suffice for all departments while another

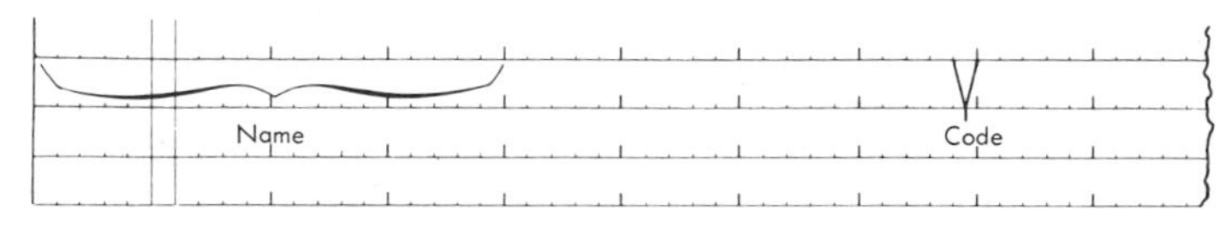

FIG. 2–5

part of the program must be divided into separate parts, one for each department. Depending on the department, the programmer should set a switch so that the program goes to the right part at the right time.

The programmer should write a FORTRAN statement telling the computer to read the data in column 40 into the storage location M. After the part of the payroll common to all departments is processed by part A of the program, the next statement should be GO TO (10,20,30,40,50), M. If the number in column 40 is a 4, the program branches to statement number 40 at this point in order to continue the processing of the payroll for department 4. When the computer has executed the instructions in part B for the payroll for department 4, it would be a mistake to reevaluate part B with the instructions in part C; yet, since the computer will take the instructions in sequence, the payroll for any department will be evaluated via the instructions in part C. Therefore, to correct the program in Figure 2–6, we must write an unconditional branch statement at the end of each set of instructions. Figure 2–7 gives the corrected program. The data includes the constant to be read into location M. Notice that the instruction to take the next data card is also accomplished by an unconditional branch statement. While both the unconditional and conditional GO TO statements involve the branching out of the natural order, one automatically branches, while the other branches on a switch which was previously set by a decision made earlier in the program.

In the following programs, the COMPUTED GO TO and the GO TO statements are only a few of the instructions which comprise the entire pro-

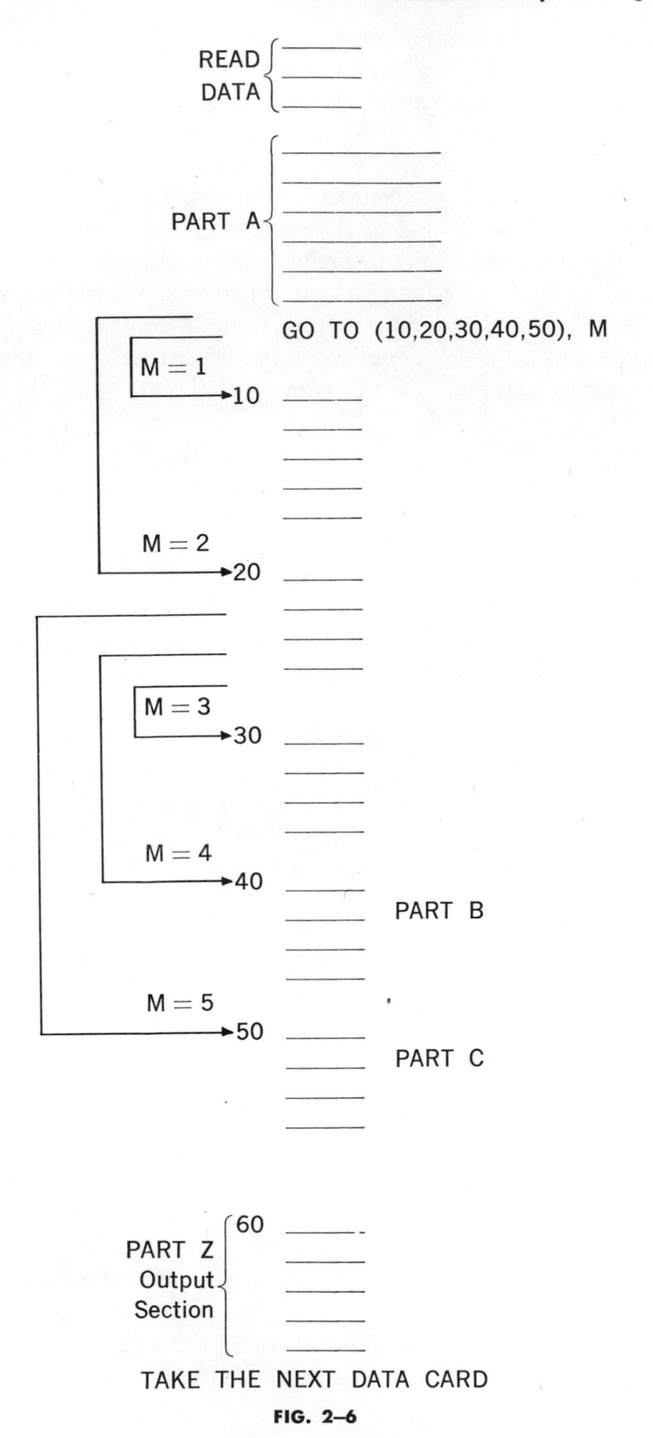
READ DATA
PART A
GO TO (10,20,30,40,50), M
M = 1
10
M = 2
20
M = 3
30
M = 4
40
PART B
M = 5
50
PART C
60
PART Z
Output
Section
TAKE THE NEXT DATA CARD

FIG. 2–6

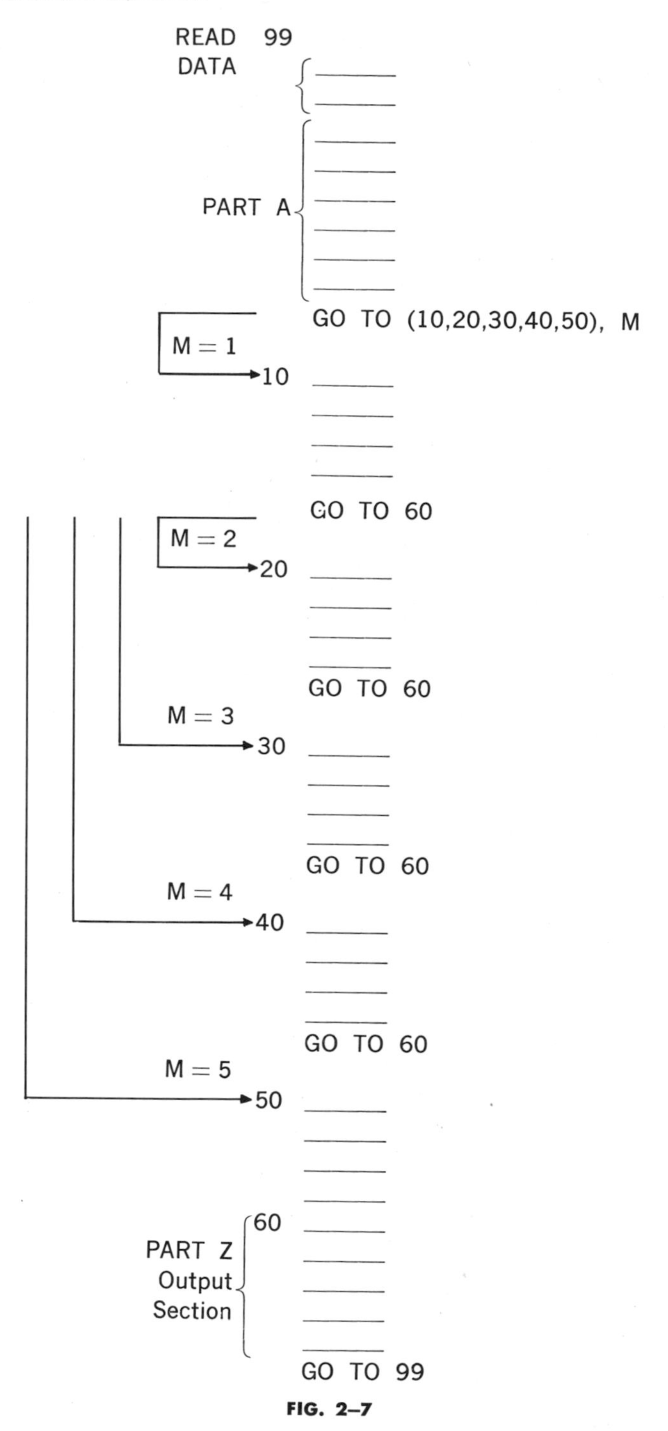
READ 99
DATA
PART A
GO TO (10,20,30,40,50), M
M = 1
10
GO TO 60
M = 2
20
GO TO 60
M = 3
30
GO TO 60
M = 4
40
GO TO 60
M = 5
50
60
PART Z
Output
Section
GO TO 99

FIG. 2–7

gram; i.e., many calculations and decisions must be written into the program before the program will be of any practical use.

A common problem is to chart some type of functional rule for all practical values; in this way, it becomes a simple task to pick the functional result from the chart for that value. For example, the functional relationship

$$PAY (X) = 2.51*X - H - .22*2.51*X - SO$$

may be a simple way to calculate the weekly salary of an hourly employee—

X—represents the hours worked.
H—represents health insurance.

SO—represents the other contributions. Let us assume that the possible number of hours worked per week will be listed only in multiples of 5 hours from 5 hours to 60 hours.

```
      DIMENSION PAY (12)
      H = 2.76
      R = 5
      SO= 1.25
    2 I= R/5.
      PAY (I) = 2.51 * R-H-.22 * 2.51 * R-SO
      K=R
      WRITE (6,100) K, PAY (I)         }
                                       }To be explained later
  100 FORMAT (5X, I3, 20X, F 10.4)     }
      R= R+5.
      I= I+1
      GO TO (2,2,2,2,2,2,2,2,2,2,2,2,2,3),I
    3 STOP }
           }To be explained later
      END  }
```

Even with this simple problem, the programmer must use ingenuity to enable the programmer to use the computer to solve the problem. Notice that there must be 14 statement numbers in the COMPUTED GO TO statement, because I has the value 2 in this statement when only one value has been calculated by the computer; since 12 values must be calculated, the thirteenth statement number must be the number 2 so that control is transferred back to statement number 2 for the twelfth calculation. After the twelfth calculation, control is transferred to statement number 3 to end the program. The only reason for the statement K = R is to eliminate the decimal point from the output (this is not necessary in every version of the FORTRAN compiler).

The FORTRAN compiler does provide the programmer with more logical power via the "IF" statement and the "DO" statement; but before we analyze these two statements in detail, the actual decision-making process is examined more closely in the next section.

2.3. Looping

We shall introduce the concept of looping by means of the following example in which a group of values are added together and the total is then divided by the number of values; this is called the arithmetic mean of the values.

We assume that not only the values but also the number of values have been read into the machine. The actual values have been placed in the array X, and the number representing the number of values has been placed in location K. If we knew there would be 30 values, the following arithmetic statement would solve the problem:

REAN =X (1) +X(2) + X(3)+ . . . . +X(30) /30. (2–1)

Notice that the location which will contain the mean is called REAN instead of MEAN; since MEAN is a fixed-point variable, the decimal part would be truncated if the storage location for the result was called MEAN.

A problem confronts the programmer who tries to use one arithmetic statement for a program to calculate the mean of 20 numbers, 30 numbers, 65 numbers, 99 numbers, etc.; or any amount of numbers from 1 to 100. The number of values will not be known when the program is written. We may assume that the person who will use the program knows the number of values at the time he runs the program on the computer; the number of values will be denoted by the variable N. Certainly the programmer would have to reserve 100 spaces for the array, X, via the statement DIMENSION X(100). Assume that the programmer can instruct the computer to read the number of values into location N and those N values of X into locations X (1), X (2), . . . ,X (N) (the details of the READ statement will be covered in detail in Chapter 3). The programmer cannot write one arithmetic statement with a variable number of values; in other words, the programmer can either write a statement with 4 values on the right of the equal sign, 10 values, 67 values, or 99 values, but once he has written down 10 values, such as:

X (1)+X (2)+X (3)+X (4)+X (5)+X (6)+X (7)+X (8)+X (9)+X (10)

the statement will be compiled with 10 values and not any other number of values. Therefore, the only possible arithmetic statement is

REAN =(X (1) + X (2)+ . . . +X(100)) /P (2–2)

in conjunction with an earlier statement, P=N, to avoid a mixed mode expression.[1]

[1] The dots imply all 100 subscripted variables are written in the statement.

Even if the programmer places all 100 subscripted variables in the arithmetic statement, difficulties are still present. A particular problem might be to take the mean of 15 values; for statement (2–2) to be correct, one must assume the values in locations X(16), X(17), . . . , X(100) to be zero. In section 1.7 it was pointed out that the FORTRAN compiler, to avoid the possibility of error in making this assumption, will print out an error message at compile time proclaiming the variables X(16), X(17), . . . , X(100) to be undefined, because the compiler is not satisfied that these locations can take on a value before their appearance in (2–2). The variables X(1), X(2), . . . , X(15) can take on a value since they appear in an input list (to be discussed in detail in chapter 3), but the variables X(16), X(17), . . . , X(100) do not appear in an input list. A variable can be defined by its appearance in an input list, such as,

```
READ, A
```

as well as by its appearance on the left side of an arithmetic statement. Remember, for subscripted variables, the appearance of the variable in a DIMENSION statement only reserves storage space and does not define the variable for the FORTRAN compiler. The only way out of this predicament is to use a program loop to solve the problem; the IF statement is one possible statement (others will be introduced in later sections) which the programmer could use for creating a program loop.

A program loop is an iterative process; certain operations are performed many times in the same way with only a parameter or a few parameters being changed each time the operation is performed by the computer. To calculate the mean of a group of values, the only operation needed in the loop will be to add one value at a time until all the values have been summed to get a total; the total is then divided by the number of values to obtain the mean. The key to using this plan in the program will be to use some location as an index; initialize this index at one; increment by one every time another value is added into the total; and keep testing to see if the index is equal to the value in location K—this constant represents the number of values read into the program. Instead of using the last few sentences to describe the plan of procedure, we can use a pictorial representation called the flow chart.

2.3.1. Flow Charting

The rectangular box represents anything but a decision box, which is diamond shaped. A pictorial representation is usually much more convenient than a verbal description when illustrating the procedure for more complicated programs. A flow is a pictorial summary of the program which focuses on the places in the program where decisions are made; in other words, a pictorial representation of the program logic.

There are two advantages of using flow charts:

1. Usually the programmer finds it easier to work out the logic in the flow chart before getting down to the very detailed job of writing the program; i.e., by eliminating all the details needed to make the program work on the computer but unnecessary to the logic needed to solve the problem, the programmer can pinpoint his thinking to the more important and difficult part of the program.

2. A well-written flow chart serves as a good documentation of the program. Assume that a programmer, during the time he is employed by an industrial firm, writes a large program. After a period of time the programmer leaves the company for some reason; then, due to some technological

FLOW CHART

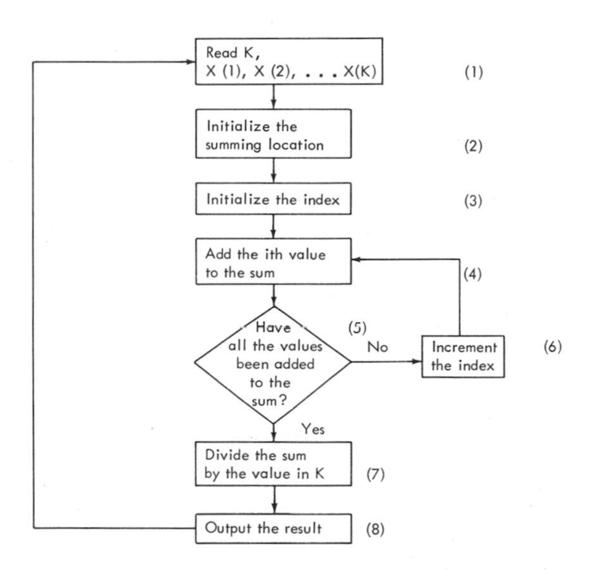

change, it becomes necessary to make a minor change in the program. Now a new programmer must be assigned to change the program. A short study of the flow chart might save the new person the tedious and difficult task of tracing through the program to find the part to change; actually, the new person must change his thinking to follow the program, since no two people will write a large program in exactly the same way.

A person need not work in industry to benefit from drawing a flow chart for his program. It is very easy to forget the method used for a particular program which was written a year or two ago. A quick reference to a flow chart should refresh the programmer's memory.

Utilizing the flow chart given earlier, the next step is to write the program to find the mean of up to 100 values. Steps (1) and (8) in the flow chart represent the input of the data and the output of the result respectively; input and output statements will be encountered later in the present chapter.

```
99  ----------------------------------------------  (1)
    TOTAL=0                                         (2)
    I=1                                             (3)
30  TOTAL=TOTAL+X(I)                                (4)
    IF (I-K) 10,20,20                               (5)
10  I=I+1                                           (6)
    GO TO 30
20  R=K
    TOTAL=TOTAL/R                                   (7)
    ----------------------------------------------  (8)
    GO TO 99
    END
```

Any location, such as TOTAL, which is used to keep a running sum of a group of values in a program which has the ability to read data and solve the problem on a continuous basis (i.e., to read one set of data and solve the problem for that set of data, then read another set of data and solve a second problem, etc., without operator interruption) must be initialized for each new set of data; otherwise, the summing location would have a number other than zero for each new set of data. The placing of the constant zero in the location in which the sum is to be stored before each new set of data is part of the initialization procedure. An index is needed to locate each value to be added to the total and also to keep track of how many values have been added to the total at any time. After the problem has been solved for one set of data, the constant in the location representing the index is the number of values which were read into the computer for the previous problem. Like the case of the location used for accumulating the sum, the index must be initialized every time a new set of data is introduced to the program. However, the initial value of the index should be one and not zero, as is the case for the initial value of the total; the reason is that a zero subscript in FORTRAN will result in an error (as explained in an earlier section). Initialization is shown on the flow chart in steps (2) and (3). In step (4) a value is added into the total; the particular value to be added to the total is determined by the value of the index I at the time the computer executes the statement

```
TOTAL=TOTAL+X(I)
```

If I has the value 5, then X(5), or the constant in the fifth variable of the array X is added to the total. The above arithmetic statement used for the operation of summing the values can be interpreted in the following way—the new value of the total is equal to the old value of the total plus the value in location X(I).

2.4. The IF Statement

To facilitate the decision necessary in step 5, FORTRAN provides the programmer with the IF statement. Formally, this statement is written as

```
IF (      ) N1,N2,N3;
```

an arithmetic expression (with or without functions—functions will be explained in a later chapter) should be written within the parenthesis. N1, N2, and N3 are the numbers of statements which appear somewhere in the program. An error message will be printed out at compile time if a statement number is written for N1, N2, and N3 which does not appear somewhere in the program. Of course, the rules for arithmetic expressions hold for the expression within the parenthesis. The FORTRAN compiler first instructs the computer to evaluate the arithmetic expression; then a decision is made depending on the result of the expression. If the result of the expression is less than zero, the computer is instructed to execute statement number N1; if the result of the expression is zero, the computer is instructed to execute statement number N2; and if the result of the expression is greater than zero, the computer is instructed to execute statement number N3. In the present example we would like to know whether the constant in location I, the index giving the number of values which have already been added into the total, is equal to or greater than the constant in location K, the number of values of which we must calculate the mean. Actually, the constant in location I will never exceed the constant in location K unless the constant in location K is zero, the reason being that initially I has the value 1, and it is increased by 1 every time another value is added into the total. Therefore, if the decision is written in the form of the IF statement,

```
IF(K-I)10,10,20
```

the first 10 will have meaning only in the instance where K takes on the value 0, which in itself is meaningless and could result only if the input card were punched wrong. To avoid this slim possibility, the first 10 in the above statement could be replaced with another number, say 40, which would refer to an output statement instructing the machine to print an error message; the following is possible:

```
30  TOTAL=TOTAL+X(I)
    IF(K-I)40,10,20
```

```
20  I=I+1
    GO TO 30
40  PRINT_____
    STOP
10  R=K
    TOTAL=TOTAL/R
```

With the slim possibility of error, the extra effort is unnecessary.

Output statements and error routines will be discussed further in a later section, as will the STOP statement.

Since the method to solve the problem is dependent upon instructing the computer to keep adding more values into the total until all the values have been added in, we want the computer to next execute statement number 20 if the number in I is less than the number in K; number 20 is placed in position N3, therefore, since the computer will go to statement number N1 if the expression (K−I) is positive. When the number in I equals the number in K, the computer should branch to statement number 10 in order to continue with the problem of calculating the mean, because the last value has been added into the total. Steps 6 and 7 instruct the computer to increment the index I (the new value of I equals the old value of I plus one) and then go back and add the next value into the total by executing statement number 30. When all the values have been added into the total, we divide by the constant in location K to get the mean. Notice that statement 10 takes the floating-point equivalent of the constant in location K and places this value in location R. The presence of statement 10 eliminates the mixed mode error which would occur if the arithmetic expression which calculates the mean would be written as:

TOTAL/K

The use of the statement GO TO 99 before the END statement is used to prepare the computer to read the next set of data after the completion of the first problem. If there are no more sets of data ready at that time, the computer will stop; however, it is only necessary to push one button to restart the computer and to continue calculating the mean of other sets of data if they are brought to the computer before some other application. More will be said about the above material in the section on input data.

The previous example employs the IF statement solely for the purpose of inquiring into the status of the index; that is, the present value of the index is compared to its maximum possible value. The test of the index is one of three steps which are vital to creating a loop; a program loop uses the same statements many times as opposed to a program which utilizes a different statement for each value to be added into the total, or one that moves each value to another place, or any other procedure which must be repeated many times, each time for a different value. Besides testing the index, the other important steps in writing a program loop are initializing the index and incrementing the index. A general flow chart for a program loop follows:

FLOW CHART

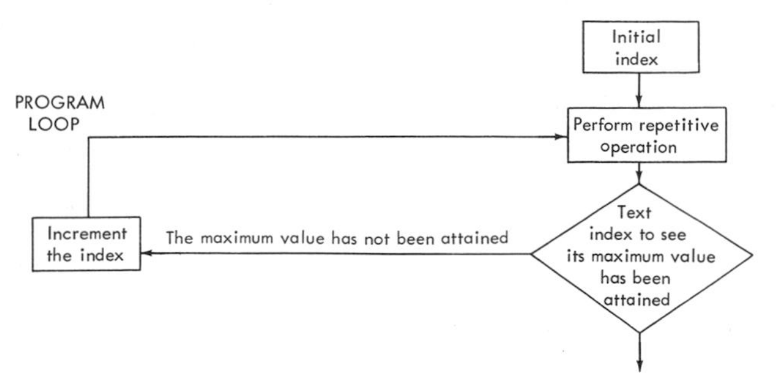

The IF statement can be employed to evaluate a much more complicated mathematical expression than (K−I). For instance,

```
IF(20.*X**5.2+Y*Z**3−25.*R**5)35,25,25
```

states that the statement number 35 should be the next one to be executed if $20 \cdot X^{5.2} + Y \cdot Z^3 - 25 \cdot R^5$ is less than zero; or, if $20 \cdot X^{5.2} + Y \cdot Z^3$ is less than $25 \cdot R^5$. But, if $20 \cdot X^{5.2} + Y \cdot Z^3$ is greater than or equal to $25 \cdot R^5$, the computer should next execute statement number 35. We can conclude that the IF statement is a 3-way (or less if the programmer wishes) switch.

The DO statement, to be introduced in next section, is designed specifically for the type of logic needed in the example to calculate the mean of a group of values. Initializing, testing, and incrementing the index can all be done via the DO statement. In more complicated programs, both the IF statement and the DO statement are needed to solve the problem as well as to reduce programming time and computer running time.

2.5. The DO Statement

The FORTRAN language provides the programmer with the capability of initializing, testing, and incrementing an index all in one statement—the DO statement.

$$\text{DO n L} = m_1, m_2, m_3$$

The letter n denotes a statement number which must be mentioned somewhere later in the program. The letters m_1, m_2, and m_3 are either fixed-point constants or fixed-point variables; in FORTRAN II, expressions are not permitted in the places denoted m_1, m_2, and m_3. The letter L stands for a fixed-point variable which acts as the index in the program loop. The fact that DO statements are designed for use in programs loops can be illustrated by the following general example.

```
      TOTAL=0
      DO 20 K=1,N,1
   20 TOTAL=TOTAL+A(K)
```

This sample program instructs the computer to add N numbers into a location which we have named TOTAL. Since N may be read into the machine at run time, the program is general in the sense that the computer can take the sum of 20 numbers, 35 numbers, or 73 numbers. Again we want to stress the necessity for the programmer to estimate the maximum amount of numbers of which he will wish to take the sum; this maximum number is placed in a DIMENSION statement so that sufficient space may be reserved for the array A; such as DIMENSION A(100), if the maximum amount of numbers will be 100. The variable K serves as an index; it keeps track of the amount of numbers already placed in the sum as well as specifying the particular number to be added into the total the next time through the loop.

The DO statement manipulates the index through the constants or variables placed in positions m_1, m_2, and m_3.

DO 20 K=1,N,1

This statement instructs the computer to initialize the index K by placing the constant 1 in K. Every time the computer passes through the loop the value in location K is incremented by 1; this operation is comparable to the arithmetic statement, K=K+1. The new value in location K is equal to the old value in location K plus 1. The computer is instructed to repeat the loop if the value in location K plus 1 is less than or equal to the value in location N; however, when the value in location K plus 1 exceeds the value in location N, the computer is instructed to leave the loop. When written as

DO n $L=m_1,m_2,m_3$

a flow chart is given in the following way:

FLOW CHART

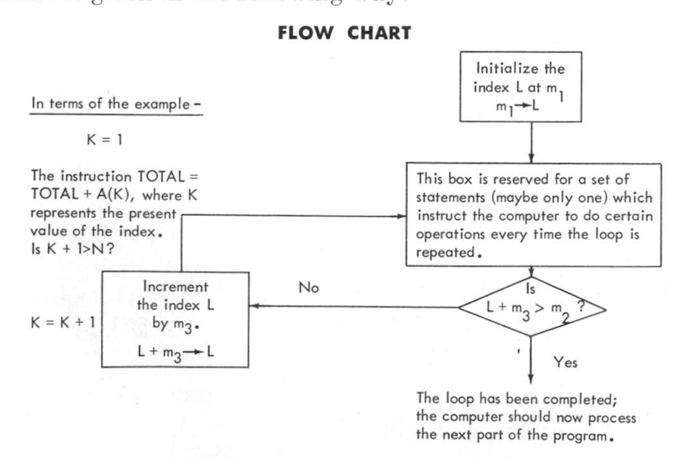

Another example is the following:

```
                m1 m2 m3
DO  20  I=1, 10, 2
          ______ } (Room for other statements,
          ______ }  if necessary)
          ______ }
20  TOTAL=TOTAL+X(I)
```

The example is carried out according to the following procedure:

1. Initialize the index I at 1.
2. Perform operations, one of which is the addition of the value in storage location X(1) into a location named TOTAL.
3. Is 1, the current value of the index I, plus 2, the value of m_3, greater than 10, the value of m_2? Since the answer is no, add 2, the value of m_3, to the current value in location I, namely 1.

Steps 1 through 3 are repeated until the answer to the question in 3 is yes. When the answer to 3 is yes, the loop has been completed and we go to the next part of the program. The values added to the location TOTAL during the loop are X(1), X(3), X(5), X(7), X(9). X(11) is not added since $9 + 2 > 10$. The reader should compare the above example with the example program given to calculate the mean of a group of numbers. Let us now compare the DO statement for the same calculation with the previous program for the IF statement.

With DO statement

```
    TOTAL=0
    DO  20  K=1,N,1
20  TOTAL=TOTAL+X(K)
    R=N
    TOTAL=TOTAL/R
```

With IF statement

```
    TOTAL=0
    K=1
30  TOTAL=TOTAL+X(K)
    IF(N-K) 10,10,20
20  K=K+1
    GO TO 30
10  R=N
    TOTAL=TOTAL/R
```

A comparison of the two programs indicates that the program utilizing the DO statement requires only five statements while the program employing the IF statement requires eight statements; the reason for this difference in the number of statements can be traced to the fact that the DO statement takes the place of the following four statements:

K=1	Initialization
IF(N−K) 10,10,20	Testing
K=K+1	Incrementing
GO TO 30	Completing the loop

The initialization of the index takes place with the execution of the DO statement; it is the very first step in the utilization of the loop. The testing and the incrementing of the index takes place just after execution of the last statement of the "DO" loop; that is, just after the execution of statement number 20 in the following program:

```
      DO  20  K=1,N,1
          ______
          ______
          ______
   20 TOTAL=TOTAL+X(K)
```

As we pointed out in a previous section, the IF statement can be used more effectively in handling the logic involved with more complicated mathematical expressions; on the other hand, the DO statement was specifically designed to provide the programmer an easy means of instructing the computer to execute a program loop.

The letter m_3 may be ignored if it assumes the value 1; for example, the statement DO 20 K=1,N,1 could be written as DO 20 K=1,N since m_3 assumes the value 1. In some programs the use of variables for m_1 and m_3 will be of distinct advantage; the point will be stressed in the later chapters on numerical methods and applications.

2.5.1. DO Loop—Rules

Like the other statements covered thus far, there are some rules which the programmer must follow to utilize correctly the DO statement. First, the programmer should not attempt to enter the range of a DO statement from outside of this range.

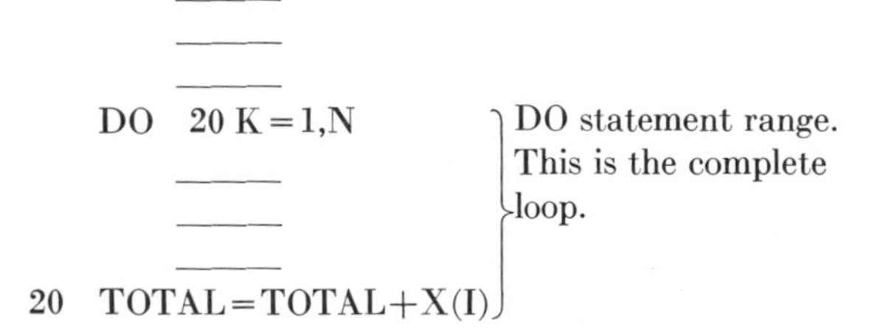

DO 20 K=1,N
20 TOTAL=TOTAL+X(I)
DO statement range.
This is the complete
loop.

The range of a DO statement starts with the DO statement itself and carries through all statements up to and including the statement number n, i.e., the statement number mentioned in the DO statement. Rule 1 implies that a branch into the range of the DO range (loop) is illegal.

```
                        ┌──── GO TO 40
                        │   ┌ DO 20 K=1,N
Error.                  │   │
                        │   │     ______
Executing a             └─→ │40   ______
branch into the             └20 TOTAL=TOTAL+X(K)
```

```
range of the loop        ____
from outside its         ____
range.                   ____
```

Secondly, a transfer statement may not be the last statement of the DO loop. In the FORTRAN II language the statements,

```
DO
IF (expression)
IF (sense switch) (to be explained in the next
                   section)
GO TO (n1,n2,n3, . . . . .n7),L
GO TO n1
```

constitute the transfer statements; i.e., either they transfer control from one part of the program to another (unconditional branch) or have the ability to do so based upon a result of a decision (conditional branch, including another DO loop).

The following program violates rule 2

```
                                    DO  20 K=1,N
                                          ____
                                          ____
                                          ____
Violates Rule 2—transfer →20        GO  TO 50
statement is                              ____
last statement in                         ____
DO loop                        50         ____
```

It may be the case that the logic of the program prevents the programmer from using any of the statements we have mentioned, other than a transfer statement, as the last statement of a "DO" loop. The FORTRAN language provides the dummy statement, CONTINUE, to present the programmer with a means of getting out of the dilemma. The following program is correct:

```
    DO 20 K=1,N

       ____
    GO TO 50
20  CONTINUE
50     ____
       ____
       ____
```

The CONTINUE statement tells the computer to execute "no-operation"; in other words, the contents of the control counter is incremented, but nothing else is done. Because the CONTINUE is the last statement of the DO loop, the next instruction will tell the computer to test the index to see if the loop has been completed so as to either repeat the loop or go to the next part of the program.

The third rule involves the definition of the looping index. The FOR-

TRAN compiler will point out an error if you redefine an index within the range of a DO loop

```
                                          DO 20 K=1,N
                                             ______
                                             ______
                                             ______
This statement redefines the index }
for the loop.                      }-->   K=K+L
                                             ______
                                             ______
                                             ______
                                       20 TOTAL=TOTAL+X(K)
```

Although it is not possible to enter a DO loop from outside of its range, it is possible to reenter the "DO" loop under certain conditions; in this case the looping index must not be redefined as stated in rule 3.

```
                           DO 20 K=1,N
The statements from           ______
the DO statement              ______
through statement 20,         ______
along with those           GO TO (35,25),L
statements enclosed            ______
in the broken           25     ______
lines below, form              ______
the range of the        60     ______
"DO".                          ______
                               ______
                               ______
                        20 TOTAL=TOTAL+X(K)
                                  ______
                                  ______
                        ---------------------------
                        35        ______           }  These statements are in
                           K=K+I                   }- the "range" of the "DO"
                        55 GO TO 60                }  statement
                        ---------------------------
```

When L takes on the value 1 in the above program, the next statement to be executed is statement number 35. Since K, the looping index, is undefined before returning to statement number 60, there is a violation of rule 3. However, the replacement of the statement K=K+I by another statement, say K=J+I would give a correct program; thus, we see it is possible to reenter the "DO" loop.

We have used the above example to demonstrate that the index may not be altered in the loop or the extended loop (extended by the instruction from statement number 35 through statement number 55), but it certainly is possible to use the index as a variable anywhere in the loop or the extended loop. For instance, statement number 35 might be R=X(K) or R=K+5. The inference here is that the index is defined whenever we branch out of the DO loop (whether we reenter to give what has been called the extended loop or we do not reenter the loop and continue with the remainder of the program).

The two possible ways of leaving the DO loop are to branch out or to exit normally; to branch out means to leave the loop before the index has attained its maximum possible value, m_2; to exit normally means to leave the loop after the execution of the last statement in the loop when the index has attained its maximum possible value, m_2.

The normal means of exit from the DO loop leaves the index in an undefined state (the FORTRAN compiler assumes no value has been placed in the location for the index) and therefore not available for use as a variable until it is redefined.

Program 1

```
      DO 20 K=1,N
         ______
         ______
         ______
20       ______
      L=K+2
```

A normal exit from the loop has left the index K undefined; therefore the statement following statement number 20 has an undefined variable on the right-hand side of an arithmetic statement. An error message will be typed out.

Program 2

```
      DO 20 K=1,N
         ______
20       ______
      K=5+I*2
      L=K+2
```

Correct

Program 1 is incorrect because the programmer has neglected to redefine the index K. Program 3 is correct; the index K need not be redefined because the program branches out of the DO loop instead of taking the normal way out of the DO loop.

Program 3

```
    DO  20  K=1,N
        ______
        ______
    GO TO 30
        ______
        ______
20      ______
        ______
        ______
        ______
30  L=K+2
```

2.5.2. Nested DO Loops

A great deal of the logical power of the DO loop can be traced to the ability of the FORTRAN compiler to translate a complicated "nest" of "DO" loops.

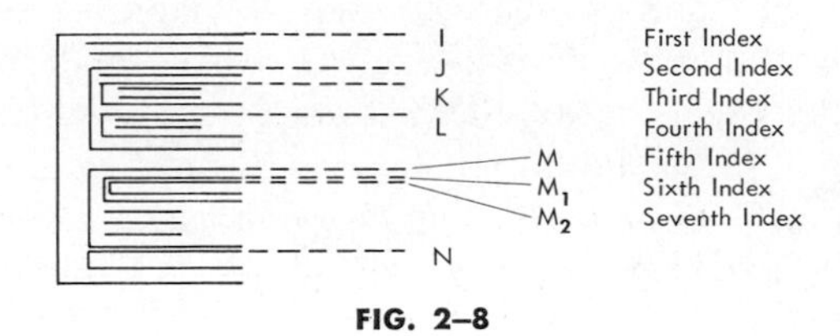

FIG. 2–8

The first step in the program shown in Figure 2–8 would be to initialize the index of the outside loop, I. Then the index J is initialized and next, K. If the range of the index K is from 1 to 10, this loop will be repeated 10 times, while the computer will hold the indices I and J at their initial values. Let us assume that the index L can take on values from 1 to 15; then the computer executes the loop with index L 15 times, while holding the indices I and J at their initial values. The next will be to increment the index J and repeat the loop with index J; if J can take on values from 1 to 10, this loop which contains two smaller loops will be repeated 10 times. Upon repetition of the J loop (this will be shorthand for "the loop with index J"), the computer will again hit the first statement of the K loop; at that point the index K is redefined at its initial value, namely 1. Remember that if the computer originally took a normal exit from the K loop, the index K was undefined prior to this reinitialization step. The remainder of the nest of "DO" loops follows the same pattern. The principal of a nest of DO loops can be easily explained by reference to the following simple nest of DO loops.

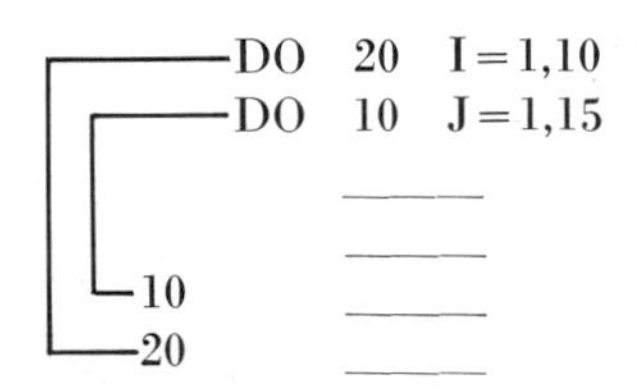

The inner loop (the J loop) will be repeated 15 times for every time through the I loop. If the computer is permitted to take the normal exit from the I loop, the I loop will have been repeated 10 times and the J loop 150 times, 15 times for each value of the index I. It is possible for the same statement to serve as the last statement for both DO loops.

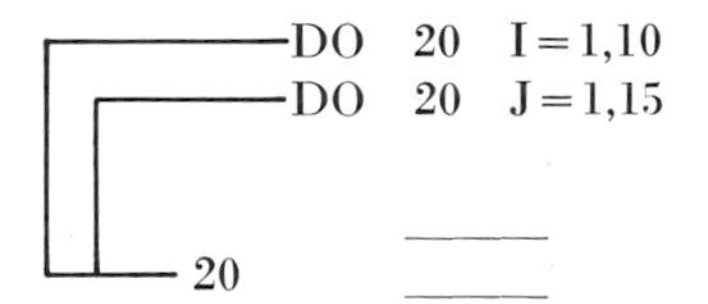

A practical example of the use of a nest of 2 DO loops is the following addition, element by element, of two arrays to get a third array. Given the arrays A and B, each having 15 rows and 10 columns:

Array A					*Array B*				
$a_{1.1}$	$a_{1.2}$	$a_{1.3}$	..	$a_{1.10}$	$b_{1.1}$	$b_{1.2}$	$b_{1.3}$	..	$b_{1.10}$
$a_{2.1}$	$a_{2.2}$	$a_{2.3}$	..	$a_{2.10}$	$b_{2.1}$	$b_{2.2}$	$b_{2.3}$	..	$b_{2.10}$
.	.	..	..	.	.	.	..	..	.
.	.	..	..	.	.	.	..	..	.
.	.	..	..	.	.	.	..	..	.
$a_{15.1}$	$a_{15.2}$	$a_{15.3}$	..	$a_{15.10}$	$b_{15.1}$	$b_{15.2}$	$b_{15.3}$	..	$b_{15.10}$

The problem is to produce a third array, C, each element $c_{ij}=a_{ij}+b_{ij}$; in other words, to obtain the element in row i and column j of the C array, add the element in row i and column j of the array A to the element in row i and column j of the B array.

Program

```
      DIMENSION A(15,15), B(15,15), C(15,15)
      DO 20 I=1,15
      DO 20 J=1,10
   20 C(I,J)=A(I,J)+B(I,J)
```

We assume that the A array and the B array are already in the computer. The double DO loop operates in a way to initialize I at 1, then to initialize J at 1, then take the value in the (1,1) location of the A array (remember this is really the first location in the A array, stored one-dimensionally, that is, the A array is stored as

A(1,1)	A(2,1)	•••	A(15,1)	A(1,2)	A(2,2)	•••	A(15,2)	A(1,3)
		•••				•••		

The first column is stored first, then the second column, etc.; we say columnwise) and the value in the (1,1) location of the B array, add them in a register, then place the sum in the (1,1) location of the C array. The next location to take on a value will be C(1,2), since I is held at the value 1 while J takes on all values from 1 to 10. After the location C(1,10) takes on a value, the inner or J loop is completed; at this point the test for the I loop becomes the following: Is 1, the current value of I, plus 1 ($m_3=1$) greater than 10? Because the answer is no, I is incremented by 1 ($m_3=1$), and the computer returns to the first statement of the J loop: i.e., DO 20 J=1,10. Now J is reinitialized at 1; therefore, the next location to take on a value will be C(2,1). The last location to take on a value will be C(15,10).

2.5.3. Comparison of IF Statements and DO Statements

To appreciate the effectiveness of the nested DO statements in the above example, below we present the same example using two IF statements.

FLOW CHART—Two Combined IF Statements

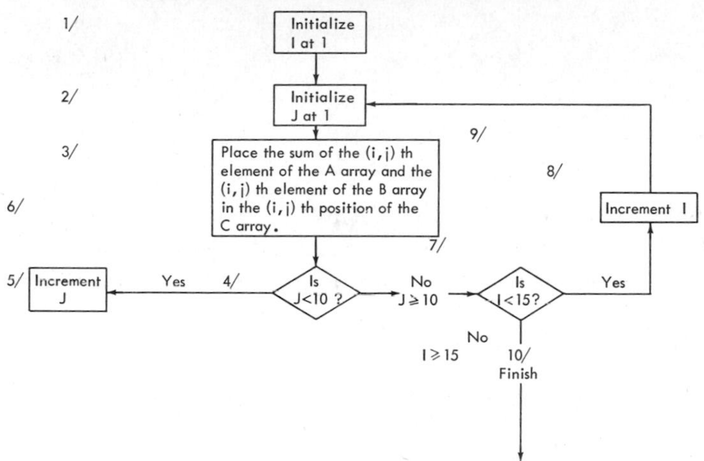

Reference		*Program*
		DIMENSION A(15,15), B(15,15), C(15,15)
1		I=1
2	15	J=1
3	30	C(I,J)=A(I,J)+B(I,J)
4		IF(J−10)20,10,10
5	20	J=J+1
6		GO TO 30
7	10	IF(I−15)25,35,35
8	25	I=I+1
9		GO TO 15
10	35	_____
		_____
		_____

Note that at the completion of the J loop, the I index is incremented and the J index is reinitialized at 1; for every number in the range of the I index the program must repeat the J loop 10 times. A comparison of the program utilizing the nest of two DO loops with the above program shows the former program required three main steps, while the latter required nine main steps. By placing the decision boxes after incrementing the indices, the programmer may take advantage of the ability to transfer which is built into the IF statement; in this way the programmer may eliminate the two GO TO statements.

Reference		*Program*
		DIMENSION A(15,15),B(15,15),C(15,15)
1		I = 1
2	15	J = 1
3	30	C(I,J) = A(I,J) + B(I,J)
4		J = J + 1
5		IF (J−10) 30,30,10
6	10	I = I + 1
7		IF(I−15) 15,15,25
	25	______
		______
		______

Notice that the logic of both IF statements had to be altered from that given in the previous program so that the programmer could change the order of the statements and still be logically correct.

FLOW CHART

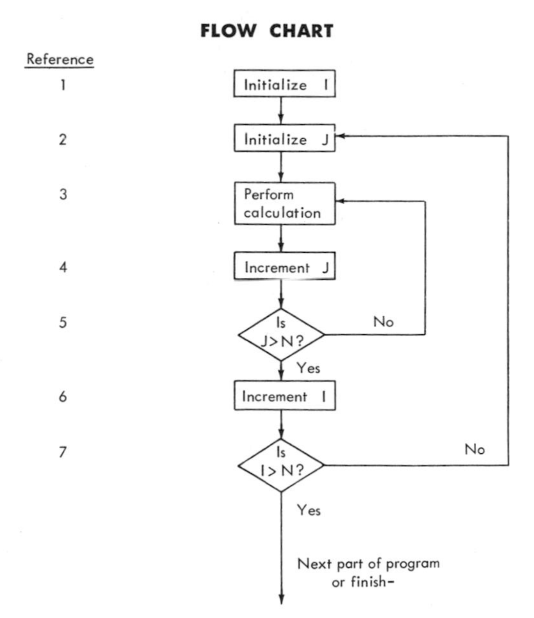

Now, the calculation is repeated if J is equal to or less than 10; because the index is incremented after the calculation, the loop must be repeated for the last index value, 10. Only when the index J exceeds 10, will all values of the index have taken part in the calculation.

2.5.4. Complementation of IF and DO Statements

To complete the discussion of DO and IF statements, we present an example designed to illustrate a need for both types of statements. The problem is to take the mean of a group of 1 to 100 numbers (remember, to take the mean of a group of values, add the values together and then divide by the number of values) and at the same time take the product of the odd-spaced numbers; i.e. the first, third, fifth, seventh, etc. (X(1),X(3),X(5),X(7), . . .).

Program

```
      DIMENSION X(100)
      PROD=1
      SUM=0
      DO 20 I=1,N
      J=I/2
      IF(2*J-I)15,20,20
   15 PROD=PROD*X(I)
   20 SUM=SUM+X(I)
      P=N
      REAN=SUM/P
```

As before, we assume that a value has been read in for the variable N, and then values have been read into the N locations X(1),X(2), ... ,X(N); the details of input to the computer will be explained in the next chapter. The reader should focus attention on the two statements

```
      J=I/2
      IF(2*J-I)15,20,20
```

which decide whether the index I, is even or odd. When I takes on an odd value, such as 9, J equals 9/2. Since the division operation is executed in fixed-point arithmetic, the decimal part of 4.5 is dropped to give a result of 4. Now 2*4−9 equal −1; that is, whenever I takes on an odd value, the result of the calculation 2*J−I will give a negative result. However, when I takes on an even value, such as 10, J equals 10/2 or 5 with no decimal part to be dropped; in this case the result of the calculation 2*J−I will always give a zero result (2*5−10). The program has been written so that a zero result for the calculation (2*J−I) will give a branch to statement number 20, so the value is added into the location SUM; but, a negative result for the calculation (2*J−I) will give a branch to statement number 15 so the value is multiplied by the previous product of odd numbers and then the value is added to the location SUM.

2.5.5. Modification of Example for Computer Run

At this point, it would be very worthwhile for the reader to punch the statements of the last program in IBM cards and run the problem on the computer. To run the problem the reader should place the following two statements immediately after the DIMENSION statement:

```
[2]99  READ (5, 101) N, (X(I), I = 1,N)
101    FORMAT (I3/(5F5.1))
```

After the statement, REAN= SUM/P, include the following statements:

```
[2]    WRITE (6,102) REAN
102    FORMAT (F 10.3)
       GO TO 99
       END
```

The reader must also punch the following data cards to be included at the end of the deck of instruction cards.

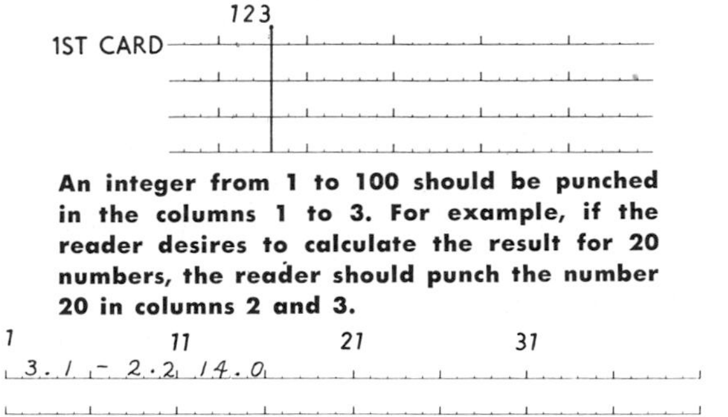

123
1ST CARD
An integer from 1 to 100 should be punched in the columns 1 to 3. For example, if the reader desires to calculate the result for 20 numbers, the reader should punch the number 20 in columns 2 and 3.
1
11
21
31
3.1 -2.2 14.0

If the number is negative, the sign should go in to the left of the first non-zero digit. To demonstrate, let us take the case of N = 3, as specified on the first card; then, the second card would look as above. The decimal point must be punched in each field.

2.6. The IF SENSE SWITCH Statement

Computers are usually equipped with four or more switches, which are placed on the exterior of the computer; the IF SENSE SWITCH statement tests one of these exterior switches as opposed to the IF statement, which acts as an internal switch. An internal switch is one that can be handled only through programming the computer to do so, whereas an

[2] These statements refer to tape input and tape output as is usually used for medium to large size computers, such as, the IBM 7040/44, IBM 7090/94, GE 625, etc. If the program is to be run on a smaller machine, such as the IBM 1620, where magnetic tape is unnecessary because of slower internal speed, these two statements become,

```
99 READ 101, N, (X(I), I = 1,N)
   PUNCH 102, REAN
```

external switch can be controlled manually by the operator. The manual type can be used to advantage in certain circumstances. Say the program is being written for the benefit of many users; some of the users may wish the results in printed form, while others desire the results in punched cards. At the time the program is run, the user tells the operator to put switch 1 up or on if he desires one type of output and to put switch 1 down or off if he desires the other type of output. For example, the program is to be written such that, switch 1 on means punching cards and switch 1 off means printing on paper.

```
       IF(SENSE SWITCH 1)20,30
    30 PRINT
       GO TO 40
    20 PUNCH
    40  _____         Statements for the
        _____         continuation of
        _____         the program or to
                      stop the computer
```

Upon execution of the IF(SENSE SWITCH n)n_1,n_2 statement, the computer will execute statement number n_1 if the switch is on; if the switch is off, the computer will take statement number n_2 for its next instruction. An error message will be typed at compile time if there is no statement number n_1 or n_2 in the program.

2.6.1. General Sense Switches

Correct use of the IF(SENSE SWITCH n) statement could lead to a multiway switch and save vital internal memory space. The IBM 1620 computer comes equipped with four external switches, presenting the user with the possibility of a 16-way switch. As an example, we will use three of the switches to demonstrate an eight-way switch.

```
       IF(SENSE SWITCH 1) 10,20
    10 IF(SENSE SWITCH 2) 30,40
    20 IF(SENSE SWITCH 2) 50,60
    30 IF(SENSE SWITCH 3) 200,300
    40 IF(SENSE SWITCH 3) 400,500
    50 IF(SENSE SWITCH 3) 600,700
    60 IF(SENSE SWITCH 3) 800,900

   200 _____       This statement will be executed if all three switches are
       _____       on
       GO TO 99
   300 _____       This statement will be executed if switches 1 and 2 are on
       _____       and switch 3 is off.
       GO TO 99
```

400 ——— This statement will be executed if switch 1 is on, switch 2
——— is off, and switch 3 is on.
GO TO 99
500 ——— This statement will be executed if switch 1 is on, switch
——— 2 is off, and switch 3 is off.
GO TO 99
600 ——— This statement will be executed if switch 1 is off, but
——— switches 2 and 3 are on.
GO TO 99
700 ——— This statement will be executed if switch 1 is off, switch 2
——— is on, and switch 3 is off.
GO TO 99
800 ——— This statement will be executed if switch 1 is off, switch 2
——— is off, and switch 3 is on.
GO TO 99
900 ——— This statement will be executed if all switches are
——— off.
99 This is a common branch for the above eight parts, similar to the example, on page 42 involving departmental payroll; the payroll example used the COMPUTED GO TO statement, whereas this example uses external switches.

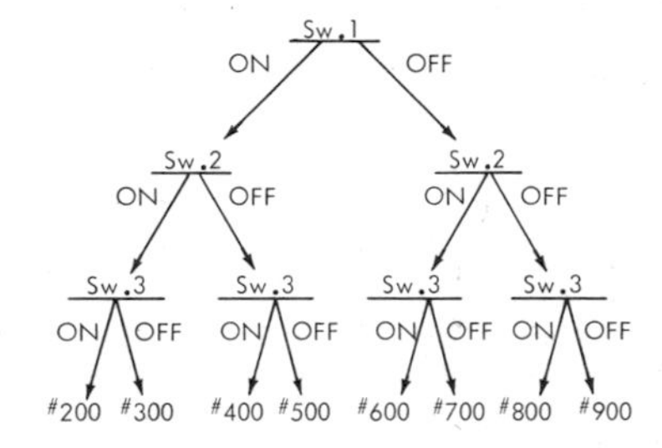

Diagrammatically:

It is obvious that the decision to plan the switch on or off should be made before the program starts to run. If it is necessary to change the position of the switch after executing part of the program, the computer should be given the instruction to halt; due to the extreme speed of the computer, the amount of instructions which have been executed is very hard to estimate; therefore, if the position of a manual switch is changed while the computer is running, the IF(SENSE SWITCH) instruction may have been executed while the switch was still on the old position.

Besides the four manual switches on the computer console, the programmer may reference switches 6,7, and 9. Switch 6 is turned on when the computer senses that the reader is trying to read an illegal character. Either the computer will stop at this point or take the next sequential instruction despite the illegal character (another manual switch makes this option available). The next instruction should be an "IF(SENSE SWITCH 6)" statement, which then directs the machine to execute an error-correction routine.

To illustrate the use of switch 6, assume that a great many cards have been punched for a certain computer (these are instructions) and now must be run on a different computer. Rather than change all the old cards so that they can be run on the new computer, the programmer can set up a table which gives the new computer equivalent of the old computer statements.

TABLE

Old Statement	*New Statement*
_____	_____
_____	_____
_____	_____
_____	_____

After a card has been read into the computer, switch 6 must be tested to see if the old statement is not acceptable to the present computer. If the old statement is not acceptable, a program must be written which instructs the computer to search the above table to look for the new computer equivalent of the old statement. The new statement is then placed in the memory of the computer; if the old statement does not appear in the table, the program instructs the computer to stop.[3]

```
        _____
              READ
        _____
      IF(SENSE SWITCH 6) 10,20
  10  Start of table-look-up routine—If there exists
      an equivalent new statement, it is placed in the
      computer memory, and then the computer pro-
      ceeds by taking the next part of the program.
      When the old statement is not in the table, the
      computer is stopped.
  20  __________
        _____
        _____                Remainder of
        _____                  Program
```

In the sample program the discussion has centered around switch 6; however, switch 7 serves the same purpose for output.

2.6.2. Other Sense Switches

A previous example has illustrated the calculation of the mean when the user knew the number of values of which he wanted to take the mean; this

[3] Although this discussion is centered around the IBM 1620 computer, the principle holds with minor changes in procedure for all computers.

number was punched in a card and entered at run time. To count the number of values may be quite a problem if the number of values exceeds 100. Switch 9 can be used by the programmer to enable the user to calculate the mean of any number of values, without counting the number of values before the program is run.

Switch 9 is activated by the movement of a small spring in the reader hopper (cards to be entered into the computer are placed in the hopper). As long as there are any cards in the hopper, the weight of the cards keep the spring in a compressed position. When the last card in the data deck is read into the computer, there will be no cards in the hopper, and the spring then uncoils. Switch 9 is turned on by the recoiling of the spring, and therefore can be used to signal the fact that the last card has been read in to the computer.

Program

```
      DIMENSION  X(1000)
   99 SUM=0
      DO  20  I=1,1000
      READ  X(I)
      SUM = SUM + X(I)
      IF (SENSE SWITCH 9) 10,20
   20 CONTINUE
   10 P = I
      REAN = SUM/P
      PRINT 7, REAN
    7 FORMAT(E14.8)
      GO TO 99
      END
```

By placing the "IF(SENSE SWITCH 9)" statement in the DO loop, the last card causes a branch out of the DO loop, therefore preserving the index, I, which serves to count the number of cards which have been read into the computer. In the program, one value is read for each card; however, that is not necessary. If four values are read in per card, then the total number of values to be included in the calculation of the mean are four times the value in location I when the last card causes the branch out of the DO loop.

In addition to switches 1,2,3,4,6,7, and 9, switches 11,12,13, and 14 are available to the programmer; the latter switches allow the programmer to use the IF (SENSE SWITCH) statement in the same way he uses the IF statement(in fact, these switches are used by the FORTRAN compiler in the translation of the IF statement).

2.6.3. Internal and External Switches

Not all computers are equipped with switches which may be manipulated manually at the computer operation panel; some computers are equipped with switches which function in the same way as the manual switches (can be turned on and off and tested) except that they are manipulated by control statements (internally) instead of manually; some computers have both types of switches.

Without manual switches, analysts who make use of general programs would be forced to submit control cards so that the internal switches could be utilized—one example might be the choice of printing the results on the printer or punching the results on cards. Of course, internal switches are advantageous for any decision which is more or less independent of the individual user. In Chapter 5 the reader will be introduced to FORTRAN statements which can operate internal switches; on computers such as the IBM 7040/44 and 7094, the internal switches are called sense lights and the external switches are called sense switches.

2.7. The PAUSE, STOP, and END Statements

The PAUSE statement instructs the computer to halt; then upon pressing the START button on the computer console, the computer will take the next sequential instruction.

```
R=S*T
T=A**2/5.3
PAUSE
B=R*T**2
```

In the above example the computer will halt upon execution of the PAUSE instruction; when the operator presses the START button, the computer will execute the instruction B=R*T**2.

The STOP statement acts like the PAUSE statement in that the computer will halt and take the next sequential instruction when the operator pushes the START. However, in addition to the halt instruction, the FORTRAN compiler translates the STOP instruction into an unconditional branch to a place in the memory.

```
Core Position 00000    GO TO 25
                       ______
                       ______
                       ______
                       R=S*T
                       A=B*C/D   The STOP instruction translates
                                 as a machine-language halt and
                    25 STOP      GO TO core position 00000.
                       S=B/C**5
```

In other words, the STOP statement creates a loop composed of three instructions.

1. A machine-language halt.
2. A transfer to a position in core holding another transfer instruction.
3. A transfer back to the halt statement.

The only way to restart the machine is to type in an instruction from the console typewriter; this technique is extremely time consuming. Therefore, a STOP statement should be used only if there is no intention of running the program more than once. The example here is not a general program in the sense that the program ends after the processing of one problem (one

```
      DIMENSION A(100)
      READ N
      DO 20 I=1,N
   20 READ A(I)
      ——— Process the numbers in the A array.
      PRINT
      STOP
```

set of data), because the processing of a second set of data would require the manual operation of the console typewriter. The general program, capable of processing more than one set of data at any computer run, would be written in the following way:

```
      DIMENSION A(100)
   30 READ N
      DO 20 I=1,N
   20 READ A(I)
      ———
      ——— Process the members
      ——— in the A array.
      PRINT
      GO TO 30
```

After printing the answers to problems utilizing the first set of data, the computer will branch to the first READ instruction to begin the processing of the second set of data. If there is no second set of data, the computer will halt, and an indicator will light on the computer console, indicating the state of operations. To process a second set of data which originally was not placed in the card reader, depress the READER START button on the card reader; otherwise the run is terminated and the procession of another program begins on the computer. The next section will be devoted to the technical aspects of input and output statements.

2.8. The END Statement

The END statement is required to be the last statement of every program written in the FORTRAN language; it is a signal to the FORTRAN compiler that there are no more cards in the source deck. The END statement is not involved with program logic and is not utilized as an instruction to the computer at run time.

Problems

2.1. Punch the following program on IBM cards and run on the computer.

```
C     SOLUTION OF LINEAR EQUATION AX + B = 0
 99   READ (5, 75) A, B
 75   FORMAT (2F5.2)
      IF (A) 10,20,10
 20   IF (B) 60, 40, 60
 40   WRITE (6,76)
 76   FORMAT (26H BOTH COEFF ARE ZERO – X = 0)
      GO TO 99
 10   IF (B) 50,30,50
 30   WRITE (6,77)
 77   FORMAT (10X,6H X = 0)
      GO TO 99
 60   WRITE (6,78)
 78   FORMAT (21H NO FEASIBLE SOLUTION)
      GO TO 99
 50   X = – B/A
      WRITE (6,79) X
 79   FORMAT (7X, 4HX = , F 20.8)
      GO TO 99
      END
```

The input data cards should be punched as follows:

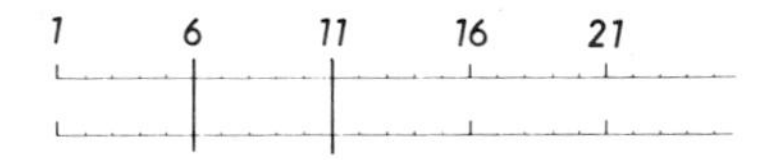

Input data is of the form xx. xx or – x.xx, where the decimal point should be punched in the field.

(See note on input/output statements given earlier for FORTRAN II; e.g., READ 75, A, B.)

Write a flow chart for the above problem.

Are all the above tests necessary to solve the problem; why are they included?

Is the program completely general?

2.2. In this chapter a program was given for the calculation of the arithmetic mean of a group of numbers in two different ways. In one case, the number of values was counted and punched on the first card; in the other case, it was not necessary to count the cards due to the use of the SENSE SWITCH 9 instruction.

Suppose the computer has no sense switches; is there any way of calculating the mean of a group of 1 to 100 numbers (HINT—try a code on the last card).

For the program given in the chapter, run the program on the computer by including the following cards (see page 46):

```
      DIMENSION X (100)
   99 READ 7, N, (X(I), I = 1, N)
    7 FORMAT (I3/(F6.2))
```

The statements preceding the GO TO 99 statement should be:

```
      PUNCH 6, TOTAL
    6 FORMAT (10X, F20.8)
```

2.3. Punch out the following program for solution on the computer.

Modify the above program to calculate the median in addition to the arithmetic mean; the median is the value which divides the numbers into two equal groups. If there are five values, 2.1, 3.2, 5.1, 2.6, 5.7, the median value is 3.2 because the numbers 2.1 and 2.6 are less than 3.2 and the numbers 5.1 and 5.7 are greater than 3.2. Use the same READ and PRINT statements and the same input data format.

2.4. Point out all the FORTRAN errors in the following program:

```
      X = 1
      R = X/Z
      I = I + 1
      GO TO (20,30) I
      GO TO 40
   30 K = 1
   25 R = K * 2
   40 F = 2.5
      DO 50, I = 1, K
      S = K/I
   20 L = I + 1
   50 IF (I-K) 30,40,60
   60 PAUSE
      END
```

2.5. *Arithmetic Progression.* Find the sum and last term of any arithmetic progression.

Let A represent the first term
" D " " common difference
" N " " number of terms
" L " " last term
" S " " sum of the terms

using the following definitions for L and S:

$$L = A+D \cdot (N-1)$$
$$S = N \cdot (A+L)\ /2$$

2.6. *Geometric Progression.* Find the sum and last term of any geometric progression.

Let L represent the last term
" A " " first "
" N " " number of terms
" R " " common ratio
" S " " sum of the terms

using the following definitions for L and S:

$$L = AR^{(N-1)}$$
$$S = (A-RL) / (1-R)$$

2.7. *Simultaneous Equations—2 Variables.* Write a program that will solve any pair of simultaneous equations in two variables.

$$AX+BY=C$$
$$DX+EY=F$$

Include tests for zero in denominator.

2.8. *Four-Digit Numbers.* The four digit number 3025 has the following property: if the number formed by considering only the first two digits (30) is added to the number formed by considering only the last two digits (25), the total will be 55; if this number (55) is squared, the result will be the original number.

$$(55)^2 = 3025$$

Find all four-digit numbers having this property.

2.9. *Monkey Problem.* There are three shipwrecked sailors and a monkey on a desert island who have gathered a pile of coconuts which are to be divided the next day. During the night one sailor arises, divides the pile into three equal parts and finds one coconut left over, which he gives to the monkey. He then hides his share. Later during the same night, each of the other two sailors, in turn, arise and repeat the performance of the first sailor. In the morning all three sailors arise, divide the pile into three equal shares, and find one left over which is given to the monkey. How many coconuts were in the original pile? Since the result is not unique, find all values from 1 to 1,000 which satisfy the conditions. (One answer is 79).

2.10. *Standard Deviation.* Write a FORTRAN program which will calculate the standard deviation of a group of N values; where the standard deviation, σ, is defined as:

$$\sigma = \sqrt{\frac{\sum_{i=1}^{N} (x_i - \bar{x})^2}{N}}$$ which is the same as

$$\sqrt{\frac{\sum_{i=1}^{N} x_i^2}{N} - \left(\frac{\sum_{i=1}^{N} x_i}{N}\right)^2}$$ Since $\bar{x} = \frac{\sum_{i=1}^{N} x^i}{N}$.

The input to the program should be the following (the total number of values is N, where $1 \leqslant N \leqslant 999$):

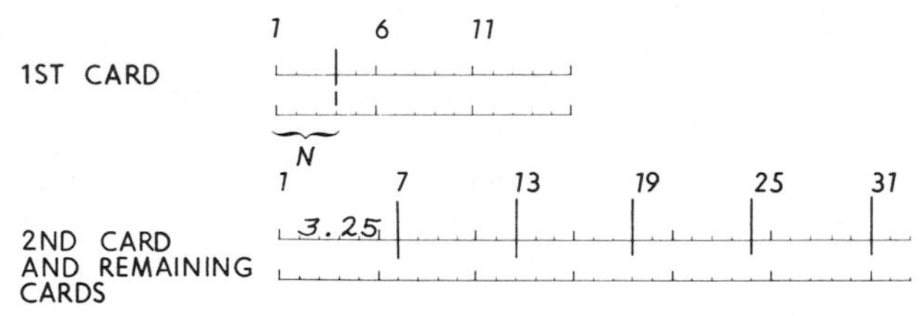

Ten values per card; each value is allowed 6 columns (from column 1 to column 60) and a decimal point must be punched in each field.

Use the following input and output statements:

```
      DIMENSION X (999)
      READ 8, N, (X (I), I = 1, N)
    7 FORMAT (I3 / (10F 6.2))
```

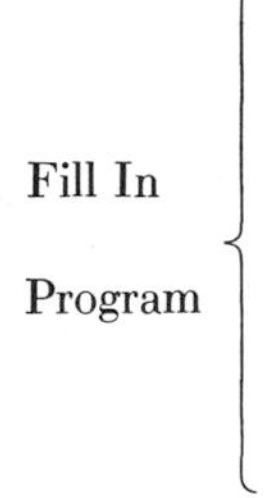


```
                          PUNCH 37
   37 FORMAT (33HCALCULATION OF STANDARD DEVIATION)
      PUNCH 38, N, SD
   38 FORMAT (/25TOTAL NUMBER OF VALUES = , I4, 10X, 12HSTD.
      DEV. = , E 14.8)
```

2.11. *Binary Search.* Write a FORTRAN IV program which will search a table of arguments to find the functions of these arguments:

(x)	$f(x)$

First, read in the cards composing the table; say each card has the value x and the value $f(x)$. Now punch a deck having an argument x in each card; for each x, find its corresponding functional value, $f(x)$.

One possible method would be to sort the arguments in ascending order, either in the machine or before the cards composing the table enter the machine. Start the search by looking at the argument in the location which divides the table in two; actually this location number should be a power of two, so it may not divide the table into exactly two parts. Compare the number in this location with the argument in question (i.e., the argument whose function we need) to determine in which half of the table the argument lies. Keep repeating this process of halving the available locations until the argument is encountered.

FLOW CHART

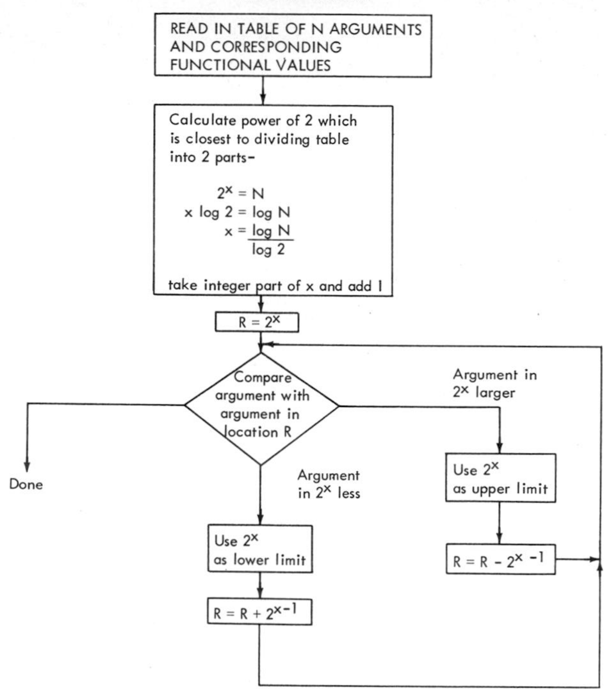

Use the following READ Statements—
To read in table

```
      READ 7, N, (X(I), Y(I), I=1, K)
    7 FORMAT (I3/ (2F6.2))
```

To read in data (arguments)

```
      READ 9, K
      I = 1
      READ 8, Z
    9 FORMAT (I 3)
    8 FORMAT (F6.2)
```

Table Cards—

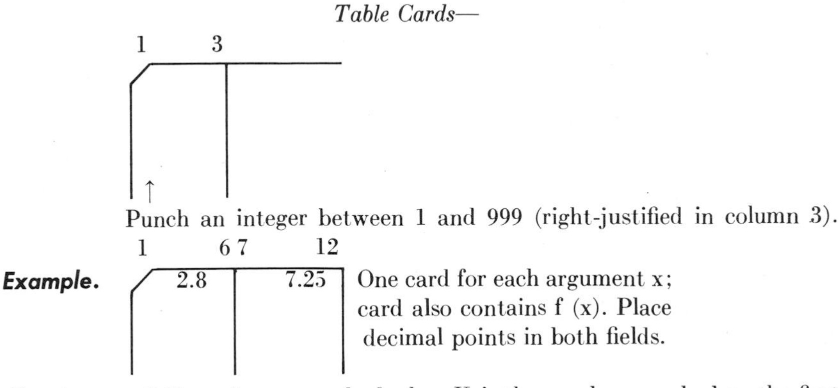

Punch an integer between 1 and 999 (right-justified in column 3).

Continue until K cards are punched when K is the number punched on the first card.

Data Cards

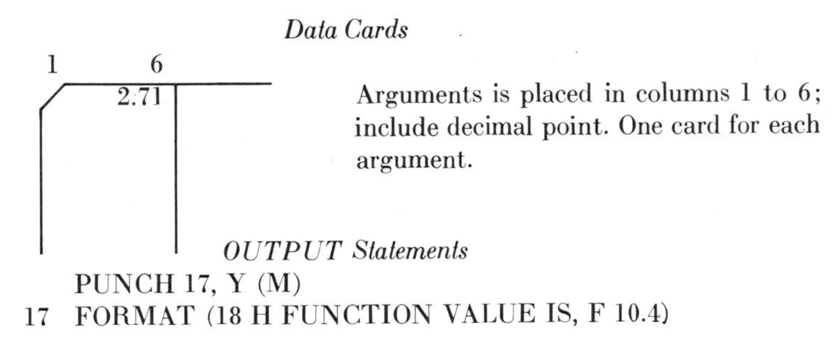

1 6
2.71
Arguments is placed in columns 1 to 6; include decimal point. One card for each argument.

OUTPUT Statements

```
   PUNCH 17, Y (M)
17 FORMAT (18 H FUNCTION VALUE IS, F 10.4)
```

2.12. Write a FORTRAN program to solve for elements of triangles. The ambiguous case may be skipped.

Procedure

Data is entered via punched cards. The angles are punched first, and then the sides, on the same card. An unknown element is left blank. Angles are punched in degrees, minutes, and seconds; format I4 for degrees and I3 for minutes and seconds; the sides are punched in format F8.4. There should be correspondence between angles and sides, i.e., the first angle being the opposite of the first side that appears on the card, etc.

The angles and sides are read, and the angles are transformed to radians.

The number of angles which are not zero is counted. The same procedure is applied to the sides.

The three possible cases are:

3 sides	0 angles
1 side	2 angles
2 sides	1 angle (between them)

The sum of the sides and angles has to equal 3, otherwise the case is impossible; but also the sum of the angles has to be different from 3.

When two sides are found, the angle between them is checked. If that angle is 0, we are at the ambiguous case, and so it is bypassed.

Consider:

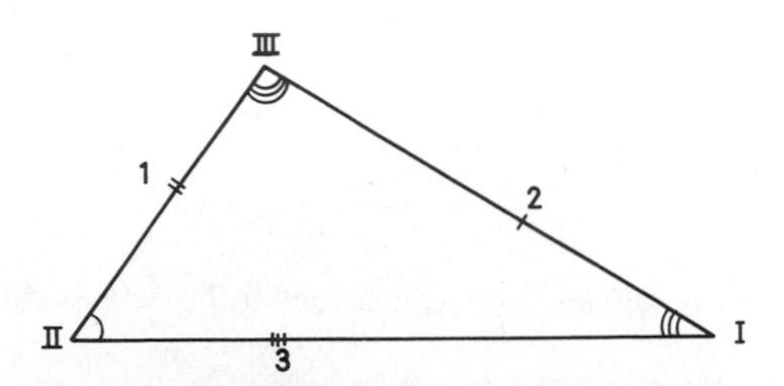

Notice that the number corresponding to angle III is 6 – (1+2), or 6 – (sum of sides forming the angle). This procedure is used throughout the program.

Flow Chart—in Descriptive Terms

The data is read; the angles are transformed to radians, the number of angles not equal to 0, and also the number of sides not equal to 0, are counted. If the sum of the angles not equal to 0 and the sides not equal to 0 is not 3, the case is impossible. If the sum is 3, the sum of the angles not equal to 0 is checked; if that sum is 3, the case is impossible.

Case III

When three sides are given, the angles are calculated by the formula:

$$\text{Tan}\,\frac{A}{2} = \frac{R}{S-a} \qquad \text{Tan}\,\frac{B}{2} = \frac{R}{S-b}$$

$$\text{T}\quad\frac{C}{2} = \frac{R}{S-c}$$

where

$$S = (a+b+c)\,/\,2$$

and

$$R = \sqrt{\frac{(S-a)\,(S-b)\,(S-c)}{S}}\,.$$

Case II

When two sides and one angle are given, the angle between them is calculated by 6 – $LS(1)$ – $LS\,(2)$. $LS(1)$ contains the number assigned to the first nonzero side, and $LS(2)$ the number assigned to the second nonzero side.

If that angle is 0, we are at the ambiguous case. Otherwise the side opposite that angle is calculated by the law of cosines, and the remaining angles are calculated by formula (1).

Case I

When one side and two angles are given, the third angle is calculated, and the law of sines is used.

2.13. *Prime Factor Problem.* Find the prime factors and their powers for any given positive integer N.

3. Input/Output

The process of entering data into and receiving data from the computer is a vital part of using the computer. Obviously, the data going into the computer must be of the form and order that the program is written to process. Usually the handling of data is more complicated in business applications than in scientific applications. However, in order to justify the use of a computer for scientific applications, in most companies there is a need for presenting results to management in a neat form.

The output of the results will be covered before the input of data, because the rules for output can and must be more strict than the rules for input. Suppose that the reader operated a computer operation and rented time to someone else on the computer; the reader might want to publish some standard programs to offer to the customer to lure him away from some other computer. Let us assume that these potential customers have a great many data cards which must be processed; the data on these cards has a certain configuration which is determined by the particular application. The computer center faces many potential users, all having different configurations of data on their input cards. If the reader offers one and only one possible input configuration to the customer, the reader is in effect saying to the customer: "You must convert all of your data cards in order to use my program." The expense and the time involved in making this conversion would, in all likelihood, dissuade the potential user from renting time on the reader's computer. To make the program available to more customers, the FORTRAN compiler should allow a general input. The difficulty of writing rules for input does not lie in the fact that the computer must be able to receive many different forms of data, but in the fact that the programmer cannot know the form of the data before the data reaches the computer. The unknown factor introduces the need for many more rules than would be needed if the form were known.

Since the results of the program are formed in the computer, the programmer will know the form before the results are taken out of the computer. Even though the user will be offered many types of output, the choice is certainly going to be made before the user rents time on the computer; i.e., the user will choose one of the output types before the program is placed on the computer. Therefore, in the case of output, the programmer will know the form of the numbers in the computer at the time he writes the program (how many significant figures, where the decimal point belongs, etc.), thus enabling the FORTRAN language to have strict output rules.

The statements for instructing the computer on the methods to bring data into, and to send results out of, the computer fall into two categories, the input/output statements and the FORMAT statements. The former category deals with the task of informing the computer whether the mode of input-output is to be the card reader, magnetic tape units, or some other mode; also, this group of statements specifies the locations in the machine into which the data is sent or from which locations the results are to be taken for some output media. The FORMAT statements instruct the computer as to the exact forms of the data and the results going to and coming from the locations specified in the input/output statements.

Because the FORMAT statements actually control the form of the input or output material, these statements will be the group to show differences between input and output. The input/output statements are almost identical in form; input/output statements will be discussed together in section 3.1. The FORMAT statements will be discussed in section 3.2, with separate discussions for input and output FORMAT statements because the output format will follow a strict and direct set of rules, whereas the input format must be more general in nature and therefore contain many exceptions.

3.1. Input/Output Statements

The computer can place the results or other material which is created by the program on either cards, magnetic tape, magnetic disk file, paper tape, "on-line" printer, or "on-line" typewriter. The same devices are used to send data or instructions into the computer. We must make the distinction between "off-line" printers and "on-line" printers. The internal speed of the computer in handling data is much greater than that of any printer; however, the speed with which the computer can place the output on magnetic tape is comparable with the internal speed of the computer. When the computer, processing a problem which involves a significant amount of data handling in comparison with the internal calculations, places the output on a printer directly connected to the computer ("on line"), the speed of the entire operation is reduced. Therefore, the output is placed on magnetic tape, and later the tape is removed and a machine, less costly than the large computer, is used to print the material on the tape. The latter technique is referred to as "off-line" printing because the printer is not connected directly to the main computer and therefore does not interfere with the internal calculating speed of the computer.

3.1.1. Available Input/Output Statements—FORTRAN II

Data can be placed into the computer via the card reader, paper tape, magnetic tape, magnetic disk file, or the console typewriter. FORTRAN II for the IBM 1620 provides the following input and output statements:

Input	*Input Media*
ACCEPT n, input list	Console typewriter
TYPE n, input list	Console typewriter
READ n, input list	Card reader
READ TAPE n, input list	Paper tape
Output	*Output Media*
PRINT n, output list	The printed page
PUNCH n, output list	Punched cards
TYPE n, output list	The typed page
PUNCH TAPE n, output list	Paper tape

FIG. 3–1

The letter n in each of these statements is a statement number of a FORMAT statement which the FORTRAN language provides so that the user may specify the exact form of output or general form of input on the output or input media (printed pages, IBM cards, paper tape, or typewriter) which he chooses. FORMAT statements work in conjunction with the associated output statement, and their usage will be covered in the next section.

3.1.2. The Implied DO Loop

The input or output list may contain variables (both floating and fixed), subscripted variables, or an implied DO loop. An implied DO loop operates much the same as the regular DO statement; the implied DO is available only for items in an input or output list.

Implied DO Statement

```
      PRINT  5,(A(I) , I=1 , 10)
    5 FORMAT..............................
```

Regular DO Statement

```
      DO  10  I=1 , 10
   10 PRINT  5,A(I)
    5 FORMAT...................
```

FIG. 3–2

Both of the above programs will print out the values in locations A(1), A(2), . . . , A(10); however, there is a difference between the two types of DO loops. In the next section, concerning FORMAT statements, we shall explore the difference in DO loops and show why we use one instead of the other at one time and vice versa at another time. Before examining a typical list, we shall examine two-dimensional arrays. The notational importance of the double subscript to address elements of a two-dimensional array will be discussed in the first chapter on numerical methods. At the present it should be noted that the first subscript refers to the row and the second subscript refers to the column.

	1st column	*2nd column*	*3rd column*	. . .	*nth column*
1st row	$a_{1,1}$	$a_{1,2}$	$a_{1,3}$	. . .	$a_{1,n}$
2nd row	$a_{2,1}$	$a_{2,2}$	$a_{2,3}$	. . .	$a_{2,n}$
3rd row	$a_{3,1}$	$a_{3,2}$	$a_{3,3}$	. . .	$a_{3,n}$
.	.	.	.		.
.	.	.	.		.
.	.	.	.		.
nth row	$a_{n,1}$	$a_{n,2}$	$a_{n,3}$	. . .	$a_{n,n}$

FIG. 3–3

In the computer the elements are stored in a one-dimensional array; i.e., let us say that the variable $a_{1,1}$ has been assigned location 10000 in the computer memory. Then if the maximum size specified by the programmer in the DIMENSION statement is 10 rows and 15 columns, $a_{2,1}$ is assigned location 10001, $a_{10,1}$ is assigned location 10009, $a_{1,2}$ is assigned location 10010, $a_{2,2}$ is assigned location 10011, $a_{2,10}$ is assigned location 10019, and eventually $a_{10,15}$ is assigned location 10149. We say that the array is stored "columnwise"; this means that the first subscript varies faster than the second subscript. FORTRAN always instructs the computer to reserve space for a two-dimensional array such that the array appears columnwise in the computer memory.

3.1.3. Input/Output Lists

A typical list might be R,S(5), (K(I),I=1,15),(A(J,L),J=1,10),(B(L1), L1=1,N,3),((C(I,K1),I=1,10,2),Z(K1),K1=3,6,2); the order of variables printed from the computer is as follows:

S(5) . . . . The fifth variable in the one-dimensional S array

K(1)
K(2)
. . . . The one-dimensional K array
.
.
K(15)

A(1,L) A(2,L) . . . A(10,L)	The two-dimensional array A has been set up in memory by the Fortran compiler via the DIMENSION statement—A(1,L) is the Lth element of the *first row of the A array*, where L must be previously defined.
B(1) B(4) B(7) B(10) . . . B(N)	The one-dimensional B array; again, the variable N must be previously defined.
C(1,3) C(3,3) C(5,3) C(7,3) C(9,3) Z(3) C(1,5) C(3,5) C(5,5) C(7,5) C(9,5) Z(5)	The two-dimensional C array, with I, the inner index of the implied DO, varying the fastest, and taking on the values 1,3,5,7, and 9; K, the outer index, takes on the values 3 and 5; the third and fifth values in the Z array are also addressed.

FIG. 3–4

If a variable which has not been defined appears in an output list, the FORTRAN compiler will instruct the computer to print an error message at compile time.

The notation for the implied DO loop may be reduced even further if it is desirable to output the entire array. Instead of the statement PRINT 10, (A(I,J),I=1,10),J=1,15) the programmer is allowed to write the statement PRINT 10,A. The reader may recall that we have explained that the arrangement of the variables of an array in the computer memory could be imagined to be one-dimensional with the first subscript varying faster than the second (that is, columnwise). Because of the standard arrangement of the variables of an array, the FORTRAN compiler can get almost as much information from the abbreviated notation as from the regular notation. In either case, the array, being composed of subscripted variables, must have been dimensioned at the start of the program. Since the abbreviated notation does not allow manipulation of the upper limit of either the first or the second subscript, the statement PRINT 10,A prints out all 150 values (assuming the statement DIMENSION A(10,15)) which compose the entire array even if the specific problem only used the first, say, 25 values.

$$\begin{array}{cccccccc}
a_{1,1} & a_{1,2} & \cdots & a_{1,5} & a_{1,6} & \cdots & a_{1,15} \\
a_{2,1} & a_{2,2} & \cdots & a_{2,5} & a_{2,6} & \cdots & a_{2,15} \\
\cdot & \cdot & & \cdot & \cdot & & \cdot \\
\cdot & \cdot & & \cdot & \cdot & & \cdot \\
\cdot & \cdot & & \cdot & \cdot & & \cdot \\
a_{5,1} & a_{5,2} & \cdots & a_{5,5} & a_{5,6} & \cdots & a_{5,15} \\
a_{6,1} & a_{6,2} & \cdots & a_{6,5} & a_{6,6} & \cdots & a_{6,15} \\
\cdot & \cdot & & \cdot & \cdot & & \cdot \\
\cdot & \cdot & & \cdot & \cdot & & \cdot \\
\cdot & \cdot & & \cdot & \cdot & & \cdot \\
a_{10,1} & a_{10,2} & \cdots & a_{10,5} & a_{10,6} & \cdots & a_{10,15}
\end{array}$$

FIG. 3–5

The statement PRINT 10,((A(I,J),I=1,K),J=1,L) does permit the printing of any part or the entire array through the variable upper limits, K and L.

Output statements have been used to demonstrate "lists" in the above examples, but input statement lists could have been used just as well, since they both operate on exactly the same principle.

3.2. Numerical FORMAT Codes—Output

This section is devoted to the group of statements which enable the FORTRAN compiler to describe the output in a very distinct manner and the input in a more general manner, whether the input media be the card reader or paper tape, or whether the output media be the printed page, the punched card, punched paper tape, or the keyboard typewriter. The input/output statement instructs the computer to input or output the value of each variable, in turn, appearing in the output list. Before the instruction is issued to the computer, the FORTRAN compiler consults the associated FORMAT statement to get the form which the value of the variable should assume on the output media.

Before writing the FORMAT statements necessary to specify the form of the output, the user should design the form of the output sheet, tape, or card. To design the output, the user must concentrate on the basic unit of output, the record. In the IBM 1620 computer the input and output media with the associated records are listed in the following table:

Input/Output Medium	*Record*
Cards........................	80 characters (in other words, the entire card)
Paper tape....................	87 characters
Console typewriter.............	87 characters

FIG. 3–6

3.2.1. Fixed-Point; I-Code

Numerical format codes are those used to bring both fixed- and floating-point numbers out of the computer, but not letters, special symbols, or coding to cause manipulations such as spacing. The codes are:

Fixed point. . . . . I*w*
Floating point. . . . . F*w*·*d*
or E*w*·*d*

where *w* represents the number of places in the field on the card or page and *d* represents the places reserved in the field for digits following the decimal point.

A typical output code specifying the form of output for a fixed-point variable might be the following:

```
  PUNCH 7, J1
7 FORMAT(I6)
```

The FORTRAN compiler translates these statements into instructions which tell the computer to punch the contents of location J1 on the card according to the associated FORMAT statement. The compiler then analyzes the FORMAT statement and translates it into these instructions for the computer:

> The left-hand parenthesis is used to instruct the machine to ready the card punch to punch a card; the value in location J1 will be a fixed-point constant and therefore the code for this type of constant, Iw, is specified in the FORMAT statement and is translated into an instruction to the computer to reserve the first six places on the card for the value in location J1; the right parenthesis is then translated into an instruction to the computer saying that no more space is to be reserved on the first card.

A more detailed discussion of the functions of the parenthesis will appear in a later section; here the discussion will be centered on the code Iw, where the w refers to the length of the field on the card.

The length of the storage location and the number of nonzero digits (other than nested zeros) in that location will be the keys to specifying the correct code. In the IBM 1620 the field length for fixed-point numbers can vary from 4 to 10, but must be fixed on the first card of the source deck; assume this length for this discussion to be five places. For the purposes of explanation, consider the following examples:
The length of the storage location and the quantity Λ are the keys to specifying the correct code:

$$\Lambda = (\text{Storage length of the location in digits}) — (\text{Number of zeros preceeding first nonzero digit})$$

On Cards

Example 1

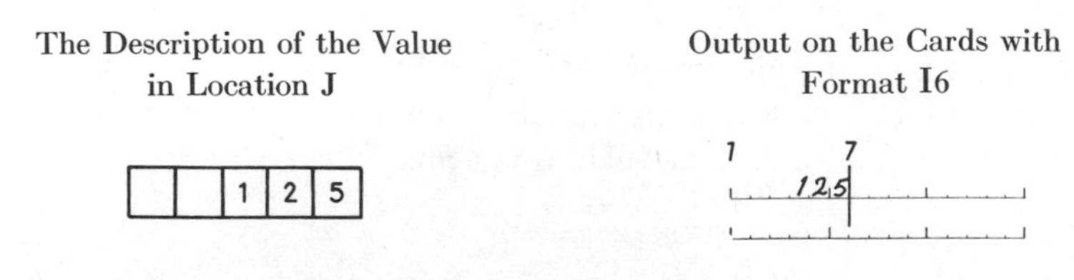

FIG. 3–7

The number is right-justified in the field, i.e., the low-order digit 5 is punched in column 6.

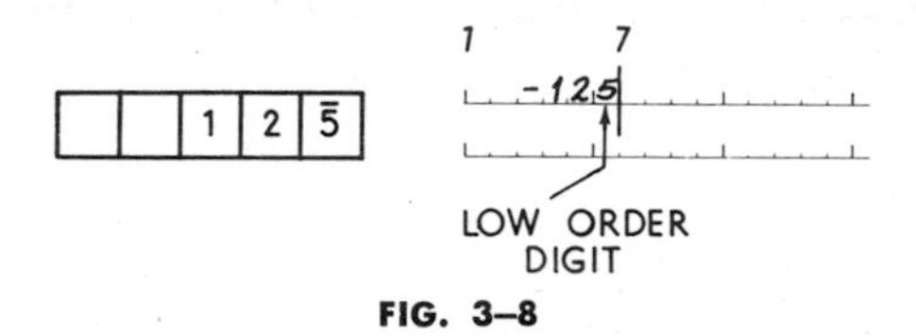

FIG. 3–8

We assume that the dash over the 5 represents a minus number in the computer; the minus sign will be punched immediately to the left of the high-order digit as in the figure on the right. Even if the number is positive, a placed is reserved for the sign. Columns 1 and 2 remain blank *on the card.*

Example 2

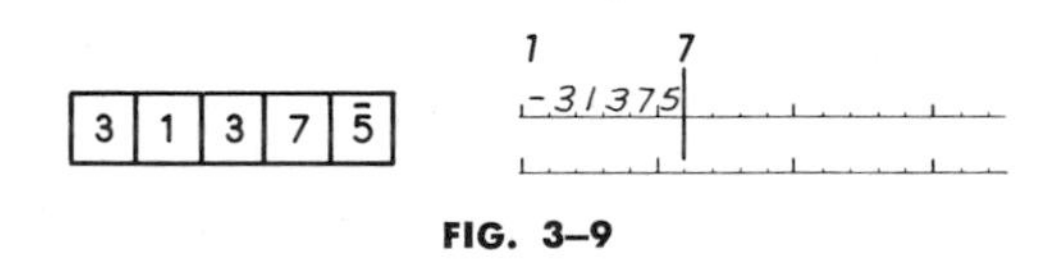

FIG. 3–9

Because the maximum length of Λ in the computer is five (remember we assumed that the length of storage location for fixed-point numbers is five digits), a field length of six digits will always be sufficient to hold the number including the sign. However, if the FORMAT statement was

FORMAT (I5)

the field may not be sufficient to hold the number including the sign.

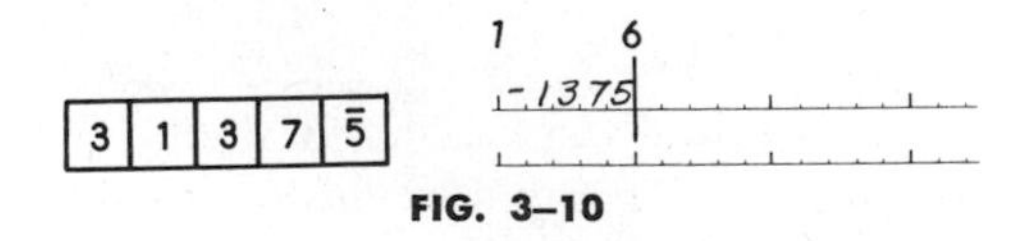

FIG. 3–10

In case the field length is not large enough to hold the number, including the sign, the high-order digit is lost in output; it goes without saying that the programmer should be aware of the number of nonzero digits, when using the I-type code for FORMAT.

The reader should recall the discussion concerning fixed-point numbers in the first chapter; fixed-point numbers should only be used for calculations when the calculations are not very complicated. Then the programmer should know Λ.

3.2.2. Floating-Point; F-Code

The format codes F*w.d* or E*w.d* may be utilized by the programmer to specify the form of the output for floating-point numbers. The *w* part specifies the length of the field, including a space for the decimal point and a space for the sign; the *d* part specifies the number of spaces reserved for nonzero digits after the decimal point. Again, the use of these codes will be illustrated by examples. We assume that the length of storage locations for floating-point numbers is eight digits (as explained in Chapter 1, these eight characters are for the mantissa of the number—two additional digits are reserved for the exponent).

The output statement and associated FORMAT statement will be

```
   PUNCH  10,A
10 FORMAT(F6.2)
```

In the following examples the exact description of the number in memory will not be given, but only its internal representation.

Example 1

The internal representation of the number is $.21X10^1$ or 2.1. (see Chapter 1 for a discussion of the internal representation of floating-point numbers)

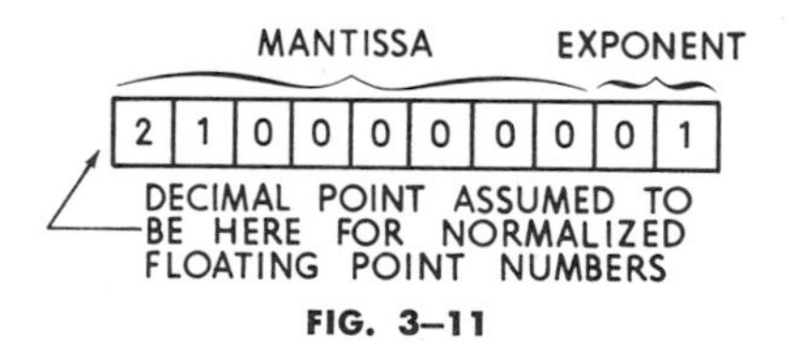

FIG. 3–11

Internal Representation
2.1
−2.1
Output

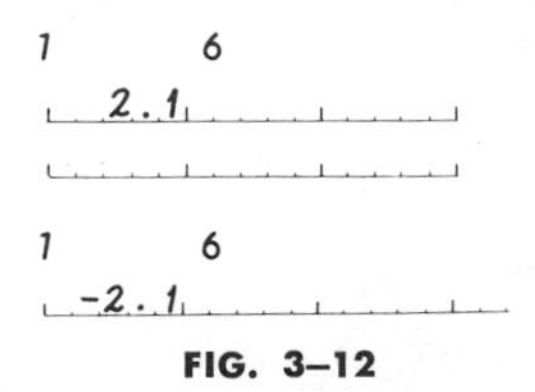

FIG. 3–12

The sign, if negative, will appear immediately to the left of the first nonzero digit; if the sign is positive, a blank will appear on the card.

Example 2

Internal Representation
3.875
Output

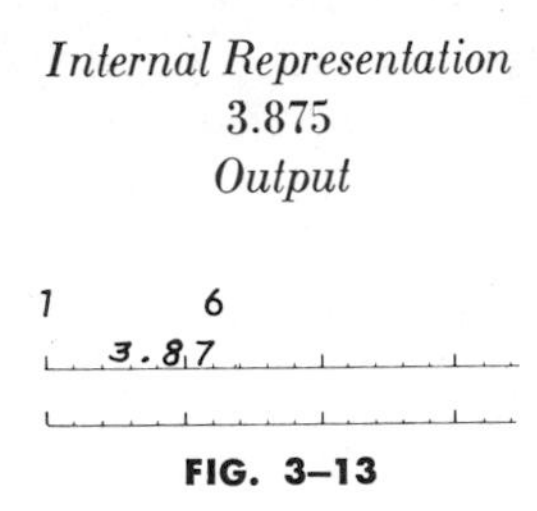

FIG. 3–13

If the number of nonzero digits following the decimal point is greater than the value d in the code F$w.d$, the low-order figure is truncated to give a d decimal places. Here, then, is another way to truncate decimal numbers in FORTRAN; the method offered in Chapter 1 to truncate decimal numbers was to place the floating-point variable on the right-hand side of an arithmetic statement and a fixed-point variable on the left of the statement—the statement, I=A, will truncate the decimal part of the number in location A.

Example 3

Internal Representation
321.75
Output

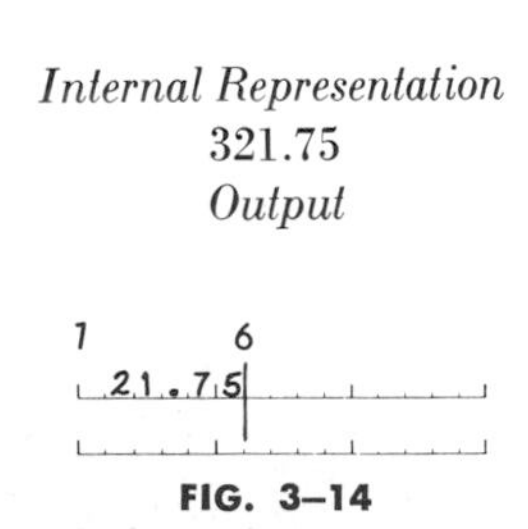

FIG. 3–14

The high-order digit, 3, has been lost because a place must be reserved for the sign even though it is positive. Since the programmer may not be able to give the exact length of a floating-point number, this error could be extremely troublesome. Therefore, to avoid truncation of the high-order digit when using the code F$w.d$, the FORTRAN compiler automatically converts the code F6.2 to the code E14.8. The output of the number 321.75

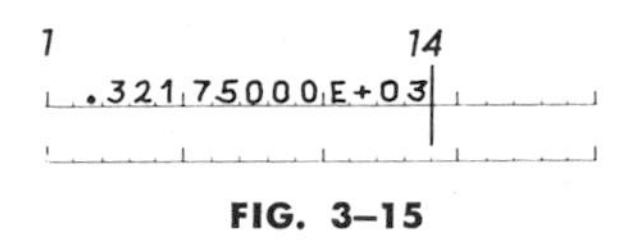

FIG. 3–15

will then be that given in the above figure. Six spaces in the field on the card are reserved for the sign, the decimal point, and for the exponent, E±XX. To understand why the punched number is .32175000E+03 instead of .75000000E+00, one must consider the instructions set up by the compiler to punch out a number under the E-type FORMAT code. The number in the computer is because the number will be in normalized floating-point form; therefore, under the code E14.8, the compiler need

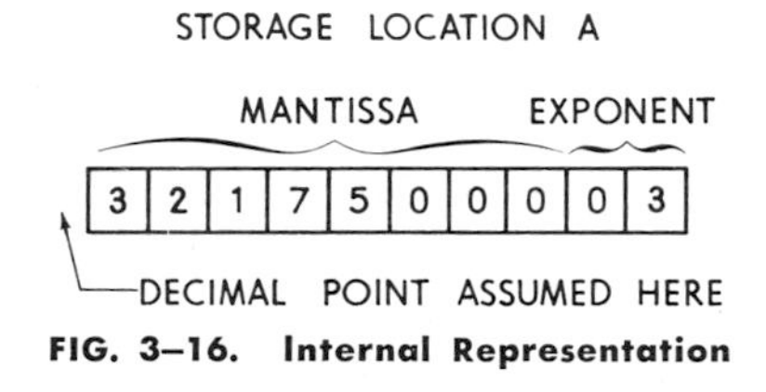

FIG. 3–16. Internal Representation

only issue an instruction to print out the eight decimal place value in storage location A in between the decimal point and the letter E, and to print the two digit exponent of the number after the symbols "E±." Although the conversion from the F-type format to the E-type format will

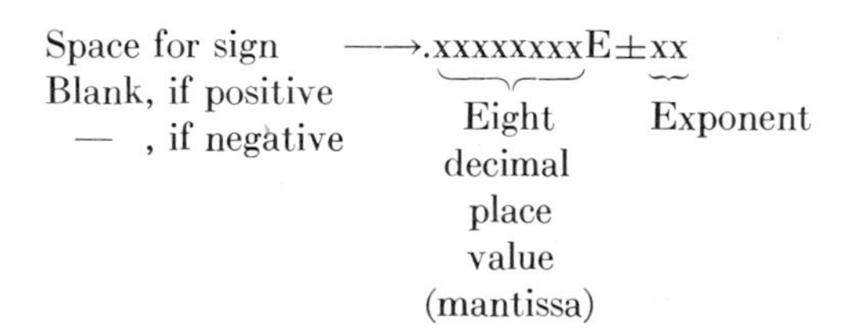

FIG. 3–17. Printed Value

prevent the truncation of the most significant part of the number, another type of error may be created in the process. If the programmer plans to use the full 80 columns of the card, some fields may be pushed off the card because the conversion has used eight spaces more than the original plan.

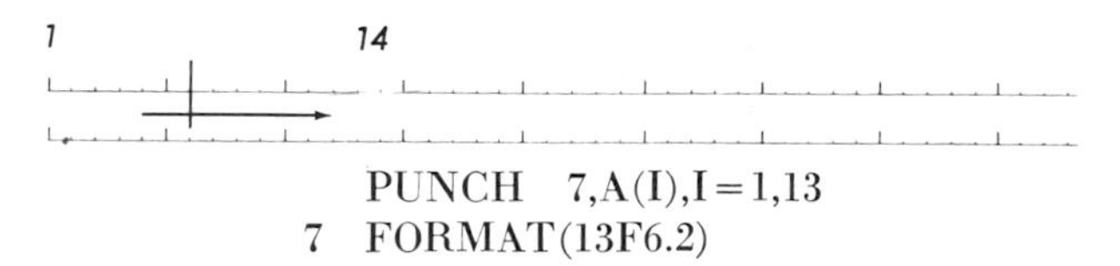


```
  PUNCH  7,A(I),I=1,13
7 FORMAT(13F6.2)
```

In the above example, the value in location A(13) would not be able to be punched on the card because of the additional eight spaces taken in the conversion of the F-type format to the E-type format.

The reader may notice in the above example the specification (13F6.2); this specification is equivalent to $\underbrace{\text{(F6.2,F6.2, ... , F6.2).}}_{\text{13 times}}$

3.2.3. Floating-Point; E-Type

Earlier in the chapter the symbol, Λ, was defined to be (Length of storage location)—(Number of zeros which precede the first nonzero digit in the location). It is desirable to remove the burden of needing to know the number of digits which precede the decimal point and the number of digits of which follow the decimal point. E-type FORMAT codes operate much like the principle of floating-point numbers and thereby remove this burden from the programmer. Two simple rules are presented to aid the reader in the use of the E-type FORMAT code.

$$w=b+s+d+6$$

The above equation simply equates the whole to the sum of its parts. The width of the entire field, w, is composed of the following: six spaces for the sign, decimal point, and the exponent E±XX; d, the number of nonzero digits following the decimal point; s, the number of nonzero digits preceding the decimal point; and b, the number of blank spaces.

$$s+d\leq 8$$

The number of digits in Λ to the right and left of the decimal point cannot be greater than the width of the storage location (this length was assumed to be eight characters). In addition to these two equations, the FORTRAN compiler has established a heirarchy in the evaluation of the E-type format code—the six spaces for the sign, decimal point, and the exponent are the first spaces to be reserved in the field; spaces for the number of digits in Λ before and after the decimal point are the next spaces to be reserved in the field; and finally, the spaces left over are to be blank

Internal Representation		*Output*
−3.1753172		
$w=10$	Format E10.4	.3175E+01
Subtract six spaces for the sign, decimal point, and exponent; this leaves four spaces; $d=4$, so the remaining four spaces are reserved for the digits of Λ which follow the decimal point. The exponent, 1, moves the decimal point to the correct place.		

Internal Representation	*Output*
$w=11$ Format E11.4 Subtract six spaces for the sign, decimal point, and exponent; this leaves five spaces. Since $d=4$, one space still remains for either s or b. If there are more than four digits of Λ in the storage locations, s is delegated one space, because space for s is reserved before the space for b. In this example there are eight nonzero numbers so s is delegated one space in field leaving no spaces for b.	−3.1753E+00
$w=15$ Format E15.4 Subtract the six necessary spaces; this leaves nine spaces. Since $d=4$, five spaces remain for s and b. Because $s+d$ must be equal to or less than eight, there will be at least one blank space. Four spaces will be reserved for s in this example because Λ contains eight digits. One blank space will be reserved immediately to the left of the sign.	b−3175.3172E−03
If the number was 3.1753172, the output would contain two blanks, one for the b part and one for the + sign, which is not punched into the field.	bb3175.3172E−03
−32.4 Format E15.4 $w=15$ Subtract the six necessary spaces; this leaves nine spaces. There are only three nonzero digits and $d=4$, so no places will be reserved for s. Therefore, the number of blanks will be five spaces.	bbbbb−.3240E+02
−6.5135148 Format E16.10 $w=16$ Subtract the 6 necessary spaces leaving 10 spaces. Now d is	b−.6513514800E+01

Internal Representation	*Output*
specified as 10, which implies the programmer wishes the remaining 10 spaces to be reserved for d even though there are only 8 nonzero figures. The remaining 2 places will be filled with zeros.	

3.3. Numerical Format Codes—Input

3.3.1. Fixed-Point; I-Type

The I-type format is provided by FORTRAN to enable the reading of fixed-point numbers into the computer. Like the I-type code on output, the I-type code for input is Iw; w gives the number of spaces in the field on the card or on the tape which is going to be entered into the location specified by the variable name in the input list.

```
  READ  1,K
1 FORMAT(I5)
```

The left parenthesis in the FORMAT statement is a signal to start reading the card, and the code I5 is an instruction to the computer to consider the first five columns as the field; the numbers in the first five columns are placed in the storage location named K.

Example 1

Input Numbers	**Internal Representation**
1 5 125	1 2 5
1 5 1	1 0 0

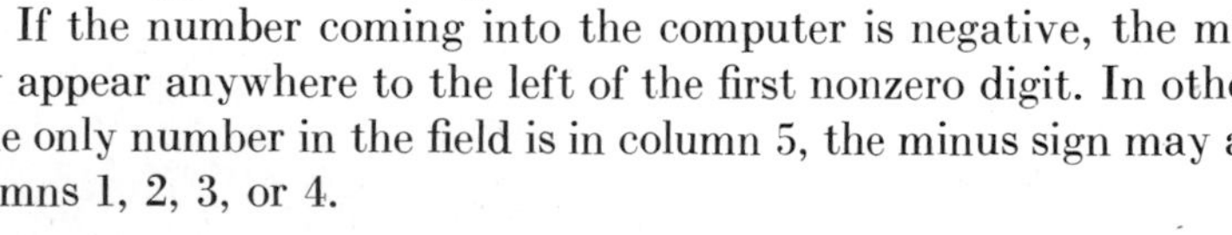

FIG. 3–18

Zeros are supplied on the right side so that number 1 in column 3 becomes 100. If the number coming into the computer is negative, the minus sign may appear anywhere to the left of the first nonzero digit. In other words, if the only number in the field is in column 5, the minus sign may appear in columns 1, 2, 3, or 4.

Example 2

3-1

FIG. 3–19

Of course, the minus sign may not appear between two numbers in the field. An inspection of the above description of the I-type format for input does not reveal much generalization from the I-type format for output. However, it should be recalled that one can find few variations when using fixed-point numbers. The F- and E-type format codes will offer more options when used for input.

3.3.2. Floating-Point; F-Type

One major option available to the programmer who uses the F-type format code for input of floating-point numbers is the option of actually punching the decimal point in the field. The first group of examples illustrate input without the decimal point in the field.

Example 1

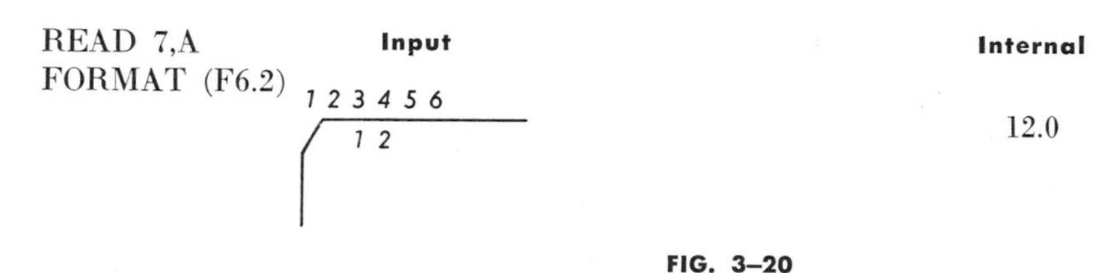

FIG. 3–20

The FORTRAN compiler supplies zeros to the right of the number; then the decimal point is placed between columns 4 and 5. The number of decimal places is determined by counting *d* places to the left from the right end of the field. Since the decimal place is not punched in the card, the full six spaces may be used for the number.

Example 2

Input **Internal**

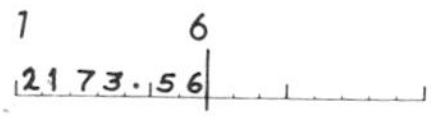

2173.56

1 6
2173.56

FIG. 3–21

A minus or plus sign may appear anywhere to the left of the first non-zero digit in the field

Example 3

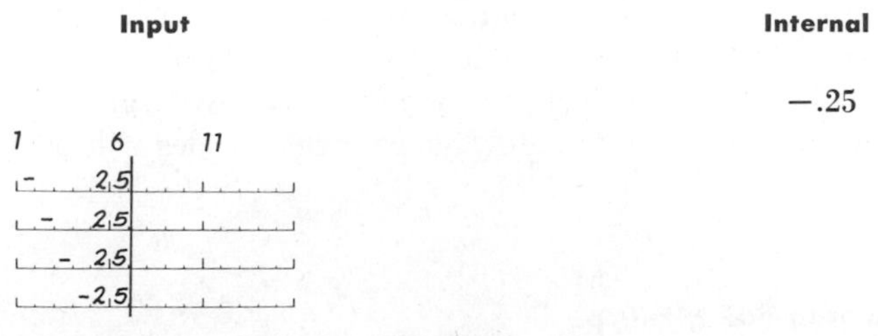

FIG. 3–22

The user may override the d part of the F$w.d$ format code by punching a decimal point in the field.

Example 4

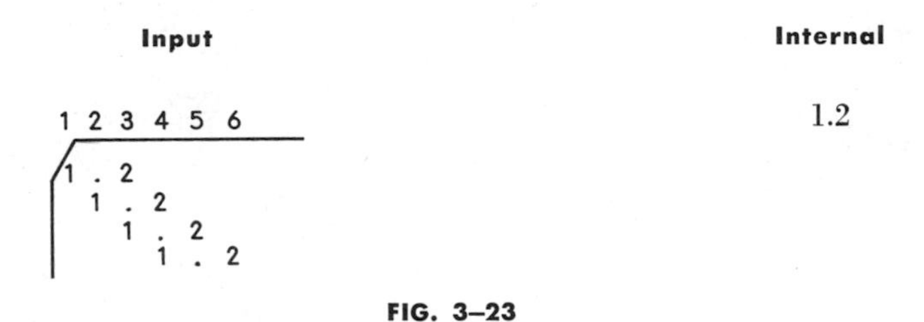

FIG. 3–23

No matter where in the field the number 1.2 is punched, its internal representation will be 1.2 because the two decimal places specified in the format code, F6.2 has no effect when the decimal point is punched into the card. Again the sign, plus or minus, may be punched anywhere to the left of the first non-zero digit.

Example 5

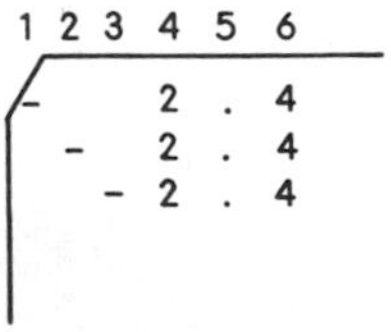

```
1 2 3 4 5 6
-     2 . 4
  -   2 . 4
    - 2 . 4
```

FIG. 3–24

Of course, when the decimal point is punched into the card there can be only five non-zero digits in the field. The option of punching the decimal point or not punching the decimal point allows the user a much more general input than would be available without this option.

3.3.3. Floating-Point; E-Type

As one might expect, the E-type format code allows the most general form of input. In addition to the option of punching the decimal point, there are alternative ways of punching the exponent and if he wishes, the user need not punch an exponent.

Example 1

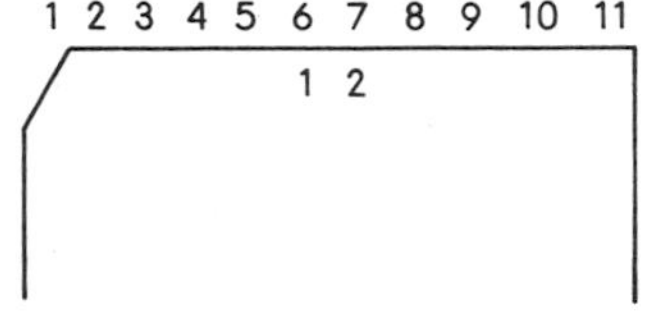

FIG. 3–25

The compiler fills in zeros to the right of the number and since there is no exponent, the decimal point is assumed to be four places to the left of the right end of the rightmost zero; in this example the zeros go in the right end of the field because there is no exponent. If the user wishes to punch an exponent of 10^2 into the field, he has many alternatives.

E+02	E+ 2
+ 02	E +2
+ 2	E 2
+02	E+2
+2	E2

Example 2

Input **Internal**

1 67 11
12 E2

$.12 \times 10^2 = 12.0$

FIG. 3–26a

Application of the same format, E11.4, with the data for example 2 leads to the same internal representation, namely, 12.0. The decimal point is assumed to be four places to the left of the first character in the exponent; therefore, the decimal point is assumed to be immediately to the left of the high-order digit, 1, in the number 12.

The programmer has the option of specifying the decimal point.

Input	Internal
1 6 11 15	1.2
1.2	
1.2	
1.2	
1.2	
1.2	

FIG. 3–26b

Again the negative sign may appear anywhere to the left of the first non-zero digit. Even if the decimal point is specified in the input field, an exponent, taking one of the forms mentioned above, may be specified in the input field.

Example 3

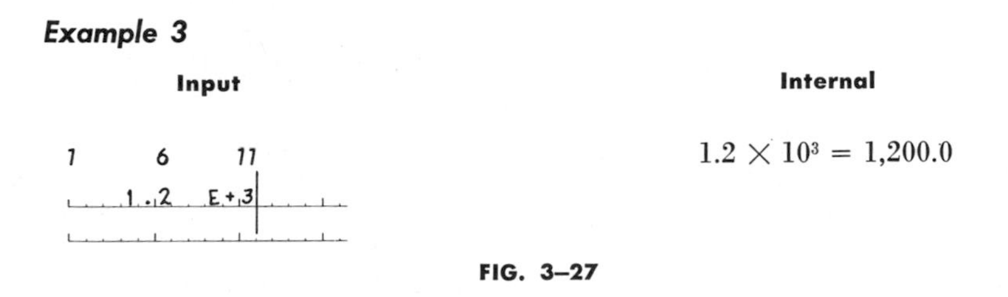

FIG. 3–27

3.4. FORMAT Code for Blank Spacing, X-Type

3.4.1. Output

Numeric format specifications provided for blanks in the output field only as a last resort. For example, a specification of E12.4 would provide blank spaces only if the number of digits in Λ is less than six. Six spaces are reserved for the sign, decimal point, and the exponent; four spaces are reserved for numbers following the decimal point; this leaves only two spaces for digits of Λ to the left of the decimal point or blank spaces. When the number of digits in Λ are less than or equal to four, these digits will all appear to the right of the decimal point.

If the number of digits in Λ is 5 or 6, then the 1 or 2 most significant figures will appear to the left of the decimal point.

For some reason the first field on the output media may be limited to 14 spaces. From the above analysis of numeric format specifications, a programmer who uses the E-type format could not guarantee any blank spaces in the left part of this field because of the assumption that storage locations for floating-point numbers are eight characters in length.

Format	*Internal Number*	*Output*
E14.8	−12.356731	−.12356731E+02
E14.4	−12.356731	−1235.6731E−02

To guarantee at least one blank space on the left for the number −12.-356731, would require the *w* part of the format E*w.d* to be at least 15. Since the output field is limited to 14 spaces, the only remaining possibility is a special format code to guarantee blank spaces. The FORTRAN language provides the format *w*X, for specifying a blank field *w* spaces in length.

Format	*Internal Number*	*Output*
3X,E11.4	−12.356731	bbb−1.2356E+01

↑
This comma is optional.

By using the X-type format, the above example demonstrates a guarantee of the three blanks in a field of 14 spaces in length. Of course, if the number of digits in A is less than or equal to four, an additional blank will be provided via the format E11.4.

The use of the X format enables the user to space the output so that it is easier for the reader.

```
  PUNCH  7,A,B,C
7 FORMAT(10XF10.4,12XF8.3,10XF10.4)
```

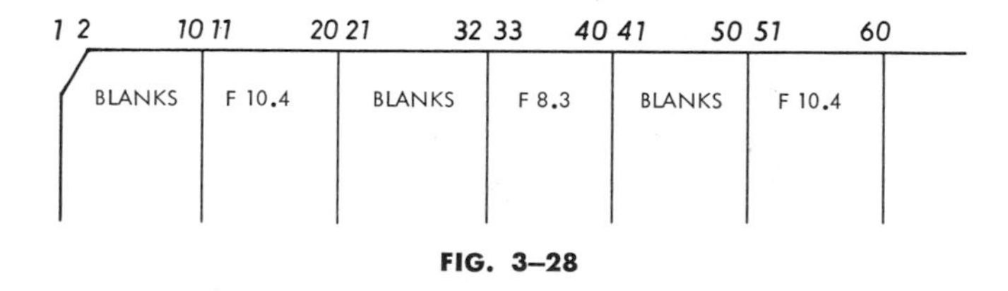

FIG. 3–28

If the results in locations A,B, and C were to be punched under the same format, say F10.4, using the same spacing, the following statements would suffice:

```
  PUNCH  7,A,B,C
7 FORMAT(3(10XF10.4))
```

3.4.2. Input

X-type specifications are useful to input as well as output. Data cards for input to a program may not have the important data in successive fields.

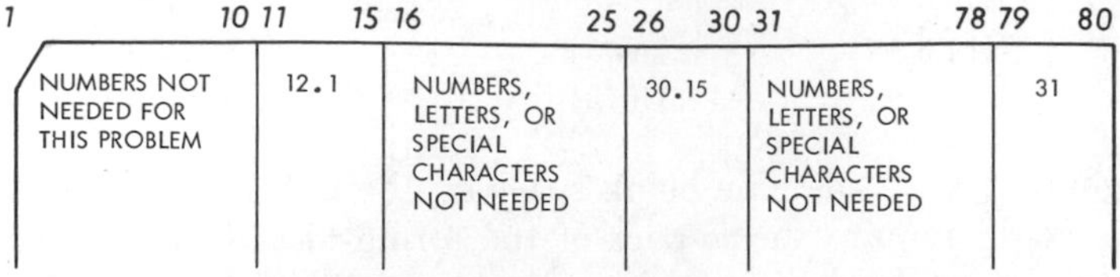

1–10	11–15	16–25	26–30	31–78	79–80
NUMBERS NOT NEEDED FOR THIS PROBLEM	12.1	NUMBERS, LETTERS, OR SPECIAL CHARACTERS NOT NEEDED	30.15	NUMBERS, LETTERS, OR SPECIAL CHARACTERS NOT NEEDED	31

FIG. 3–29

Columns 11 to 15, 26 to 30, and 79–80, contains the data for the program; all other numbers (0 to 9), letters (A to Z), or special characters (/,$)(.) are to be ignored in this program. The input statements

```
  READ 7,A,B,K
7 FORMAT(10XF5.1,10XF5.1,48XI2)
```

will place the number 12.1 in location A, the number 30.15 in location B, and the number 31 in location K. Any other numbers, letters, or other characters are not placed in any addressable storage location; they are essentially ignored by the FORTRAN compiler.

3.5. Computer Example

Example

Input of one-dimensional array, perform simple manipulations on the array, and output of both the original array and the new array.

```
   DIMENSION A(20), B (20)
99 READ 7,N
 7 FORMAT (I2)
   READ 8,(A(I), I=1, N)
   L = N/2
   DO 10 I = 1, L
   R = I
10 B(I) = A(I) * R
   K = L+1
   DO 20 I = K,N
   R = I
20 B(I) = A (I)/R
   PUNCH 30,(A(I), I = 1, N)
   PUNCH 30,(B(I), I = 1, N)
30 FORMAT (5(5X, F10.3))
 8 FORMAT (5F6.2)
   GO TO 99
   END
```

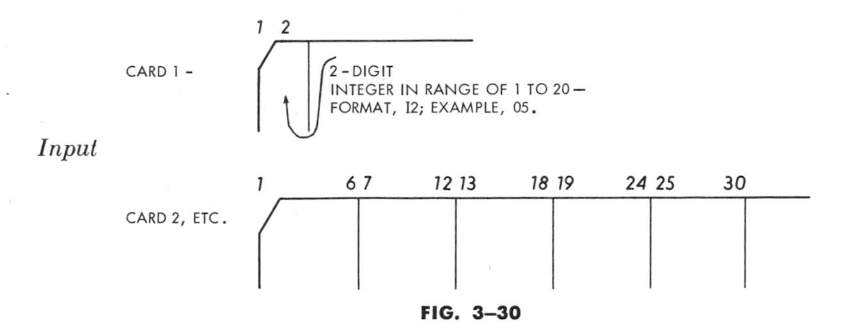

FIG. 3–30

On each card there will be five fields, except for the last card which may contain any number of fields from 1 to 5. Each field should contain a floating-point number under format, F6.2; for example, −3.1 or

1	2	3	4	5	6
−	3	8	7.		

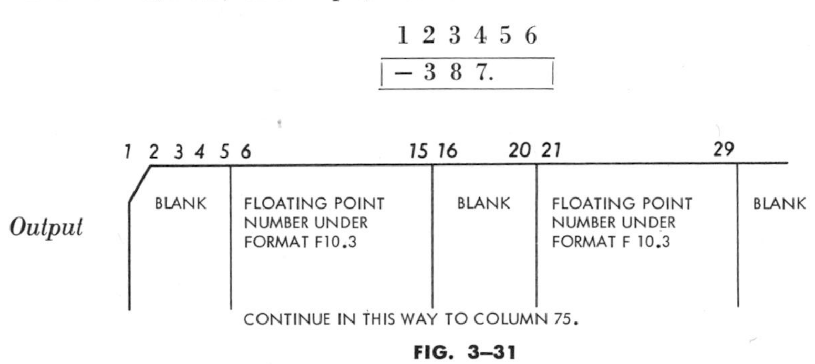

FIG. 3–31

After running the above program on the computer, the reader will notice that the output format is still not in "presentable" form; i.e., it is not clear enough to be understandable to many people. To improve the output format, one would require the ability to skip one or more lines, put a heading on the page as well as subheading, and any pertinent comments. In the next two sections the reader is introduced to the methods offered by the FORTRAN compiler to solve these problems.

3.6. Alphameric Format Specificiations

3.6.1. Output; H-Type FORMAT

Most times the results of a program are useless unless they are presented in an "easy-to-read" form. One of the most important parts of a good output format is the headings and other descriptive notation, which consists of letters and special characters, such as dollar signs, parentheses, commas, etc. In addition to the need for letters and special characters for headings and other descriptive notation, letters are absolutely essential for company names, individual names, and departments, in commercial data processing. FORTRAN allows the use of two alphameric (numbers, letters, or special characters) format codes, *w*H and A*w;* again, the *w* specifies the width of the field for input or output. A typical heading for a student's program would be his/her name, the date, the class, and the section.

MATH 301 –SECTION C *47 spaces* MARCH 17, 1966
MORRIS OSBORNE *53 spaces* PROBLEM 1

The following FORTRAN statements instruct the computer to punch the above heading.

```
   PUNCH 7
7  FORMAT(20HMATHb301bb–SECTIONbC,47X13HMARCHb17,1966)
   PUNCH 8
8  FORMAT (14HMORRISbOSBORNE,53X9HPROBLEMb1)
```

Notice that no output list is needed when only alphameric coding is specified in the FORMAT statement. The absence of a list eliminates the need for a comma after the FORMAT statement number; the comma becomes optional. The FORTRAN compiler counts the field length starting with the place immediately to the right of the *H* in the code *w*H. Any alphameric character within the *w* spaces to the right of H will be punched exactly as it is written in the FORMAT statement. In the above example, the first output card will contain the following:

MATH 301–SECTION C	Starts in column 1 and ends in column 8. Column 5 is left blank. Columns 9 and 10 are punched blank and a dash is punched in column 11. The word section is punched in columns 12 through 18; column 19 is blank; and a "C" will be punched in column 20. The X-type format is used for blanks.
MARCH 17,1966	The date is punched in columns 68 through 80 with column 73 left blank.

A miscount of the number of spaces desired in the "H" coding is one of the most common errors for the beginning programmer. The FORTRAN compiler will instruct the computer to print out an error indication at compile time for most input/output format errors, including a miscount of specified field length. An alternative to the use of *w*X code in statement 7, would be to actually leave 47 blank spaces in the FORMAT statement; however, this method is more time consuming and would necessitate a continuation card for the FORMAT statement.

```
   PUNCH 7
7  FORMAT(80HMATHb301bb–SECTIONbCbbbbb . . . . bbbbbb
                                    \_______________/
                                           47
                                                 MARCHb17,1966)
```

Two major descriptive methods of presenting results are illustrated in the next two examples. In the first case, the program is used to solve a system of three simultaneous equations for many successive sets of data; the answers will be called X1, X2, and X3.

```
  PUNCH 7
7 FORMAT(10X2HX1,25X2HX2,25X2HX3)
```

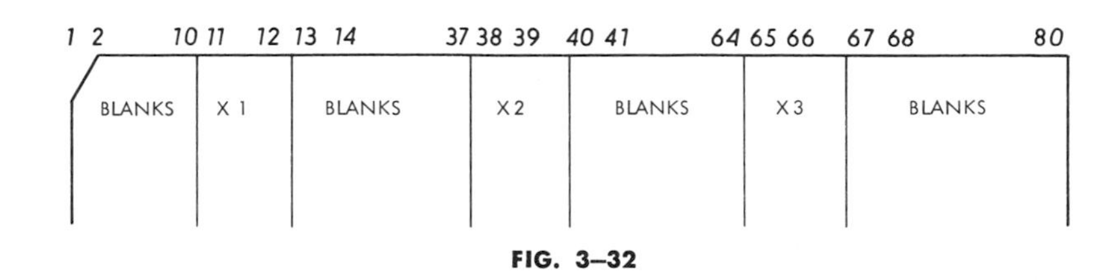

FIG. 3–32

```
  PUNCH 8,X1,X2,X3
8 FORMAT(7XF8.3,19XF8.3,19XF9.3)
```

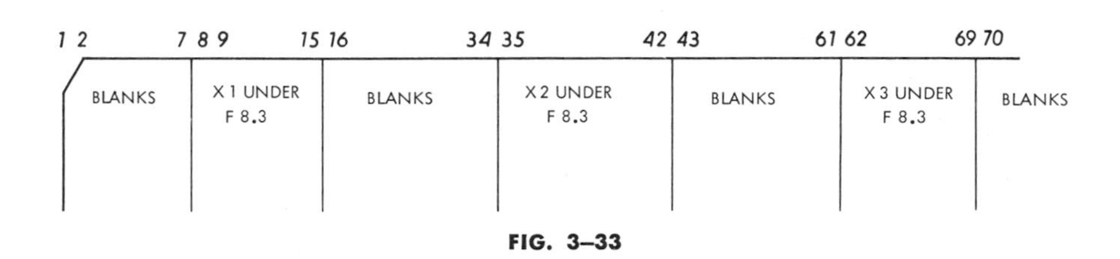

FIG. 3–33

The second group of statements will be used once for every set of data cards; in other words, one set of answers will be punched for every problem.

X1	X2	X3	
______	______	______	1st problem
______	______	______	2nd problem
.	.	.	
.	.	.	
.	.	.	
______	______	______	*n*th problem

FIG. 3–34

Another possible output for the above problem would have descriptive material before each answer. Assume that the program is written to solve a system of simultaneous equations; the number of equations can range from 2 to 10.

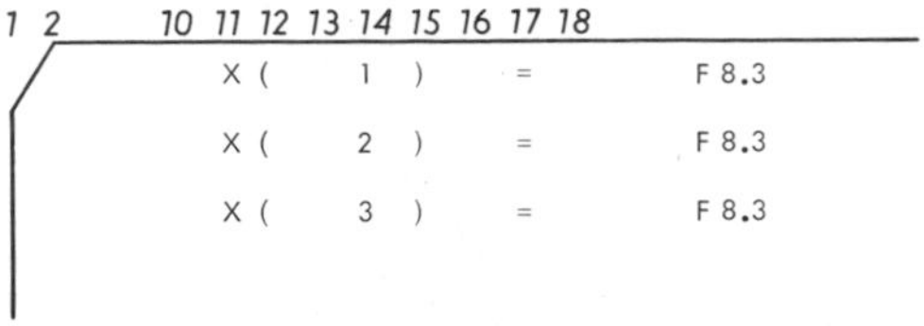

```
1 2      10 11 12 13 14 15 16 17 18
              X (     1  )     =          F 8.3
              X (     2  )     =          F 8.3
              X (     3  )     =          F 8.3
```

FIG. 3–35

If there are two equations, only two answers are to be punched out; if there are seven equations, seven answers are to be punched out, etc.

```
      PUNCH   7,I,(X(I),I=1,N)
    7 FORMAT(10X2HX(,I2,4H)b=b,F8.3)
```

Every time the computer executes the PUNCH statement, another card is punched out. The implied DO loop (X(I),I=1,N), is equivalent to the list 1,X(1),2,X(2) , ... N,X(N), in the sense that only one card is necessary to punch out the results from all the locations. Of course, the programmer cannot vary the length of the list once the program has been compiled; this is the reason for the implied DO loop. In this example, only two values are punched per card, because of the right parenthesis in the format statement. The FORTRAN compiler analyzes the FORMAT statement via the following steps:

1. Hit left parenthesis, start column 1.
2. The first field consists of 10 blank spaces.
3. The next field will be alphameric and two spaces in length, actually the next two characters in the FORMAT statement, X(, will be punched in columns 11 and 12.
4. The next field will be two spaces long and will contain the fixed-point number which is stored in location I at the time of execution of the statement.
5. Columns 15,16,17, and 18 will be occupied by an alphameric field; namely,)b=b.
6. Now the floating-point result which is stored in location X(I) is punched in columns 19 through 26
7. The right parenthesis ends the card, and if there are more items in the list, another card will be placed in a position to receive the remaining output; therefore, another card is always ready to be punched unless the last value, X(N) has been punched out. The subject of parenthesis will be explained in greater detail in a later section.

Although it would be possible to punch many values on one card with the implied DO loop as given in the above example, the user can reduce this number of values via different types of FORMAT statements.

Typical Output

X(1)=5.215
X(2)=3.718
X(3)=21.516
X(4)= −1.756

3.6.2. Input; H-Type FORMAT

For use of the H code in commercial work, the programmer may need to use the same FORMAT statement for input and output. A sales analysis application may require the program to accept cards which contain the company name in columns 1 through 20 and other pertinent information in columns 21 through 30, 41 through 50, and 71 through 80. The other fields do not contain useful information. After the calculations necessary to obtain the results have been completed, the output should contain the company name in columns 1 through 20, with other desired results to be punched in columns 21 through 30, 41 through 50, and 71 through 80. The other fields are to be left blank.

```
   READ   17,A,B,C
17 FORMAT(20Hbbbbb . . . bbbb,F10.3,10XF10.3,20XF10.3)
```

(20 blanks)

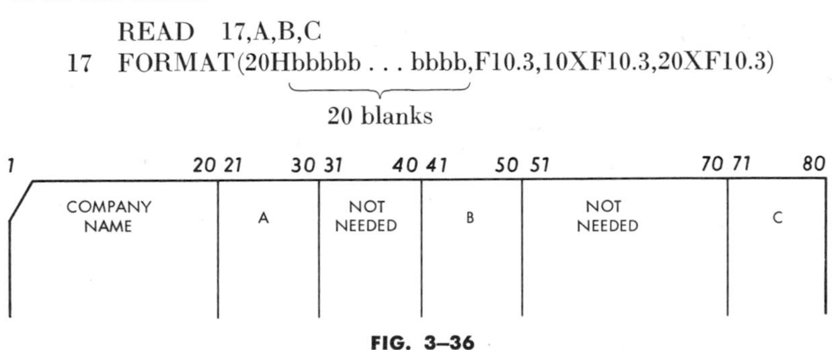

FIG. 3–36

The first 20 characters in the card are read into a 20-position storage location in the machine; the FORTRAN compiler associates this location with FORMAT statement 17. The programmer cannot address this location; a correspondence exists between this type of storage location and the storage register. A register, as opposed to a normal location, usually cannot be directly addressed by a FORTRAN statement; that is, the user can give a symbolic name to a storage location and place a value in the location by writing that symbolic name on the left side of an arithmetic statement. The user cannot utilize the same procedure for addressing registers. In a like manner, the only way the programmer can put characters into the storage location associated with FORMAT statement 17 is via that statement. The value in columns 21 through 30 is read into location A, the value in columns 41 through 50 are read into location B, and the value in columns 71 through 80 are read into location C.

```
PUNCH   17,A,B,C
```

The output statement necessary to create the format desired in the problem must refer to the same FORMAT statement which is utilized by the input statement. The reader may picture the input statement as reading the company name off the card and placing these characters in the first 20 positions of the FORMAT statement. Then the output statement will use the H-type FORMAT in the normal manner; and the characters in the first 20 positions of the FORMAT statement following the "20H" will be punched into the first 20 positions of the card.

```
       READ  17,A,B,C
    17 FORMAT(20Hbbb.bbb,F10.3,10X,F10.3,20X,F10.3)
```

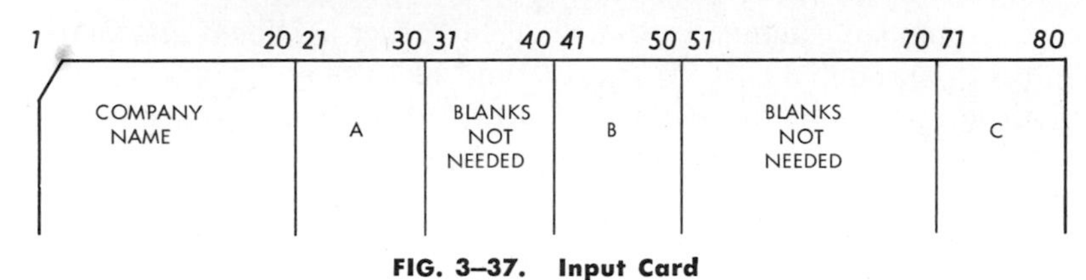

FIG. 3–37. Input Card

Assume the FORMAT statement to be:

```
    17 FORMAT(20HCOMPANY NAME       ,F10.3, 20X,F10.3)
       PUNCH 17,A,B,C
```

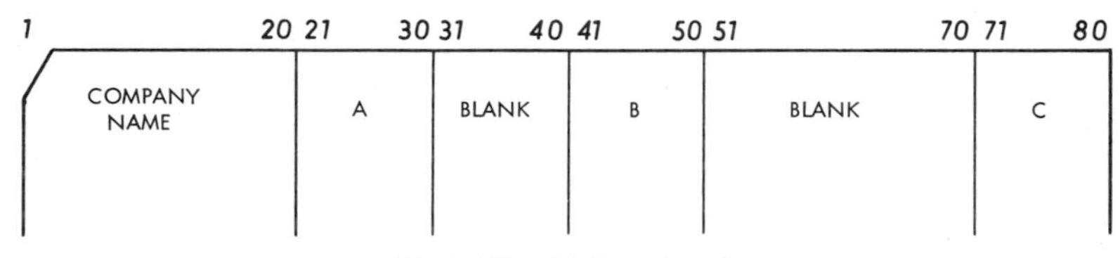

FIG. 3–38. Output Card

A deck of input cards for a practical sales analysis problem might contain thousands of cards; to handle the above problem without the use of the same FORMAT statement for both input and output would require a different FORMAT statement for each input card. Each FORMAT statement would contain a different company name in the alphameric field. For a sales analysis problem with two input cards (two companies), the following procedure would be sufficient.

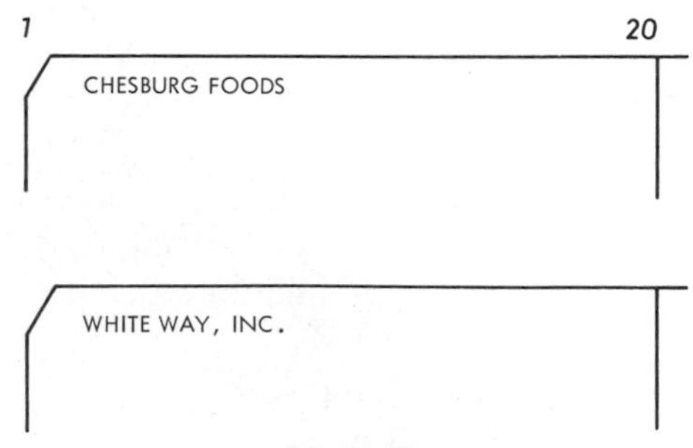

FIG. 3–39

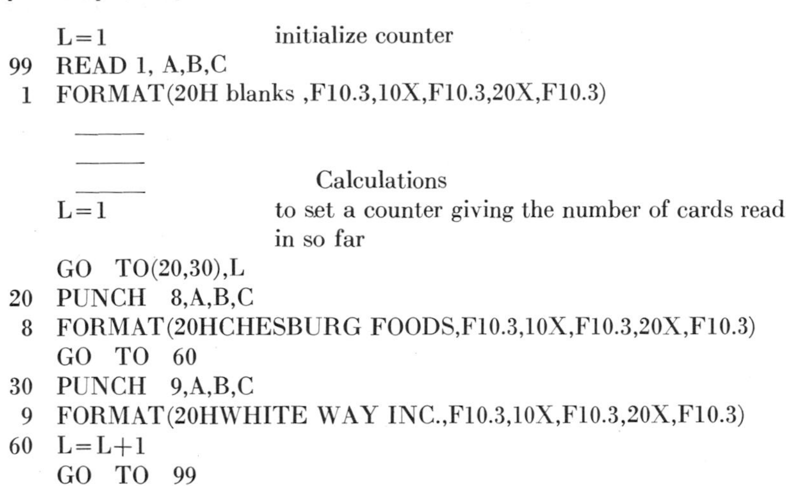

```
      L=1                    initialize counter
   99 READ 1, A,B,C
    1 FORMAT(20H blanks ,F10.3,10X,F10.3,20X,F10.3)
      ______
      ______
      ______                    Calculations
      L=1                    to set a counter giving the number of cards read
                             in so far
      GO  TO(20,30),L
   20 PUNCH  8,A,B,C
    8 FORMAT(20HCHESBURG FOODS,F10.3,10X,F10.3,20X,F10.3)
      GO  TO  60
   30 PUNCH  9,A,B,C
    9 FORMAT(20HWHITE WAY INC.,F10.3,10X,F10.3,20X,F10.3)
   60 L=L+1
      GO  TO  99
      END
```

The above method for handling output of results is clearly useless when the number of input cards becomes sizable. To solve the practical problem, the program must have a dynamic method of bringing in alphameric fields and punching out the same fields for many different cards. A single FORMAT statement will solve the problem if the FORMAT on the card for output is exactly the same as that for input. However, when the fields are to be shifted in going from input to output or new fields are to be added in the transition from input to output, another general method must be devised to solve the problem of punching the alphameric characters.

Example

The input card is to be similar to that in the previous examples, but the name is to be punched out in column 61 through 80

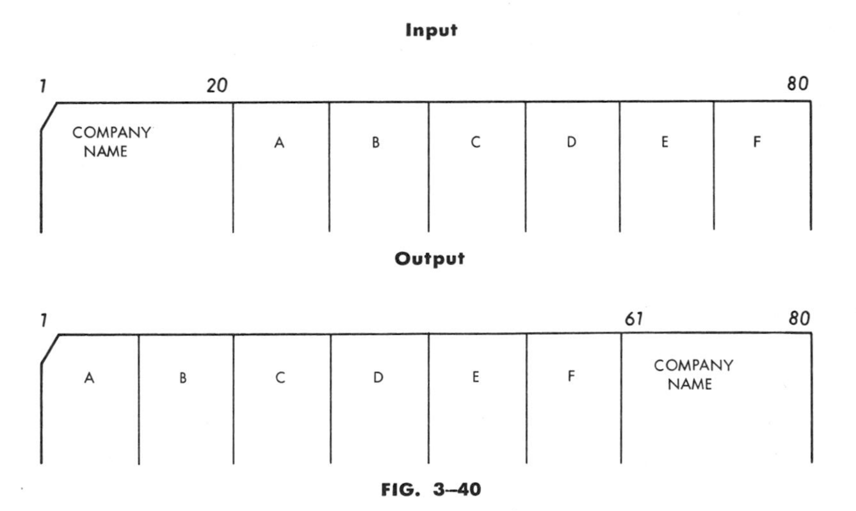

FIG. 3–40

This example can illustrate the problems presented to the programmer by changing the positions of fields or introduction of new fields in going from input to output with cards which must contain alphameric information. Now, a common FORMAT statement for input and output is impossible.

```
  READ 7,A,B,C,D,E,F
7 FORMAT(20H__________,6F10.3)
             20 blanks
  PUNCH 7,A,B,C,D,E,F
```

As was illustrated earlier, the above sequence of statements will punch the company name in the same columns of the output card as the input card.

```
  PUNCH 8,A,B,C,D,E,F
8 FORMAT(6F10.3,20H blanks )
```

Two separate FORMAT statements will not suffice because the company name is put into a storage location associated with FORMAT statement 7; a reference to FORMAT statement 8 will result in a field of blanks in columns 61 through 80.

3.6.3. A-Type FORMAT

To overcome the above difficulty, the programmer must be able to address directly the storage locations containing alphameric characters in the same way that the programmer can address locations containing numeric characters: that is, by the appearance of the symbolic name of the location on the left-hand side of an arithmetic statement or in the list of a READ statement. A second type of alphameric format code, the Aw code, is provided in the FORTRAN language to enable the programmer to address directly storage locations containing alphameric characters. The rules for giving names to storage locations containing fixed- and floating-point numbers apply to naming storage locations for alphameric characters. Let us continue to assume that the length of storage locations for fixed-point numbers are 5 characters long and for floating-point numbers the length of storage locations are 10 characters (8 for the mantissa and 2 for the characteristic).

Each individual cell in the computer can only be used to represent the digits, 0 through 9. Therefore, two adjacent cells must be utilized by a two-digit code allowing the programmer to represent alphameric characters. For instance, the numbers from 40 to 49 could represent the digits 0 to 9, the numbers from 50 through 75 could represent the letters A to Z, and the numbers in the 20's and 30's could be used to represent special characters. Computers are usually designed to read in alphameric code or numeric code.

In the IBM 1620 computer a "36" computer operation code (in machine language) is utilized by the computer to read each column of information into one storage location in the memory of the computer, whereas a "37" computer operation code is utilized by the computer to read one column of information from the card into two adjacent storage locations in coded form. The FORTRAN compiler translates an "A"-type code into a "37" operation code.

By providing the programmer with directly accessible storage locations, FORTRAN provides the solution to problems of moving alphameric fields on the card when going from input to output.

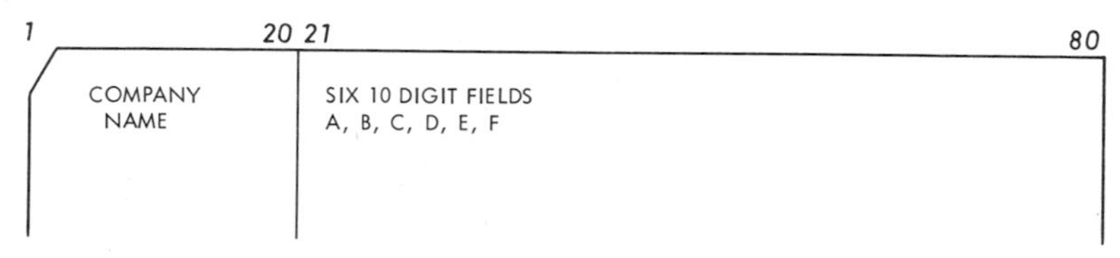

FIG. 3–41. Input Card

```
  DIMENSION R(4)
  READ 7,(R(I),I=1,4),A,B,C,D,E,F
7 FORMAT(4A5,6F10.3)
  PUNCH 8,A,B,C,D,E,F,(R(I),I=1,4)
8 FORMAT(6F10.2,4A5)
```

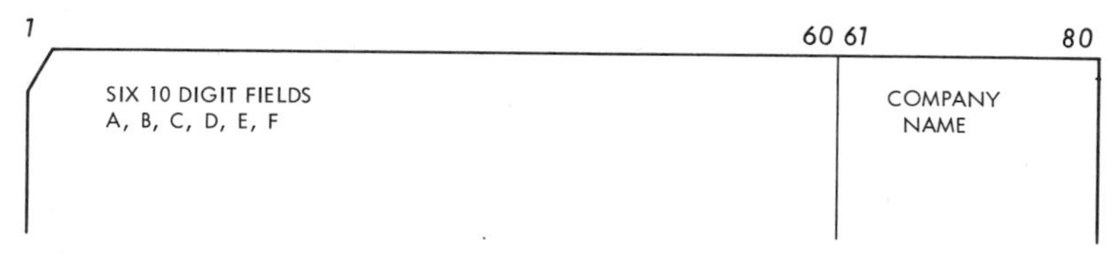

FIG. 3–42. Output Card

By reading the company name into the four locations, R(1),R(2)R(3), and R(4), the programmer can use two different FORMAT statements to solve the above problem: one FORMAT statement for input and a second FORMAT statement for output. The number of input cards is now irrelevant, because each new name comes into locations R(1), R(2), R(3), and R(4) from the first 20 positions on the card and destroys the alphameric information placed into those storage locations from a previous input card.

40 storage locations divided into 4 fields

R(4)	R(3)	R(2)	R(1)

Each alphameric character (including blanks) is read into two cells in coded form; since there will be 20 alphameric characters, four storage locations which may contain floating-point numbers are needed. Storage locations given a symbolic name starting with the letters other than I,J, K,L,M, or N are assumed to be 10 characters in length; if fixed-point storage locations were to be specified, then 10 locations would be required, since each location would contain only two alphameric characters (five cells divided by two spaces per character gives two possible characters).

Although the programmer can move alphameric information from one location to another in the computer, the process of changing one alphameric word to another by internal operations is still difficult.

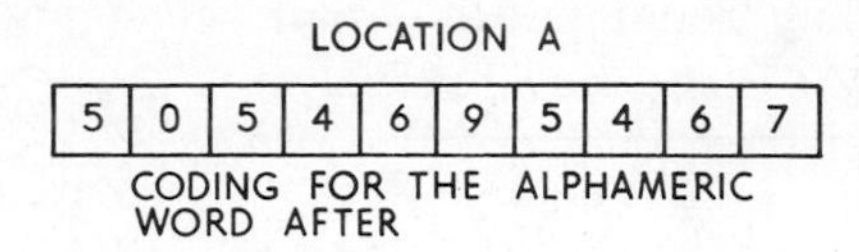

To change the word in location A to "ART OR" would necessitate the addition of the value in location B to location A; the result would appear in location C.

LOCATION B

0	0	1	3	0	0	1	0	0	0

$C = A + B$

LOCATION C

5	0	6	4	6	9	6	4	6	7

Before and after the addition has been performed by the computer, the programmer must consider the possibility of negative numbers and length of fields. We present this example to illustrate the futility, if not the impossibility, of using the basic FORTRAN language for manipulation of symbols and for more complicated business-oriented problems.

3.7. The Use of the Slash "/" and the Parenthesis "()" in FORMAT Specifications

3.7.1. Computer Operations

To provide a solid basis for the presentation of the slash and the parenthesis format codes, it is necessary to go into greater detail on the techniques used in computers for input and output.

```
  PUNCH  7,A,B,C,D
7 FORMAT(4F10.2)
```

Eighty positions of memory are reserved for an output area by the computer; the information to be punched into the output card may consist from

0 to 80 characters. The output process (as well as the input process) takes place in two steps:

1. The FORTRAN compiler instructs the computer to take the value in location A and place it in the first part of the output area; then the value in B is placed in the output area, then the value in C, and finally the value in D. The right parenthesis is a signal to the computer to close the output area and proceed to step 2.
2. The characters in the output area are punched into the card, and the output area is opened to enable this area to accomodate the next record to be punched out on the next card (a record for card input/output is 80 characters, the length of the card).

The intermediate input and output areas are called buffers, because they are designed to balance the very fast internal speed of the computer with the relatively slow speed of reading and punching cards; in other words, step 1 takes place much faster than step 2. The buffer areas allow the computer to perform some calculations internally while the contents of the buffer is punched into the output card or read into the buffer from the input card. In either case, the buffer is locked until it is emptied, so that the first set of values is not destroyed by the new set of values.

3.7.2. Parentheses

In the above illustration the PUNCH list was the same length as the number of numerical format specifications, since 4F10.2 is equivalent to F10.2,F10.2,F10.2,F10.2

```
      PUNCH   17,A, B, C,D,E
   17 FORMAT(4F10.2)
```

Output Cards

1st. card A,B,C,D	Under F10.2
2nd. card E	Under F10.2

If the input/output list is longer than the number of numerical format specifications, then the right parenthesis is a signal to lock and empty the buffer after the values in A,B,C, and D have been transferred to the buffer. Then the FORMAT statement returns to the left parenthesis and the value in location E is transferred to the buffer, if it has been reopened; if not, the computer will be tied up for a time. At this point there are no items in the output list; the record is completed when either the right parenthesis is encountered and no items remain in the list or a numerical format specification is encountered and no items remain in the output list. The completion of the record is a signal to close the buffer and punch the contents of the buffer into the next card. Only the value in location E was in the buffer when it was closed; therefore, the second output card will contain only the value in location E (under FORMAT F10.2).

The above example can also be applied to illustrate the case of less items in the list than numeric format specifications.

```
      PUNCH  7,A,B,C
    7 FORMAT(4F10.2)
```

The record is closed when there are no items in the input/output list and either the extreme right parenthesis or a numeric specification is encountered in the FORMAT statement. In the above example the last of the four F10.2 codes appearing in the FORMAT statement closes the record; at that time the contents of the buffer containing the values which are also in locations A,B, and C are punched into an output card.

3.7.3. Slashes

Slashes in the format can provide spacing on the printed output; if the results are to be printed on the console typewriter, the return of the carriage and a line skip are the result of the format slash; if the results are to be punched on cards which are later to be taken to a fast printer, slashes cause blank cards, which later create blank lines on the printed report.

```
      PUNCH  7,A,B,C,D
    7 FORMAT(2F8.3/F10.2,F6.3)
```

Output Cards

1st. card A,B	According to format F8.3
2nd. card C,D	According to format F10.2 and F6.3

The slash serves to close the buffer and then to cause the contents of the buffer to be punched into the first card. When the buffer is reopened, the contents of location C and D are sent into the buffer and then punched into the second card when the computer encounters the extreme right parenthesis (in this example) there is only one parenthesis, so the word extreme may be dropped—however, when more than one set of parenthesis is employed in the FORMAT statements, the rightmost parenthesis will be the right parenthesis, which will close a record; the use of two or more sets of parentheses will be explained later in this section).

To provide blank cards, more than one slash must be specified in the FORMAT statement.

```
      PUNCH  8,A,B,C,D,E,F,G,
    8 FORMAT(2F8.3//2F5.1,F4.1///F5.2)
```

Output Cards

1st. card A,B	Under F8.3
2nd. card Blank	
3rd. card C, D, and E	C and D under F5.1 and E under F4.1
4th. card Blank	

5th. card Blank	
6th. card F	Under F5.2
7th. card G	Under F8.3

The first slash closes the buffer and allows the contents of A and B, which were in the buffer, to be punched into the first card. When the buffer is reopened, the second slash is encountered, thereby causing the buffer to be closed again and its contents to be punched into the second output card. Since no characters were transferred into the buffer, only blanks are punched into the second card. The remainder of the format specifications should be analyzed in the same way. Three successive slashes cause two blank output cards (or two blank lines on the printed page); in general, n successive slashes cause $(n-1)$ blank output cards. The last record ends on the second F8.3 format.

```
  PUNCH  8,A,B,C,D,E,F,G,H
8 FORMAT(2F8.3//2F5.1,F4.1///F5.2)
```

Output Cards

1st. card A,B	Under F8.3
2nd. card Blank	
3rd. card C,D and E	C and D under F5.1 and E under F4.1
4th. card Blank	
5th. card Blank	
6th. card F	Under F5.2
7th. card G,H	Under F8.2
8th. card Blank	

In the above example another variable, H, has been added to the output list. Now the last record ends on the first of slashes; however, a record must close with the end of the output list and a numeric format specification.

Because a slash code is not a numeric format specification, the final record closes with the first F5.1 format specification. In the meantime, the second of the two successive slashes has caused the punching of a blank card. If, instead of the two slashes, the FORMAT statement contained the code 5HERROR, the last output card would be:

7th. card G,H, ERROR

Slashes may be placed at the beginning or ending of the FORMAT specifications as well as in the middle with the same effect.

```
  PUNCH  7,A,B,C,D
7 FORMAT(/F7.2,2F4.1/F5.2/)
```

Output Cards

1st. card Blank	A under F7.2
2nd. card A,B,C	B and C under F4.1
3rd. card D	D under F5.2
4th. card Blank	

The first slash causes an empty buffer to be punched into the first card; therefore, the first card is blank. The last slash causes the closing of the buffer which contains the contents of storage location D; this value is then punched into the third output card. After the buffer is reopened, the extreme right parenthesis again closes the buffer, which now contains no values; the fourth output card will then contain only blanks.

3.7.4. Multiple Pairs of Parentheses

More than one pair of parentheses may be used in a single FORMAT statement.

```
   PUNCH  27,(A(I),I=1,61)
27 FORMAT(F4.1,2(F6.3,2(F5.2,2F4.2)/2(F5.1,2F5.3)F4.2)F6.1)
```

Output Cards

```
1st. card A(1) , A(2) , A(3) , A(4) , A(5) , A(6) , A(7) , A(8)
          F4.1   F6.3   F5.2   F4.2   F4.2   F5.2   F4.2   F4.2
2nd. card A(9) ,A(10) ,A(11) ,A(12) ,A(13) ,A(14) ,A(15) ,A(16)
          F5.1  F5.3   F5.3   F5.1   F5.3   F5.3   F4.2   F6.3
2nd. card A(17) ,A(18) ,A(19) ,A(20) ,A(21) ,A(22)
          F5.2   F4.2   F4.2   F5.2   F4.2   F4.2
3rd. card A(23) ,A(24) ,A(25) ,A(26) ,A(27) ,A(28) ,A(29) ,A(30)
          F5.1   F5.3   F5.3   F5.1   F5.3   F5.3   F4.2   F6.1
4th. card A(31) ,A(32) ,A(33) ,A(34) ,A(35) ,A(36) ,A(37)
          F6.3   F5.2   F4.2   F4.2   F5.2   F4.2   F4.2
5th. card A(38) ,A(39) ,A(40) ,A(41) ,A(42) ,A(43) ,A(44) ,A(45)
          F5.1   F5.3   F5.3   F5.1   F5.3   F5.3   F4.2   F6.1
6th. card A(46) ,A(47) ,A(48) ,A(49) ,A(50) ,A(51) ,A(52) ,A(53)
          F5.1   F5.3   F5.3   F5.1   F5.3   F5.3   F4.2   F6.1
7th. card A(54) ,A(55) ,A(56) ,A(57) ,A(58) ,A(59) ,A(60) ,A(61)
          F5.1   F5.3   F5.3   F5.1   F5.3   F5.3   F4.2   F6.1
```

For all practical purposes, the programmer would undoubtedly use less complicated and shorter FORMAT statements. A long FORMAT statement, such as the one used in the above example, can profitably be used for academic purposes because of the many questions inherent in such an example. It should be noted that only the extreme right parenthesis closes the buffer and causes the computer to punch out the contents of the buffer. In the above example the extreme right parenthesis causes the punching of the third output card. Notice that the FORMAT statement returns to the left parenthesis next to the outside left parenthesis when the computer recognizes the extreme right parenthesis. However, the multiplier of that set of parentheses is ignored when the computer repeats the FORMAT statement.

```
27 FORMAT (F4.1,2(F6.3,2(F5.2,2F4.2)/2(F5.1,2F5.3)F4.2)F6.1)
```

This multiplier is ignored when the FORMAT statement is repeated.

These multipliers are not ignored when the FORMAT statement is repeated.

After repeating once, the FORMAT statement will always return to the left innermost parentheses.

Although the multiplier of the larger set of parentheses is ignored when the computer repeats the FORMAT statement, the same is not true of the multipliers of the sets of innermost parentheses. Special treatment is accorded to the innermost parenthesis, because these will be needed to handle the format for complex numbers (these will be discussed in detail in Chapter 5). The reader should also note that the first repeat of the FORMAT statement differs from all successive repeats. For all repeats of the FORMAT statement after the first repeat, the FORMAT statement always returns to the left innermost parenthesis; the multiplier of this set of parentheses continues to stay in effect through all following repeats.

3.7.5. Practical Examples

To close the discussion on FORMAT statements for the basic FORTRAN II language, two examples will be presented to illustrate practical uses of FORMAT statements and the use of the "implied DO loop" as opposed to the "regular DO loop."

Suppose that the final step in a certain program is the need to punch out a one-dimensional array of values which have been calculated during the program. The maximum size of the array has been set in the DIMENSION statement at 10; the minimum size of the array is 1 value.

Desired Output

```
1st. card X(1)
2nd. card X(2)
  .       .
  .       .
  .       .
nth. card X(N)      N is any number from 1 to 10
```

Required Output Statements

```
      PUNCH 7. (X(I),I=1,N)
 7    FORMAT(F10.3)
            or
      DO 10 I=1,N
10    PUNCH  7,X(I)
 7    FORMAT(F10.3)
```

Of course, in either case, the variable N must be defined prior to its appearance as an index in the series of output statements. The implied DO loop PUNCH 7, (X(I),I=1,N) causes only one card to be punched (remember, a card is punched whenever the computer executes a PUNCH statement), because the implied DO loop is equivalent to a long list (as explained in an earlier example). However, every time the extreme right parenthesis is encountered by the computer, the buffer is closed and the values in the buffer are punched into the next card. Therefore, N cards will be punched with one value per card. In the second case, the computer executes the PUNCH statement N times under control of the regular DO loop index I. The output card format and the number of cards would be exactly the same, if, in the second case, the statement:

```
7  FORMAT(10F10.3)
```

were to be substituted for the given FORMAT statement. Now, the second F10.3 in the FORMAT statement causes the buffer to be closed, because the list contains only one variable.

A more difficult problem of the same nature is the output of a two-dimensional array of variable size. Assume the maximum size of the array has been set in the DIMENSION statement at 10 rows and 10 columns, i.e. DIMENSION A(10,10). The minimum size of the array will be two rows and two columns; the first subscript denotes the row and the second subscript denotes the columns.

Desired Output

Array—5 rows and 5 columns
1st. card A(1,1), A(1,2), A(1,3), A(1,4), A(1,5)
2nd. card A(2,1), A(2,2), A(2,3), A(2,4), A(2,5)
. . . . . .
. . . . . .
. . . . . .
. . . . . .
5th. card A(5,1), A(5,2), A(5,3), A(5,4), A(5,5)
Array—3 rows and 6 columns
1st. card A(1,1), A(1,2), A(1,3), A(1,4), A(1,5), A(1,6)
2nd. card A(2,1), A(2,2), A(2,3), A(2,4), A(2,5), A(2,6)
3rd. card A(3,1), A(3,2), A(3,3), A(3,4), A(3,5), A(3,6)

Assume there are to be M columns and N rows; i.e. $A(M,N)$

```
      DO  10  I=1,M
   10 PUNCH  7,(A(I,J),J=1,N)
    7 FORMAT(10F6.2)
```

At least one card will be punched each time the computer executes statement 10—the actual number of cards punched depends on the FORMAT statement. By assumption, the upper limit to N is 10; therefore, after N values have been transferred into the buffer and it has been closed, one card will be punched out containing the N values which were sent to the buffer. Actually, the entire first row is punched into the first card (if there is enough room on the card to accomodate all the values in the row—if not, the remaining values in the row will be punched into a second card). Every time the regular DO loop with index I is repeated, another row is punched out into an output card. It should now be clear that there will be M output cards each containing N values.

Problems

3.1. For the following OUTPUT statements, show how the output cards will appear:

```
a)        PUNCH 27, A, B, C, D, K, F, G, H
       27 FORMAT (2F5.1/F6.2 (2F6.3/F6.2))
b)        PUNCH 35, (A(I), I = 1, N)
       35 FORMAT (F 5.2)
c)        PUNCH 47 (A(I), I = 1, N)
       47 FORMAT (/ 5F6.1 /)
d)        DO  29 I = 1, M
          DO  29 J = 1, N
       29 PUNCH 15 A (I,J)
       15 FORMAT (5F6.2 /)
e)        DO 30 I = 1, M
          DO 30 K = 1, N
       30 PUNCH 17 (A(I,K,J), J = 1, L)
       17 FORMAT (5F6.2)
```

3.2. *Given:* $-99 \leq I \leq 99$. It is desirable to punch the sign of I in column 8 and the digits of I in columns 9 and 10.

```
     PUNCH  1, J
   1 FORMAT(7X,I3)
```

The above statements will not produce the desired result if $-9 \leq I \leq 9$; why not? Write a group of statements which will punch out the sign (if negative) in column 8 and the number in columns 9 and 10. Modify these statements so that a + sign will be punched out in column 8 if I is positive (normally, column 8 would be left blank if I were positive).

3.3. *Part I. Given:* A one-dimensional array of M (M$\leq$ 1000) floating-point numbers, X, in the range $-99.99 \leq X \leq 99.99$. Write the PUNCH and FORMAT statements necessary to obtain the following output FORMAT when the punched cards are printed:

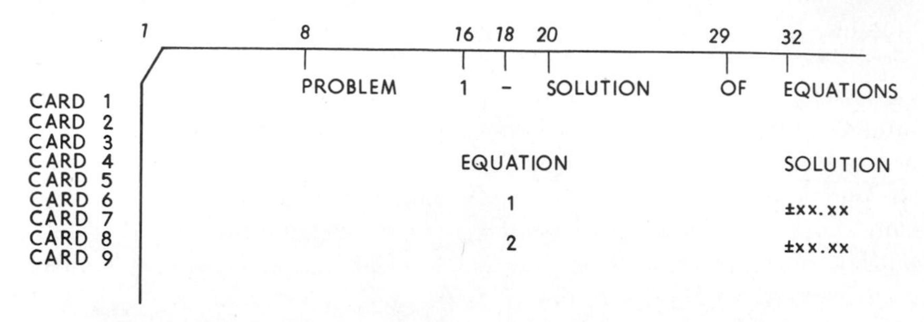

Part II When the output cards are taken over to the printer, the analyst must consider the number of lines available to him per page. Suppose that there are 60 lines per page available for printing the results. The actual results start in column 6, and because every other line is to be skipped, only 28 values can be printed per page according to the specified format.

If every page starts on line 3 (due to the wiring of the printer), line 3 would contain the following:

n xx. xx

where n is the number of the equation and xx. xx is the solution for equation number n. There will be no heading on all pages following the first page. The reader should modify the program in Part I so that the following heading appears on all pages after the first page.

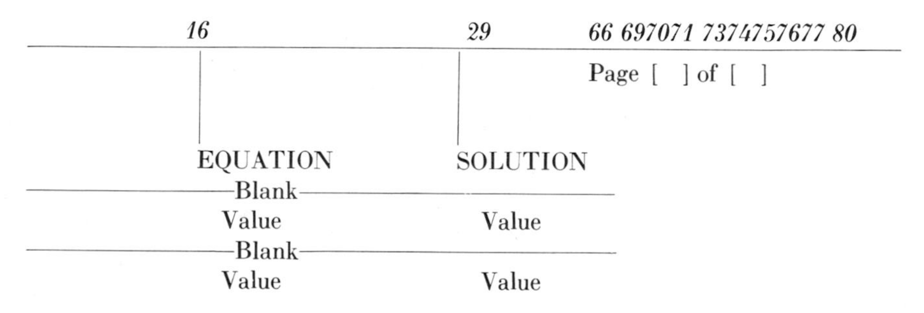

3.4. Use the following input instructions with the output instructions for the problem 3.3 to test your answer to problem 3.3.

```
    READ   100,(M,X(I),I = 1, M)
100 FORMAT(I4/ (10F6.2))
```

Test Data

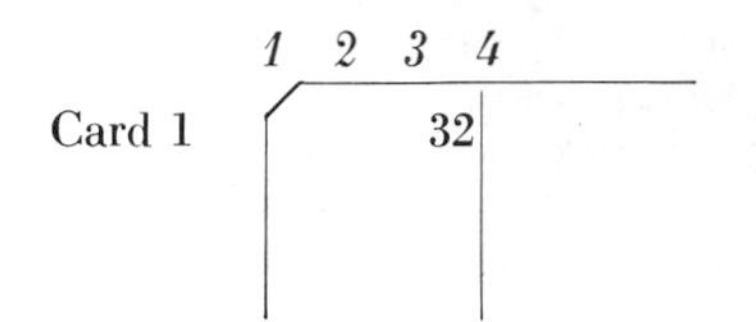

Card 2

1–6	7–12	13–18	19–24	25–30	31–36	37–42
2.8	−3.12	3.1	2.6	−1.3	3.75	8.1

43–48	49–54	55–60	61–80
−1.2	31.21	−81.77	

Card 3

1–6	7–12	13–18	19–24	25–30	31–36	37–42
1.2	3.7	−3.8	−81.51	3.7	51.3	4.7

43–48	49–54	55–60	61–80
5.27	3.278	5.71	

Card 4

1–6	7–12	13–18	19–24	25–30	31–36	37–42
1.2	3.856	−1.2	−8.756	−8.7	3.7	− 3.75

43–48	49–54	55–60	61–80
−1.	15.251	3.72	

Card 5

1–6	7–12	13–18	19–24	25–80
8.25	7.15	−1.2	75.12	

3.5. Write a FORTRAN program which will evaluate the formula $y = ax+b$, for x in increments of .1 starting at zero with an upper limit of 4 for different values of a and b.

Include in your program a group of instructions which will plot the y values as ordinate against the x values as abscissa; also write a heading and label both axes.

For example:

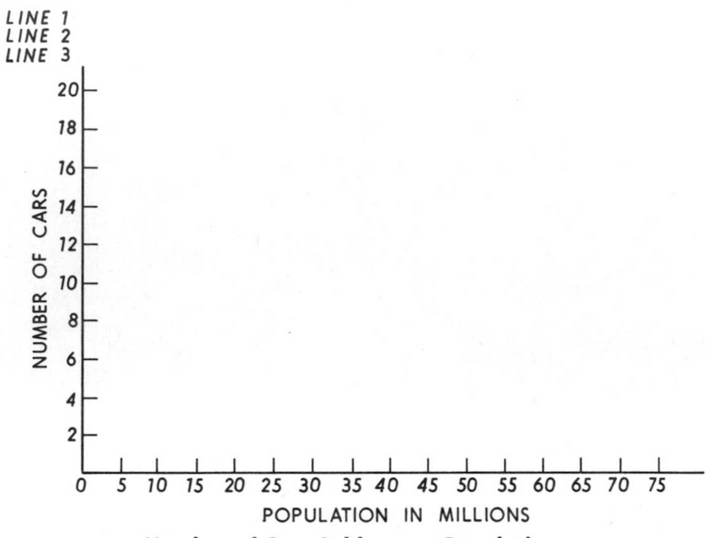

Number of Cars Sold versus Population

The ordinate can be labeled manually. One problem which arises is obtaining the right scale for the axis; in the case of the linear function $y = ax+b$, it is not difficult to find the scale, because the minimum and maximum occur at the extreme values of x. If $a = \frac{1}{4}$ and $b = 0$, then for a range on x of 0 to 75 we have the following range:

$$y = \tfrac{1}{4}\ (0) = 0 \text{ and } y = \tfrac{1}{4}\ (75) = 18\tfrac{3}{4}\ .$$

There are 50 lines available on the printed page (from 5 to 55) for the graph (not including the heading); therefore, the programmer must fit a range on y of 0 to 20 (as a round figure) in 50 lines. One solution would be to start labeling the ordinate at line 10 as 20; then, at every fifth line down (i.e., line 15,20, . . . ,50), punch out y as 18, 16, . . . ,2.

Scale the abscissa on line 55, label on line 57, and put the heading on line 59. For the actual plotting points use asterisks(*). Place alphameric blanks into two one-dimensional array with 65 (leaving room for labeling and heading) locations, using A-type format:

```
     READ   7,(K(I), I = 1, 65)
   7 FORMAT(65 A1)
     READ   7,(J (I), I = 1, 65)
```

Input card 1 ________________________
All blanks

Input card 2 ________________________
All blanks

Now read a card filled with asterisks into an array J1:

Input card 3 ________________________
****

When it is decided into which column (x—value) the asterisk should be placed for each y, say position I, where I = 30, the programmer can write the statement J(I) = J1 (I). After punching this value, the blank working field is regenerated by moving a blank from the K array to the J array; J(I) = K(I).

3.6. Find two whole numbers which between them make use of each of the 10 digits 0,1,2,3,4,5,6,7,8, and 9 just once. The two numbers are respectively the square and the cube of the same number.

3.7. Given a group of data cards under the following FORMAT—

1 2 — 10	11 — 15	16 — 25	26 — 30	31 — 34	35 — 79	80	
Name of person (alphameric)	xx. xx rating factor	Job de- scrip- tion	xxxxx Job num- ber	xxxx Code of last dept.	Comments (alphameric)		Always blank

The last card has a code letter A in columns 79,80.

Write a FORTRAN program which will read the above material into memory and then punch the output in two ways:

(1) *Job*

Persons	*Rating*	*Present Dept.*
______	______	______
______	______	______
______	______	______

Assume that the cards are in order by JOB number.

(2) *Dept.*

Persons	*Job*	*Rating*
______	______	______
______	______	______
______	______	______

3.8. *Calculation of Bowling Averages.* Write a FORTRAN program which will accept the following input—total pins for three-game series, high game for last three games, games bowled to date, total pins to date, high game to date, high

Calculate new average, total pins to date, high game for season, and high three-game series to date.

Design the output for one week so that it can be used for input to the next week.

3.9. Following is the description and flow chart for writing a FORTRAN program which can be used to calculate a student's grade point average. Write a FORTRAN program, following the given instructions and flow chart.

The student's name is punched in columns 1 through 40. Starting in column 41, a letter grade is punched, followed by the number of credit hours in that course.

Two columns are devoted for this, one for the grade, the next one for the number of credit hours in that course.

Column 79 is always blank. If any character is punched in column 80, the program assumes that the next card that follows is again punched with grades. They are punched in columns 1 through 78. Column 79 is blank and if column 80 is punched with any character, another card is assumed. A total of eight continuation cards can be included (or 331 grades). If a card with an * in column 1 appears in the program, the information in columns 2 through 80 of that card appears as a heading in the output. If a $ is punched in column 2 of this card, the program assumes the next card that follows to be the criteria to determine the letter grade (A+, A−, B+, B−, C+, C−, D+, D−, E)

Explanation of the Flow Chart

A card is read. If an * is in column 1, this is a header card; in this case, column 2 is checked for a $. If this $ is present, the next card is assumed to be a criteria card, which is read. Notice that a group of students can be graded to a certain criteria and another group with another criteria. If no * is present in column 1, this card is assumed to be a student card. The name of the student is assumed to be in columns 1 through 40, and the grades in columns 41 to 78. Column 80 is checked and if it is not blank, the next card is assumed to have grades in columns 1 through 78. This process is repeated until a card with a blank in column 80 is read, or until a total of 8 cards are read.

In the IBM 1620 the alphameric codes for A, A, C, D, and E are respectively 41, 42, 43, 44, and 45. Because of the fact that the fixed-point precision is 4, any information read in format A1 is left adjusted, i.e., an A goes as 4100.

The grading uses the 4.0 system. If each letter in storage is divided by 100, and the result subtracted from 45, we obtain 4 for A, 3 for B, 2 for C, etc. This number is multiplied by the number of credit hours in that course, and in this way the number of points is obtained. The floating-point precision is 6. The average is obtained with six significant digits, in the form x. x x x x x. To round the number, 0.005 is added to this average. The average is then reduced to x. xx000 by multiplying by 100, storing the result in fixed-point location, re-storing the result back in a floating-point location and dividing by 10.

Once the average is obtained, a letter grade has to be given according to this average, and the criteria eight numbers are stored in core. They are the lower criterias for A , A−, B , B−, C ,C−, D and D−. The obtained average is compared to each one of these numbers. If the average is greater than the criteria in say, J, of this array, then a C− should be punched. In the first part of the fixed-point location "LETER" the letter grade is stored, in the second part, the sign (+ or −) is stored. Notice that if J is odd, the sign is plus; if J is even, the sign is −. Also we have the following $J \ \underbrace{1{,}2}_{A} \ \underbrace{3{,}4}_{B} \ \underbrace{5{,}6}_{C} \ \underbrace{7{,}8}_{D}$

Then (J+1)/2 will yield:

$$
\begin{aligned}
1 &\text{ for } J = 1 \text{ or } 2\\
2 &\text{ for } J = 3 \text{ or } 4\\
3 &\text{ for } J = 5 \text{ or } 6\\
4 &\text{ for } J = 7 \text{ or } 8
\end{aligned}
$$

If (J + 1)/2 is multiplied by 1,000 and added to 4,000, we obtain the codes for A if J is 1 or 2, B if J is 3 or 4, and so on.

For the sign, a minus sign is represented by 20, a plus sign by 10. So 20− (J−J/2 * 2) * 10 will be equal to 20 if J is even and equal to 10 if J is odd. In this way the statement LETER = 4,000+(S+1)/2*1000+20−(J−J/2 * 2) *10 stores the corresponding letter with its sign in the fixed-point location "LETER"). This code punched in format A2 will yield A , A−, B , B−,etc.

FLOW CHART

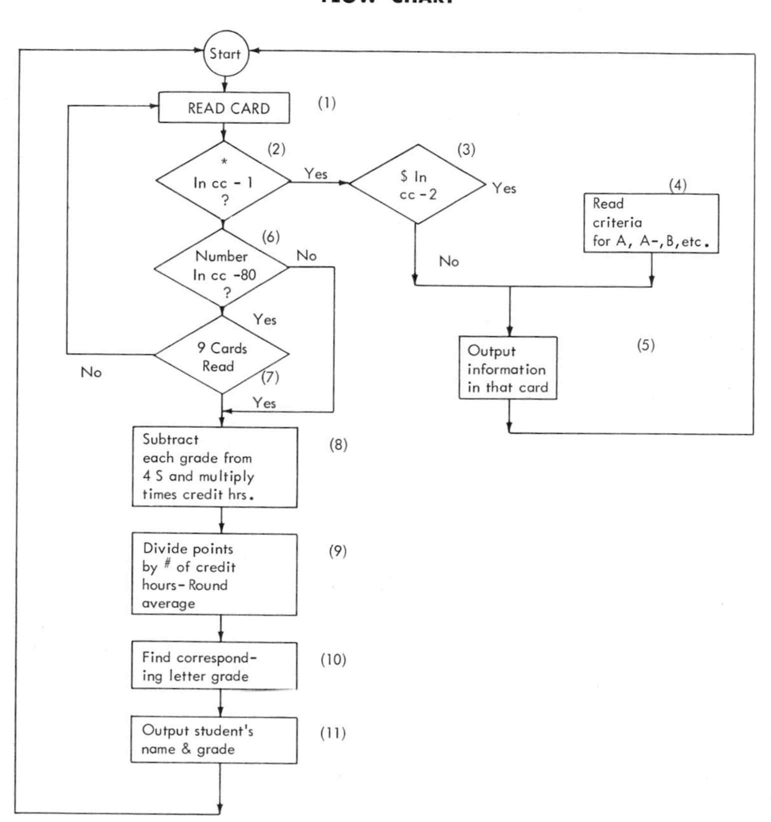

3.10. Explain the FORMAT statements for the programs in the problems at the end of Chapter 2.

4. Functions and Subroutines

A general definition of a subroutine is a "group of statements (maybe only one) which serve to accomplish some purpose through utilization of the computer." Even though the above definition is general in nature, it might lead one to form a picture of a difficult program broken down into parts or modules. As the student progresses to more and more difficult programs, he should incorporate into the difficult program as often as possible, short, simple programs, which he has previously written. In other words, the programmer should build up a file of programs and use these programs, with the aid of a minimal number of other instructions, to solve more complex problems. In this way, he would not only save a great deal of time and effort on his part, but he may also save computer time and storage.

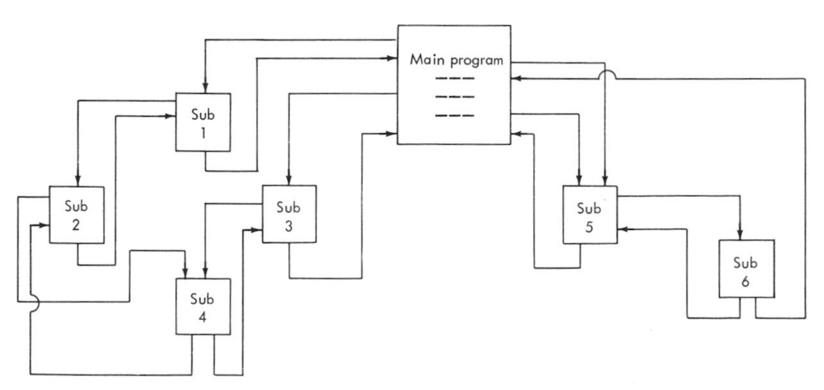

FIG. 4–1. Main Program and Associated Subprograms

In the above program the main program utilizes the subprogram, Sub 1, which in turn utilizes the subprogram, Sub 2, which in turn utilizes the subprogram, Sub 4. In addition, the main program utilizes the subprograms, Sub 3 and Sub 5. Subprogram Sub 3 utilizes the subprogram, Sub 4, and the subprogram, Sub 5, utilizes the subprogram, Sub 6. This illustrates the method by which a programmer, with a relatively few main instructions, can utilize the computer to solve difficult problems. By using the file of programs built up through previous problems by the programmer or utilizing programs written by other computer users, the programmer eliminates the need of writing an entirely new program for every problem. A relatively few instructions may serve to specialize the existing programs to solve a great many problems.

4.1. Closed and Open Routines

Subprograms which appear only once, no matter how many times they are used in the main program, are called closed subprograms.

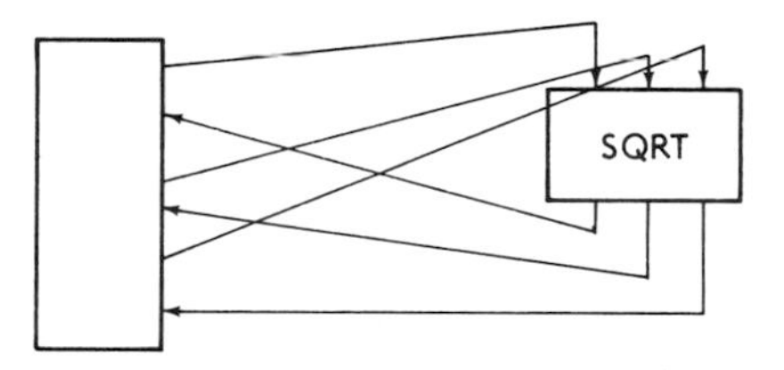

FIG. 4–2. Closed Subprogram

To use a closed subprogram, such as the subprogram to calculate the square root of a number, shown above, the computer must be instructed to do the following four steps:

1. Transfer the argument(s) to the subprogram so that the subprogram can instruct the computer to operate on them.
2. Branch to the first instruction of the subprogram.
3. Transfer the result of the calculations back to the main program.
4. Branch back to the instruction following the last executed instruction in the main program.

The set of instructions which are necessary to instruct the computer to perform the above operations are called linkage instructions. In accordance with the policy we established in the first three chapters, we shall again go into only as much machine language as we need to give a meaningful explanation of the FORTRAN statements which enable the programmer to use subprograms. The fourth step is the most difficult to accomplish, because the reentry to the main program may take place at any statement in the program; the address of the statement at which reentry is to take place must be supplied at the time the subprogram is to be used. In the IBM 1620 computer a machine-language statement is available which transmits the address of the argument to the subprogram and transmits the address of the next sequential instruction to a special register.

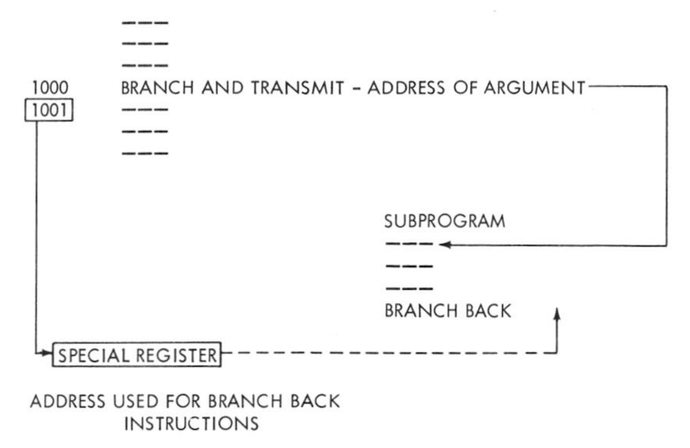

FIG. 4–3. Linkage Instructions

The "BRANCH AND TRANSMIT" instruction places the next sequential address, namely 1001, in a special register; also the address of the argument is transmitted to the subprogram; and finally, the computer executes an unconditional branch to the first instruction of the subprogram. At the end of the subprogram, a machine-language statement, the BRANCH BACK, executes an unconditional branch to the address specified in the special register (this corresponds to a "GO TO n" statement; but now n cannot be specified; it becomes a special register which then gives the address of the statement to which the computer must execute the branch). The address of the location into which the result is placed by the subprogram is transmitted to the main program via an unconditional BRANCH statement. These instructions are the linkage instructions.

A subprogram which is placed in the direct line of instructions is called an "open subroutine."

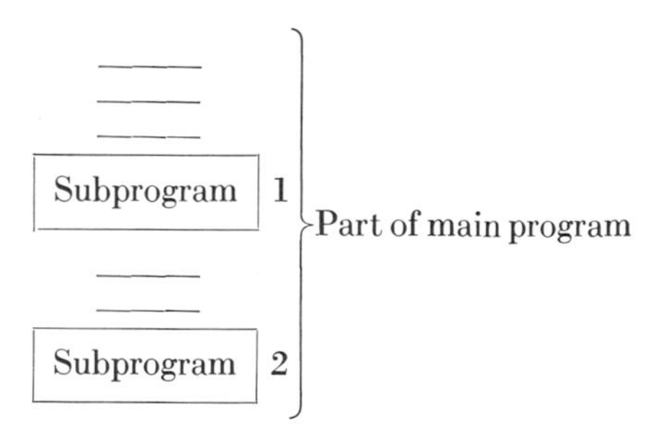

FIG. 4–4. Open Subprograms

An open subroutine creates none of the linkage problems involved with the closed subroutines. If the subprogram is to be used only once or twice in the program, an open subroutine will be faster than a closed subroutine because of the computer time necessary to evaluate the linkage instructions. However, if the subprogram is going to be used many times in the same program, a great deal of computer memory space is wasted by writing open subroutines, because the same instructions must be written many times.

4.2. Subroutine Operations

In the FORTRAN language there are three operations involved with the use of functions and subroutines:

1. *Naming or Coding*—Assignment of a symbolic or code name to a function or a subroutine always serves one purpose and may serve a second purpose. The FORTRAN compiler uses the symbolic name of the function as the address of the location which contains the first instruction of the subroutine.

GO TO SYM   Symbolic name of the subroutine; usually a machine-language address, say, 13158.

The branch to the subroutine is effected by a statement like BRANCH AND TRANSMIT—The GO TO statement is used here only for the purpose of illustrating the branch to the first instruction of the subroutine.

		Subroutine	
The first instruction of the subroutine is located at the machine-language address, 13158	13158	______	SYM
		______	
		______	
		______	

Rather than reservation of an actual storage location with the symbolic function name, the appearance of the function name in the transfer statement to the subroutine causes the compiler to substitute the address of the first instruction of the subroutine. In other words, the symbolic name of the function is utilized by the compiler in setting up the linkage instructions.

Because the compiler does not reserve a storage location for the function name, a reference to the name in the subroutine will set up a new storage location in the subroutine.

Main Program	*Subroutine* *GAMMA*
A FORTRAN instruction to utilize the subroutine GAMMA	→ 1st instruction
	121 GAMMA = A*B

The location called GAMMA is defined in statement 121, and at run time a value will be placed in location GAMMA. In this way, the storage location may be used to send the result of the subroutine back to the main program; i.e., the address of the location containing the result, GAMMA, is transferred to the main program.

2. *Defining or Writing*—Similar to the case of variables, a function or subroutine is defined in terms of the FORTRAN compiler when the compiler can assume (at compile time) that the functional rule will be available to the program at run time. Say, the programmer tries to use the subroutine, PAYRL, in a certain program:

Main Program

____
____
____

125 [________] ←Statement which attempts to utilize the subroutine PAYRL. At this time, if the subroutine is available to the program, the computer will use the subroutine statement(s) in order to return a result to the main program.

____
____

To assure the availability of the subroutine at run time, the compiler must be satisfied (at compile time) that the subroutine will be available to the main program when statement 125 is executed by the computer.

At this point the reader should be able to draw a correspondence between the definition of variables and the definition of functions.

A variable becomes defined, to the compiler, when the compiler can assume (at compile time) that a value will be placed in the location, specified by the variable name, at run time. For a function or subroutine to be defined, the compiler must be able to associate a group of instructions (maybe only one) with the symbolic name of the subroutine.

Nonsubscripted Variable		*Arithmetic Expression*
A	=	B + C

Function Name		
GAMMA	Linkage Instructions may take on several forms, to be explained later in this chapter.	A group of instructions written to accomplish some purpose (a subroutine)

The group of instructions composing the subroutine serve the same purpose as the arithmetic expression on the right-hand side of the arithmetic statement; the compiler may assume that the value (the result of the calculations) will be transferred from the subroutine to the main program when a reference is made to the symbolic name of the subroutine.

Sometimes, the process of defining a subroutine is called, "writing the subroutine," because the statements composing the subroutine must be written out, i.e., specified in order to define the subroutine.

3. *Using or Calling*—In order to get a result back from a subroutine, a linkage must be set up between the main program and the subroutine; included in this linkage must be a means of transmitting the argument(s) to the subroutine. If a function or subroutine has been defined, a reference to the symbolic name of the subroutine which supplies the arguments will allow the programmer to use, or call for the use of, the subroutine.

In the basic FORTRAN II language, four types of subroutines are available to the programmer. The following four sections discuss these subroutines in detail, along with the auxiliary statements provided in the FORTRAN language to enable the programmer to take full advantage of the subroutine.

4.3. Library Subroutines

A name consisting of four to seven alphameric characters, the last of which must be the letter F, and the first of which must be a letter, may be given to library subroutines. If the first letter is an X, the result calculated by the subroutine will be a fixed-point constant; any other letter used for the first letter will cause a floating-point result to be calculated. Examples: SINF, RANDF, SYMBF, ABSF.

Library subroutines are defined by a machine-language program which must be included in the FORTRAN compiler. Several of the most commonly used subroutines were written as part of the compiler in order to enable the programmer to use these subroutines and still punch only one main deck, instead of having to punch several decks.

4.3.1. Given Library Subroutines

The following subroutines were incorporated into the Fortran compiler:

1. SINF(argument)
2. COSF(argument)
3. ATANF(argument)
4. LOGF(argument)
5. EXPF(argument)
6. SQRTF(argument)
7. ABSF(argument)

In each case only a single real argument was permitted, and only a single value would be calculated by the subroutine for transfer to the main program. For the trigonometric sine, cosine, and arctangent subroutines, the argument must be specified in radians.

Hastings' approximation or a Taylor's series expansion (see Chapter 6) are the rules by which the trigonometric sine is computed in FORTRAN. The trigonometric cosine is computed using the series for the sine, but taking as the argument, $\pi/2-$ (the argument specified for the cosine in radians).

The trigonometric arctangent, the natural logarithm ($\log_e$), and the exponential function (e^x), are calculated by use of Taylor's series expansion, or some modification thereof which will converge more quickly. If the argument for the subroutine ABSF is positive, the result will be the same as the argument; however, if the argument is negative, the result will be the same as the argument with the sign changed to positive. Examples of some of the above subroutines will be given in Chapter 6 (since a knowledge of mathematical series is not assumed for this volume, not all of the above subroutines will be explained in Chapter 6). Each of the first six subroutines may be carried to as many significant places as is desired. Usually the number of significant figures is made equal to the length of storage locations for floating-point variables.

4.3.2. Difficulties in FORTRAN Programming—Need for Library Routines

Many times, the programmer may have to use machine-language instructions to solve some small part of the large problem. Now the programmer benefits by using FORTRAN as much as possible, but for certain applications, such as character manipulation, data transfer, decision making, and report control, the FORTRAN language is either inefficient or will not work at all.

Although the FORTRAN language cannot profitably be used (if it can be used at all) to program problems in the above areas, the programmer still may benefit by the use of FORTRAN if the main body of the problem is concerned with scientific calculations. To use FORTRAN for the main program and also to handle the troublesome areas mentioned above, it is necessary to write a subroutine in a machine-type language. In the basic FORTRAN II language for smaller computers (IBM 1620), the only way to write subroutines to handle the afore-mentioned areas is to write them in actual machine language and incorporate the subroutine into the FORTRAN compiler. Because this book does not explain machine language or the linkage necessary to place a subroutine into the compiler, the discussion of library subroutines for the basic FORTRAN II language will not be examined further. Chapter 5, which extends FORTRAN II to larger machines and to FORTRAN IV, will show that the calling instruction in the FORTRAN language for the larger machines is very simple and that the subroutine itself may be written in symbolic language. As far as programming ease, this symbolic language lies between actual machine language and FORTRAN.

4.3.3. Operations—Library Subroutines

When the programmer calls for a library subroutine, either one originally in the compiler or one written by the programmer and added to the compiler, the actual machine-language statements comprising the subroutine are duplicated and placed in the object program. If the library subroutine is not called by the programmer, it is not duplicated and placed in the object deck, therefore using the memory space only when it is necessary.

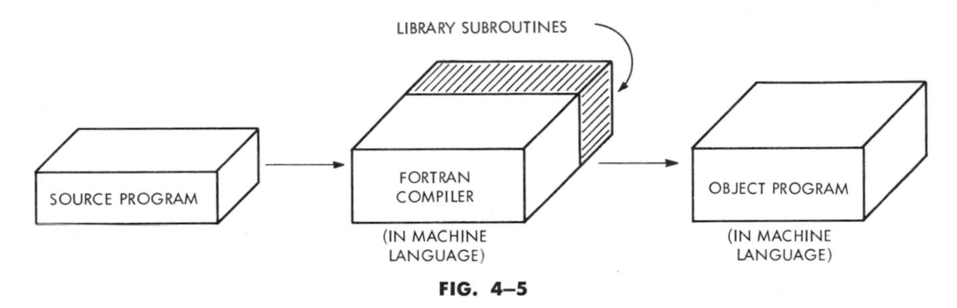

FIG. 4–5

The appearance of the name of the library subroutine on the right-hand side of an arithmetic statement will cause the FORTRAN compiler to punch the subroutine as part of the object program and to establish the linking instructions necessary to utilize the library subroutine at run time.

```
Y = 2.528 + R - 3.156*SIN(A)
Z = F+G
```

Assume that R, A, F, and G have been defined prior to this statement. At compile time the statements which comprise the SIN subroutine are placed in the object program. When the computer is running the program and reaches the above arithmetic statement, the following steps take place:

1. The value in location A is transferred to the subroutine to serve as the argument (actually, only the address corresponding to the symbolic storage name A is transferred to the subroutine).
2. A branch to the first statement of the subroutine, SIN, is effected by a transfer instruction.
3. A result is calculated by the computer as it executes the subroutine statements.
4. The address of the result is transmitted back to the main program.
5. Control is transferred back to the main program; to the instruction following the instruction causing the transfer to the subroutine.

6. The value in the address transmitted by the subroutine (the result of the calculation) is multiplied by 3.156, and the product is then subtracted from the sum of the value in location R and 2.528.
7. The next sequential instruction, Z = F + G, is executed by the computer.

4.4. Arithmetic Statement Functions

These functions are named in the same manner as library subroutines; i.e., four to seven alphameric characters, the first of which must be a letter (X for a fixed-point result) and the last of which must be the letter F. However, unlike the library subroutines, arithmetic statement functions are defined in one FORTRAN statement. Consider the definition of the function, named FRSTF:

$$\text{FRSTF(X)} = \text{U}*\text{X} - \text{Z}$$

The above arithmetic statement establishes a rule or a correspondence between two sets of points.

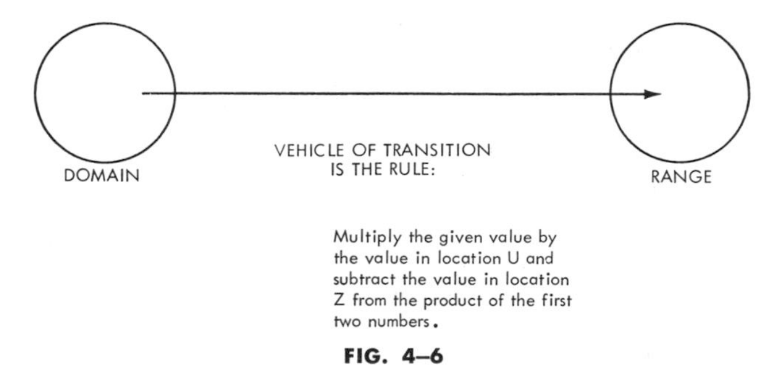

FIG. 4–6

The domain is the set of values which may be taken on by the variable X or the set of values which are allowed to go into location X; upper and lower limits may be placed on this set of values by the programmer (i.e., for some reasons connected with the particular problem, X is allowed to take on rational [floating-point] numbers between 0 and 2000) or by the physical size of the storage location. At compile time the FORTRAN compiler associates the rule—take the argument and multiply it by the value in location U, then subtract the value in location Z from this product—with the name FRSTF. In other words, FRSTF can be regarded as the symbolic address of the location of the first machine-language instruction needed to provide the calculation comprising the rule or function. The result of the calculations specified in the arithmetic statement is a set of values, namely, the range. For each value in the domain, there is a value in the range. Only a single value can be calculated by an arithmetic statement function.

4.4.1. Dummy Variables and Regular Variables

In defining the arithmetic statement function, FRSTF(X) = U*X−Z, variable X, serving as an argument, is not the ordinary type of variable name in the sense of taking up a storage location. When the function FRSTF, is used at run time, it would be advantageous for the programmer to be able to use any floating-point variable as the argument for the function, not only the variable X; if only X could be used as the argument, it would be necessary to write an arithmetic statement defining the value X before using the function. In other words, X serves as a "dummy" variable for R(1) or Y or some other variable when the program is run. Because X will serve as a dummy and not assume a value in its own right, the FORTRAN compiler allows the programmer to use the variable X to specify another storage location besides its position in the functional rule.

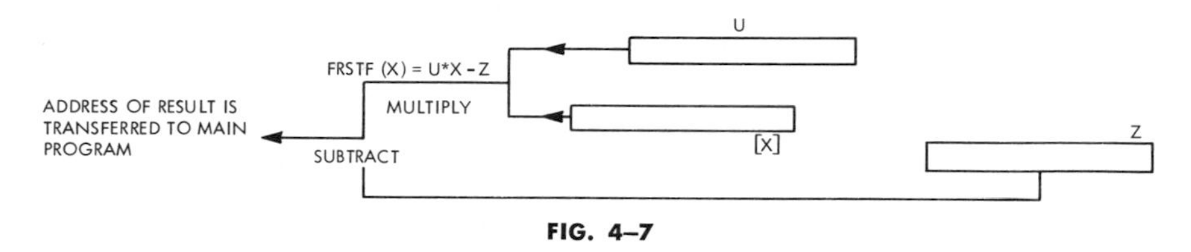

FIG. 4–7

[X] is not actually a storage location, but a space in an instruction.

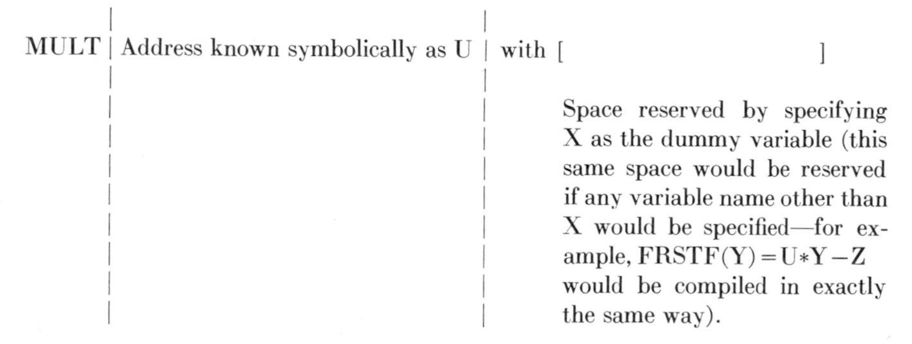

MULT
Address known symbolically as U
with [ ]
Space reserved by specifying X as the dummy variable (this same space would be reserved if any variable name other than X would be specified—for example, FRSTF(Y)=U*Y−Z would be compiled in exactly the same way).

At run time the address of the variable to be used as the argument will be placed in the space reserved by the dummy variable. To be a dummy variable, the variable must appear on both sides of the arithmetic statement which defines the function. In the above example only the variable X was a dummy variable, but it is permissible to have many dummy variables.

TENTHF(A,B,C,D)=A*B+C**2*D+5.216*R

Now A, B, C, and D are all dummy variables, the variable R being the only regular variable (by a regular variable we mean a variable specifying an actual storage location).

Library subroutines may be used in the definition of arithmetic statement functions, because the compiler knows that the library subroutines are predefined and are included in the compiler; in this way, the compiler can assume that the entire rule will be available when it is referred to at run time (again this is the definition of being defined to the compiler).

NINTHF(S)=R*SINF(S)

Variables (dummy or regular) to be used in the arithmetic statement defining the function must not be subscripted because the appearance of a variable in such a statement serves as a signal to the compiler to reserve a storage space for that variable. It would not be feasible for the compiler to reserve a location which must also be part of an array. Say the subscripted variable R(3), appeared in the definition of an arithmetic statement function:

TWELFHF(R(3))=S*R(3)+T —wrong—subscripted dummy variable
or TWELFHF(T)= S*R(3)+T —wrong—subscripted regular variable

In either of the above statements, a position in storage is reserved for the symbolic name R(3). Whether a DIMENSION statement for the array R is placed before or after either of the above statements, a conflict develops in the compiler rules, because the DIMENSION statement serves to reserve space for arrays. To avoid this conflict of possibly assigning two different addresses to the same symbolic name, the compiler must set up a testing procedure for the appearance of subscripted variables in the definition of arithmetic statement functions or to rule out the use of subscripted variables in the definition of arithmetic statement functions; the latter alternative was chosen, because there is no advantage to using subscripted variables in the definition of these functions.

The conflict between the reservation of storage space for variables used both in functions and in other applications also leads to the rule that arithmetic statement functions must be defined before the first executable statement of the program (all control statement are executable statements). Nonexecutable statements include the following:

FORMAT
DIMENSION

After one arithmetic statement function has been defined, it may be used in the definition of another arithmetic statement function.

FRSTF(X)=U*X−Z
SCNDF(Y,R)=F*2.561+R*FRSTF(Y)

4.4.2. Calling of Arithmetic Statement Functions

Thus far the discussion has been centered on the definition of arithmetic statement functions. Like library subroutines, arithmetic statement functions are called or used by their appearance on the right-hand side of an arithmetic statement.

FRSTF(X)=U*X+S	Definition of the function FRSTF. This statement must appear before the first executable statement of the program.
R=X*2.167+FRSTF(Z(I))	Use of the function FRSTF.

After the execution of the above statement, the value in location R will be the result of the calculation:

X*2.167+U*Z(I)+S

The variable X in the definition statement is a dummy variable for the variable Z(I), at run time. At this time, the variables X,U,I,Z(I), and S must be defined to the compiler. Notice that the variable X serves both as a dummy variable and a regular variable; since the appearance of X in the arithmetic statement defining the function only serves as part of a rule and not to reserve a storage location, it is perfectly legal to later use X as a regular variable (regular, in the sense that a storage location is associated with the symbolic name X). Notice also, subscripted variables may be used as arguments when the arithmetic statement function is called to product a result.

Arithmetic statement functions can be compounded to give the programmer a powerful set of rules utilizing closed subroutines (i.e., subroutines which appear only once, even though they may be used many times). Following is a set of six arithmetic statement functions presented to illustrate the way in which these functions are compounded as well as to illustrate, once more, the difference between dummy variables and regular variables.

(1) FRSTF(X)=U*X−V
(2) SCND(U,X)=U*X−V
(3) THRDF(R)=3.275+FRSTF(F)*R
(4) FRTHF(A,B)=B**2*SCNDF(FRSTF(A),B)
(5) SIXTHF(J)=I*J+5*J

Statements which call the above functions:

(i) Y=2.731+FRSTF(Z(K))
X is a dummy variable for Z(K)

The value to be placed in storage location Y is the result of the calculation:

2.731+U*Z(K)−V

The variables U,V,K, and Z(K) are regular variables and therefore must be defined before their appearance in the calling statement.

(ii) L=3.716+4.276*SCNDF(R,S)

Now both U and X are dummy variables, for R and S respectively. The value to be placed in location L will be the value calculated by

3.716 + 4.276 * (R*S−V)

However, the result will be truncated and placed in location L, because L signifies a fixed-point location. The variables R, S, and V are regular variables and therefore must be defined before their appearance in the calling statement.

(iii) S=6.75/THRDF(Z)

X is a dummy variable for F and R is a dummy variable for Z. The value to be placed in S is calculated by

6.75/((3.275+U*F−V)*Z).

U, F, V, and Z, being regular variables, must be defined prior to the calling statement.

(iv) G=FRTHF(P,Q)+Z**2.*P

A is a dummy variable for P, and B is a dummy variable for Q; in addition, U and X, in (2), are dummy variables for the value calculated by the FRSTF with argument A, and the variable B, respectively. In (1), X is a dummy variable for A; it is interesting to note that A is, in turn, a dummy variable for P. The value to be placed in location G is calculated by:

Q**2* (U*P−V)*Q−V +Z**2.*P

Q, U, P, V, Z, and P are regular variables.

(v) I21=200./SIXTHF(K*J(3))

Although the computation for the SIXTHF will be done in fixed-point arithmetic, the resulting value will then be floated, because the function name does not start with X.

Of course, the floating result is then fixed once more and placed in location I21, since this specifies a fixed-point location.

Any calculations which requires a double change of mode is wasteful of computer time; a more efficient way to handle the function would be:

```
 Definition
   XSIXTHF(J)=I*J+5*J
Calling
    I21=200/XSIXTHF(K*J(3))
```

In either case, J is a dummy variable for the expression (K*J(3)). The value to be placed in location I21 is the result of the calculation:

200/(I*K*J(3)+5*K*J(3))

I, K, and J(3) are regular variables and, therefore, must be defined prior to execution of the above statement. If, at time of execution of the above statement, the values in locations I, K, and J(3) were 2, 3, and 4 respectively, then the result would be

200/(2*3*4+5*3*4)=200/84=2,

truncation being caused by fixed-point division. Now, in (5), the following would occur:

2 ——————→ 2.0	——————→ 2
Floated because SIXTHF starts with a letter other than X	Fixed because I21 is a fixed-point variable

The student may use the function XSIXTHF and therefore eliminate these two steps. Four possible mode configurations are possible for functions of one argument or for functions of more than one argument, provided all the arguments are of the same mode. These four possibilities are:

1. Fixed argument(s), fixed result
2. Floating argument(s), fixed result
3. Fixed argument(s), floating result
4. Floating argument(s), floating result

Dummy variables serve to set the mode and the number for the regular variables which are going to replace them.

Definition

TENTHF(A)=A**2+R*2.1

Calling

Y=TENTHF(K)

ERROR: The mode in the function, TENTHF, is set for floating point by the dummy variable A. An attempt to use the value in location K will result in a mixed mode expression.

Definition

TWENTYF(R,S,T)=3.*R+S*T

Calling

Z=3.27*TWENTYF(A,B)

ERROR: The function requires three values for arguments while the calling statement only supplies two arguments.

4.4.3. Application of the Arithmetic Statement Function

The advantage of using an arithmetic statement function can be appreciated by the following comparison:

VARIABLE is to CONSTANT
as ARITHMETIC STATEMENT FUNCTION
is to ARITHMETIC EXPRESSION.

An arithmetic statement function may be thought of as a storage location for the arithmetic expression itself, not the value of the arithmetic expression; in this sense, the arithmetic statement function can hold many arithmetic expressions—the function is the same but the parameters are changed from one time to the next.

Suppose the function, $f(x,b) = \dfrac{ax^2+b}{cx}$

must be used three times, as in the following program:

```
      FUN (X,B) = (A * X ** 2+B)/ C*X
      READ 27, Y,Z, A,C,R,S,K
   27 FORMAT (6F6.2,I4)
      D = (R * 2.12) / S** 1.4
      DX = S *FUN (Z, D) / EXPF(Y)
      U1 = Y * Z+A * S
      K = S / R
      F = E
      DY = F / FUN (U1,F)+DX ** K
      U2 = (DX+DY) /2.+R
      DZ = U2 *FUN (U1, U2)
      PUNCH 37, DX, DY, DZ
   37 FORMAT (E 16.8, 10 × E 16.8, 10 × E 16.8)
      STOP
      END
```

The name FUN may be thought of as a location (actually, it is not a location, but a rule) which holds a series of different arithmetic expressions (not values), (A * X ** 2+B)/C * X, one for each combination of the values X and B.

4.5. FUNCTION Subprograms

These functions may be given a name consisting of one to six alphameric characters, the first of which must be a letter and the final character must not be an F if the name is more than three characters long. To call a FORTRAN FUNCTION subprogram, its name must appear on the right side of an arithmetic statement—in a fashion equivalent to library subroutines and arithmetic statement functions. The major difference between the three types of functions is the way in which the programmer defines them. For a problem which requires a function that cannot be defined in one FORTRAN statement or that is not used often enough to justify its inclusion in the compiler (and does not need the character manipulation power of machine language), the programmer should write a FUNCTION SUBPROGRAM.

As its description points out, the FORTRAN subprogram is defined in a separate FORTRAN program. FORTRAN FUNCTION subprograms may be placed behind the main program and compiled with the main program (or the subprograms may be compiled separately).

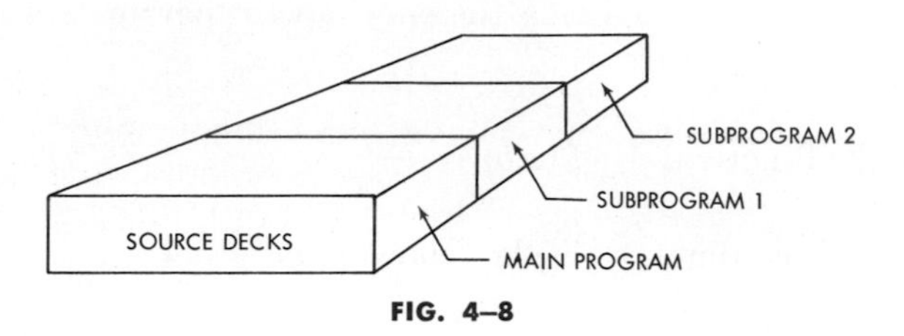

FIG. 4–8

Subprograms may not be placed between two statements of any FORTRAN program, whether it be a main program or another subprogram.

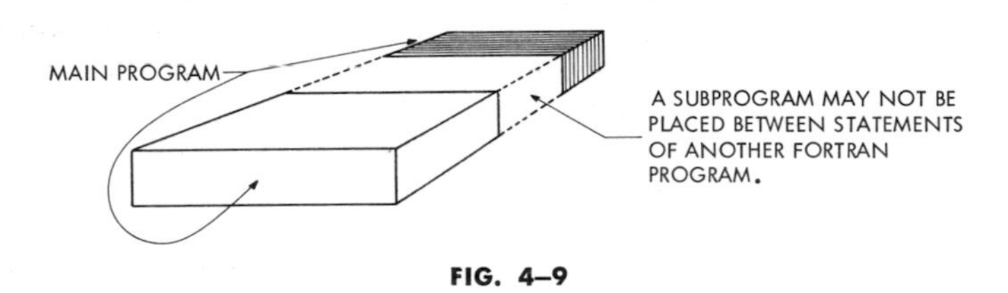

FIG. 4–9

4.5.1. FUNCTION Subprogram Definition and Use—Compiler Operations

Each FORTRAN FUNCTION subprogram must contain the following statements:

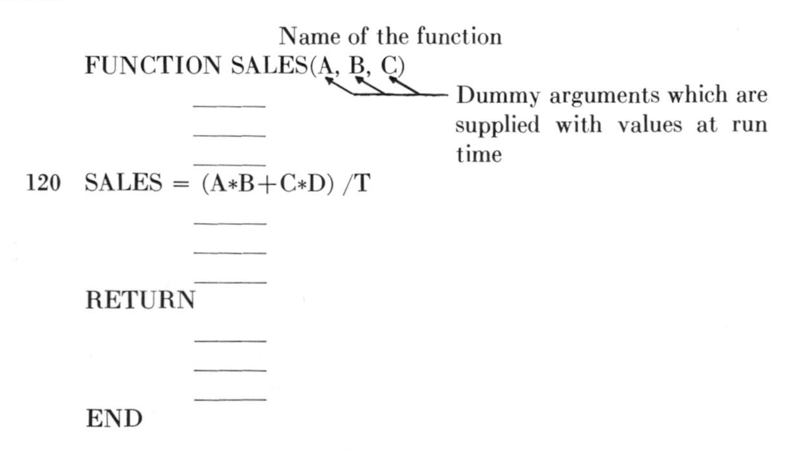

The first statement of the subprogram must be a FUNCTION statement, which includes the name of the function and at least one variable which serves as a dummy for some regular variable in the calling program at run time.

Y = 3.726*SALES(R, S, T)

At compile time the FORTRAN compiler analyzes the above statement in the following way:

1. The symbolic name, "SALES," must either be a FUNCTION subprogram or an array, because some arguments follow the name. A check is then made with symbolic names listed in the DIMENSION statement; since SALES does not appear in the DIMENSION statement, the FORTRAN compiler will treat SALES as the name of a FUNCTION subprogram.

2. A location in the memory is reserved, and it is associated with the name SALES (notice that the location SALES may be used only in conjunction with the FUNCTION subprogram named SALES). The machine address of this location is then transmitted to a certain place in memory, say 18000.

Location	*Contents*	*Name*
12151		SALES
18000	12151	

3. The machine addresses equivalent to the variables R,S,T are placed in storage locations. Of course, R,S, and T must be defined before their appearance as arguments of the FUNCTION subprogram, SALES.

Location	*Contents*	*Name*
10110		R
10120		S
11572		T
20000	10110	
20001	10120	
20002	11572	

Movement of Addresses of Arguments to Special Storage Locations

4. Instructions are set up by the compiler which will create a transfer, at run time, to the first instruction of the subprogram and also which will place the address of the next sequential instruction in a special register (to enable a return to the main program at the instruction after the instruction which caused the transfer to the subprogram).

Location	*Contents*
05000	Transfer instruction to address 18000
Special register	05001

TRANSFER INSTRUCTION

After compiling the main program, the FORTRAN compiler compiles the subprogram (actually the subprogram may be compiled at an entirely different time, even ahead of the main program, because the two compilations are entirely independent). Of course, when the program is run, both the compiled main program and the compiled subprogram must be present. The FUNCTION statement indicates to the compiler that this is a subprogram; therefore, the addresses at which the arguments are located will be found in locations 20000, 20001, and 20002 (these addresses are just used for illustration purposes).

Location	*Contents*
20000	10110
20001	10120
20002	11572

The addresses in location 20000, 20001, and 20002 are associated with the symbolic names A, B, and C.

A is the symbolic name for location 10110.
B is the symbolic name for location 10120.
C is the symbolic name for location 11572.

Thus, A, B, and C serve as dummy variables for R, S, and T, in much the same way as the dummy variables in the arithmetic statement functions. However, in the subprogram itself, A, B, and C are regular variables; that is, they are symbolic names for storage locations, in addition to serving in the functional rule. In arithmetic statement functions, the use of a symbolic name for a dummy variable did not prevent the use of the symbolic name to serve as another storage location; the reason being that dummy variables served only to reserve positions in the functional rule.

The RETURN statement is compiled into an unconditional transfer statement with the address of destination being located in the special register.

RETURN is equivalent to GO TO address located in special register (the address was placed there in the compilation of the calling statement).

Since the subprogram is a separate FORTRAN program, an END statement must be the last statement of the subprogram. The RETURN statement must be placed after the last statement of the subprogram which the programmer wishes to be executed by the computer; it need not be immediately before the END statement.

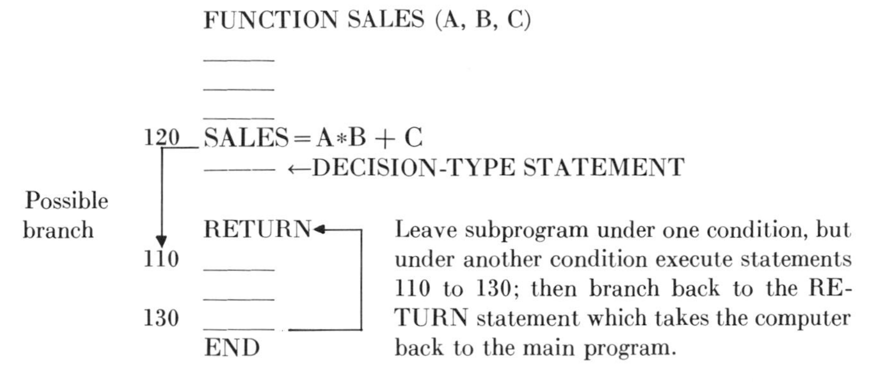

120 SALES = A*B + C

Possible branch

SALES, a storage location in the subprogram, is defined by its appearance on the left side of an arithmetic statement: namely, statement 120. A reference in the subprogram to SALES, is a reference to the address in location 18000; therefore, the location named SALES in the main program is equivalent to the location associated with the function SALES, in the main program. The location named SALES is used to bring back the result from the subprogram; this location may take on a value either through its appearance on the left side of an arithmetic statement (as in the example) or in a READ list.

The arguments which appear after the function name in the calling statement may be any of the following;

1. A constant
2. A variable (nonsubscripted or subscripted)
3. An arithmetic expression

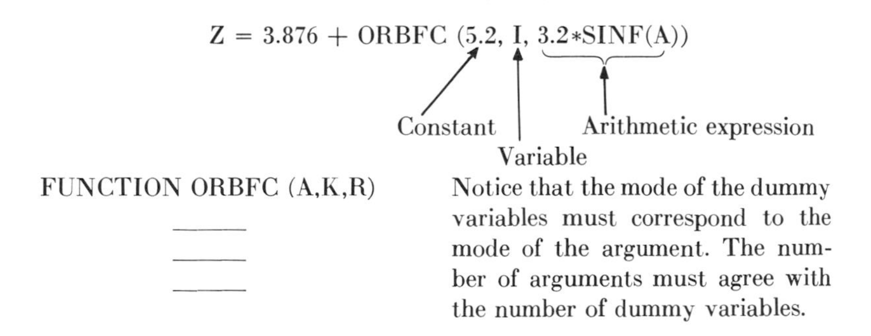

Z = 3.876 + ORBFC (5.2, I, 3.2*SINF(A))
Constant
Variable
Arithmetic expression
FUNCTION ORBFC (A,K,R)
Notice that the mode of the dummy variables must correspond to the mode of the argument. The number of arguments must agree with the number of dummy variables.

If an array name appears as an argument in the calling statement, its size must correspond to the size of the array appearing in the subprogram, and each array must appear in a DIMENSION statement in its own program.

Main Program

```
   DIMENSION A(10)
       ______
       ______
       ______
   S = 2.716 * ABTRO (A)
```

Subprogram

```
   FUNCTION ABTRO (C)
   DIMENSION C(10)
   ABTRO = 0
10 DO 10 I = 1, 10
   ABTRO = ABTRO + C(I)
   RETURN
   END
```

In the above example the function ABTRO computes the sum of an array of 10 numbers, the result being transmitted back to the main program via the name of the function, ABTRO. This result is then multiplied by 2.716, and the final result is placed in location S.

4.5.2. Implicit Arguments and the COMMON Statement

Thus far, one method has been presented by which arguments can be transmitted from the main program to the subprogram, namely, by the appearance of the variables, serving as arguments, after the name of the function in the calling statement. Another method for transferring values between two programs is available in the FORTRAN language through the use of the COMMON statement.

```
COMMON A,B,C,D
```

The FORTRAN compiler reserves locations for the variables A,B,C, and D starting from the upper end of the memory. If the upper end of memory is location 32000, the symbolic name, A, will be associated with location 32000; the symbolic name, B, with location 31999, etc.

Location	*Name*
32000	A
31999	B
31998	C
31997	D

An array name may be placed in a COMMON statement if it also appears in a DIMENSION statement in the same program.

```
COMMON E, R
DIMENSION R (10)
```

Location	*Name*
32000	E
31999	R(1)
31998	R(2)
______	______
______	______
______	______
31990	R (10)

Because the FORTRAN compiler assigns storage to variables appearing in COMMON statements, in the same way in all FORTRAN programs, values may be transmitted between programs in this way.

Main Program

```
COMMON A, B
    ______
    ______
    ______
Y = R+AFUNC(Z)
    ______
    ______
    ______
```

Subprogram

```
FUNCTION AFUNC(V)
COMMON R,S
    ______
    ______
    ______
AFUNC = R*S+V**2
RETURN
END
```

In the above example, R and S in the subprogram serve as dummy variables for A and B of the main program because of the COMMON statement.

Main Program		*Subprogram*	
Location	*Name*	*Location*	*Name*
32000	A	32000	R
31999	B	31999	S

A reference to R in the subprogram is a reference to location 32000, the address associated with the symbolic name A in the main program. Therefore, the COMMON statement has made R, in the subprogram, equivalent to A, in the main program. The variable V, in the subprogram, is a dummy variable for Z in the main program, by the first method of transmitting values between programs. At run time, the statement:

```
AFUNC = R * S+V ** 2                    (1)
```

yields the result to be returned to the calling program in the statement:

```
Y = R+AFUNC (Z)                         (2)
```

The values of R, S, and V in (1) could have been transmitted from the main program or they could have been supplied by input-output or arithmetic statements in the subprogram prior to (1). It is not required that the variables A,B, and Z in the calling program take on values prior to (1). For example, it would be possible to have the statements:

```
     READ 7, R, S
   7 FORMAT (2F6.2)
     V = (R-S)/S ** 2
```

precede (1) in the subprogram. In this case, the values in the locations, A, B, V, and Y after execution of (1) in the calling program will be the following:

Calling Program

A	Contains the value read in for R in the subprogram
B	Contains the value read in for S in the subprogram
Z	Contains the value of the expression (R−S)/S ** 2 as evaluated in the subprogram
Y	Contains the result of the calculation Y = R+AFUNC (Z) which is equivalent to Y = R+(A*B+((A−B)/(B ** 2)**2)) Where the variable R must have taken on a value in the calling program prior to (2)

4.5.3. Multiple Results in the FUNCTION Subprogram

As illustrated in the previous programs, one result from the FUNCTION subprogram is returned to the calling program via the name of the subprogram. However, more than one result may be returned to the calling program from the FUNCTION subprogram via the variables which are placed in COMMON storage. Those results transmitted via COMMON variables are available to the calling program at the statement following the calling statement; whereas, the result transmitted via the name of the FUNCTION subprogram is available in the calling statement.

Main Program

```
     COMMON (A, B, C)
     A =5.268
     R =7.3825* A+2.6
     READ  1, F, G
  23 B = R * A + F * G
  27 USUB1 = 3.278 * ROLE (R)
```

```
29  D = YSUB1 + B * (3.516 + C)
    ______
    ______
    ______
    END
    Subprogram
    FUNCTION ROLE (A)
    COMMON (U, V,W)
    T = A * 3.15 * U
    ROLE = SQRTF (U + 2. * V) + U ** .57
127 W = ROLE * T
    READ  7, R
    ______
    ______
    ______
117 V = R * W ** 3
    RETURN
    END
```

Both the variables B and C, which appear in the COMMON statement of the main program, are used to bring back results from the subprogram; it is interesting to note that the variable B serves both to send a value to the subprogram and to bring a value back from the subprogram. When the variable V in the subprogram, the dummy variable for B, takes on a value in statement 117 of the subprogram, the variable B in the main program takes on the same value, because V and B are the same location in the memory. Therefore, the value which was in B before the execution of statement 117 has now been destroyed (replaced by a new value). If the programmer desires to preserve the value which was placed in location B in statement 23 of the main program, this value should be transferred to another storage location before the execution of the calling statement, 27; such an instruction would be:

TEMP = B

The values in locations B and C of the main program, in statement 29, will have the values which were placed in locations V and W through statements 127 and 117 of the subprogram. Variable R of the main program also serves to transmit an argument to the subprogram via the dummy variable, A. For a variable in the COMMON storage area to transmit a value back to the main program, that variable must appear on the left-hand side of an arithmetic statement or be a member of a READ list in the subprogram.

Results being transmitted via the COMMON variables A and C can be utilized by the calling program in any statement from statement 29 to the end of the program; the result returned via the function name, ROLE, is utilized for calculations in statement number 27.

4.5.4. EQUIVALENCE Statements and Their Interaction with COMMON Statements

A single location in any FORTRAN program may be given two or more different names through the use of the EQUIVALENCE statement:

```
EQUIVALENCE (A, B)
```

Now any reference to location A will be a reference to location B, because they are one and the same location.

For a very large program which must be assigned to two or more programmers, it is advantageous to go through the two or more parts of the program (considering one part for each programmer) and put locations which serve the same purpose into an EQUIVALENCE statement. A considerable amount of memory space may be saved in this way.

The programmer should be aware of the fact that putting A and B in an EQUIVALENCE statement is not the same as writing the arithmetic statement, A = B. In the latter case there are two distinct locations, A and B; after execution of the arithmetic statement, both locations have the value which was in B.

Variables in the subprogram which serve as dummy arguments for variables in the main program should not appear in an EQUIVALENCE statement of the subprogram. The linkage created by the calling statement does not allow the programmer to specify his own address (i.e., another variable name) for dummy arguments. Since the appearance of a dummy variable in an EQUIVALENCE would amount to exactly specifying his own address; this is forbidden.

Main Program

```
______
______
______
Y = SUBR (R, S)
______
______
______
END
```

Subprogram

```
FUNCTION SUBR (A, B)
EQUIVALENCE (C, B)
______
______
______
RETURN
END
```

ERROR—The location which is named B has already been given an address: namely, the same address as variable S in the main program. An address is now assigned to C by the compiler without knowledge of the address transmitted by the linkage instructions. Since B cannot reference two different locations in the same program, an error is created in the subprogram.

If the variable carrying the argument is placed in COMMON instead of after the function name in the calling statement, then the corresponding dummy variable (also in the COMMON area) in the subprogram may appear in an EQUIVALENCE statement.

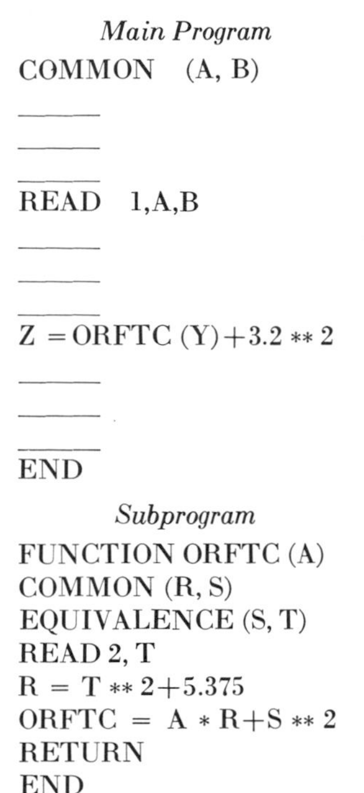

Main Program

```
COMMON   (A, B)
______
______
______
READ   1,A,B
______
______
______
Z =ORFTC (Y)+3.2 ** 2
______
______
______
END
```

Subprogram

```
FUNCTION ORFTC (A)
COMMON (R, S)
EQUIVALENCE (S, T)
READ 2, T
R = T ** 2+5.375
ORFTC = A * R+S ** 2
RETURN
END
```

The appearance of the variable S in both the COMMON and the EQUIVALENCE statements changes the order of the variables in the COMMON storage area.

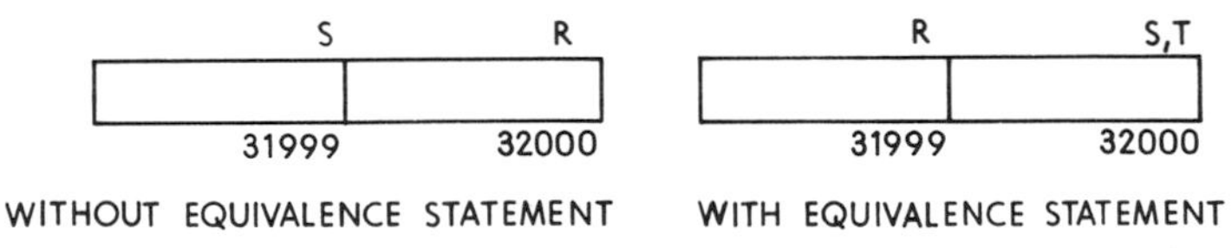

FIG. 4–10

Now the variable R serves as a dummy for the variable B of the main program, and both the variables S and T (S and T refer to the same location because they appear in an EQUIVALENCE statement) serve as dummy for the variable A of the main program. A rearrangement of the COMMON storage area will take place in any FORTRAN II program under the above circumstances.

In connection with the use of both COMMON and EQUIVALENCE statements in the same program, we might consider a few more cases which might be hard to interpret for the reader without special mention.

COMMON R,V
DIMENSION S(3)
EQUIVALENCE (R, S (3))

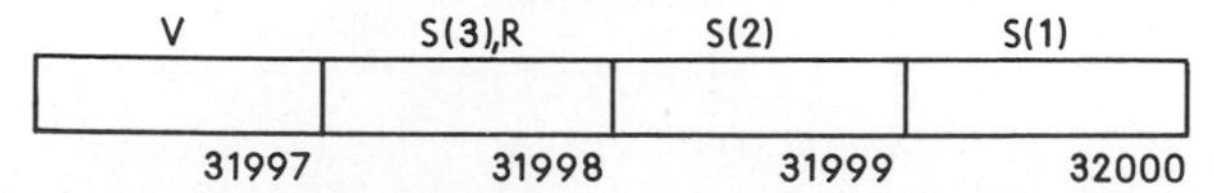

FIG. 4–11. Arrangement of the COMMON Storage Area

Since the programmer specified that he wants R and S(3) to reference the same storage location, the compiler will name the first location S (1), the second location S(2), the third location both S(3) and R, and the fourth location V.

Another possible combination of the COMMON and EQUIVALENCE statements might lead to the following example:

COMMON Y, Z, V
DIMENSION R (4)
EQUIVALENCE (Z, R)

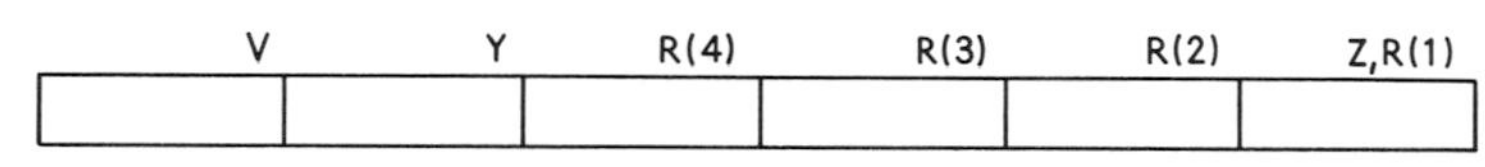

FIG. 4–12. Arrangement of the COMMON Storage Area

Notice that when the nonsubscripted variable, Z, is made equivalent to the array, R, and when no subscript is specified for the array, the compiler assumes that the programmer wishes the nonsubscripted variable to be equivalent to the first element of the array, i.e., R(1). Because Y is not to be made equivalent to any other element of the R array, Y is given the fifth location in the COMMON storage area; in other words, a gap of three spaces in the COMMON storage area is left for R (2), R (3), and R (4).

Finally, more than one array may be included in the EQUIVALENCE statement.

COMMON U, V, W
DIMENSION A (4), B (2)
EQUIVALENCE (V, A, B(2))

W	U	A(4)	A(3)	A(2)	V,A(1),B(2)	B(1)

FIG. 4–13. Arrangement of the COMMON Storage Area

A slight change in the above combination would result in the following allocation of the COMMON storage area.

COMMON U, V, W
DIMENSION A (4), B(2)
EQUIVALENCE (V, A, B)

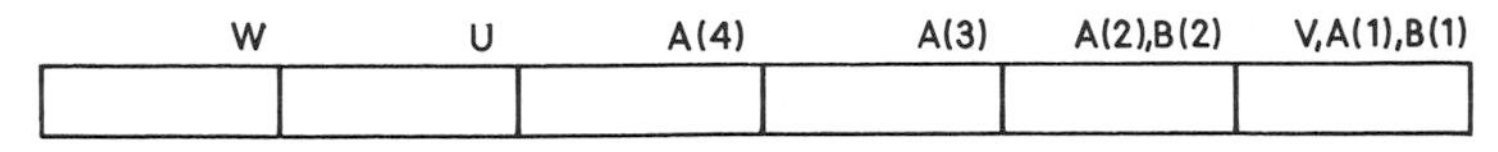

FIG. 4–14. Arrangement of the COMMON Storage Area

The programmer has now forced A(2) to be equivalent to B(2) by specifying that V be equivalent to both A(1) and B(1).

4.6. SUBROUTINE Subprograms

Most of the explanation in the previous section on FUNCTION subprograms holds for SUBROUTINE subprograms; the differences are listed below:

1. A SUBROUTINE statement instead of a FUNCTION statement must be the first statement of the subprogram.
2. The SUBROUTINE subprogram is called (used) through the appearance of its name (the SUBROUTINE subprogram is named in the same way as the FUNCTION subprogram) in a CALL statement.
3. No arguments need be specified in the CALL statement (remember —at least one argument is required in the arithmetic statement which calls the FUNCTION subprograms).
4. More than one value may be returned from the SUBROUTINE subprogram through variables placed in the COMMON storage area. The FUNCTION subprogram can return only one value to the main program through its calling statement; however, like the SUBROUTINE subprogram, the FUNCTION subprogram can return many values through variables placed in the COMMON storage area. These values which have been placed in the COMMON area may be utilized in any statement following the calling statement in both the case of the SUBROUTINE subprogram and the FUNCTION subprogram.
5. Alphameric characters may be used as arguments following the CALL statement; any alphameric characters used for arguments must be preceded by an n H, where n is the number of characters, including blanks, following the H.

```
CALL FACT (5, 2, A, K, F (3), R*S+3.1, 5HERROR)
```

Arguments, as illustrated in the above CALL statement, may be fixed or floating constants, fixed or floating variables, arithmetic expressions, and alphameric characters. For SUBROUTINE subprograms the mode of the variables, whether they appear in the CALL statement or in the COMMON statement, determine both the mode of the arguments and the results, since the variables are used to transmit them between the main program and the subprogram. The name of the subroutine has nothing to do with the mode of any of the results. In the FUNCTION subprogram, the result returned in the calling statement is transmitted via the function name; therefore, the mode of the result is affected by the name of the FUNCTION subprogram.

The following example is presented to illustrate the use of subroutines and the methods followed by the compiler in compiling them. All the necessary details are included to familiarize the reader with subroutines. Two times are important in the following analysis, compile time and run time.

	Locations in the memory		
Symbolic name of the location	ALPHA (1)	BETA (2)	
READ 1, ALPHA	(10) [XXX]		
FORMAT (F 6.2)			
CALL FOUL (BETA. ALPHA)			
PRINT 1, BETA		(19) [XXX]^2	
STOP END	(5)	(5)	(6)
Symbolic name of the location	T	S	Y
SUBROUTINE FOUL (S, T)	(11) [XXX]		
S = T ** 2	→	(13) [XXX]^2	
CALL BAT (Y, S)			
S = Y RETURN		(18) [XXX]^2 ←	(17) [XXX]^2
END			
Symbolic name of the location		(9) Y	(9) X
SUBROUTINE BAT (X, Y)		(14) [XXX]^2 (15)	
X = Y			[XXX]^2
RETURN			
END			

The steps listed on the following pages are placed in parentheses.

ANALYSIS—COMPILE TIME

STEPS

READ 1, ALPHA

1. A location is set up in the memory to correspond to the symbolic name ALPHA, since this is the first appearance of the name ALPHA. Incidentally, the name ALPHA is also defined in this statement, because the compiler can assume that, at run time, a value will be placed in this location via the READ statement.

CALL FOUL (BETA, ALPHA)

2. A location is reserved in the memory to correspond to the symbolic name BETA, because this is the first appearance of the name. The appearance of the name BETA is not sufficient to define that variable for the compiler, because the compiler cannot assume that BETA will take on a value through this statement.
3. The machine-language instructions which are necessary to link the main program with the subprogram FOUL are compiled by the compiler.
4. The appearance of the variables S and T in the SUBROUTINE statement serves to define these variables in the subprogram. Compiler must assume that S and T will contain values transmitted to them from the main program via the linkage instructions. In fact, neither variable will contain values at run time. Compilation of the machine-language instructions which are necessary to transmit, at run time, the machine addresses of the locations named BETA and ALPHA from the main program to a subprogram are compiled.

SUBROUTINE FOUL (S,T)

5. The machine addresses of the locations carrying the addresses of the arguments BETA and ALPHA from the main program are associated with the names S and T, respectively. In other words, the location named BETA in the main program may now be called S in subroutine FOUL, and the location named ALPHA in the main program may now be called T in subroutine FOUL. At this point in the program, S will not contain a value, because there was no value in BETA when the subprogram was called by the main program. If the programmer is to be allowed to compile the main program and its subprograms at different times, this possibility of error cannot be avoided.

CALL BAT (Y, S)

6. In the subroutine FOUL, a location is reserved in memory and is made to correspond with the name Y, because Y has not appeared before in this subroutine. Location S, which appears as an argument in the CALL statement of subroutine FOUL, has the same address as the location S

which appears as a dummy variable in the SUBROUTINE statement. In the same program a symbolic name can be associated with only one location (otherwise, there would be havoc).

7. The machine-language instructions which are necessary to link the main program with the subprogram BAT are compiled by the compiler.

8. Machine-language instructions which are necessary to transmit, at run time, the machine addresses of the locations named Y and S from subroutine FOUL to another subprogram are compiled.

SUBROUTINE BAT (X, Y)

9. The location named Y in the subroutine FOUL may now be called X in subroutine BAT, and the location named S in the subroutine FOUL may now be called Y in the subroutine BAT. For a more detailed explanation, see step 5. Notice that the location named Y, in subroutine FOUL, is not the same address as the location Y in subroutine BAT.

Only the statements directly involved with subprograms were considered in the above discussion; the other statements were considered in earlier chapters of this book.

RUN TIME

READ 1, ALPHA

10. A value is read from the card under format, F 6.2, into location ALPHA.

CALL FOUL (BETA, ALPHA)

11. The value read into location ALPHA is now in location T of subroutine FOUL.

12. Control is transferred to the first instruction of subroutine FOUL.

S= T**2

13. The value in location T is squared and placed in location S (the value originally in location T is undisturbed).

CALL BAT (Y,S)

14. The value in location S of subroutine FOUL, is now in location Y of subroutine BAT.

15. Control is transferred to the first instruction of subroutine BAT.

X = Y

16. The value in location Y is placed in location X.

RETURN

17. Control is returned to the statement following the CALL statement

in subroutine FOUL. As a result of the linking instructions, the value in location X of subroutine BAT is now in location Y of subroutine FOUL.

S = Y

18. The value in location Y is placed in location S. Notice that the same value $(XXX)^2$ was already in location S; this value having been placed there in step (13).

RETURN

19. Control is returned to the statement following the CALL statement in the main program. As a result of the linking instructions, the value in location S of subroutine FOUL is now in location BETA of the main program.

PRINT 1, BETA

20. The original value squared, is now printed out of location BETA. Therefore, the entire combination of three programs simply was used to obtain the square of a value; however, the main purpose of the program is to illustrate subprograms.

4.6.1. Calculation of Binomial Coefficients

A more practical use of subprograms is illustrated with the following example, in which, a very practical program is written as a subprogram. This subprogram in turn utilizes an even more basic subprogram. The basic subprogram calculates factorials. N factorial, denoted N! is defined as (N) . (N−1).(N−2) . . . (2). (1) and 0! is defined to be 1. Although factorials may be defined for negative numbers, the subprogram will not consider them.

```
      FUNCTION IFACT (N)
      IFACT = 1
      IF (N) 20, 20, 10
10    DO 30 I = 1, N
30    IFACT = IFACT*I
20    RETURN
      END
```

N is a dummy variable carrying the argument from the main program. A typical calling statement requiring calculation of N! might be:

NFCT = IFACT (N)

It is only a coincidence that the argument, N, and its dummy in the subprogram, N, have the same name.

Both the argument, N, and the result, IFACT, are fixed-point variables. The number of factorials which can be calculated is limited by the length of the storage location; if this length is 9 decimal digits, then the largest factorial which can be calculated is 11! To go to floating-point notation would permit more factorials to be calculated; however, it should be remembered that the number of significant figures is still limited by the length of the storage location. In other words a number, such as 20!, could be computed, but it would not mean much due to the fact that only nine significant figures are available. To get larger factorials, the programmer could write a library subroutine which permits greater length of storage locations.

ANALYSIS

IFACT = 1	This statement serves to initialize the location in which the factorial is formed; if the location is not initialized the product will build up from one program to the next. To take care of the case of 0! the location carrying the result is set to 1; if a test for an 0 argument is positive, control is transferred back to the main program at that point.
IF (N)20, 20, 10	The IF statement is the test for a zero argument referred to in the above explanation. Notice that a negative argument will also cause a return to the main program with a result of 1. It may be desirable to write the statement as IF (N) 50, 20, 10 where statement 50 would either cause the computer to stop or to execute an error routine. The probability of a negative argument and the seriousness of the error should dictate which route to follow. We assume a small probability for getting a negative argument. When the argument is zero, the computer branches to statement 20, which in turn causes a return to the main program with the result 1. When the argument is greater than zero, the DO loop is executed by the computer.
10 DO 30 I = 1, N IFACT = IFACT * I	The DO loop computes N! When I = 1, the computation is 1 * 1 = 1, which is unnecessary and could be avoided if we took the following approach. IF (N − 1) 20, 20, 10 10 DO 30 I = 2, N 30 IFACT = IFACT * I Now a value of 1 will be returned to the main program if the argument is either 0 or 1; this is correct because 0! = 1 and 1! = 1. In this way the program is made more efficient.

The FUNCTION subprogram, IFACT, will be utilized by the FUNCTION subprogram BINOM in the following example. BINOM will calculate binomial coefficients, such as, $\binom{N}{K}$; $\binom{N}{K}$ is defined as $\frac{N!}{K!\,(N-K)!}$ and is a coefficient of the binomial expansion $(a+b)^N$. Among other applications, $\binom{N}{K}$ represents the number of possible ways of picking K things out of N things (we will use this fact latter). It will be assumed that K is equal to or less than N.

```
      FUNCTION BINOM (N, K)
      BINOM = 1
      IF (N-K) 10, 10, 20
   20 BINOM = IFACT (N) / (IFACT (K) * IFACT (N-K))
   10 RETURN
      END
```

ANALYSIS

BINOM = 1 IF (N−K) 10, 10, 20	These two statements are included for the sole purpose of avoiding the use of the subprogram, IFACT, when N≤K. In this case BINOM=1; therefore, it is much quicker to skip the subprogram. However, to decide which method is better one must know the approximate percentage of times that N will equal K. If N never equals K, the statements BINOM = 1 IF (N−K) 10, 10, 20 waste computer time.
20 BINOM=IFACT (N) / (IFACT (K) * IFACT (N−K)	Fixed-point division is allowable here because binomial coefficients are always integers. If a binomial coefficient could be a decimal number, fixed-point division would result in truncation.

In these examples SUBROUTINE subprograms were used to call SUBROUTINE subprograms and FUNCTION subprograms were used to call FUNCTION subprograms; this was a coincidence and should not be interpreted as a rule.

4.6.2. Example: Binominal Probabilities

Calculation of binomial probabilities—a variable Z possesses a binomial probability distribution if Z can take on only discrete values and the probability $f(z)$ that Z takes on the value z is:

$$P\,(Z = z) = f(z) = \frac{n!}{z!(n-z)!}\,p^z q^{n-z},\ (z = 0, 1, \cdots, n)$$

where $q = 1 - p$.

Calculate the probability that $(z_1 \leq Z \leq z_2)$, i.e.

$$\sum_{z = z_1}^{z_2} \frac{n!}{z!(n-z)!}\,p^z\,q^{n-z}$$

where n, z_1, z_2, and p are given.

FLOW CHART

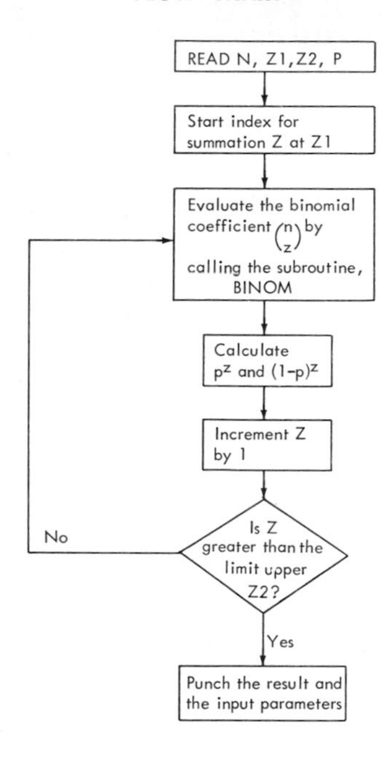

Program

```
      PROB = 1
   99 READ 77, N, J1, J2, P
   77 FORMAT (I3, 2I2, F5.2)
      DO 20 I = J1, J2
   20 PROB = PROB * BINOM (N,I)* P **I* (1.-P)**I
      PUNCH 67
   67 FORMAT (20HBINOMIAL PROBABILITY/)
      PUNCH 68, N, J1, J2, P
   68 FORMAT (4HN = ,I3, 7X,5HZ1 = ,I2, 7X,5HZ2 = ,I2,
     17X, 4HP = , F5.2)
      PUNCH 69, PROB
```

```
69  FORMAT (21HTHE PROBABILITY IS, F10.4)
    GO TO 99
    END
```

4.6.3. Example: FORTRAN Function Subprogram to Calculate Multinomial Probabilities

The multinomial probability distribution is defined as

$$P_{rm}\{A_1, \ldots, A_k\} = \frac{n!}{A_1! \ldots A_k!} B_1^{A_1} \ldots B_k^{A_k}$$

where we have k mutually exclusive and exhaustive outcomes $X_1, \ldots, X_k$ with probabilities $B_1, \ldots, B_k$, and $\sum_{i=1}^{k} B_i = 1$. Then P_{rM} gives the probability of obtaining X_i exactly A_1 times; of obtaining X_2 exactly A_2 times; . . . ; of obtaining x_k exactly A_k times in a sample of size N. Following is a FORTRAN function subprogram for calculating multinomial probabilities.

```
    PMULT (A,N,B,K)
    DIMENSION A(10),B(10)
    QMULT=1.
    DO 20 I=1,K
    L=A(I)
20  QMULT=QMULT * FACT (L) * B(I) **L
    PMULT=FACT(N)/QMULT
    RETURN
    END
```

This routine uses the FORTRAN function subprogram, FACT, to calculate the factorials.

4.6.4. Example: A Program Which Utilizes the Multinomial Function Subprogram of Example 4.6.3. to Read Parameters, Calculate Multinomial Probabilities, and Print Results

```
    DIMENSION A (10), B (10)
99  READ 47, K, N, (A (I), B(I), I = 1, K)
47  FORMAT (I2, I4/ (F4.0, F5.2))
    PRODT = PMULT ( A,N,B,K)
    PUNCH 51
51  FORMAT (5X, 22HMULTINOMIAL DISTRITION)
    PUNCH 52
52  FORMAT (/ 60X, 9HPROBLEM 1)
    PUNCH 53
53  FORMAT (/ 10X, 10HINPUT DATA)
    PUNCH 54, K, N
```

```
54  FORMAT (14H# OF GROUPS = ,I2, 10X,14HTOTAL ITEMS = ,I4)
    PUNCH 55
55  FORMAT (15HNUMBER  IN GROUP, 10X,11HPROBABILITY)
    DO 59 I = 1,K
59  PUNCH 56, A(I), B(I)
56  FORMAT (7X,F4.0, 14XF6.2)
    PUNCH 62, PRODT
62  FORMAT (33H THE PROBABILITY OF THIS DIST. IS, F6.2)
    GO TO 99
    END
```

4.6.5. Example: Calculation of Sin (X) by Taylor's Series Expansion

Use of factorial function in calculation of the sin function by the Taylor's series expansion.

The Taylor's series expansion of sin (x),

$$\sin(x) = x - \frac{x^3}{3} + \frac{x^5}{5} - \frac{x^7}{7} - + \cdots$$

$$\text{or } \sin(x) = (-1)^n \frac{x^{2n+1}}{(2n+1)!} \text{ for } n = 0, 1, 2, \ldots$$

The error from truncation due to stopping at the kth term is equal to or less than the absolute value of the kth term.

Write a FORTRAN program to calculate the sin of a given agrument; provide for reading the allowable error.

```
99  READ 10, X, E
10  FORMAT (F6.2,F10.6)
    SSIN = 0
    DO 20 I = 1, 100
    N = I - 1
    R = N
    TERM = -1.**N*X**(2.*R+1)/(2.* R+1.)
    IF (ABS(TERM)-E) 20,20,40
40  SSIN = SSIN+TERM
20  PUNCH 35, X, SSIN
35  FORMAT(20X, 4HSIN(,F6.2,4H) = ,F 14.8)
    GO TO 99
    END
```

Problems

4.1. Given any function $f(n)$, the rth difference of $f(n) \equiv \Delta^r f(n) = f(n+r) - \binom{r}{1} f(n+r-1) + \binom{r}{2} f(n+r-2) \ldots (-1)^{r-1} \binom{r}{1} f(n+1) + (-1)^r f(n)$.

Write a FORTRAN function subprogram to calculate the rth difference of a function of the argument, n; use the function, BINOM (N,K) to calculate the binomial coefficients.

4.2. Demonstrate that

$$\sum_{i=0}^{n} \binom{n}{i} = 2^n$$

for several positive integers, n. Use the binomial function subprogram, BINOM (N,I).

4.3. Write a FORTRAN subroutine to evaluate the following function for various N, n, and r.

$$f(r,n) = \sum_{m=0}^{N} (-1)^m \binom{N}{m} \left(1 - \frac{m}{n}\right)^r$$

4.4. Write a FORTRAN program to find the maximum point of the following function which represents consumption of cabinets; $x^a e^{-bx}$ for $a = 5.21$, $b = 0.014$. Use a method consisting of increasing x until the rate of increase of $f(x)$ starts to decrease; then, examine this area closely by using smaller increments of x.

4.5. Write a FORTRAN program to find the discounted rate of return, r, which will reduce the present worth of a series of fixed cash flows, A, to zero.

$$A + rA + r^2A + \cdots + r^{n-1}A = \frac{A(1-r^n)}{1-r} = R$$

Solve for the r, given A and n, which will reduce R to zero.

4.6.

```
FRST (A) = A/B+C
SCND (R,B) = A * R+B**2
THRD (F,G) = SCND(F)+ FRST(G)/SCND(G,E)
FRTH (F1,F2) = THRD (F1,SCND(F2,F3))/SCND(F1,FRST(F2))
```

What is the arithmetic expression for: Y = FRTH (S,T)*2.165 + S? (That is, expand FRTH(S,T) into components.) Which are the dummy variables and which are the regular variables?

4.7. Write a FORTRAN program and accompanying flow chart to evaluate the following (make the program general):

$$\sum_{k=0}^{n} \binom{a}{k} \binom{b}{n-k}$$

where $a > n$, $b > n$ and where $\binom{c}{x}$ is a binomial coefficient which can also be written

$$\frac{c\,!}{x!\,(c-x)\,!}$$

and take 0 ! = 1

4.8. Examine the following main program and attendant subprograms:
Question—What is the value of X (3) printed?

```
      COMMON (F1,F2)                SUBROUTINE TAB (I)
      DIMENSION X(10)               COMMON X
      F1=1                          T=I - 1
      DO 1 I = 1, 10                X=X+T
      CALL BAT (T, I)               CALL CAB (T)
      X(I) = T                      I=I+1
    1 PRINT 2, I, X(I)              RETURN
    2 FORMAT (I3, F10. 1)           END
      STOP
      END
```

```
      SUBROUTINE BAT (Y,L)          SUBROUTINE CAB (X)
      COMMON (Z)                    COMMON (E, F)
      Y=L/11                        F = E+X
      M = 1                         RETURN
      M1 = L                        END
    1 IF (M - L+1) 2,2,3
    2 CALL TAB (M1)
      M = M1 - 1
      GO TO 1
    3 Y = Y+Z
      RETURN
      END
```

4.9. After execution of the following programs, what value is printed for A2?

```
C     TEST PROBLEM                  SUBROUTINE JOHN (AI)
      COMMON (A1,A2,L,F2)           COMMON (R,S,K,T)
      CALL JOHN (R)                 K = 1
      A2 = A1 *F2                   DO 10 I = 1, 5
      PRINT 1, A2                   S = K/I
    1 FORMAT (E 14.7)               CALL JACK
      STOP                       10 CONTINUE
      END                           A1 = S
                                    RETURN
                                    END
```

```
      SUBROUTINE JACK               FUNCTION GEORGE (V1)
      COMMON (B2, A1, L3, B1)       COMMON (C1, C2, K1, R)
      B1 = 2.* A1                   C1 = 2.+V1
      A1 = B1** 2                   R = C1+C2
      B2 = GEORGE (A1)              GEORGE = R
      RETURN                        RETURN
      END                           END
```

4.10. What is the result in location A after the following program segments?

```
   Main Program             SUBROUTINE SUB(Q,R)
     ______                 IF(Q-R) 1,1,2
     ______              2  Q = R
     ______              1  RETURN
   CALL SUB(5.,2.)          END
   A = 5.
```

4.11. Given that the following relations exist between the delays and sales; delays and production cost:

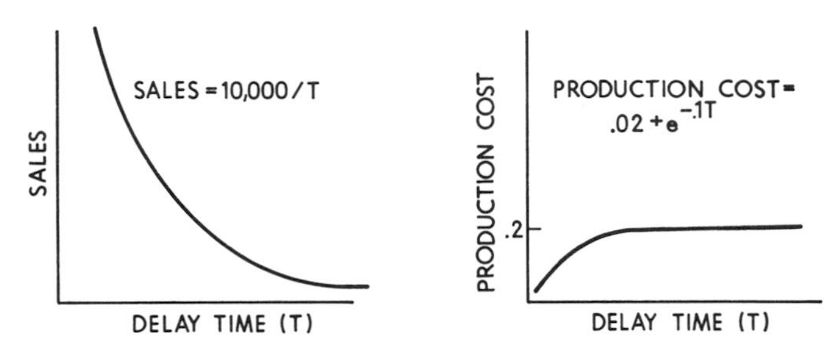

In other words, as the time between the placing or an order and the delivery date increases, the amount of sales decreases; in fact, the two variables, sales and delay time, are related by the function:

$$\text{Sales} = 10{,}000/T$$

Similarly, as the factory tries to reduce the time between the placing of an order and the delivery of the order, production cost increases because of overtime; production cost is related to delay time by the function,

$$\text{Prod. Cost} = .02 + e^{-.1T}$$

where T is the delay time.

We assume that the company is trying to maximize net income: where net income, $NI = 10{,}000/T\ (.98 - e^{-.1T})$. Net income is equal to the amount sold ($10{,}000/T$) with a given delay time, multiplied by the income derived from each unit sold; where the income from 1 unit is, 1 − cost of each unit sold.

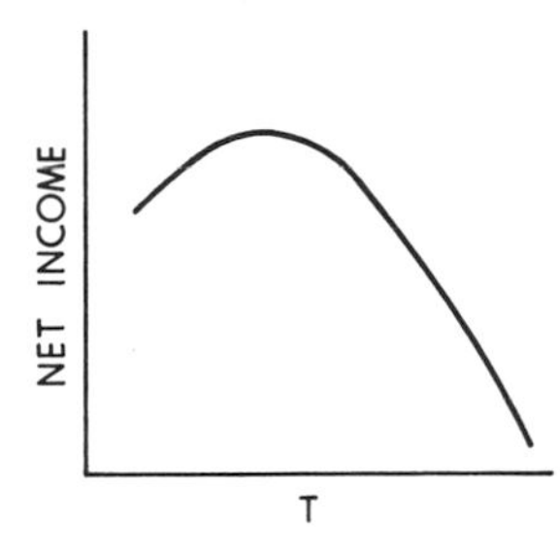

Write a FORTRAN program to find the maximum of the net income versus delay time curve using the following method:

1. Evaluate the function, $10{,}000/T\ (.98-e^{-.1T})$, at some convenient intervals (say, intervals of .1 unit in T) until there is a change in sign.
2. Now go back *two* intervals and repeat the procedure over these last two intervals, but using a much smaller interval, say .01; again stopping when there is a change in sign.
3. Repeat the cycle by going back two intervals from the point at which there was a change in sign.

5. Extension to FORTRAN IV and FORMAC

Chapters 1 through 4 were devoted to the FORTRAN II language. FORTRAN II contains only the basic components, because the relatively small computers for which it is designed have memories of limited size and lack other features. It became apparent that with an increase in memory capacity and addition of certain other features, the larger computers could profitably utilize a more powerful FORTRAN language. Recently, therefore, IBM released FORTRAN IV, a new version of the FORTRAN language, which extended and improved on FORTRAN II.

In this chapter, we turn from the basic FORTRAN II language to FORTRAN IV. We shall discuss the extension of FORTRAN II to the larger computers and point out the differences between FORTRAN II and FORTRAN IV. To conclude the chapter and the discussion of the FORTRAN language itself, a few paragraphs will be devoted to a translation of FORTRAN II to FORTRAN IV, and FORMAC, an extension of FORTRAN IV which provides more power in the symbolic manipulation of mathematical expressions, will be discussed briefly.

5.1. Fixed Word Length and Double Precision

Most large computers designed for scientific problems have a fixed word length: i.e., the number of digits per storage location is fixed. For example, the IBM 7040, 7044, 7090, and 7094 have a capacity of 36 binary bits per storage location. (We shall assume that the smallest numbers of bits that can be addressed is 36. This is not strictly true, but will simplify the following explanation.) Numbers in the binary base system can take on only the values zero or 1; each binary number is called a binary bits. The first bit (reading from the right to the left) may be taken as the power to which we

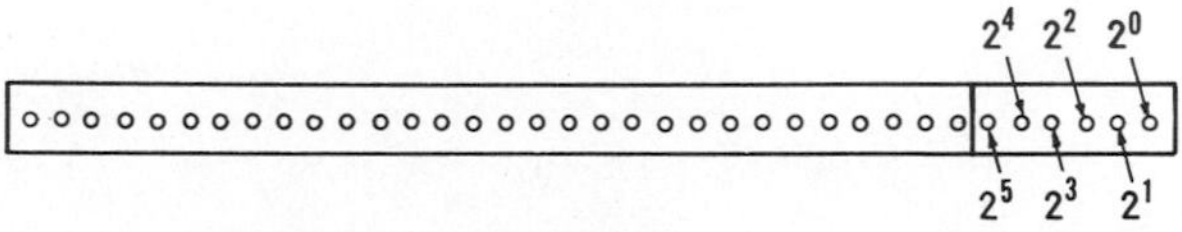

2^4 2^2 2^0

o o o o o o o o o o o o o o o o o o o o o o o o o o o o o o | o o o o o o

2^5 2^3 2^1

FIG. 5–1

raise the number 2. If the leftmost bit represents the sign 1 (a binary bit must either assume the value 0 or 1; 0 would signify + and 1 would signify −), there are 35 binary bits remaining with which to represent the number. For integers, the largest number that could be represented would be $2^{35}-1$ (if there were 36 bits, it would be 2^{35}); in the base 10, $2^{35}-1$ is a number with 11 decimal digits.[1]

For decimal numbers, part of the number is devoted to the exponent, leaving the equivalent of one to nine decimal digits; the exponent has a range of 10^{-38} to 10^{+38}. The programmer can get nine significant decimal digits if the first digit is equal to or less than 3, but only eight significant decimal digits if the first digit is greater than 3.

3 5 6 7 8 9 1 6 5

Two binary bits can represent the digits 0–3.

Both off ≡ 0	o o
First off, 2nd on ≡ 1	o •
First on, 2nd off ≡ 2	• o
Both on ≡ 3	• •

For the digits 4 to 7, the computer needs another binary bit.

5 5 6 7 8 9 1 6 5

Thus the 9-digit number starting with 5 requires more space than is available in the word.

Some scientific problems involve a great many arithmetic operations, which seriously reduce the number of significant figures in important quantities; therefore, it may be necessary to carry more than eight or nine significant figures. In fixed word length machines, the programmers can obtain

---

[1] At this point, the reader may wish to refer to some of the references in the appendix in order to learn how to convert binary to decimal and viceversa; because FORTRAN automatically translates the decimal input to binary and back to decimal for output (if desired), this chapter will refer to binary only if necessary to explain the methods used in FORTRAN.

up to 16 digits by utilizing one word for the most significant part and another word for the least significant part; the range for numbers of this significance is 10^{+38} to 10^{-29}.

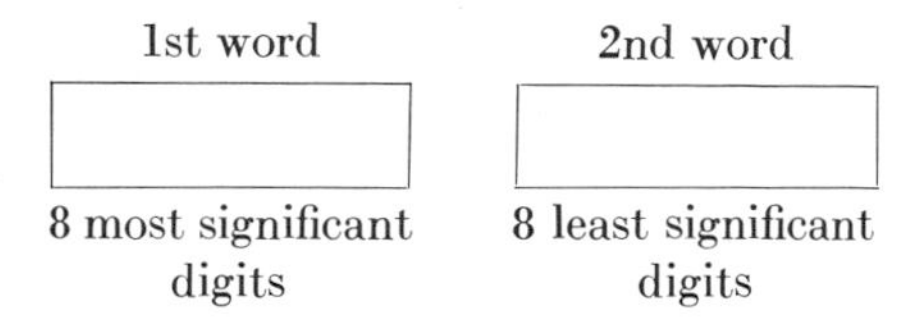

5.1.1. FORTRAN II

The technique of combining two storage locations (words) to represent one number is called "double precision." It is provided for by both FORTRAN II and FORTRAN IV for the floating-point numbers. As is the case with single-precision floating-point numbers, double-precision numbers are input to the computer either through a read list or via an arithmetic statement. In FORTRAN II the variable R is defined to be double precision; it takes on the value 12.1256712853 in Figure 5–2. The letter D

COLUMNS 1 2 3 4 5 6 7 8 9 72 73 ••• 80

D R = 12. 1256712853

FIG. 5–2

in column 1 is a signal to the compiler that two storage locations be used for the variable R; the most significant part, 12125671, will be stored in one location, and the least significant part, 28530000, will be stored in a second location. Also, the programmer may use a scale factor following the letter E to denote double-precision numbers, as he does with single-precision numbers.

D	R = 6.23E4
or D	R = 6.23E + 4

Of course, there are only 3 figures here, but these numbers may be known to 10 significant digits, the remaining 7 digits being zero.

Only single-precision floating point numbers may be input or output; that is, a D in column 1 of an input or output statement has no effect on the precision. If it is necessary or desirable to read in (or write out) double-precision numbers, one variable may be used for the more significant part and another for the least significant part; this method is not at all awkward if only single variables, and no arrays, are to be input (output). In either case, the usual modes for floating-point single-precision numbers, E and

F, cannot be used to input both parts of the number (especially the most significant part), because the most significant part is rounded in input or output. To avoid rounding the most significant part of the number, the programmer may use the O (octal)-type format.

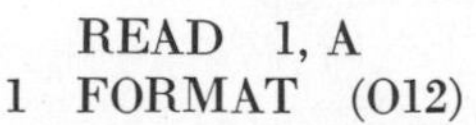

```
  READ 1, A
1 FORMAT (O12)
```

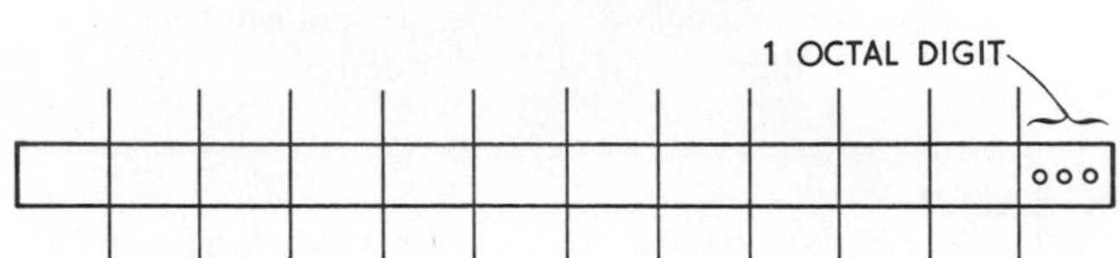

FIG. 5–3. Thirty-six Binary Bits Give 12 Octal Digits

Three binary bits are used for one octal digit.

2^2	2^1	2^0		*Octal Digit*
o	o	o	all off	0
o	o	•		1
o	•	o		2
o	•	•		3
•	o	o		4
•	o	•		5
•	•	o		6
•	•	•		7

The above read statement calls for 12 octal digits from the card. If less

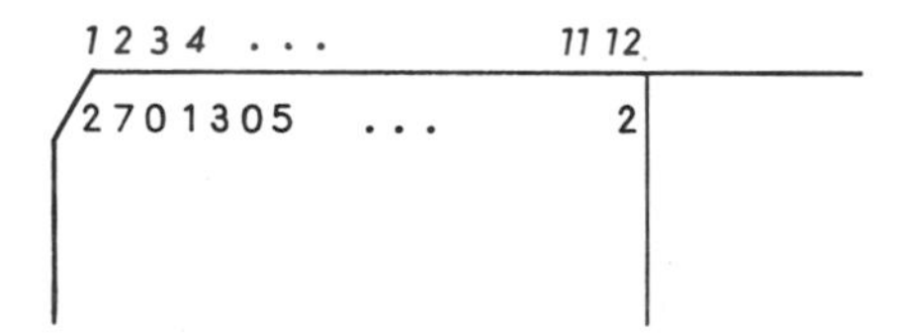

FIG. 5–4. An Octal Digit May Be 0 to 7 (Base 8)

than 12 octal digits are specified in the format Ow, (w represents the number of spaces in the field on the card), the field is read in and right justified in the core location. Either a fixed or floating variable name may be used

```
  READ 1, I
1 FORMAT (O7)
```

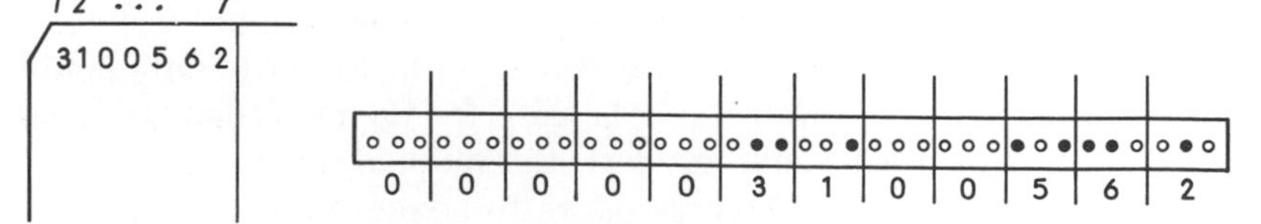

FIG. 5–5. *Left:* On the Card; *Right:* In Core

with the octal-type format; the principal advantage in using the octal-type format is the elimination of the rounding process. (Another advantage is that the translation from octal to binary is easier than the translation from decimal to binary. However, considering that the compiler uses the machine to do this very quickly, this advantage is small.) To avoid rounding each number in large data processing problems in which large blocks of data must be moved in and out of the core (to magnetic tape) because of storage limitation in core, the octal-type format is essential.

A single variable (as opposed to an array) may be read into the computer in the following way:

```
      READ   1, R (1), R (2)
    1 FORMAT (2O12)
```

The FORTRAN II compiler will interpret the variable as a one-dimensional array of two elements, R(1) and R(2), which contain the most and least significant parts of the constant being read into these two locations. Later in the program, a reference to R in an arithmetic statement which has a D in column 1 will reference both locations, R(1) and R(2).

D	Z = R	No error because R does not appear in a DIMENSION statement and appears both subscripted and unsubscripted in the same program. Z now becomes a double-precision variable; in other words, two storage locations are allocated to Z. The above statement is really equivalent to two statements: Z(1) = R(1), and Z(2) = R(2)

It is permissible to refer to the variable R in an arithmetic statement which does not have a D written in column 1.

V = R, or V = R(1)

In this case, the most significant part of the double-precision constant in location R—actually the number in location R(1)—is transferred to location V; V is a single-precision floating-point variable. The programmer may refer to the least significant part in an arithmetic statement by using the subscript 2.

W = R(2)

For this statement to be correct, it is necessary for the variable R to appear in a double-precision DIMENSION statement.

```
D         DIMENSION   R
```

One should note that reference to the least significant part of the number must be preceded by its appearance in a double-precision DIMENSION statement unless the reference to the least significant part is made in an input (output) statement.

There is also provision in FORTRAN II for arrays of double-precision variables; like arrays of single-precision variables, any double-precision subscripted variable must first appear in a DIMENSION statement which has the letter D in column 1.

```
D          DIMENSION  S(10,10)
           ______
           ______
           ______
D          B = 8.27365138516
D          S(5,6) = 3.1657158321
D      21  Z = S(5,6) * B
```

B and S(5,6) are defined to be double-precision variables and given values as shown in the above example. In statement 21, the value in location S(5,6) is multiplied by the value in location B, using double-precision arithmetic because statement 21 contains the letter D in column 1; the double-precision result is placed in location Z (of course, Z refers to two locations—one for the most significant part and one for the least significant part).

Double-precision arithmetic refers to arithmetic operations performed on double-precision numbers; in other words, a 16-digit number is added to, multiplied by, subtracted from, or divided by another 16-digit number, with the rounding process affecting the least significant digit.

A reference to a double-precision subscripted variable in an arithmetic statement without a letter D written in column 1 would yield only the most significant part.

```
V = S(5,6)
```

Only the eight most significant digits would be transferred to the single-precision storage location V as a result of this arithmetic statement. To refer to the least significant eight digits of a double-precision subscripted variable, the programmer must add the dimension of the last subscript to the last subscript of the variable. If the programmer wishes to reference the least significant part of the variable S(5,6), the dimension of the last subscript, 10, must be added to the last subscript.

```
W = S(5,16)
```

Input (output) of double-precision subscript variables is a bit tedious, because it necessitates a change in variable.

```
    DIMENSION  A (10), B(10)
    READ  7, (A(I), B(I), I = 1,10)
  7 FORMAT (2O12)
```

Each input card contains two 12-position fields; the octal constant in the first field is read into the position of the A array specified by the index, I, and the octal constant in the second field is read into the position of the B array specified by the index, I.

```
D          DIMENSION  U (10)
           ______
           ______
           ______
           DO 20 I = 1, 10
      10   V (I) = A (I)
           J = I + 10
      20   U(J) = B(I)
```

In statement 10 the most significant part of the number is placed in the V array, while in statement 20 the least significant part of the number is placed in the U array.

Double-precision expressions may be tested in the IF statement which includes the letter D in column 1; however, only the most significant part will figure in the test.

```
D          IF(C-D) 10,20,30
or
D          IF(C(1)-D(1))10,20,30
```

Presumably, C and D have been given double-precision values earlier in the program. The above statement will then compare the most significant part of the variable C with the most significant part of the variable D. If the programmer wishes to compare the least significant parts of some variables, he must use the subscripting method which was indicated by an earlier example.

```
D          DIMENSION E(2), F(2)
           ______
           ______
           ______
D          IF(E(2)-F(2)) 10,20,30
```

Double-precision variables in FUNCTION and SUBROUTINE subprograms will be explained in detail later in this chapter.

5.1.2. FORTRAN IV

The handling of double-precision variables and constants in FORTRAN IV is more convenient than in FORTRAN II. Double-precision constants may be specified to the FORTRAN IV compiler by writing a constant containing more than nine figures, or less than nine figures but containing a D exponent, or both. For example,

5716. 3517165
35. 317 D3
.36852 D0
628. 37582165 D3

A zero exponent is permissible in specifying a double-precision constant.

As in FORTRAN II, double-precision variables in FORTRAN IV have the same names as single-precision floating-point variables; however, unlike FORTRAN II, the D in the first column of every statement using double-precision variables is no longer needed. Now all variables which are to be double-precision must be placed in a type statement.

```
      DOUBLE-PRECISION C,D, E(10), F(10), R, S
   99 READ 7, C, D, (E(I), I = 1,10)
    7 FORMAT (D21.14)
              ______
              ______
              ______
      DO 20 I = 1,10
      F(I) = E(I)*C + D
      R = C * D + 3.7125612375
      S = R**2
        ______
        ______
        ______
      PRINT 7, (F(I), I=1,10),R,S
      GO TO 99
      END
```

Double-precision variables may now be read into the computer, appear in arithmetic statements, and be printed out in the same way as single precision variables. The data on the input card may now actually be double precision.

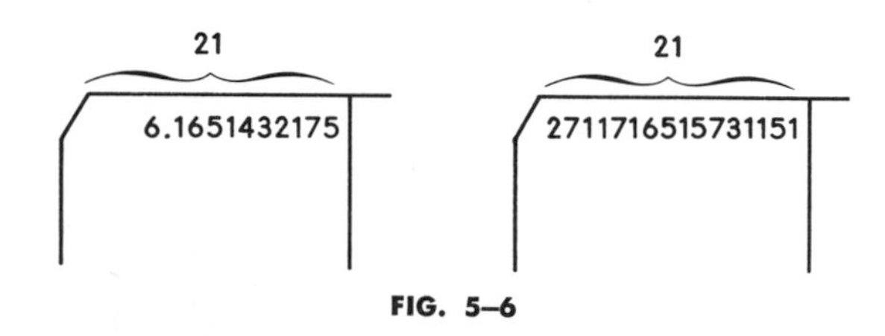

FIG. 5–6

Like the E-type format for single-precision floating-point variables, the D-type format for double precision may be overridden by writing down the decimal point.

If the variable T, a single-precision floating-point variable, appears on the left-hand side of an arithmetic statement containing a double-precision arithmetic expression of the right-hand side, the most significant part of the double-precision result is placed in location T.

```
DOUBLE PRECISION A,B
      ______
      ______
      ______
T = A * B
```

In FORTRAN IV, however, unlike FORTRAN II, it is not possible to address the least significant part of a double-precision variable through an arithmetic statement; however, it is possible to write a subprogram in a machine-type language which will accomplish this purpose.

5.1.3. Double-Precision — Example

Example 1

Calculate e to as many significant places as is possible, using double-precision location lengths and double-precision arithmetic; e may be evaluated by the following series expansion:

$$e = 2 + \frac{1}{2!} + \frac{1}{3!} + \frac{1}{4!} + \cdots$$

```
    DOUBLE PRECISION E,X,Y,E1,Z
    E  =  2.0D0
    X  =  2.0D0
    Y  =  1.0D0
    DO  10  I = 1,1000
    Z  =  I
    E1  =  E + Y/FACTD(Z)
    IF(ABS(E1-E))40,40,10
    X  =  X * (Z + 1.0D0)
 10 E  =  E1
    PUNCH  101,E1
101 FORMAT(5X4HE = ,E24.17)
    STOP
    END
```

Note that the IF statement tests the present value of E with the previously calculated value of E; a test result of zero indicates that E has been calculated to as many significant figures as is possible, given the length of the two storage locations which make up the double-precision variable. Also note that all calculations are made in double precision, because the variables and the constants involved in the arithmetic statements are all double precision. We assume that a FUNCTION named FACTD is available to calculate factorials in double-precision. Double-precision subprograms are explained in a later section.

5.2. Complex Constants and Variables

5.2.1. FORTRAN II

The extended version of FORTRAN II, and FORTRAN IV, permit the programmer to handle operations with complex numbers without having to write a machine-language subprogram. Complex constants are composed of two single-precision floating-point constants, one for the real part and one for the imaginary part; these constants are treated in a way very similar to double-precision constants by the FORTRAN II compiler. Like double-precision variables, complex variables are given floating-point variable names and are treated by the compiler as one-dimensional arrays consisting of two elements.

```
I        R = (2.82, - 3.15)
```

Instead of a D in column 1, the programmer specifies a complex variable by punching a letter I in column 1. Real and imaginary parts are to be separated by a comma and enclosed in a set of parentheses. The appearance of a variable, previously defined to be complex, in an arithmetic statement with no letter I in column 1 will give only the real part of the number.

S = R or S = R(1)

The location named S will now contain the floating-point number, 2.82. If an I is placed in column 1, S will also be a complex variable, containing the complex constant (2.82, −3.15). To address the imaginary part without addressing the real part, the programmer should place the variable in a complex DIMENSION statement and then use the second subscript—exactly the same procedure as in the case of addressing the least significant part of a double-precision variable.

```
I        DIMENSION D
         ______
         ______
         ______
I        D = (2.135,7.1246)
         ______
         ______
         ______
      21 T = D(2)
```

After the execution of statement 21, location T will contain the floating-point number, 7.1246.

In the previous section it was explained that the FORTRAN II compiler does not permit input (output) of both parts of a double-precision constant; the same is true for complex constants. Now the programmer need not worry about rounding off the first part of the word, since the imaginary part of a complex number is not a continuation of the real part; therefore, it is not necessary to use the O-type format for input (output) of complex constants.

```
         READ 17, U(1), U(2)
      17 FORMAT (F10.2, F10.4)
```

Arrays of complex constants are permitted, but again, as in the case of double-precision constants, a change of variables is necessary for input (output). This makes the process a much more tedious one.

```
I        DIMENSION W(10)
         DIMENSION S(10), T(10)
         READ 10, (S(I), T(I), I = 1,10)
      10 FORMAT (2F10.3)
         DO 20 I = 1,10
         W(I) = S(I)
         J = I + 10
      20 W(J) = T(I)
```

Notice that the imaginary part of the complex constants, the floating-point constants read into the T array, are placed into their correct locations by using a subscript containing the dimension of the W array as an addend. In the above example, the dimension of the W array is 10; therefore, in order to address the imaginary part of each variable in the W array, 10 must be added to the last subscript.

Another example using a two-dimensional array is:

```
I        DIMENSION Z(10,10)
         DIMENSION A(10,10), B(10,10)
         READ 20, ((A(I,J), B(I,J), I = 1,10), J = 1,10)
      20 FORMAT (2F8.2)
         DO 30 I = 1,10
         DO 30 J = 1, 10
         Z(I,J) = A(I,J)
         K = J + 100
      30 Z(I,K) = B(I,J)
```

Now the dimension of the Z array is 100, so 100 must be added to the last subscript in order to address the imaginary part of the number. The same procedure holds for arithmetic statements.

```
       1 R = Z(4, 5)
       2 S = Z(4, 105)
I      3 T = Z(4, 5)
```

In statement 1, reference is made to the real part of the constant in the fourth row and fifth column of the Z array. The variable S, in statement 2, will assume the imaginary part of the constant in the fourth row and the fifth column of the Z array. T will be a complex variable containing both the real and imaginary parts of the constant in the above position.

5.2.2. FORTRAN IV

Complex variables, like double-precision variables are defined in a type statement:

```
COMPLEX R,S,T(10,10,10)
     ______
     ______
     ______
R=(3.271, - 4.21 E3)
S=R**I
READ 7(((T(I,J,K),I=1,10),J=1,10),K=1,10)
     ______
     ______
     ______
```

R and S are complex variables and T is a three-dimensional array of complex numbers. Notice that the T array is dimensioned in the type statement and therefore must not appear in a regular DIMENSION statement. In FORTRAN IV, unlike FORTRAN II, a complex variable and a floating-point variable may not appear on opposite sides of the equal sign.

```
COMPLEX  Z,F
R = Z Not allowed
V = 3.716
F = V Not allowed
```

Therefore, it is not possible for the programmer to address the imaginary part of the number in FORTRAN IV without writing a subprogram in a machine language.

In the example before the last, the complex variable R was raised to an integer power (I); it is not possible to raise a complex variable to a floating point power. More will be said about real functions of complex variables in a later section of this chapter.

5.2.3. Complex Variables — Example

Write a FORTRAN IV program to calculate the hyperbolic sine of a complex argument, $z = x + iy$.

$$\sinh(z) \frac{e^z - e^{-z}}{2}$$

where

$$e^z = e^x(\cos y + i \sin y)$$

Analysis:

$$\sinh(z) = \frac{e^x(\cos y + i \sin y) - e^{-x}(\cos(-y) + i \sin(-y))}{2}$$

$$= \frac{(e^x + e^{-x}) \cos y + (e^x - e^{-x}) i \sin y}{2}$$

Since

$$\cos(-y) = - \cos(y)$$

and

$$\sin(-y) = \sin(y)$$

Program

```
      COMPLEX Z
      DIMENSION A(2)
      EQUIVALENCE (Z,A(1)),(A(1),ZREAL),(A(2),ZIMAG)
99    READ(5,1) Z
 1    FORMAT(2F6.2)
      ETODX = EXP(ZREAL)
      ETODMX = EXP(-ZREAL)
      COSY = COS(ZIMAG)
      SINY = SIN(ZIMAG)
      SZREAL = COSY * (ETODX + ETODMX)/2.
      SZIMAG = SINY * (ETODX - ETODMX)/2.
      WRITE (6,2) Z, SZREAL, SZIMAG
 2    FORMAT(24H THE HYPERBOLIC SINE OF ,E14.8,3H I ,E14.8,3X3H IS,
     1/14H REAL PART   ,E14.8,19H IMAGINARY PART   ,E14.8)
      END
```

5.3. Boolean and Logical Variables

Before explaining the differences between FORTRAN II and FORTRAN IV in the area of Boolean operations, we will briefly consider an introduction to Boolean algebra and logic and present a few examples.

5.3.1. Boolean Algebra

In Boolean algebra there are only two values to consider, 0, and 1. Three operations are defined: addition, multiplication, and complementation.

Addition

$$0 + 0 = 0$$
$$0 + 1 = 1$$
$$1 + 1 = 1$$

The addition operation is commonly referred to as the logical "or"; 0 or 0 is 0, 0 or 1 is 1, and 1 or 1 is 1.

Multiplication

$$0 \cdot 0 = 0$$
$$0 \cdot 1 = 0$$
$$1 \cdot 1 = 1$$

The multiplication operation is commonly referred to as the logical "and"; 0 and 0 is 0, 0 and 1 is 0, and 1 and 1 is 1.

Complementation

$$\text{Not } 0 = 1$$
$$\text{Not } 1 = 0$$

Since only two symbols, 0 and 1, are available, if a symbol is not 0, it must be 1, and vice versa.

In terms of symbols, the "or" and "and" operations are:

$$\begin{array}{ll} \mathrm{R} + 0 = \mathrm{R} & \mathrm{R} \cdot \mathrm{R} = 0 \\ \mathrm{R} + 1 = 1 & \mathrm{R} \cdot 1 = \mathrm{R} \\ \mathrm{R} + \mathrm{R} = \mathrm{R} & \mathrm{R} \cdot \mathrm{R} = \mathrm{R} \end{array}$$

where R may take on the values 0 or 1.

It is easy to see that both the "or" and "and" functions possess the properties of commutativity and associativity.

$$A + B = B + A \qquad \text{Commutativity (or)}$$

$$\left.\begin{array}{l} 0 + 1 = 1 + 0 \\ 0 + 0 = 0 + 0 \\ 1 + 0 = 0 + 1 \\ 1 + 1 = 1 + 1 \end{array}\right\} \text{Possibilities}$$

0 or 1 is one and so is 1 or 0; etc.

$$\begin{array}{rl} A \cdot B = B \cdot A & \text{Commutativity (and)} \\ (A + B) + C = A + (B + C) & \text{Associativity (or)} \\ (A \cdot B) \cdot C = A \cdot (B \cdot C) & \text{Associativity (and)} \end{array}$$

In the same way it can be shown that both functions possess the property of distributivity with respect to each other.

Cases

$$A=1, B=0, C=0 \qquad A \cdot B + A \cdot C = A \cdot (B + C) \tag{1}$$

$$\underbrace{\underbrace{1 \cdot 0}_{0} + \underbrace{1 \cdot 0}_{0}}_{0} \qquad \underbrace{1 \cdot \underbrace{(0 + 0)}_{0}}_{0}$$

$$A=1,B=1,C=0 \qquad \underbrace{\underbrace{1\cdot 1}_{1} + \underbrace{1\cdot 0}_{0}}_{1} = \underbrace{1\cdot \underbrace{(1+0)}_{1}}_{1} \tag{2}$$

$$A=0,B=1,C=0 \qquad \underbrace{\underbrace{0\cdot 1}_{0} + \underbrace{0\cdot 0}_{0}}_{0} = \underbrace{0\cdot \underbrace{(1+0)}_{1}}_{0} \tag{3}$$

$$A=0,B=0,C=0 \qquad \underbrace{\underbrace{0\cdot 0}_{0} + \underbrace{0\cdot 0}_{0}}_{0} = \underbrace{0\cdot \underbrace{(0+0)}_{0}}_{0} \tag{4}$$

$$A=0,B=0,C=1 \qquad \underbrace{\underbrace{0\cdot 0}_{0} + \underbrace{0\cdot 1}_{0}}_{0} = \underbrace{0\cdot \underbrace{(0+1)}_{1}}_{0} \tag{5}$$

$$A=0,B=1,C=1 \qquad \underbrace{\underbrace{0\cdot 1}_{0} + \underbrace{0\cdot 1}_{0}}_{0} = \underbrace{0\cdot \underbrace{(1+1)}_{1}}_{0} \tag{6}$$

$$A=0,B=0,C=1 \qquad \underbrace{\underbrace{1\cdot 0}_{0} + \underbrace{1\cdot 1}_{1}}_{1} = \underbrace{1\cdot \underbrace{(0+1)}_{1}}_{1} \tag{7}$$

$$A=1,B=1,C=1 \qquad \underbrace{\underbrace{1\cdot 1}_{1} + \underbrace{1\cdot 1}_{1}}_{1} = \underbrace{1\cdot \underbrace{(1+1)}_{1}}_{1} \tag{8}$$

In the same way,

$$\begin{aligned}
A + B\cdot C &= (A+B)\cdot(A+C) && \\
&= (A+B)\cdot A + (A+B)\cdot C && \text{Distributivity} \\
&= \underbrace{A\cdot A} + B\cdot A + A\cdot C + B\cdot C && \text{"} \\
&= A + B\cdot A + A\cdot C + B\cdot C && A\cdot A = A \\
&= A\underbrace{(1+B+C)} + B\cdot C && \text{Factor} \\
&= \underbrace{A\cdot 1} + B\cdot C && 1+B+C=1 \\
&= A + B\cdot C &&
\end{aligned}$$

Many Boolean algebraic expressions may be established by using the above rules. For example:

$$A + (A \cdot B) = A \cdot (1 + B) = A \cdot 1 = A$$

From the definition of the complementary operation, the following equations hold:

$$\begin{aligned} A + \tilde{A} &= 1 \qquad \text{where} \sim \text{implies "not"} \\ A \cdot \tilde{A} &= 0 \\ \tilde{\tilde{A}} &= A \end{aligned}$$

In the first equation:

$$\begin{array}{ll} \text{if } A = 0 & 0 + \tilde{0} = 0 + 1 = 1 \\ \text{if } A = 1 & 1 + \tilde{1} = 1 + 0 = 1 \end{array}$$

The other equations are proved in the same way.

$$\begin{array}{lccc}
\text{Also} & \widetilde{A \cdot B \cdot C} & = & \tilde{A} + \tilde{B} + \tilde{C} \\
\text{verification} & & & \tilde{0} \quad \tilde{0} \quad \tilde{0} \\
A=0, B=0, C=0 & \widetilde{\underbrace{0 \cdot 0 \cdot 0}_{\underbrace{\tilde{0}}_{1}}} & & \underbrace{1 + 1 + 1}_{1} \\
 & 1 & & \\
A=0, B=0, C=0 & \widetilde{\underbrace{0 \cdot 0 \cdot 1}_{\underbrace{\tilde{0}}_{1}}} & = & \underbrace{\tilde{0} + \tilde{0} + 1}_{\underbrace{1 + 1 + 0}_{1}} \\
 & 1 & = & 1 \\
A=0, B=1, C=0 & 1 & = & 1 \\
A=0, B=1, C=1 & 1 & = & 1 \\
A=1, B=0, C=0 & 1 & = & 1 \\
A=1, B=0, C=1 & 1 & = & 1 \\
A=1, B=1, C=0 & 1 & = & 1 \\
A=1, B=1, C=1 & 0 & = & 0
\end{array}$$

and $\quad \widetilde{A + B + C} = \tilde{A} \cdot \tilde{B} \cdot \tilde{C}$

where $\quad \widetilde{A + B + C}$ implies "not" (A or B or C).

Again these basic rules may be used to deduce other relations.

$$\widetilde{X \cdot \tilde{Y} \; + \; \tilde{X} \cdot Y}$$

$$\Downarrow$$

$$\widetilde{X \cdot \tilde{Y}} \quad \cdot \quad \widetilde{\tilde{X} \cdot Y}$$

$$\Downarrow$$

$$(\tilde{X} + \tilde{\tilde{Y}}) \quad \cdot \quad (\tilde{\tilde{X}} + \tilde{Y})$$

$$\Downarrow$$

$$(\tilde{X} + Y) \quad \cdot \quad (X + \tilde{Y})$$

$$\Downarrow$$

$$\tilde{Y} \cdot X + Y \cdot X \quad + \quad \tilde{X} \cdot \tilde{Y} + Y \cdot \tilde{Y}$$

$$\Downarrow$$

$$Y \cdot X \quad + \quad \tilde{X} \cdot \tilde{Y}$$

$$\Downarrow$$

$$Y \cdot X \quad + \quad \widetilde{(X + Y)}$$

where $\Downarrow$ means "implies."

One application of Boolean algebra is switching networks and computer components. Below are switches representing the operations "or," "and," and "not." The first produces a signal if there is a signal on either C or D.

$C \longrightarrow$ (OR) $\longrightarrow$
$D \longrightarrow$

The next produces signal only if there is a signal on both C and D:

$C \longrightarrow$ (AND) $\longrightarrow$
$D \longrightarrow$

The one below produces a signal if and only if there is no signal on C—if there is a signal on C no signal will be generated from the device.

$C \longrightarrow$ (NOT) $\longrightarrow$

A possible two-way signal might be a positive voltage for a "1" and a negative voltage for a "0."

The greatest advantage of the Boolean algebra notation may be traced to the fact that a different physical circuit is represented by expressions which are mathematically equivalent. For example, the equation:

$$A \cdot B + C \cdot D = (A + C) \cdot (A + D) \cdot (B + C) \cdot (B + D)$$

illustrates two possible circuits:

$A \longrightarrow$ [AND]
$B \longrightarrow$

[OR] $\longrightarrow A \cdot B + C \cdot D$

$C \longrightarrow$ [AND]
$D \longrightarrow$

(a)

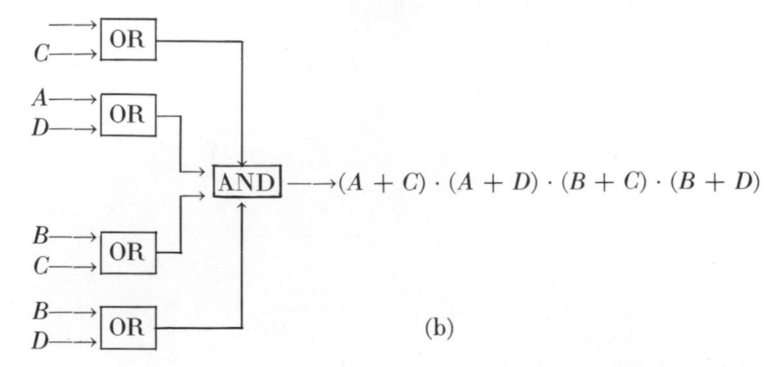

(b)

Circuit (a) requires less components than circuit (b), so it would be advantageous to use design (a) which is equivalent to design (b).[2]

5.3.2. FORTRAN II

Both FORTRAN II and IV allow the programmer to handle the logical operations which were illustrated above. In FORTRAN II, the symbols +, *, and − denote the operators OR, AND, and COMPLEMENT, respectively; the operator * is higher in the hierarchy of operators than is the operator +. The complementary operator is highest because it is part of the expression or symbol to which it applies.

Boolean operations are performed on the entire 36 binary-bit word, and these operations take place in arithmetic statements containing the letter B in column 1.

```
B        R = A * B + C * D
B        S = (A + C) * (A + D) * (B + C) * (B + D)
B        T = -(A + B + C)
B        F = (- A) * (-B) * (-C)
```

If the Boolean variables, which must have floating-point names, are to take on the values 0 or 1, these variables must be defined in a READ list or on the left-hand side of an arithmetic statement.

```
B        R = 1
B        S = 0
         or
         READ  7, A,B,C,D
       7 FORMAT (4O12)
```

[2] For further references to switching theory and Boolean algebra, see R. K. Richards, *Arithmetic Operations in Digital Computers* (Princeton, N.J.: D. Van Nostrand Co., Inc., 1955).

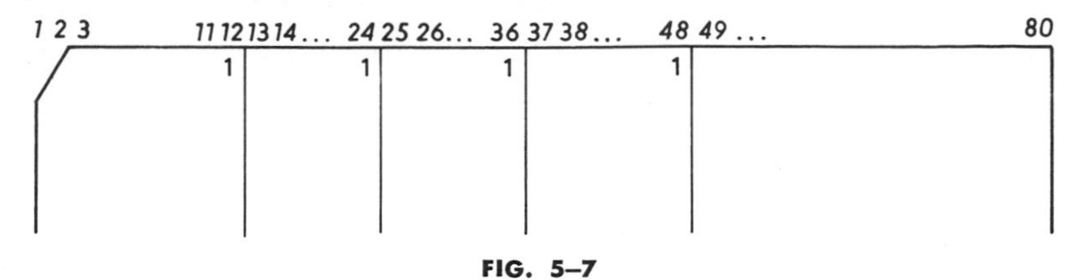

FIG. 5–7

Actually, the programmer is using only the rightmost of the available 36 bits in each machine location when he performs Boolean algebra in FORTRAN II. Complex networks may be represented by one variable through the use of Boolean algebraic symbols; the value of the network at any time will depend on the value of its components on the Boolean equation. This type of logic is not limited to computer design or switching circuits; the same general ideas appear in logic, systems engineering, and other far-reaching topics.

In logic a student may be able to tell from established facts whether certain phrases are true or false. From a knowledge of phrases and the way these phrases are logically combined to form sentences, the student, by writing out the sentence in symbolic logic, can tell if the sentence is true or false. Let us consider a very simple example:

The cause of the riot in Alfredo Street following the speech can be attributed to:

$$\underbrace{\text{Rival gangs}}_{A} \text{ or } \underbrace{\text{Hot weather}}_{B} \text{ and } \underbrace{\text{The fact that some of the audience was agitated by outsiders}}_{C}$$

In this example we will assume there was a riot and try to see if the above statement is true. Logically, the sentence can be broken down to the statement, $A + B * C$. $R = A + B * C$. The value of R, the truth or falsity of the statement, can be found if the truth or falsity of its component phrases, A,B, and C are known. If A is true, B is false, and C is true, the value of R is true.

$$\text{T or } \underbrace{\text{F and T}}$$
$$\underbrace{\text{T or F}}$$
$$\text{T}$$

True can be represented by a 1 and false by a 0 in terms of the variables in FORTRAN II.

Another use for symbolic logic occurs in systems engineering. In the design of an accounting system, one of the major problems arising is the timing of the flow of data; if certain data are not present, some task may be tied up. In other words, questions of the following type arise and must be answered before the system is drawn up: What type of data is needed for each task?; Where do these data come from and how long does it take to communicate between the group having the data and the group which desires the data? Having finished this preliminary study, the engineer can lay out a proposed system in symbolic logic. If a certain job is parallel to another in the sense that either job may be accomplished without results from the other, these jobs may be connected by a logical "or," but, if the one job follow another in the sense that the results of one are critical to the working of the other, then the two jobs are symbolically related by the "and" operator. Let us say some jobs are related as shown in Figure 5–8.

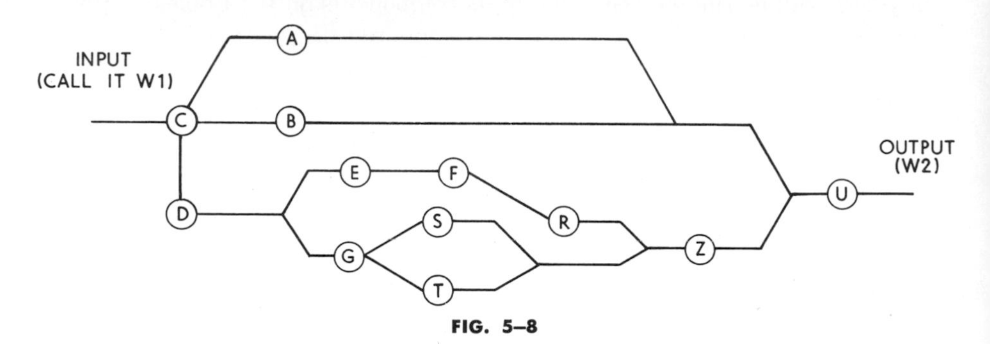

FIG. 5–8

A, B, and D are parallel in the sense that any of them may function without information from the others; none of them can be started before the completion of job C.:

```
B        V1 = S + T
B        V2 = E * F * R
B        V3 = G * V1
B        V4 = V2 + V3
B        V5 = D * V4 + Z
B        V6 = A + B + V5
B        V7 = C * V6 * U
B        W2 = W1 * V7
```

In this example the network of jobs was broken down into eight equations; the output, W2, will be true or false depending on whether the components of the system or network are true or false.

Boolean variables may be used for logical symbol manipulation in FORTRAN II via the same logical operators, +,*, and −. Say a necessary part of a certain program is to pick out the middle 12 binary bits and move them to the rightmost 12 positions of the core. Step 1 consists of keeping the middle 12 bits:

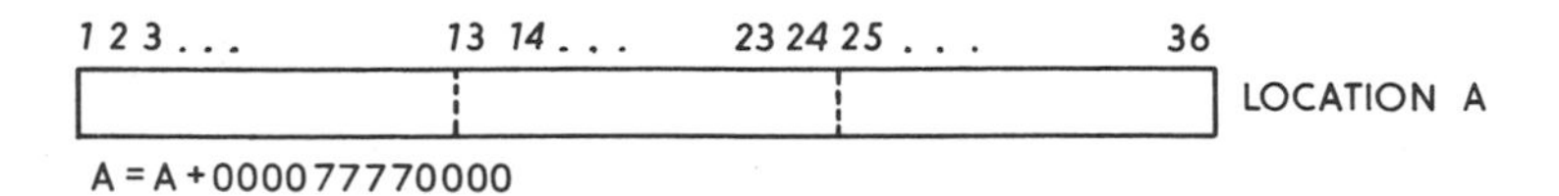

Remember that any number which is combined with a zero through the logical "and" operator will give a zero result.

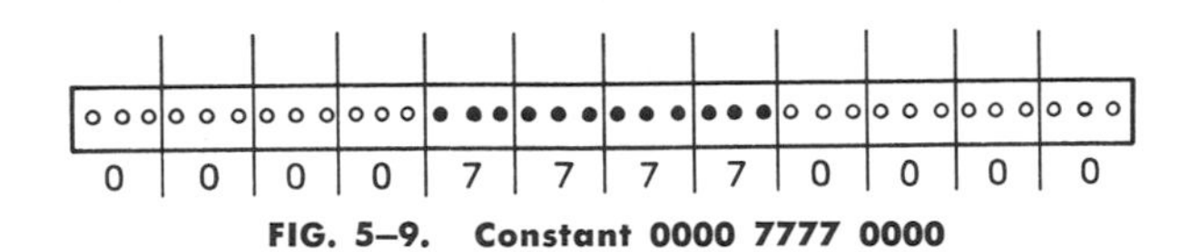

FIG. 5–9. Constant 0000 7777 0000

Therefore, any binary bit in location A which is combined with a zero binary bit will result in a 0 binary bit. Any binary bit in location A which is combined with a 1 binary bit will remain unchanged.

If Z represents a binary bit,

$$Z * 0 = 0$$
$$Z * 1 = Z$$

Note that the constant in the Boolean statement above is written in octal:

Octal	*Binary*
0	o o o
1	o o •
2	o • o
3	o • •
4	• o o
5	• o •
6	• • o
7	• • •

FIG. 5–10. Three Bits Are Equivalent to One Octal Number

The result of the Boolean statement follows:

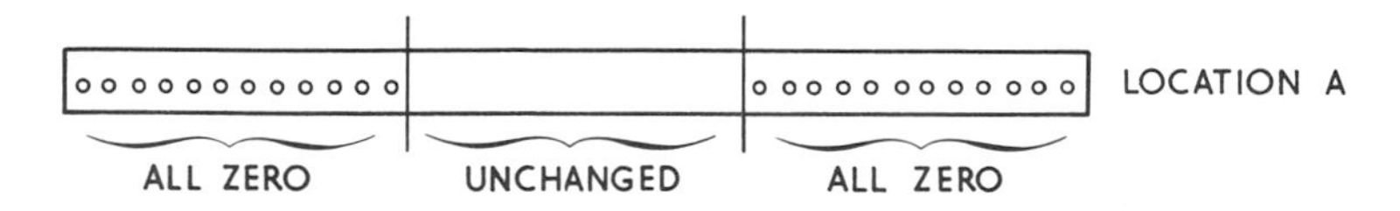

The second step will be to effect a shift to the right of 12 binary bits. To shift to the right 12 binary bits is equivalent to multiplying the value in location A by 2^{-12} or $1/2^{12} = 1/2048$. Therefore, to move the middle 12 bits to the rightmost 12 positions, the programmer must divide the value in location A by 2048. It should be noted at this point that we are treating the value in location A as an octal number (that is, considering the entire 36 bits) and not as a floating-point number. We could have used the fixed-point location K just as well. In that case, the statement is

K = K/2048

After the above statement has been executed:

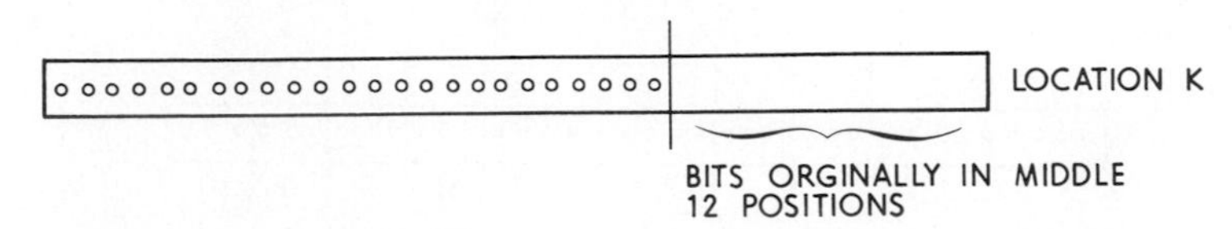

The constant 000077770000 is called a mask. In the next chapter a program which uses the above technique to generate random numbers will be explained.

5.3.3. FORTRAN IV

Logical operations are handled differently in FORTRAN IV from FORTRAN II. Operations which require that a word either be 0 or 1 can be handled more easily in FORTRAN IV; but operations requiring the use of masks—that is, operations which use the entire 36 bits for logical operations—can only be handled through the use of a subroutine written in machine language. A logical variable may have either a fixed-point name or a floating-point name, but it must appear in a type statement.

Column 7

```
LOGICAL   R,K,B (10, 10)
```

In any statement of the program following the above type statement, the appearance of R or K denotes a logical variable and the appearance of the double-subscripted variable B denotes a two-dimensional array composed of logical variables. These variables may take on only one of two values, either true or false. Logical constants may be read into the program or may appear on the right-hand side of an arithmetic statement.

```
    LOGICAL C (10)
    READ 7, (C(I), I = 1, 10)
  7 FORMAT (10L5)
```

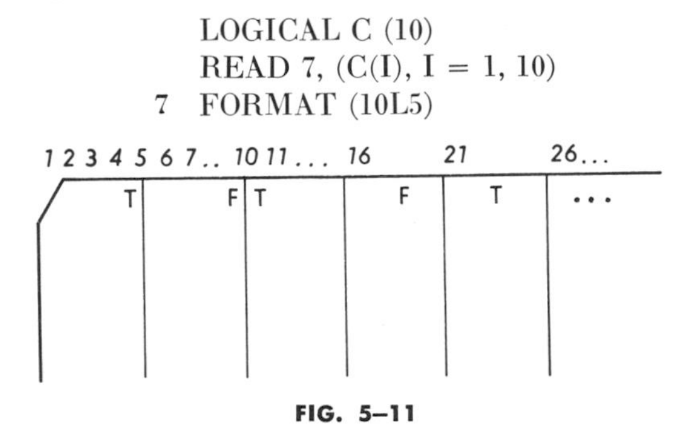

FIG. 5–11

The Lw format code is available for input (output) of logical constants; w is the width of the field. A true value will be read into the storage location if the first nonblank character is a T; the letter T may appear anywhere in the field. A false value will be read into the storage location if either the first nonblank character is an F or if the entire field is composed of blanks.

```
     LOGICAL R,S,T,K
     R = · TRUE ·
     READ 8,S,K
   8 FORMAT (2L8)
     T = R · OR · S · AND · · NOT · K
               ______
               ______
               ______
```

Because the hierarchy of logical operators is:

· NOT ·	$\sim$
· AND ·	$\wedge$
· OR ·	$\vee$

The above logical expression will be evaluated as $R \vee (S \wedge (\sim K))$; first, the value in location K is negated, and then a logical "and" operation is performed between the value in location S and the negation of the value in location K; finally, the value in location R is combined with the result of the above operation via the logical "or" operator. Notice also the appearance of both fixed-point and floating-point variables in one expression; this is legitimate in this case because the appearance of variables in a FORTRAN IV type statement overrides the normal way of naming variables; i.e., if the first letter is I,J,K,L,M, or N, the variable is fixed point, but if the name starts with any other letter the name is a floating-point one.

In addition to the use of the logical operators, FORTRAN IV provides the following relational operators which allow the programmer to handle numerical values in a logical way.

Operator	*Mathematical Symbol*	*Code*
Less than	$<$	· LT ·
Less than or equal to	$\leqslant$	· LE ·
Equal to	$=$	· EQ ·
Not equal to	$\neq$	· NE ·
Greater than	$>$	· GT ·
Greater than or equal to	$\geqslant$	· GE ·

When these operators appear in a logical expression containing either numerical variables or logical variables or both, the relational operators are below the mathematical operators but above the logical operators in the hierarchy of operators.

The Entire Hierarchy of Operators

```
* *            }
* and /        } Mathematical
+ and -        }
·LT·, ·LE·, ·EQ·, ·NE·, ·GT·, ·GE· } Relational
·NOT·  }
·AND·  } Logical
· OR · }
```

Following are some examples using all the operators:

```
     LOGICAL A,B,C,D,E
     DOUBLE-PRECISION R,S,T
     INTEGER Z
       ______  }
       ______  } Statements which read R,S,T,Z, and K
       ______  }
     A = ·NOT·(R * * 2·GE·S + T·OR·E·LT·K)
     READ 7, B,C,D
   7 FORMAT (3L6)
     E = (B·OR·A)·AND·(C·OR·D)·AND·S·GT·2.5*T**2
       ______
       ______
       ______
```

Assume that

R = 2.71358562513
S = 3.1
T = 2.1
Z = 5
K = 2
B = FALSE
C = TRUE
D = FALSE

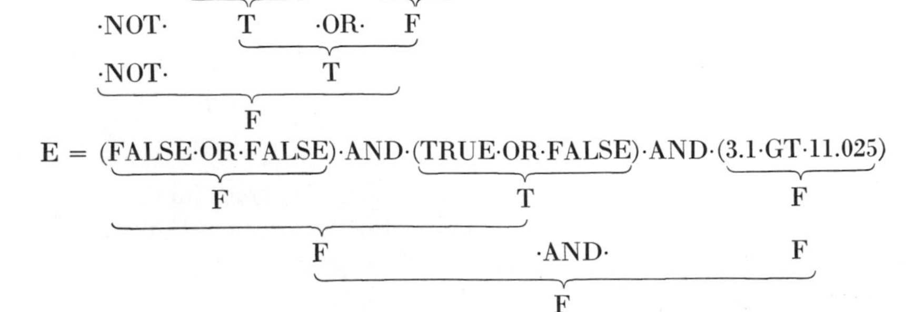

Notice that the variable name Z, normally a floating-point name, here is a fixed-point name because its appearance in the INTEGER type statement overrides the normal rules of naming. In logical expressions, both fixed and floating-point variables may appear as long as the fixed-point variable is not combined (i.e., either by arithmetic or relational operation) with a floating-point variable. Two successive operators must be separated by parentheses unless the NOT operator is one of them.

R·OR··NOT·S Correct
R·OR··AND·S Not correct

When using logical operators, only logical variables may be combined, but when using relational operators, the following types of variables may be combined:

Real with real
Real with double precision
Integer with integer

Logical expressions are built up by the combination of logical variables via logical operators or by the combination of arithmetic expressions through the use of relational operators. A logical statement consists of a logical expression on the right-hand side of the equals sign and a logical variable on the left-hand side.

To perform Boolean operations with the entire 36-bit word in FORTRAN IV, the programmer must write a subprogram in a machine-type language; more will be said about subprograms later in this chapter. Type statements are used in FORTRAN IV to type functions and subroutines as well as variables.

5.4. Control Statements

In general the control statements in the extended FORTRAN II system are the same as or similar to the control statements which are available in the basic FORTRAN II system. One important control statement which is available in FORTRAN IV and which was not available in either version of FORTRAN II is the LOGICAL IF statement.

5.4.1. LOGICAL IF Statement—FORTRAN IV

IF (A logical expression), (An executable statement other than a DO or another LOGICAL IF)

When the logical expression inside the parenthesis is true, the statement written after the parenthesis is executed by the computer. If the logical expression is false, the next sequential statement is executed by the computer.

```
        LOGICAL U,V
          ______
          ______
          ______
        IF((U·OR·V)·AND·K·GT·10), R=K+L**2
        J=K+1
        ______
        ______
        ______
     10 F=R+S
        ______
        ______
        ______
```

Assume that at the time of execution of the LOGICAL IF statement,

```
U = FALSE
V = TRUE
K = 7
```

then (U · OR · V) is TRUE and (K · GT · 10) is FALSE; therefore, the entire logical expression is FALSE and the statement, J=K+1, will be the next statement to be executed by the computer. On the other hand, if U is FALSE, V is TRUE, and K is 11, then K · GT · 10 is TRUE, and the entire logical expression becomes TRUE. In this case the next statement to be executed will be R=K+L**2; after execution of that statement, the statement, J=K+1, will be executed. If, instead of R = K + L ** 2, the statement following the parenthesis was, GO TO 10, the next statement to be executed would be F=R+S, provided that the logical expression was true.

The LOGICAL IF statement is particularly useful as the last statement of a DO loop; it is the only decision-type statement which can be used as the last statement of a DO loop.

```
        LOGICAL F,G
          ______
          ______
          ______
        DO 20 I=1,10
          ______
          ______
          ______
     20 IF(F·AND·G·AND·K·GT·I), T = S+5.1
        R = T+2.*S
          ______
          ______
          ______
```

When the logical expression in the LOGICAL IF statement is true, the statement following the parenthesis, T + S + 5.1, is executed and the DO loop is continued in the natural way; that is, if I<10, the loop is repeated and if I = 10, the statement R = T + 2 * S is executed. Again the statement following the parenthesis in the LOGICAL IF statement may be a transfer statement, such as an arithmetic IF or a GO TO statement; in this case the programmer may effect a branch out of the DO loop. When the logical statement is false, the DO loop is continued in the natural way.

In the following example the programmer is required to write a program to add together all the integers which are read into the computer, and also to multiply the odd integers.

```
      DIMENSION  K(100)
      READ  7, (K(I),I=1,100)
    7 FORMAT (16 I5)
      IPROD=1
      ISUM=0
      DO  10  I=1,100
      ISUM=ISUM+K(I)
   10 IF(2*(K(I)/2)-K(I)·LT·0),IPROD=IPROD*K(I)
```

The expression 2* (K(I)/2) − K(I) will be negative if the integer in location K(I) is odd and zero if the integer in that location is even. When the integer is odd, the logical expression in statement 10 will be true; the next instruction will then be to multiply this integer into the product. On the other hand, if the integer is even, the statement, IPROD = IPROD * K(I), will not be executed and DO loop will be continued in the normal way.

5.4.2 Sense Switch, Sense Light, and Check Switches — FORTRAN II

The control instructions for the basic FORTRAN II system included the IF (SENSE SWITCH) n_1, n_2 statement; the same type of statement is available in FORTRAN II for larger computers and FORTRAN IV. Whereas four external sense switches are available on the IBM 1620, larger machines have six switches.

IF (SENSE SWITCH k) n_1, n_2

where k = 1,2,3,4,5, or 6 and n_1 and n_2 are statement numbers.

In addition, there are four sense lights available on the larger computers; these sense lights work in essentially the same way as the sense switches except that they are located internally and therefore are much faster than the switches.

SENSE LIGHT k

where k = 0,1,2,3,4; if k = 0, all sense lights are turned off; if k = 1,2,3, or 4, sense lights 1,2,3, or 4 will be turned on, respectively.

IF (SENSE LIGHT k) n_1, n_2

where k = 1,2,3, or 4 and n_1 and n_2 are statement numbers. Whenever a sense light is tested, it will be turned off if it was originally on.

The basic FORTRAN II employed the SENSE SWITCH 14 for overflow detection; the extended FORTRAN II uses the following two statements:

IF ACCUMULATOR OVERFLOW n_1, n_2
IF QUOTIENT OVERFLOW n_1, n_2

In the larger computers there are two registers involved with arithmetic operations, the accumulator and the multiplier-quotient register. If overflow takes place as a result of floating-point arithmetic, an indicator is turned on. The above instructions interrogate these lights; when the interrogated light is on, it is turned off. When overflow occurs in either register, that register is set to the largest possible value, 377777777777 to the base 8 (octal).

Like the basic FORTRAN II, the extended version allows the programmer to test for a division for zero through interrogation of the divide check indicator.

IF DIVIDE CHECK n_1, n_2

If the interrogated switch is on, it is turned off.

FORTRAN IV provides the same decision-making power through the use of subroutines.

FORTRAN IV	*FORTRAN II*
CALL SLITE (k)	SENSE LIGHT k
CALL SLITE (k,R)	IF (SENSE LIGHT k) n_1, n_2

The variable R is set to 1 if sense light k was on; if k was off, the variable R is set to 2. Sense switch k is tested.

CALL SSWTCH (k,R)	IF(SENSE SWITCH k) n_1, n_2

The variable R is set to 1 or 2 depending on the condition of switch k. If k was up, R is set to 2, but if k was down, R is set to 1.

CALL OVERFL (k)	IF ACCUMULATOR OVERFLOW n_1, n_2
	IF QUOTIENT OVERFLOW n_1, n_2
CALL DVCHK (k)	IF DIVIDE CHECK n_1, n_2

5.5. Input/Output Statements

5.5.1. Discussion of Faster Input/Output Devices

Large computers need faster input/output devices as well as devices which allow fairly fast access to a great store of data. The following input/output devices may be available:

Magnetic tape
Magnetic drum
Disk file

A card reader / punch is usually connected to the computer; but to speed the input/output process, data is usually transferred from cards to magnetic tape by a smaller computer so that data coming into the larger machine will be from magnetic tape.

Magnetic tape offers great speed for sequential processing of large volumes of data. However, if it is not known on which part of the tape certain data is stored at the time of processing, much time is lost in skipping large parts of the tape.

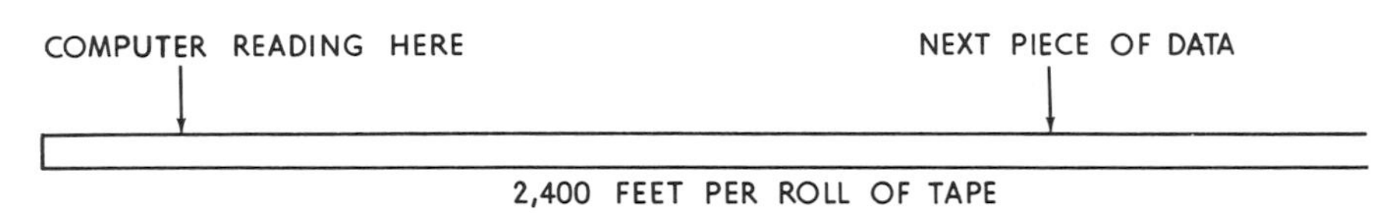

This is due to the one-dimensional, straight-line nature of a roll of tape.

To provide the same reference time to any part of the storage media, the user should avail himself of magnetic disk files; this medium is slower than magnetic tape for processing sequential data (i.e., the required data follow, one character after another, on the tape), but is much faster than magnetic tape for providing random access of data.

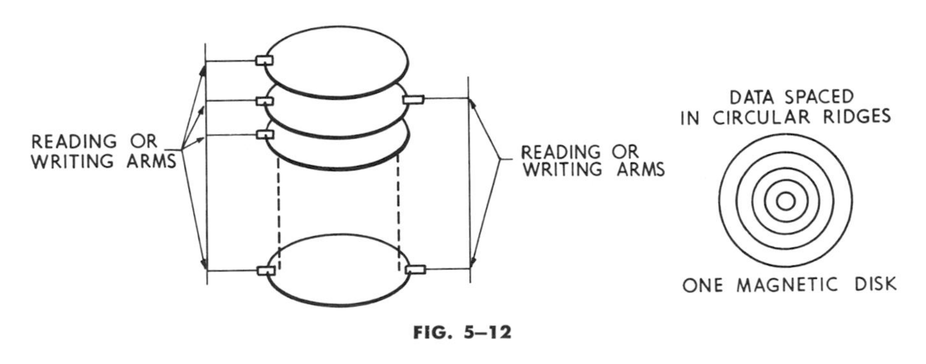

FIG. 5–12

The disk file–magnetic disk file resembles a two-dimensional array of storage shelves; the arms can go up and down to locate the right disk and then move in across the disk to locate the data. All the disks are moving at high speeds (usually about 1,800 revolutions per minute); if there is an arm for each disk, the average time to access a data record is $\frac{1}{2}$ of a revolution or .016 seconds.

Magnetic drum is essentially random access (same average access time for any character), but provides less capacity at higher speeds than the disk file.

In our discussion of input/output with FORTRAN II and FORTRAN IV, only magnetic tape and punched cards will be considered, since these two modes are most often needed; instructions for these modes are common

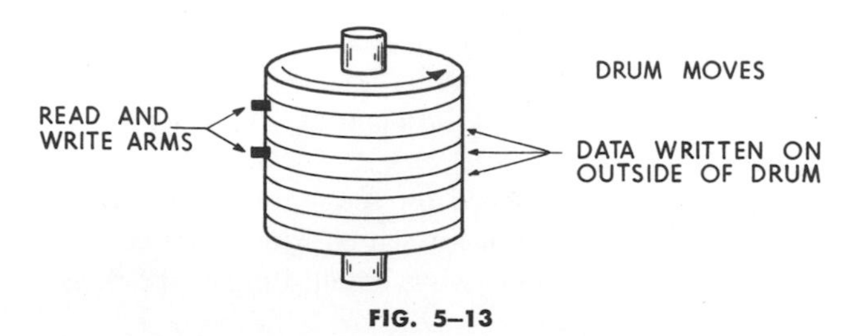

FIG. 5–13

to both versions of FORTRAN. Computer installations utilizing magnetic disk files or magnetic drum files may add these instructions to the FORTRAN Compiler.

FORTRAN II *Statements*		*FORTRAN IV* *Statments*
(1) READ TAPE	k, list	READ (k) list
(2) READ INPUT TAPE	k,n, list	READ (k,n) list
(3) WRITE TAPE	k, list	WRITE (k) list
(4) WRITE OUTPUT TAPE	k,n, list	WRITE (k,n) list
(5) READ	n, list	READ (n), list
(6) PRINT	n, list	PRINT n, list

Statements 1 and 3 are involved with binary records; statements 2 and 4 are involved with binary coded decimal records. The letter k denotes the symbolic number of the tape unit; each installation publishes a list of symbolic tape numbers:

READ (5) "list of items"

Binary information is read from tape unit 5 into the location specified in the list; a logical record (any group of binary words which are to be read by one input statement) is read by the computer. A binary tape which has been written by FORTRAN or written by some other program following the necessary formating will look like the following:

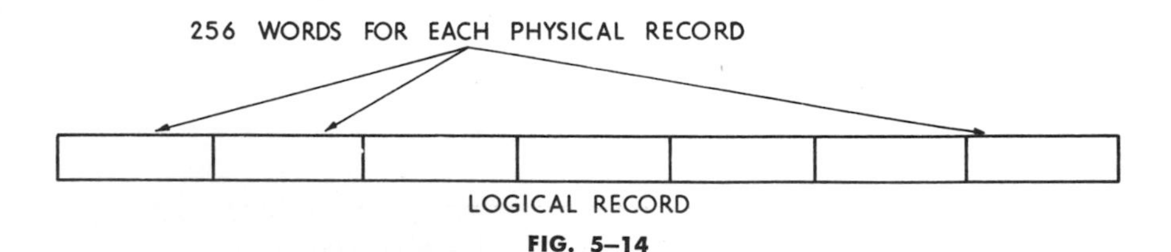

FIG. 5–14

A logical record is divided into as many physical records as needed, with the limitation that each physical record has a maximum length of 256 binary words.

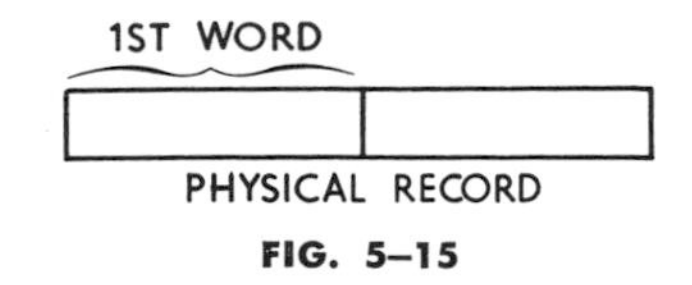

FIG. 5–15

The first word of each physical record is zero, except for the first word of the last physical record, which contains the number giving the number of physical records in the logical record; this device is automatically checked by FORTRAN to insure against the loss of a record. If the list specified in the input statement is less than the logical record, the tape will move to the next record. If the list is longer than the logical record, the computer will stop, and an error message is printed on the printer connected to the computer:

LIST EXCEEDS LOGICAL RECORD LENGTH
EXECUTION TERMINATED BY EXEM

EXEM is the Execution Error Monitor. At this point, control is transferred to the monitor, which will then consider the next program.

The statement WRITE (5) list takes the results in the locations specified in the list and writes them on tape in binary mode. All the items in the list are written as a logical record; as mentioned earlier, each logical record is broken down into physical records, each of which is at most 256 binary words in length. The first word in the last physical record gives the count of the total number of records. Since count control is kept automatically and checked by FORTRAN, there is no need to write a mark on the tape signifying the end of an information file. For applications tending toward the commercial computing side, it may be necessary to indicate the end of the information file in order to check hash totals or to initiate some data handling or modifying routine; because the data for commercial applications will almost always be in binary coded decimal mode, end-of-file routines will be discussed in regard to input/output statements for data in the binary coded decimal mode.

WRITE (k,n) list where n refers to a FORMAT statement which provides information to the compiler on the form (mode, length, etc.) of the data to be written on symbolic tape unit, k. The FORMAT statement determines the length of the records on the tape; the mode will be binary coded decimal. As many records are written as is needed to exhaust the list. If, while writing these records, the compiler encounters the end of a certain reel of tape, the full tape is backspaced one record, and an end-of-file mark is written automatically on the tape (this is also true of the WRITE (k) list, statement for data in binary mode); also, a message is printed:

END OF TAPE WRITING XX
CHANGE AND PUSH START

This message is intended strictly for use by the operator and not by the programmer; it is presented at this time to give the student a chance to understand the way in which FORTRAN handles tape operations.

For both commercial and scientific applications, more than one type of data will probably be on the same reel of tape; each type of information is usually called a file and can be identified by labels on the front and back of the file.

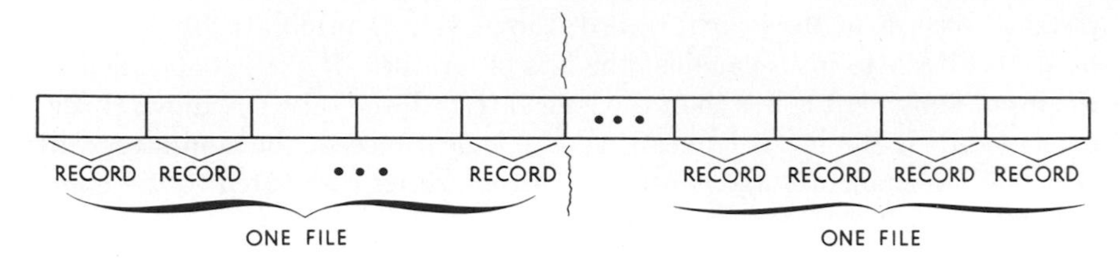

The first record of the file would contain information describing the type of data in that file. The last record of the file would contain the number of records in that file (for binary data, the end of file would be taken care of in the normal course of operations by the FORTRAN compiler) for checking

FLOW CHART

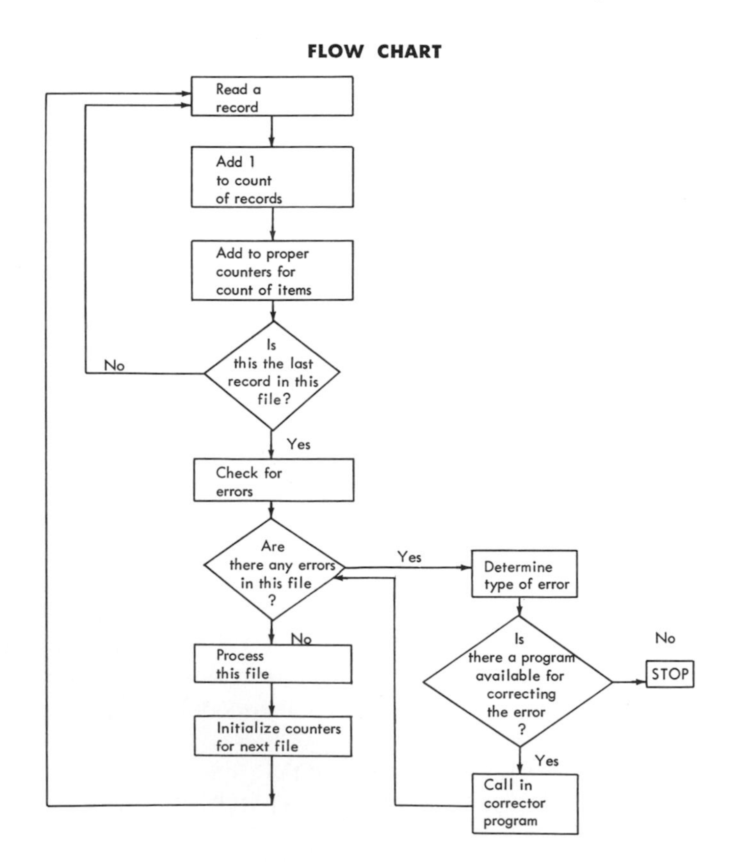

purposes, and maybe a hash total of file data handled in the program for checking purposes. (A total of items being handled may be available before the program; this is checked against the hash total to see if all items were handled by the program.) In order to check to see if all the items have not been considered, or if it is desirable to bring in a special routine to handle exceptional conditions, there must be a way to signal the last record. One field in the last record could contain a very large number; this field could be checked for every record. Upon receiving the last card signal, the programmer could instruct the computer to check for error conditions—when no errors are present, the program would proceed normally; an error condition would call in a subprogram to either analyze and correct the error condition or to stop the computer and print a message indicating the error condition.

5.4.3. Auxiliary Input/Output Instructions

The corrector program might have to reread the entire file or at least a part of the entire file in order to initiate the procedure to correct the error; for this purpose the FORTRAN language includes the statement:

BACK SPACE k

where k is a symbolic tape unit. Execution of this instruction causes the computer to backspace one record on take unit k. An example of a corrector program might be a program which would replace one of the records in the file with another record from the entire library of data which is stored on the auxiliary storage media, such as the magnetic disk file.

Additional protection may be gained by instructing the computer to place an end-of-file code after each file written in binary coded decimal mode; the instruction is

END FILE k

where k is a symbolic tape unit. When executing the instruction

READ (k, n)

the computer will automatically check for the end-of-file mark; if the computer hits an end-of-file mark while trying to read a record, the following message will be typed out to be acted on by the operator:

END OF FILE TAPE XX. TO CONTINUE THIS JOB, PUSH START.
TO GO TO NEXT JOB, DEPRESS SIGN KEY AND PUSH START.

Instructions as to the choice to make in the above situation should be given to the operator; however, the programmer should avoid stopping the computer in the middle of a program. In normal operations, the computer should be allowed to take the next job if the computer tries to read the end-of-file code.

When the program has completed the output for one part of the job (maybe the updating of a customer record tape), the tape should be rewound so that it may be processed by another part of the program or by another program at a different time. FORTRAN provides the instruction

REWIND k

for the benefit of the programmer.

In addition to the tape input/output instructions, the instructions

READ n,
WRITE n,
PRINT n,

are available for input/output of binary coded decimal information for cards and the printer attached to the computer. The letter n in the above statements represents the number of a FORMAT statement appearing in the program. Card input/output will not be described in detail because there is little difference between machines for this mode of transferring information.

5.4.4. The NAMELIST Statement

FORTRAN IV provides for the input/output of data without reference to an input/output list through the NAMELIST statement:

NAMELIST/RA/F,G,T,Z /XXX/I,R,A,K,L

Like other variable names, a NAMELIST name must consist of 1–6 alphameric characters; the first character must be a letter. Each group of variables appearing in the above statement is given a name; the name appears enclosed in slashes. Therefore, RA and XXX are the group names; group RA is composed of the variables F, G, T, and Z, while group XXX is composed of the variables I, R, A, K, and L.

For input/output of one of these groups, only the name of the group need appear in the input/output statement:

READ (5, RA)

Information in the binary coded decimal mode will be read from symbolic tape unit 5.

READ XXX

Information is read into the computer from the card reader. Notice that when reference is made in an input/output statement to a name of a group of variables in a NAMELIST statement, no FORMAT statement is necessary; this is the result of the method with which the data must be specified on the input cards or tape.

```
                C FOR COMMENT
         STATEMENT  Cont.
         NUMBER                                  FORTRAN STATEMENT
         1       5  6  7    10    15    20    25    30    35    40    45
CARD 1    $RA F=3.1,G=5,T=2.16534...
CARD 2    Z=-3.15615731256 $
CARD 3   2.165372,3.16E+5,2,4,R=2.165
CARD 4    $ 3.165,2.16518,3.158E+2
CARD 5    $ XXX I=2.127,R=6.2,2.1,3*2.712
CARD 6    A(4,3)=2,4*8,K=3.128E+1,L(4)=/$
```

FIG. 5–16. Data Cards for NAMELIST Variables

The first column of all data records (cards) is ignored when the input/output device references a NAMELIST name. If the second character is a \$, the next variable is considered to be a NAMELIST name; when this variable name matches the name in the input/output statement, the following items are considered to be data converted to the correct mode and placed in positions specified on the data cards. Another \$ signals the end of the group of data. In case that either there is no \$ in column 2 or the name following the \$ does not match the NAMELIST name specified in the input/output statement, that record (card) is ignored and the next record is examined.

In the above example, cards 1 and 2 contain data for the variables in the NAMELIST group RA; the column immediately following the NAMELIST group name must be left blank.

```
    3.1               ———→ F
    5 ———→        5. ———→ G
      Floated
    2.16534 ———→ T
                  Converted
 −3. 15615731256 ———→        −3.1561573→Z
                  To single precision
                  because Z is single
                  precision
```

The entire record need not contain data; if it is so desired, the programmer need punch only one data value per card. The \$ in the second record terminates transmission of data for the NAMELIST group RA. In record 3 the "2" in column 1 is ignored, and then the entire record is ignored, because no \$ appears in column 2. After finding a \$ in column 2 of record 4, the characters following the \$ are compared with the NAMELIST group name XXX. Since the characters following the \$ are not alphameric (there is a decimal point) and the first character is not a letter, an error will be signaled by the compiler. If instead of \$3.165, the first word had been \$ Z Z, no error would have been signaled; because Z Z does not match XXX, this record would also have been passed. Examination of card 5 reveals a match of the NAMELIST group name, XXX, with the variable name following the $ sign; therefore, the data items which follow are to read into the locations mentioned in the NAMELIST statement under group, XXX.

$$2.127 \xrightarrow[\text{to fixed point}]{\text{Converted}} 2 \longrightarrow \text{I}$$

Assume R is an array name, having appeared in a statement such as DIMENSION R (5).

6.2———→R (1)
2.1———→R (2)
2.712——→R (3)
2.712——→R (4)
2.712——→R (5)

Assume A is a two-dimensioned array having appeared in the statement DIMENSION A (4, 4).

Converted
2———→ 2. ———→A(4, 3)
to floating
point
8———→ 8. ———→A(1, 4)
8———→ 8. ———→A(2, 4)
8———→ 8. ———→A(3, 4)
8———→ 8. ———→A(4, 4)

Arrays are read in columnwise; that is, the first subscript varies faster than the second.

From these examples the reader can see that the data items may take one of the following forms:

(1) Variable Name = constant

(the variable name may be one element of an array if the subscripts are constants)

(2) Array Name = set of constants separated by commas; an alternative to placing the same constants in a sequence is a constant multiplying an item —for example 5.2, 5.2, 5.2 can be written as 3*5.2
(3) Array element (subscripted variable) = set of constants separated by commas; the first element in the list corresponds to the location specified and the remaining elements correspond to the following positions in the array.

Variable or array names may belong to as many NAMELIST names and statements as the programmer desires; however, the NAMELIST name itself (i.e., the group name) must be a unique variable name and should not be the same as any other variable or function name in the program. A variable in a NAMELIST statement cannot be used as an argument of a subroutine.

A NAMELIST statement serves to reserve space in the computer corresponding to the NAMELIST group name.

```
DIMENSION Z 1 (10), N2 (5)
NAMELIST /AA/ I,J,R,Z 1, Z 2 /BE/N1,N2,N3,F,G,K
```

GROUP NAME AA

Z2	Z1(10)		Z1(3)	Z1(2)	Z1(1)	R	J	I
		• • •						

The group of 14 storage locations may be referred to by the name AA.

GROUP NAME BE

K	G	F	N3	N2(5)		N2(2)	N2(1)	N1
					• • •			

Because the compiler must know how many locations to reserve for each NAMELIST group name, a NAMELIST statement must precede the appearance of a group name in the program. In the same vein, the compiler must know how many elements are in each array appearing in a NAMELIST statement in order to be able to reserve the correct number of storage positions; therefore, an array must appear in a DIMENSION statement before its appearance in a NAMELIST statement.

Constants used in data items for the NAMELIST statement may be integers, real numbers, double-precision numbers, complex numbers (X1, X2), and logical constants. Any of the first three forms of data may be associated with real, integer, and double-precision variables; as the examples indicate, the FORTRAN compiler will convert these forms as it becomes necessary. Complex constants may only be associated with complex variables, and logical constants may only be associated with logical variables. The NAMELIST statement allows the programmer to refer to all the information in a record by the name of the record.

```
NAMELIST/PAYRC/WORKNM, HRS, RATE, INSCD, DEPT.
READ, PAYRC
```

1ST INPUT CARD

2ND INPUT CARD

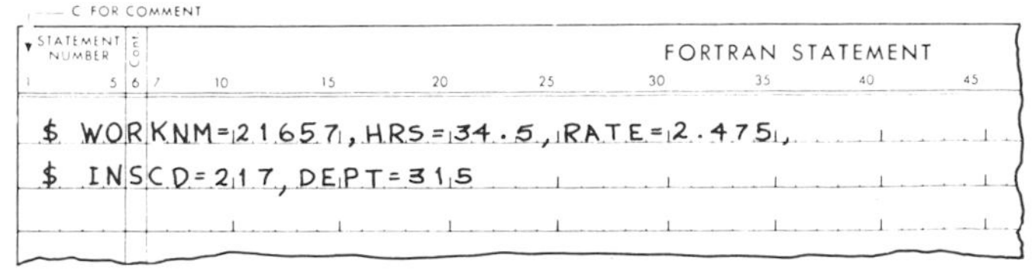

FIG. 5–17

A more flexible format on the data cards is allowed by the NAMELIST statement in the sense that only the first three columns of each record are set (blank, $, blank); however, because the format variable = . . . is not the common way to handle data, this part of the format leads to a disadvantage. An output tape or deck of cards from a FORTRAN program using a NAMELIST statement will have the correct format for input to another program or the same program using a NAMELIST statement for input.

5.4.5. The DATA Statement

In addition to the NAMELIST statement, FORTRAN IV includes the DATA statement; the latter is means of entering integer, real, logical, octal, and complex constants as well as alphameric information. One way the programmer can enter data (except alphameric data) into the object program is the arithmetic statement.

```
DOUBLE  PRECISION  A
LOGICAL  U, V
U = TRUE
V = FALSE
R = 2.12573E+2
A = 1.735D+2
```

Octal constants cannot be entered into the object program through the use of arithmetic statements; these constants must be read into the program at run time, as was pointed out earlier in this chapter in the discussion of Boolean algebra. The DATA statement may be used to enter integer, real, double-precision, complex, logical (· TRUE ·, · FALSE ·, T, or F), and alphameric characters (nH followed by n alphameric characters). Coding a letter or symbol in the binary mode requires 6 bits, and since there are 36 bits in each storage location, one storage location can hold 6 alphameric characters. If n is not a multiple of 6, the remaining characters are placed at the leftmost position of the storage location and blanks are added—for example, 11HSTART AGAIN, is coded into two storage locations:

code	code	code	code	code	code	code	code	code	code	code	code
S	T	A	R	T	b	A	G	A	I	N	b

where b represents a blank. Each octal constant (the letter O followed by 1 to 12 octal digits—O21 or O333571212757) is placed in one storage location and may be either positive or negative.

```
LOGICAL  A, B
DOUBLE  PRECISION  C,D,E
COMPLEX  F
```

```
DIMENSION  R (10), S(5), T(2), Z (5)
           ______
           ______
           ______
DATA  A,B/ T,  FALSE·/ , F / (3.2,−2.1537) /
DATA  C,D,E/2.123756452175, 3.1728D+5, − 2,173547181215/
DATA  R/5 * 3.21E+1, 2*8.175, 3* 3.1728/
DATA  (S (I), I= 1,3) / 3.128, 2.12715, − 1.32 /
DATA  (T (I), I= 1,3) / 11HSTART   AGAIN /
DATA  P, Z (4) / O 371725, 2.1754/
```

The DATA statement takes the form

$$\text{DATA list} / k_1, k_2, \ldots, k_n/, \text{list} / k_1, k_2, k_3, I * k_4, \ldots, k_m/, \ldots$$

when $k_1, k_2, \ldots, k_n$ actually are the data constants (the information itself) and I is an integer constant which may be used to save space if more than one variable is to have the same value.

Each item in the list must have a corresponding data item; as illustrated in the above examples, an implied DO loop (as is permitted in input/output statements) may be used in the list. Also as in input/output, an entire array may be brought into the object deck by specifying the array name in the list, provided that the array was previously mentioned in a DIMENSION statement; the array R in the above examples is an illustration.

Probably the most important use of the DATA statement is to bring in octal or alphameric information; octal information may be needed for Boolean or logical operations in a machine-language subroutine as was discussed earlier in this chapter.

5.6. Functions and Subroutines

FORTRAN II subprograms have been discussed in an earlier chapter; the types of subprograms include:

Type	*Comment*
(1) Built-in functions	An open subroutine
(2) Library functions	Closed subroutines Prewritten on a library tape
(3) Arithmetic statement functions	Closed subroutines Included in the program
(4) Function subprograms	Closed subroutines written as separate FORTRAN programs.
(5) Subroutine subprograms	(same as above)

5.6.1. Machine-Language Subprograms

As in the basic FORTRAN systems, subroutines coded in a machine-type language may be added to the library tape. In addition, separate subprograms written in a machine-type language may now be written by the programmer and compiled separately. Now the programmer can write a subprogram in a symbolic language, having the advantages of machine language but utilizing symbolic addresses and names, and call for it in the FORTRAN main program without putting the routine on the library tape. If the subprogram was placed on the library tape, the programmer would have to write the necessary linkage instructions in machine language; now, the machine-language subprogram may be called in the same way as a FORTRAN subprogram; i.e., via a CALL statement. If the programmer needs a machine-language subroutine for symbol manipulation and logic, but it will not be used enough to make it worthwhile to place the routine on the library tape, he could use the following procedure:

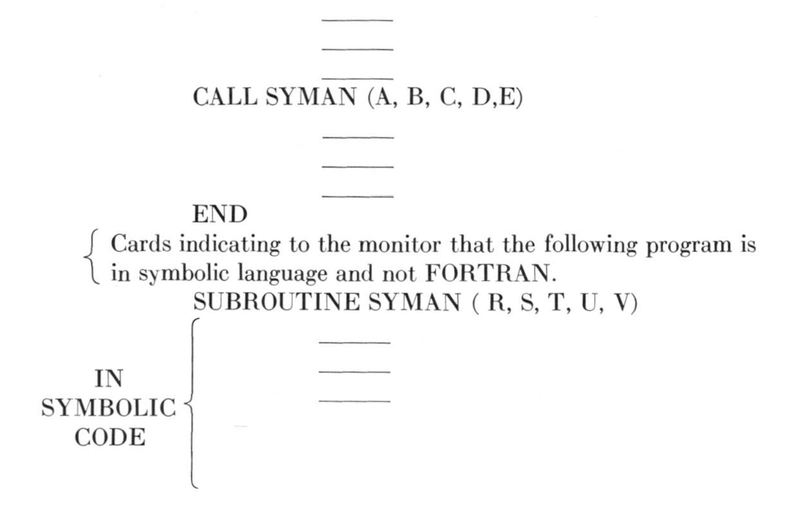

CALL SYMAN (A, B, C, D,E)
END
Cards indicating to the monitor that the following program is in symbolic language and not FORTRAN.
SUBROUTINE SYMAN (R, S, T, U, V)
IN SYMBOLIC CODE

An assembly program which translates symbolic language (FAP, in the case of the IBM 7090/94) resides on the FORTRAN II system tape and is called in by the monitor upon recognizing some code cards before the subroutine. Because monitor systems for different machines will require different code cards, the programmer must consult the reference manual for these cards. The monitor program acts like an executive program; calling in different compilers for the different tasks which must be completed to finish the job.

FORTRAN IV handles machine-language subroutines in the same way as FORTRAN II. For both versions of FORTRAN, linkage instructions are automatically (through use of system control cards) created by the compiler for subroutines written in FAP. Other languages may also be used to write subroutines for FORTRAN, but to incorporate these subroutines into the system the programmer must write his own linkage instructions and cannot use the CALL statement. FUNCTION subprograms, as well as subroutine subprograms, may be written in symbolic language.

5.6.2. Mathematical Routines

The mathematical routines which were written onthe library tape in FORTRAN II are compiled as FUNCTION subprograms in FORTRAN IV; in a sense they may still be thought of as a library of subroutines and are available on the FORTRAN processor tape.

5.6.3. Subprogram Names as Arguments

FORTRAN II for larger machines and FORTRAN IV both provide the programmer with the capability to use subprogram names as arguments for other subprograms; in this way one subprogram may avail itself upon many other subprograms by simply changing the list of arguments following the calling statement.

FORTRAN II

```
F          SQRT, EXP, COS, RAND, MANIP, FACT
           ______
           ______
           ______
           B = 2.31 ** 3.2
           ______
           ______
           ______
        1  Y = SUBA (SQRT, B)
           ______
           ______
           ______
        2  R = SUBA (EXP, B)
           ______
           ______
           ______
        3  S = SUBA (COS, R)
           ______
           ______
           ______
        4  CALL SUBB (RAND, Z1, Z2)
           ______
           ______
           ______
        5  CALL SUBB (MANIP, A1, A2)
           ______
           ______
           ______
```

```
      6  CALL SUBB (FACT, B1,B2)
         ______
         ______
         ______
         END
```

The two subprograms being called are:

```
         FUNCTION  SUBA(SUBF1, A)
    101  SUBA = SUBF1F (A)
         RETURN
         END

         SUBROUTINE SUBB (SUBF2, A1, A2)
    102  A1 = SUBF2 (A2)
         RETURN
         END
```

Notice that the subprogram name, SUBF1F, references the library function, SQRTF, when called by statement number 1; the library function, EXPF, when called by statement number 2; and the library function, COSF, when called by statement number 3. The terminal F, which must be present in the name of all library functions, should be dropped when the library function name appears in an argument list of a calling statement and in the reference list of the first statement of the subprogram. Notice, however, that the terminal F must be added when the dummy variable used for the library function in the subprogram appears in an arithmetic statement; for example, the variable SUBF1 serves as a dummy for the library functions in the function SUBA and, therefore, must contain a terminal F in statement 101 of function SUBA. The terminal F is, of course, not needed when a variable serves as a dummy for either a function subprogram or a subroutine subprogram; therefore, in statement 102 of the subroutine SUBB, no terminal F is added to the variable SUBF2.

Any library function, name, FUNCTION subprogram name, or SUBROUTINE subprogram name which is used as an argument in another subprogram must appear in an F statement as shown in the above example.

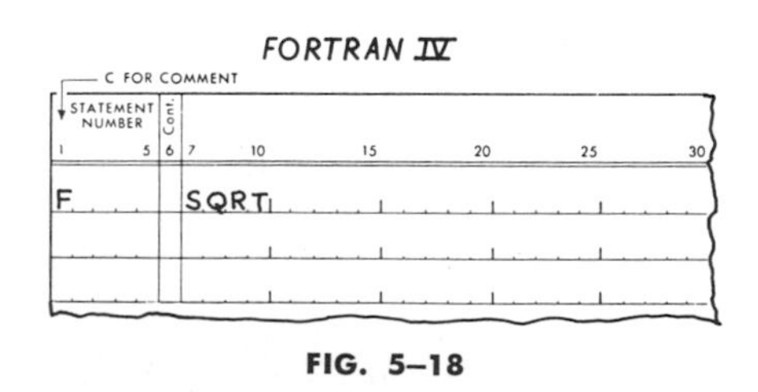

FIG. 5–18

In FORTRAN IV, the EXTERNAL statement is used instead of the F statement. Also, in FORTRAN IV, one need not be concerned with the problem of dropping or adding the terminal F, since there are no library functions as such.

In FORTRAN IV, the only difference in the above programs is the appearance of the EXTERNAL statement and the elimination of the terminal F on the dummy variable in the subprogram.

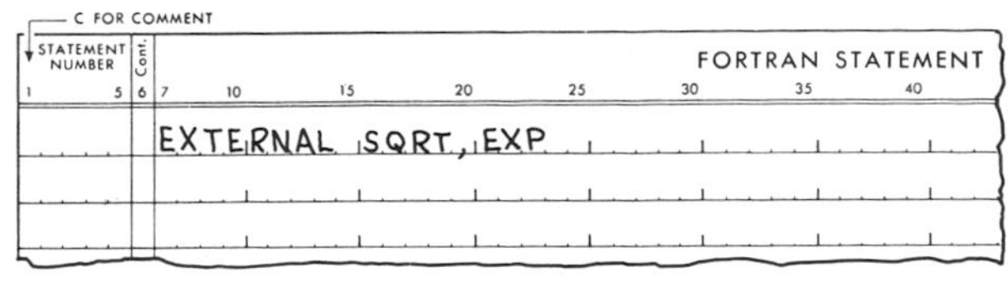

FIG. 5–19

5.6.4. Relation between COMMON and EQUIVALENCE Statements

The relation between the COMMON and the EQUIVALENCE statements are different in FORTRAN II and FORTRAN IV. In FORTRAN II, the appearance of a variable in both a COMMON statement and an EQUIVALENCE statement can affect the organization of the COMMON storage area; whereas, in FORTRAN IV, the organization of the COMMON storage area is unaffected by a COMMON variable appearing in an EQUIVALENCE statement.

FORTRAN II	*FORTRAN IV*
COMMON R,S, EQUIVALENCE (S, T)	COMMON R,S EQUIVALENCE (S,T)
COMMON Locations	*COMMON Locations*
1. S and T 2. R	1. R 2. S and T

Another difference arises when the programmer places an array in the COMMON storage area.

FORTRAN II	*FORTRAN IV*
COMMON R	N O
DIMENSION S(3)	T
EQUIVALENCE (R, S (3))	P E
COMMON Locations	R M
1. S(1)	I T
2. S(2)	T E
3. R and S (3)	D

Because the first variable appearing in the COMMON statement is placed in the first location of the COMMON storage area in FORTRAN IV, the above type of relation between COMMON and EQUIVALENCE statements is not permitted, since there would be no place for S(1) and S(2).

FORTRAN II	*FORTRAN IV*
COMMON R, S	COMMON R, S
DIMENSION T (3)	DIMENSION T (3)
EQUIVALENCE (R,T)	EQUIVALENCE (R, T)
COMMON Locations	*COMMON Locations*
1. R and T (1)	1. R and T (1)
2. T (2)	2. S and T (2)
3. T (3)	3. T (3)
4. S	

In FORTRAN II a gap is left between location R and location S; in FORTRAN IV no such gap is left between R and S.

5.6.5. Labeled COMMON Storage Area

Only the regular COMMON storage area described for the basic FORTRAN II is available for the extended version of FORTRAN II; FORTRAN IV, however, in addition to the regular (or blank) COMMON storage area provides a block (or labeled) COMMON storage area.

```
COMMON I, J, R, S / BOX 1/A (10), B / / K, Z1
COMMON / B2/ F (15), R1 (5, 5) / / L, L1, L2 /BOX1/M
```

In the above example I, J, R, S, K, Z1, L, L1, and L2 belong to blank COMMON; the array of 10 variables named A, the variable B, and the variable M belong to the COMMON block named BOX1; the array of 15 variables named F and the array of 25 variables named R1 belong to the COMMON block B2.

The student should be aware of the following points in the above example:

A labeled COMMON block name should be 1 to 6 alphameric characters, the first of which is a letter; this name must not be the same as the name of any subroutine which is used by the main program with this COMMON. The COMMON block name is indicated by its enclosure in a pair of parentheses; the list of variable names in a COMMON block is terminated by a pair of consecutive slashes or by the end of that COMMON statement. An array appearing either in a labeled or an unlabeled COMMON statement may be dimensioned in the COMMON statement; if the array is dimensioned in the COMMON statement, it must not be dimensioned in a DIMENSION statement or a TYPE statement. If the same COMMON block appears in more than one program, it must be the same size in all programs in which it appears; unlabeled COMMON may be any length in any of the programs. The programmer may not put two variables which are in the COMMON storage area in an EQUIVALENCE statement. A variable which takes up two storage locations (in other words, a complex or double-precision variable must be placed in the COMMON area in such a way that the high-order position of the variable be an even number of positions from the first location of that COMMON area, whether the area be labelled or unlabeled COMMON.

```
        COMPLEX  B
        COMMON   A, B /C/ R (10), F / D / K, L, Z
        EQUIVALENCE (A, B), (F, Z)
```

ERROR 1—The variable B has its high-order position one location away from the first element of the blank COMMON area.

ERROR 2—The variables A and B, both of which are in COMMON, must not appear in an EQUIVALENCE statement. The same is true for F and Z, which appear in two different COMMON blocks.

Labeled COMMON possesses an advantage when a program with many subprograms requires a change in the COMMON area midway through the programming or even after the entire program has been written. If certain variables are COMMON to only a part of all the programs, it is easier to change this COMMON area by putting these variables in a separate labeled COMMON block than to change the COMMON statements for all programs.

```
C       MAIN     PROGRAM
        COMMON   R, S, T (10), Z
        COMMON   /F1/ A (10), K, L, M
        ______
        ______
        ______
        END

        SUBROUTINE  BART
        COMMON   A, B, C(10), D
        COMMON   /F 1/ R(10), K1, K2, K3
        COMMON   /F 2/ S1, S2, S3
        ______
        ______
        ______
        END

        SUBROUTINE  FOUL
        COMMON   T1, T2, T3 (10), T4
        COMMON   /F2/ E1, E2, E3
        ______
        ______
        ______
        END
```

In the above example, all programs share the unlabeled COMMON area; the main program and the subprogram BART share the labeled COMMON block, F1; while the two subprograms share the labeled COMMON block, F2.

5.6.6. The BLOCK DATA Statement

Data may be entered into labeled COMMON at compile time via the BLOCK DATA subprogram which is available in FORTRAN IV. In Figure 5–20 the BLOCK DATA subprogram is used with the labeled common area of section 5.6.5.

```
C FOR COMMENT
STATEMENT NUMBER | Cont. | FORTRAN STATEMENT
      BLOCK DATA
      COMMON /F1/A(1Ø),K,L,M
      COMMON /F2/S1,S2,S3
      DATA(A(I),I=1,1Ø)3.25,4*2.1,2*3.18,2.75,2*2.178/,S3/-3.1297/
      END
```

FIG. 5–20

Notice that all the elements of any specified COMMON block must appear in the DATA BLOCK subprogram even though not all the elements appear in the DATA statement. The above subprogram was used to enter data into both COMMON blocks; this is permissable. There should be no executable statements in the DATA BLOCK subprogram; only COMMON, DIMENSION, DATA, and END statements are permitted (or other nonexecutable statements).

5.6.7. Results of Subprograms—Mode

Earlier in this chapter the student was introduced to the way in which the programmer must identify the mode or type of variable to both the FORTRAN II and FORTRAN IV compilers; the same procedure is used for specifying the mode or type of subprogram.

FORTRAN II. In FORTRAN II the double-precision and complex-value subroutines which are available to the programmer appear in the form of library functions or of built-in functions. They are named in the same way as the real-valued functions except for their name on the library tape; if it is double precision, the name starts with the letter D; if it is complex, the name starts with letter I. (This information is not needed in order to use the available subprograms except in the case where the name of a subprogram appears as an argument of another subprogram.) For example, the subprogram to take absolute values is a built-in function:

REAL (SINGLE)	DOUBLE-PRECISION	
ABSF	DABS	This appears only on the library tape.

To use the double-precision subprograms, the letter D must be written in column 1, and the letter D must be dropped before the letter A.

```
D  R = ABSF (s)
or
I  C = ABSF (Z)   Where Z is a complex variable.
```

FORTRAN II, modification 5, for the IBM 7090/94 computer has the following built-in and library functions available.

	Single-Precision	*Double-Precision*	*Complex*
	ABSF*	ABSF*	ABSF
(Truncation)	INTF*	INTF	_____
(Remaindering)	MODF*	MODF	_____
	FLOATF*	FLOATF*	FLOATF*
(Transfer of sign)	SIGNF*	SIGNF*	SIGNF*
	ATANF	ATANF	_____
	_____	ATAN2F	_____
	(Arctangent of (arg¹, arg²)		
	EXPF	EXPF	EXPF
	LOGF	LOGF	LOGF
	LOG 10F	LOG10F	_____
	SINF	SINF	SINF
	COSF	COSF	COSF
	SQRTF	SQRTF	SQRTF

The * designates a built-in function. Of course, the programmer may add complex or double-precision subroutines either to the library tape or as FUNCTION and SUBROUTINE subprograms; in the latter case he need not worry about the above D convention unless he is using the built-in subroutines for complex and double-precision add, multiply, etc.

When a subprogram name (complex or double-precision) appears as an argument of another subprogram, the programmer must not only follow the procedure given previously for real-valued subprograms concerning the terminal F, but he must also place the letter D or I before the first letter of the subprogram name in both the calling statement list and the list in the first statement of the subprogram.

Main Program

```
F        DEXP
D        ZI = FIRST F (DEXP, Z2)
```

Subprogram

```
FUNCTION  FIRST  (FUN1, S)
D           FIRST = FUN1F (S)
```

FORTRAN IV. As in the case of variables, FORTRAN IV utilizes the TYPE statement for denoting the mode or type of the function. The available TYPE statements are:

```
INTEGER  FUNCTION  RAND (A)
REAL  FUNCTION  THRDF  (FIRSTF, I,J)
DOUBLE  PRECISION  FUNCTION  FIND(S (100))
COMPLEX  FUNCTION  CMULT (Z1, Z2)
LOGICAL  FUNCTION  THRUTH  (F (10, 10))
```

Since the name of a FUNCTION subprogram can carry back the result from the subprogram, FUNCTION subprogram names must be typed as in the above example. If the name of the function does not appear in a TYPE statement, the first letter of the name dictates the mode or type.

```
FUNCTION  LOOK (I, J, K)
```

The returning result would be integer since the first letter of LOOK is the letter L.

Main Program

```
COMPLEX  S1, S2,Y
COMMON  A, B, S1, S2
S1 = (2.137, − 1.375)
READ  1,S2
Y = CMULT
END
```

Subprogram

```
COMPLEX  FUNCTION  CMULT
COMPLEX  Z1, Z2
COMMON  R, S, Z1, Z2
T1 = REAL (Z1)        (Takes real part of a complex number.)
T2 = REAL (Z2)
T3 = AIMAG (Z1)        (Takes imaginary part of a complex number.)
T4 = AIMAG (Z2)
T5 = T1 * T2 − T3 * T4
T6 = T1 * T4 + T2 * T3
CMULT = (T5, T6)
RETURN
END
```

SUBROUTINE subprograms return the results via their arguments and not the name; therefore, to type a SUBROUTINE subprogram one needs only the regular TYPE statement.

```
SUBROUTINE BOB
DOUBLE PRECISION C, D
COMMON A, B, C, D
C = (D + 2.15371628435) ** 2.1
______
______
______
RETURN
END
```

In the above example the result is placed in the double-precision location, C, for return to the main program via the COMMON statement.

Built-in functions and mathematical subroutines (prewritten FUNCTION subprograms) are automatically typed by the FORTRAN IV compiler. Any additional mathematical routines must be typed by the programmer as previously illustrated by the examples. The available routines are similar to those available in FORTRAN II; for an exact listing of the available routines see the FORTRAN manual for your particular machine published by the computer company which manufactures the machine. A good programmer will always check to see the method used by a particular FORTRAN compiler for a mathematical routine before he makes use of the routine; the result could be a saving of time or a more accurate answer. For example, some versions of FORTRAN use the following method to evaluate complex multiplication: $Z_3 = Z_1 \cdot Z_2$, where Z_1 and Z_2 are complex numbers and Z_3 is the complex result.
First, the numbers $Z1$ and $Z2$ are converted to the form

$$Z1 = r_1\ (\cos\theta_1 + i\sin\theta_1) = r_1 e^{i\theta_1}$$

and

$$Z2 = r_2\ (\cos\theta_2 + i\sin\theta_2) = r_2 e^{i\theta_2}$$

then

$$Z1 * Z2 \text{ is calculated as } (r_1 e^{i\theta_1})(r_2 e^{i\theta_2}) = r_1 r_2 e^{i(\theta_1+\theta_2)}$$

Now there is a possibility that one of the products $(r_1 r_2)$ or $e^{i(\theta_1+\theta_2)}$ is much larger than the other; as a result, significance will be lost when the two are multiplied together in floating-point mode. To avoid this loss of accuracy, the programmer may write his own subroutine, say CMULT.

Z3 = CMULT (Z1, Z2)

This subroutine has already been given in a previous example.

5.6.8. Optional Return from Subprograms

FORTRAN IV allows the programmer a choice of statement upon return from the subprogram; in other words, the return to the main program need not be to the next executable statement following the CALL statement. Say that a decision must be made in a subprogram whether to follow the normal logic of the main program or to skip to another part of the main program. In a statistical analysis of sales figures, input figures which are so far out of line as to be suspect, must be handled separately.

```
        Main Program
        DIMENSION   A(1000)
        READ 107,N, (A (I), I = 1, N)
  107   FORMAT (I3/ (5 F 10.2))
        CALL STAT (A, N, R, T, 117S)
  102 { Special program to transform
        suspicious values
      { Continuation of main program using either
      { normal analyzed values from the sub-
  117 { program or values returned from the
      { subprogram which have been transformed
      { by the above special coding.
              ______
              ______
              ______
        END

        SUBROUTINE STAT (B, K, Z1, Z2, *)
        DIMENSION   B (1000)
              ______
              ______
              ______
        IF (B (I) - Z2) 20, 10, 10
   10   RETURN 1
        RETURN
        END
```

The statement, RETURN 1, refers to the first nonstandard return; the only nonstandard return is referred to the asterisk in the argument list of the SUBROUTINE statement. The asterisk used as an argument corresponds to the argument 117S, in the argument list of the CALL statement; the desired statement number must precede the letter S. The above example illustrates one nonstandard return and one normal return; it is possible to have many nonstandard returns by proceeding in the same way. The nonstandard return feature is not available in FORTRAN II.

5.6.9. Multiple Entry Points to Subprograms

Another feature available in FORTRAN IV and not in FORTRAN II, is the ENTRY statement. One subprogram may contain several parts; some places in the main programs may require the entire subprogram while other places in the main program may only require parts of the subprogram. If the programmer could enter the subprogram at several different points, he could utilize different parts of the subprogram; therefore, fewer subprograms would be required to solve the problem.

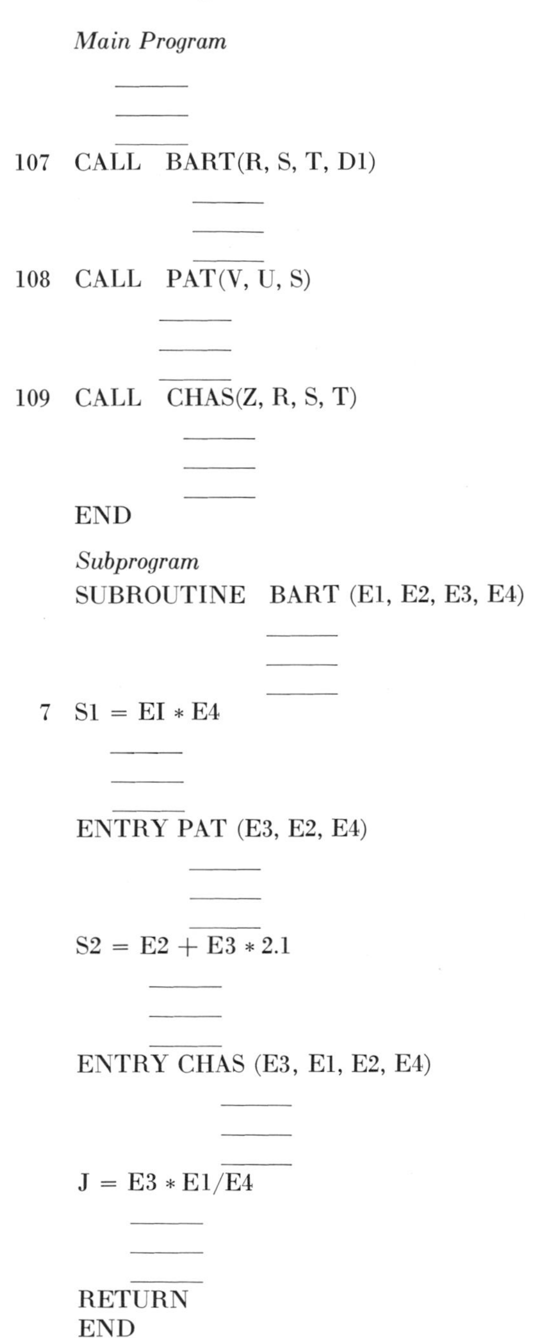

```
        Main Program
            ______
            ______
            ______
107     CALL   BART(R, S, T, D1)
                 ______
                 ______
                 ______
108     CALL   PAT(V, U, S)
               ______
               ______
               ______
109     CALL   CHAS(Z, R, S, T)
                 ______
                 ______
                 ______
        END
        Subprogram
        SUBROUTINE   BART (E1, E2, E3, E4)
                       ______
                       ______
                       ______
  7     S1 = EI * E4
            ______
            ______
            ______
        ENTRY PAT (E3, E2, E4)
                 ______
                 ______
                 ______
        S2 = E2 + E3 * 2.1
              ______
              ______
              ______
        ENTRY CHAS (E3, E1, E2, E4)
                     ______
                     ______
                     ______
        J = E3 * E1/E4
             ______
             ______
             ______
        RETURN
        END
```

Statement 107 transfers control to the first statement of the subprogram, statement 108 transfers control to the first entry point, and statement 109 transfers control to the second entry point. After control has been transferred to the first statement of the subprogram via statement 107, the entire subprogram will be executed; the ENTRY statements serve as nonexecutable statements (like a COMMENT statement) when the computer executes the program.

The number, order, and type of variables in the CALL statement must agree with the number, order, and type of variables in the ENTRY statement. It is important to realize that upon entry to the subprogram all variables serving as arguments in that ENTRY statement are redefined; that is, upon entering from statement 108, variables E3, E2, and E4 are redefined.

5.6.10. Variable Array Size in FORTRAN

Both FORTRAN II (the extended version) and FORTRAN IV provide the programmer with the ability to have variable dimensions for arrays appearing in subprograms. For a practical example, say that there is a subroutine available for multiplying two matrices:

Main Program

```
DIMENSION  A (10, 10), B (10, 10), C (10, 10)
                ______
                ______
                ______
CALL  MATMPY (A, B, C, 8, 10, 15)
                ______
                ______
                ______
END
```

Subprogram

```
SUBROUTINE  MATMPY (X, Y, Z, K, L, M)
DIMENSION  X (K,L), Y (L,M),Z (K, M)
                ______
                ______
                ______
RETURN
END
```

The dimensions K, L, and M, must not be such that the dimensions of the arrays in the main program, which must be constant integers, are exceeded.

5.7. Conclusion of FORTRAN

Two very important topics, which have not been stressed through the first five chapters, but which will be emphasized in the remaining three chapters, are checking of input data, examination of intermediate results, and documentation; because of the simplicity of the examples given thus far, only the flow chart was used for documentation. As the programs become more complex, more documentation will be needed so that someone trying to use a program other than his own can understand the type of input needed, the method of computation, the speed, the accuracy, the capability, and the output of the program.

Once again we remind the student that the material offered in the first five chapters should be taken as a guide to FORTRAN programming; for each different computer the rules may be slightly altered or some things may not be available. Therefore, the programmer should refer to the manufacturers specifications before programming a particular machine.

5.8. The FORMAC Language

FORMAC is an extension of the FORTRAN IV language: i.e., FORMAC contains all of the power of FORTRAN IV and provides additional capabilities in the area of algebraic manipulation of expressions. At the present time, FORMAC cannot work with double-precision or complex numbers.

5.8.1. Variables

In order to manipulate expressions, FORMAC must have the power to refer to an entire expression by a variable name; remember, in FORTRAN, a variable referenced a storage location which usually contained a numerical value (it was possible to use numbers as a code for symbols in FORTRAN, but this served no purpose, because FORTRAN possesses very little symbol manipulative power). There are two types of FORMAC variables: one variable represents entire expressions and the other variable represents single symbols (not necessarily numeric values).

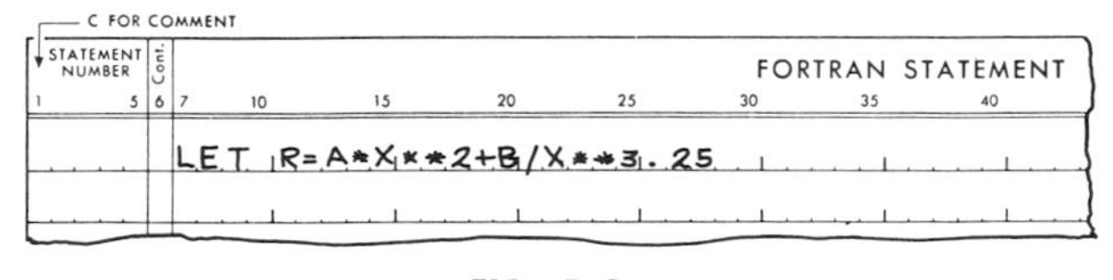

FIG. 5–21

R is the symbolic address of the memory location at which the expression begins. The total number of storage locations referenced by the variable R depends on the expression. If the expression was coded internally in binary coded decimal taking six binary bits per character, the first location of the locations referenced by the variable R would be as shown in Figure 5–22. Actually, expressions are not represented internally by their binary coded

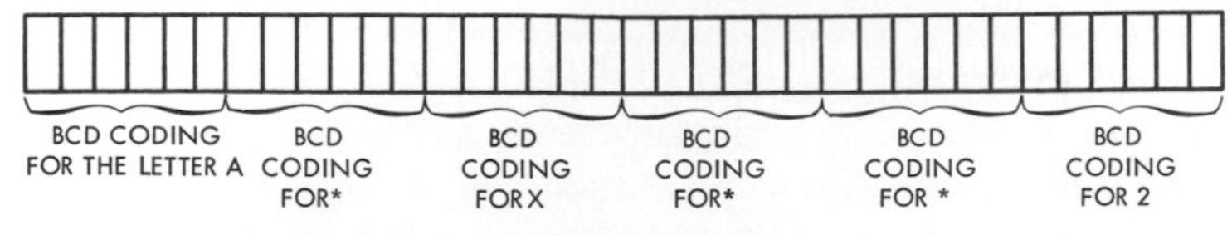

FIG. 5–22

decimal counterparts but by a much simpler representation; the programmer need not understand this internal representation, because the FORMAC compiler provides the ability to translate binary coded decimal information to the simpler coding and vice versa.

The word LET causes the FORMAC compiler to create an expression for a variable; a FORMAC variable which is not introduced by the LET statement is called an atomic variable (lowest level or most basic) and must appear in an ATOMIC statement.

```
ATOMIC   K, R (10), I, A, F
```

Atomic variables, if they are to be subscripted, must be dimensioned in the ATOMIC statement and should not appear in a DIMENSION statement; atomic variables must not appear to the left of the equal sign in a FORMAC statement; atomic variables (provided they are not subscripted) may be used as arguments in CALL statements to subroutines.

The mode of a FORMAC variable is determined by its first letter; like FORTRAN, if the first letter is I, J, K, L, M, or N, the variable is fixed point, if the first letter is any other letter, the variable is of floating-point mode. Unlike FORTRAN, FORMAC allows the programmer to use mixed-mode expressions; rules are provided for the determination of the mode. In this book all the rules of FORMAC will not be considered in detail, only the basic concept and power of FORMAC. In a FORMAC program both FORMAC and FORTRAN statements may be utilized throughout the program.

```
       ATOMIC   A, B, K, C (10)
    50 LET   Z = A*B*K+5
       READ   101, R,S,T,U
    30 LET   C (1) = U+K
    20 DO   10   I = 2, 10
       LET   C (I) = R * C (I−1)
    10 CONTINUE
    40 T3 = R * S + R
```

Statement 30 is a FORMAC statement which contains both FORMAC variables (K) and FORTRAN variables (U) on the right-hand side. Statement 20 is the regular FORTRAN DO statement. Notice that a DO loop cannot end on a FORMAC executable statement; all FORMAC executable statements start with the word LET, except for the ERASE and AUTSIM statements. Statement 40 is a typical FORTRAN arithmetic statement;

the value at location R is multiplied by the value at location S, and the result is added to the value in location T—the result of the entire calculation is placed in location T3. One may compare statement 40 with statement 50, a FORMAC statement, which gives a symbolic name or an address in the computer to the expression A*B*K+5.

FORTRAN operators have the same meaning when they appear in FORMAC expressions as in the FORTRAN language; i.e., +, −, *, /, **.

5.8.2. Functions

All the FORTRAN IV mathematical functions are still available; in addition, the FORMAC functions

FORMAC		FORTRAN
FMC EXP	Correspond to FORTRAN functions	EXP
FMC SIN		SIN
FMC COS		COS
FMC LOG		LOG
FMC ATN		ATN
FMC HTN		HTN

FORMAC functions accept FORMAC or FORTRAN expressions as arguments, whereas FORTRAN functions accept only FORTRAN expressions or constants as arguments. Four other functions are provided by FORMAC to simplify programming:

(1) FMCFAC (x) ≡ calculates the factorial of the FORMAC expression, X.

(2) FMCDFC (x) ≡ calculates the double factorial of the FORMAC expression, X.

(3) FMCOMB (x,y) ≡ calculates the combinatorial result of $\binom{X}{Y}$

(4) FMCDIF (X_1, Y_1, K_1, Y_2, K_2, . . . , Y_n, K_n) ≡ takes the derivative of expression X_1, first with respect to the FORMAC variable Y_1,—the differentiation takes place K_1 times (where K_1 gives a non-negative fixed point constant value); then the derivative is taken with respect to variable Y_2 — the differentiation takes place K_2 times; etc.

EXAMPLES—

(1) FMCFAC (R) ≡ cannot be evaluated until R takes on a numeric value; if R takes on the value 4, the value returned is

$$4 \cdot 3 \cdot 2 \cdot 1 = 24$$

(2) FMCDFC (8) = $8 \cdot 6 \cdot 4 \cdot 2 = 384$

(3) FMCOMB (A,B) = No value until A and C take on values. If A takes on the value 6, and B takes on the value 2, the value returned by the function is

$$\binom{6}{2} = \frac{6\,!}{2\,!\,(6-2)\,!} = \frac{6.5}{2.1} = 15$$

```
(4)     ATOMIC  X, T
        DEPEND (X/T)
        LET  B = A * FMCDIF (3*X**2, T, 1)
```

After execution of the above statements, location B contains the expression

A * 6 * X * FMCDIF (X, T, 1)

or

$$\left(6 * A * \frac{dX}{dT}\right) * X$$

The DEPEND statement offers the programmer a method of expressing implicit dependence between atomic variables (not LET variables or FORTRAN variables; i.e., those locations representing a numeric value). If the DEPEND statement was not included in the above example, the expression starting at location B would be A * 0.

5.8.3. Substitution

The programmer can substitute constants, variables, or expressions for other variables in expressions; he also has the ability to evaluate a particular expression for certain values of its parameters. For this purpose FORMAC provides the following statements:

SUBST = creates a new mathematical expression from the old mathematical expression by substituting other constants, variables, or expressions.

```
ATOMIC  C, D, E
LET  A = SUBST  B, (C, G), (D, R), (E, FMCDIF (2*X**3, X, 2))
```

In the FORMAC expression starting at location B, substitute the FORMAC expression starting at location G for the atomic variable C or the FORMAC function at location C, substitute the FORMAC expression starting at location R for the atomic variable at location D or the result of a FORMAC function (the result will be located at location D), etc. From this explanation, one can see that the letters enclosed in parenthesis represent pairs of parameters which take on the same values in certain FORMAC expressions.

```
ATOMIC  E, J, I, Z, L, X
READ  101, M,K
LET  A=2 * Z+ L ** 2
LET  G=M + 5 * K ** I
LET  B=4 * M + C ** 2/D + E ** 3
```

First substitute G for C in the expression starting in location B to get

4 * M + (M + 5 * K ** I) ** 2/D + E ** 3;

Then substitute R for D to get

4 * M + (M + 5 * K ** I) **2/ (2*Z+L ** 2) + E ** 3;

Then substitute the expression after operation of

FMCDIF (2 * X** 3, X, 2) for E;

in other words

6*X**2→12*X

goes into E to give

4 * M+(M+5 * K ** I) **2/(2*Z+L ** 2) + (12 * X) ** 3

Instead of listing the pairs of parameters the programmer can write the label of a list of pairs of parameters, if the parameter label has been previously defined.

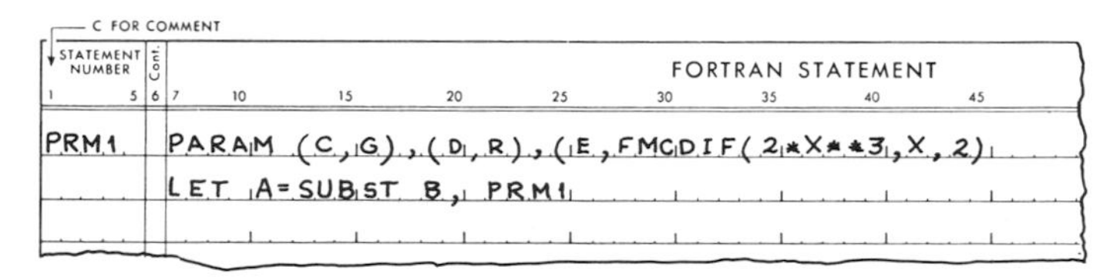

FIG. 5–23

where PRM1 is the label of the parameter statement (Figure 5–23).

5.8.4. Substitution Resulting in a FORTRAN Value

Another FORMAC statement which works in a way similar to the SUBST statement is the EVAL statement; the difference being that SUBST produces a FORMAC LET variable, whereas EVAL produces a FORTRAN value (i.e., numeric, as was discussed earlier in this section). It should be pointed out that the result of the SUBST statement may be numeric, but even in this case its internal coded form is that of a FORMAC LET variable.

```
          ATOMIC  R, F
LPRM      PARAM (R,3), (F, FMCDIF (*2 X ** 2, X, 2))
          LET   Z = 4 * R + F
          LET   B = SUBST Z,LPRM
```

the differential operator produces the result 4. Therefore, the expression becomes

4 * 3 + 4 = 16

Internally we have

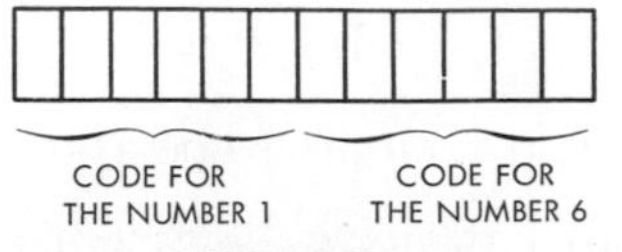

FIG. 5–24

or 16 is represented as a FORMAC expression (Figure 5–24).

If, however, the EVAL statement was used instead of the SUBST statement:

```
         ATOMIC R, F
LPRM     PARAM (R, 3), (F, FMCDIF (2 * X ** 2, X, 2))
         LET Z = 4 * R + F
212      B = EVAL Z, LPRM
```

The variable B is a FORTRAN floating-point variable; that is, it is a symbolic name of a storage location, which after execution of statement 212 contains the constant value 16 expressed as a floating-point number.

B

16	IN FLOATING POINT

Another example of the EVAL statement is

```
ATOMIC X, K
LET F = K ** 2/3 + X ** 2
LET Y = SUBST F, (K3), (X, FMCFAC(2))
AR = EVAL Y + X
```

The FORMAC compiler first uses the SUBST command to replace K and X by their corresponding elements in the parameter statement and then evaluates the FORMAC expression Y + X. In locations starting at Y we have

$$3 ** 2/3 + 2 ** 2$$

and at X, we have 2. The floating-point value 9 resides in location AR.

Computer memory limitations severly hinder an advanced programming language like FORMAC. To help save memory locations, FORMAC provides automatic simplification routines. Automatic simplification instructs the computer to collect like terms, combine constants, and similar operations.

```
LET Y = X + FMCDIF (X ** 2, X, 1)
Gives X + 2.X
Simplification gives 3.X
```

5.9. Automatic Simplification—The AUTSIM Statement

In addition to the normal operations performed after every executabel statement by the automatic simplification routine, the programmer can specify evaluation of the following through the use of the AUTSIM statement options:

AUTSIM	QUINT	*Evaluate all:* Factorial, double factorial, and combinatorial operators having constants, FORTRAN variables, or FORTRAN expressions which can be evaluated, as arguments.
	QNUM	*Evaluate all:* FMCSIN, FMCCOS, FMCLOG, FMCATN, FMCHTN, FMCEXP, and ** operators having the above list of operands as arguments.
	QNINT	Includes all operators of both QUINT and QNUM.
	ON	None of the operators in both QUINT and QNUM are to be evaluated.

If there is no AUTSIM statement, the QNINT option is assumed by the compiler.

```
      ATOMIC B
      READ 101, K
        ———
        ———
        ———
      AUTSIM ON
        ———
        ———
        ———
      LET R = 5.1 + 2.1 ** K * B/FMCFAC (K)
                  ———
                  ———
                  ———
```

Assume that the value read into location K is 2, then the expression starting at location R is

5.1 + 2.1 ** 2 * B/FMCFAC (K)

If instead of the option ON, the option QUINT had been used, the resulting expression would be

5.1 + 2.1 ** 2 * B/2

5.9.1. Input/Output—The ALGCON and BCDCON Statements

FORMAC expressions are coded internally for easier storage as was explained earlier in this section. FORTRAN input/output statements do not have the ability to translate from the regular binary coded decimal notation to the coded notation and back again; therefore, FORMAC must provide translation for FORMAC expressions which are input to the computer in binary coded decimal form and also for internally coded FORMAC expressions which are to be output in binary coded decimal form. For input FORMAC provides the ALGCON statement and for output the BCDCON statement.

```
      DIMENSION  B(10),C (5)
      READ  10,(B (I), I = 1, 10), N
 10   FORMAT (10 A 6 / I 2)
      ATOMIC R, S
         ______
         ______
         ______
      MI = 1
      LET K = EVAL (2 * S), (S, 3)
 50   LET C (MI) = ALGCON B (1), L
      MI = MI + 1
      IF (N - L) 40, 40, 50
 40           ______
              ______
              ______
```

The input cards might look as shown in Figure 5–25.

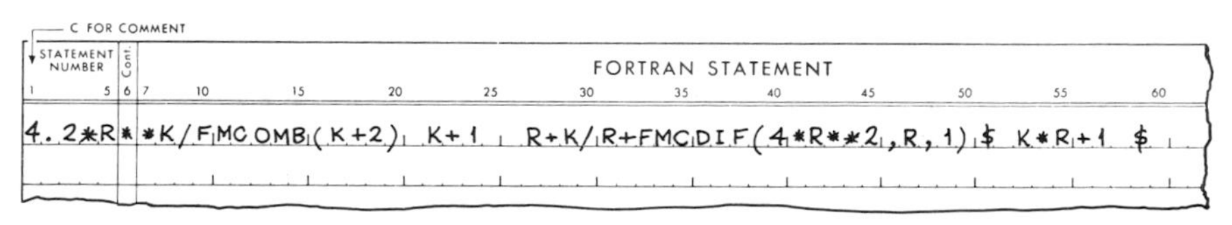

FIG. 5–25

Each FORMAC expression read in must end with a $ in binary coded decimal mode. Note that the A-type FORTRAN format is used because of the alphameric expressions. In the ALGCON statement, the FORTRAN variable B represents the array containing the FORMAC expression (s) in binary coded decimal mode. The fixed-point variable L either assumes the value zero or something else; the switch is set by the FORMAC compiler depending on whether the expression to be translated starts at the beginning of the B array or somewhere in the middle of the B array. In this way, although only one FORMAC expression can be translated for each execution of the ALGCON statement, many expressions held in the same array can be translated by the FORMAC compiler. The above example causes the FORMAC LET variables, C (1), C (2), and C (3) to take on these expressions:

Starting at location C (1), 4.2 * R ** 6/8.
at location C (2), $\underbrace{\text{R + 6./R + 8. * R}}_{\text{9. * R + 6/R}}$
at location C (3), 6. * R + 1

The BCDCON statement works in the same way as the ALGCON statement, only to translate from internal coding to binary coded decimal coding.

5.9.2. Further Simplification—The EXPAND Statement

Expression simplification beyond the automatic simplication described earlier and the AUTSIM options is available to the programmer via the EXPAND statement. The additions operations provided by the EXPAND statement are application of the distributive law, application of the multinomial theorem, and grouping an expression over a common denominator (not necessarily the lowest common denominator). The distributive law for multiplication with respect to addition is

$$a\ (b + c) = ab + ac$$

Evaluation of the expression $(x_1 + x_2 + \ldots + x_r)^n$ is found by adding all possible terms of the form

$$\left\{\begin{matrix} n \\ n_1,\ n_2,\ \ldots,\ n_r \end{matrix}\right\} x_1{}^{n_1}\ x_2{}^{n_2}\ x_3{}^{n_3}\ \ldots\ x_r{}^{n_r}$$

where

$$n_1 + n_2 + \ldots + n_r = n$$

and

$$(n_1,\ n_2,\ n_3,\ \ldots,\ n_r) = \frac{n!}{n_1!\ n_2!\ \ldots\ n_r!}$$

this is the multinomial theorem. For example, the expression $(x + y + z)^4$ would be evaluated as follows:

$$\left(\frac{4!}{4!}\right) x^4y^0z^0 + \left(\frac{4!}{4!}\right) x^0y^4z^0 + \left(\frac{4!}{4!}\right) x^0y^0z^4 + \left(\frac{4!}{3!1!}\right) x^3y^1z^0$$
$$+ \left(\frac{4!}{1!3!}\right) x^1y^3z^0 + \left(\frac{4!}{3!1!}\right) x^3y^0z^1 + \left(\frac{4!}{1!3!}\right) x^1y^0z^3$$
$$+ \left(\frac{4!}{3!1!}\right) x^0y^3z^1 + \left(\frac{4!}{!!3!}\right) x^0y^1z^3 + \left(\frac{4!}{2!2!}\right) x^2y^2z^0 + \left(\frac{4!}{2!2!}\right) x^0y^2z^2$$
$$+ \left(\frac{4!}{2!2!}\right) x^2y^0z^2 + \left(\frac{4!}{1!1!2!}\right) x^1y^1z^2 + \left(\frac{4!}{1!2!1!}\right) x^1y^2z^1 + \left(\frac{4!}{2!1!1!}\right) x^2y^1z^1$$
$$= x^4 + y^4 + z^4 + 4x^3y + 4xy^3 + 4x^3z + 4xz^3 + 4y^3z$$
$$+ 4_yz^3 + 6x^2y^2 + 6y^2z^2 + 6x^2z^2 + 12xyz^2 + 12xy^2z + 12x^2yz$$

```
ATOMIC  C,D, X
LET  A = EXPAND (C+D) ** 3 + C * (X−D)
```

After the above LET statement has been evaluated, the expression starting at location A will be

```
C ** 3. + 3. * C ** 2. * D + 3. * C * D ** 2.
    + D ** 3. + C * X − C * D
```

Automatic simplification will still be performed on the expanded expression if the expanded expression can be simplified.

```
ATOMIC  R, S, T
LET  Z = (R + S) * (R + T) / 2. + T * (1 + S) / U ** 2.
                                  + R ** 2. * (U + T) / U
LET  Y = EXPAND  Z, CODEM
```

Where CODEM indicates that there are any variables in the denominator of any part of the expression, a common denominator is desired by the programmer. Immediate expansion gives:

```
(R ** 2. + R * S + R * T + S * T) * (.5) + (T * 1. + T * S) * U ** (−2.)
    + (R ** 2. * U + R ** 2. * T) * U ** (−1.)
```

Simplification and creation of a common denominator gives:

```
(3* U** 2. * R ** 2. + U ** 2. * R * S + U ** 2. * R * T + U ** 2. * S * T +2. * T
  + 2. * T * S + 2. *R ** 2. * U + 2. * R ** 2. * T * U) ** (2. * U ** 2.) ** (−1)
```

which is

$$\frac{3 * U^2 * R^2 + U^2 * R * S + U^2 * R * T + U^2 * S * T + 2 * T + 2. * T * S + 2. * R^2 * T * U}{2. * U^2}$$

Instead of expanding an expression, the programmer may wish to factor or partition an expression, and doing so, he may want to obtain coefficients of variables in the expression. Because factoring of an expression is usually much more difficult than expanding of an expression, one might correctly assume that the factoring ability of FORMAC is of a limited nature.

```
ATOMIC  A, B, C, D
LET  Z = (A + B) * (C + D)
LET  Y = PART  Z, K
```

The FORMAC expression following the word PART (in this case, Z) is the expression to be divided up or partitioned; the expression starting in location Y is the subexpression which was cut off of the original expression. Removal of the expression Y from the original expression Z produces expression Y and another expression; this remaining expression is then moved into location Z—the original expression is therefore lost in the partitioning process. Different types of original expressions will be partitioned differently; a code indicating the type of partition is placed in the FORTRAN fixed-point variable, K. Successive partitioning can be applied to the remaining expression to reduce the expression to basic variables; when the last reduction has taken place, the set of locations starting at the address where the remaining expression has been residing now becomes available for further assignment (in FORMAC terms, the expression has been erased).

In the example given above, the expression starting at location Y is

A+B

and starting at location Z, the original has been replaced by the remaining expression,

C+D.

The number 5 is placed in location K because 5 is the code for factoring products. If the PART statement was used again with the expression starting at location Z as argument, we have

```
LET   F = PART   Z, L
```

where now F contains C and Z contains D; L contains 4, which is the code for factoring sums.

One more application of the PART statement, such as LET A1 = PART Z, M results in A1 containing the variable D and Z being freed (erased) for other expressions. The code 2 is placed in M.

A program to accomplish the same type of factoring can be written in loop form.

```
      DIMENSION R (20)
      ATOMIC   A,B,C,D
      LET   Z = (A + B) * (C + D)
      DO   10 I = 1, 20
      LET   R (I) = PART Z, K
      IF(K − 17)10, 30, 30
   10 CONTINUE
   30 _____
      _____
      _____
```

When the PART command is applied to an original expression which has been erased from core storage, the variable K takes on the value 17; the factoring of all other expressions result in a value for K which is from 1 to 16. This is to say, in the statement

```
LET   R(I) = PART Z, K
```

when the FORMAC expression starting at R (I) has been erased, the next execution of the PART command results in the value 17 going into location K. The results from the above program are

```
1st time through loop—  R (1) contains  A + B
                        Z  contains  C + D
                        K  contains  5
Branch to continue loop—
2nd time through loop—  R (2)  contains C
                        Z  contains D
                        K  contains 4
Branch to continue loop—
3rd time through loop—  R (3) contains D
                        Z  contains  nothing  (original variable is erased)
                        K  contains  2
4th time through loop—  R (4)  contains  nothing
                        Z  contains  nothing
                        K  contains  17
loop ends, branch to statement 30 to continue the program.
```

FORMAC provides the programmer the power to find the coefficients of variables or functions via the COEFF statement.

```
ATOMIC  X
LET  R = 2 * X ** 3 + F * X ** 2
LET  A = COEFF R, X ** 3, Z,
Another FORTRAN variable may be specified here.
```

In the FORMAC expression R, the programmer desires to have the coefficient of the FORMAC variable X (in place of an atomic variable, one could specify a FORMAC function of the type FMCSIN, FMCCOS, . . . , FMCHTN, FMCFAC, the type FMCDFC, FMCOMB, FMCDIF and its corresponding argument(s)) placed in the locations starting at A (this is a FORMAC LET variable); the next highest power of the specified variable is placed in the FORTRAN variable Z.

If the programmer had written

```
LET  A = COEFF R, X ** 3, Z, Z2
```

then the next lowest power of the specified variable would be placed in location Z 2. In many cases, both Z and Z 2 would contain the same thing, because there is only one power of the variable remaining. In the foregoing example, the number 2 goes into the location A as a FORMAC expression; i.e., in coded form. The number 2 also goes into the FORTRAN variable Z, because the next highest power of the variable X is 2.

For X ** 0, the next highest power is actually the lowest integer exponent and the next lowest power is the highest integer exponent.

```
DIMENSION  COF(10)
ATOMIC  Y, K
```

```
        LET   POWER = 5.2 * Y ** 7 + R * Y ** 2
                      + 3.2 * FMCFAC (K) + 3.721
                      + 3.* Y + 4.1 * Y ** (-4)
        L = 0
        LI = 1
    20  LET   COF (LI) = COEFF POWER, X ** L, X1, X2
        L = X2
        LI = LI + 1
        IF (L - 0) 20, 30, 20
    30  ------
        ------
        ------
```

The first time through the loop gives 0 as the contents of FORTRAN fixed-point variable L, the FORMAC expression 3.2*FMCFAC (K)+3.721 starting in location COF (1) because this expression does not contain the variable Y (i.e., Y ** 0), −4. as the contents of the FORTRAN variable X1 because next highest after X ** 0 actually gives the lowest integer power which is −4, and the floating-point constant 7. goes into the FORTRAN floating-point variable X2, because the next lowest power after X ** 0 results in the highest integer power of Y in the given expression. After the first execution of the COEFF statement the following results hold:

Loop Index	
2	L contains 7, COF (2) contains the FORMAC expression 5.2, X1 contains 0., X2 contains 2.
3	L contains 2, COF (3) contains R, X1 contains 7., (No higher power than 12 exists), X2 contains 1.
4	L contains 1, COF (4) contains 3., X1 contains 2. X2 contains −4. (The zero power of Y is not counted here)
5	L contains −4, COF (5) contains 4.1, X1 contains 1., X2 contains 0.

Notice that X2 goes from highest to lowest (without going to zero), then to zero; thus, the loop technique can be used to give all the coefficients.

Other FORMAC statements with associated subroutines (FORMAC statements are translated to FORTRAN IV CALL statements to subroutines added to the regular FORTRAN IV subroutines) simplify programming by providing a counting, matching, searching, and ordering FORMAC expression.

5.9.4. Counting—The CENSUS Statement

The CENSUS statement counts the number of terms or factors in an expression to give a constant which is then placed in a FORTRAN variable location.

```
ATOMIC  X,Y,K
LET  JACK = 2 * X ** 3 + Y * X * FMCFAC (K)
LET  COUNT = CENSUS (JACK, FT, 4)
```

The result in COUNT is 3; FT referring to the counting being on factors combined by addition (the number 4).

5.9.5. Mathematical Equivalence—The MATCH Statement

Two FORMAC expressions may be compared for either identity or mathematical equivalence by the MATCH statement, with the result, being either true or false, placed in a FORTRAN logical variable. The code to test for identity is ID; that for mathematical equivalence is EQ, with the programmer having the ability to specify the tolerance within which the two expressions must come to be considered equivalent.

```
     ATOMIC X, Y, Y1
     LOGICAL R, S, Q
     LET  Z = X * (Y + Y1)
     LET  T = X * Y + X * Y1
     LET  R = MATCH  ID, Z, T
     LET  U = EXPAND  Z
     LET  S = MATCH  ID, U, T
  10 LET  Q = MATCH  EQ, 0., Z, T
     ______
     ______
     ______
```

In order to be identical, two expressions must match symbol for symbol; therefore, in the above example the logical variable R takes on the value FALSE. However, when the FORMAC expression starting at location Z is expanded by the distributive law, it matches identically with the FORMAC expression starting at location T; thus, the logical variable S takes on the value TRUE in the above example. Notice that the unexpanded expression at Z is matched with the expanded expression at T in statement 10; because these two are mathematically equivalent to a tolerance of zero, the logical variable Q takes on the value TRUE. To test for mathematical equivalence FORMAC utilizes any routines needed to bring the two expressions to common terms (such as, EXPAND, EVAL, SUBST, etc.). The ordering of the expressions in the identical match test does not depend on the ordering of the expression (i.e., A + B is identical to B + A) because the FORMAC compiler reorders expressions into a certain order (lexicographic) where the expression is coded for internal storage.

To search for the appearance or dependence of one or all of a list of FORMAC atomic variables or FORMAC functional expressions (i.e., the FORMAC operators FMCFAC, FMCSIN, FMCDIF, etc., applied to a

FORMAC expression); appearance is considered to be the explicit appearance in the FORMAC expression while dependence also includes implicit relation via a DEPEND statement.

```
    ATOMIC  A, B, D, E
    DEPEND (D/E)
1   LET   R = A + B * FMCFAC (K) + D ** 2
2   LET   S = FIND R, APP, ALL, A, B,D,E
3   LET   T = FIND R, APP, ONE, A, B, D, E
4   LET   U = FIND R, DEP, ALL, A,B,D,E
```

The variable on the left-hand side of the equals sign in the LET statement using the FIND command is a FORTRAN logical variable; a TRUE value implies dependence or appearance as specified in the statement—a FALSE value implies no dependence or appearance. In the above example, the logical variable S takes on the value, FALSE, after execution of statement 2 because E does not appear explicitly in expression R; but T takes on the value TRUE in statement 3 because the FIND command states that only one of the variables A, B, D, or E, must appear explicitly in expression R. After execution of statement 4 the variable U takes on the value TRUE because the variable E, although not appearing explicitly in expression R depends on variable D (E appears in the DEPEND statement with D); therefore the variables A,B,D, and E appear either explicitly or implicitly in expression R.

5.9.6. Order of Factors for Output—The ORDER Statement

Before printing (BCDCON) or dumping (FMCDMP), the programmer may wish to specify a particular order of factors in a product or terms in a sum; FORMAC provides the order statement for this purpose.

```
ATOMIC  Y, Z
LET   R = ORDER   Z*Y ** 2 + 3 * Y * Z ** 2 +Y ** 3 *Z * 2.1, INC, (X)
```

The resulting expression starting at R will be

```
3 * Z ** 2 * Y + Z * Y ** 2 + 2.1 * Z * Y ** 3
```

because the programmer asked for the ordering to be on increasing powers of the variable X.

5.9.7. Preservation of Storage—The ERASE Statement

A compiler which operates on expressions will necessarily take a great deal of the core storage space of the computer; therefore, it is necessary for the programmer to tell the compiler when an expression is no longer needed so that the compiler can use that space again. The ERASE statement permits the programmer to give a signal to the compiler when certain expressions are no longer needed to solve the problem.

ERASE A, B, C, D, E

where A, B, C, D, and E are all LET variables.

To help the programmer debug his program, FORMAC provides the FMCDMPstatement. The programmer receives the address, BCD name, mode, numeric value (if a FORTRAN variable), and atomic or LET identification (if a FORMAC variable). Options exist as to when the dump is to take place, the subroutines desired, which type of variables, and the form of the FORMAC variables.

For a more detailed discussion of the FORMAC rules, see IBM FORMAC reference manual.[1] This discussion of FORMAC is meant only to throw some light on the possible extensions of FORTRAN. The FORMAC compiler, developed by IBM and the Massachusetts Institute of Technology is presently used only in a few installations and can be regarded as experimental. For further information, contact IBM.

FORMAC Executable Statements

ALGCON	ERASE	LET
AUTSIM	EVAL	MATCH
BCDCON	EXPAND	PART
CENSUS	FIND	SUBST
COEFF		ORDER

Problems

5.1. Write a FORTRAN IV program to find the hyperbolic cosine of a complex variable z; do not use the complex exponential function. The hyperbolic cosine of z is defined as

$$\cos h\ z = \frac{e^z + e^{-z}}{2}.$$

5.2. The TVRAT company has sent out questionnaires to 1,000 selected viewers; among the questions to be answered was whether these viewers had their TV sets on at a certain time of the evening and at a certain date. If the sets were on, the viewers were asked to indicate which of 4 channels was being viewed and whether or not the commercial was watched. The questionnaire consisted of a card which was to be marked as follows:

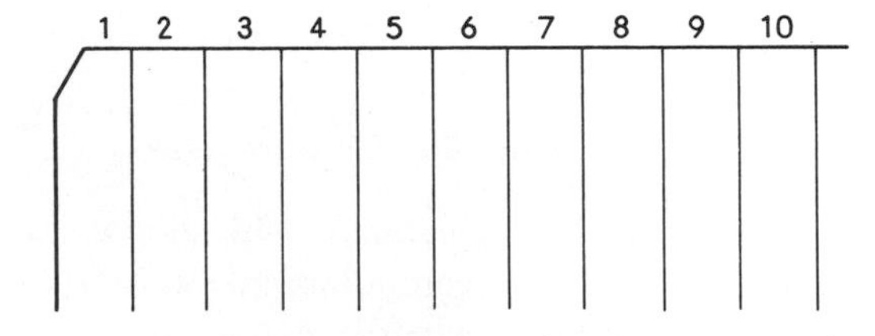

[1] Share General Program Library, FORMAC 7090R2 IBM0016; 1965.

The instructions given were as follows:

Mark Column 1, "T" if the TV set was on; if off, leave the first 6 columns blank. Mark one of columns 2, 3, 4, or 5 with a "T" if the following channel was on—

Channel 2	column 2 ≡ T
Channel 5	column 3 ≡ T
Channel 7	column 4 ≡ T
Channel 9	column 5 ≡ T

ONLY MARK ONE OF THESE 4 COLUMNS.

If you watched the commercial, mark a "T" in column 6; otherwise, leave column 6 blank. If column 6 is marked, then make some comment as to the value of the commercial by the following code:

Rating	*Column to be marked "T"*
Superior	Column 7
Good	Column 8
Fair	Column 9
Would have left the TV set for a snack, but was too lazy	Column 10

Write a FORTRAN program to summarize the questionnaires in the following groups:

Total number of Questionnaires ______
Total people who watched TV ______
People who watched Channel 2 ______
Watched commercial ______
Commercial rating
A ______
B ______
C ______
D ______
People who watched Channel 5 ______
Watched commercial ______
Commercial rating
A ______
B ______
C ______
D ______
People who watched Channel 7 ______
Watched commercial ______
Commercial rating
A ______
B ______
C ______
D ______

People who watched Channel 9 ________
Watched commercial ________
Commercial rating
A ______
B ______
C ______
D ______

5.3. Use Boolean algebra and FORTRAN IV to write a program which will help doctors to get a fast breakdown on the number of patients with symtoms A, B, C, or D who had ailments X, Y, Z. It is not possible for a patient who has A and B to have symptom C; also it is not possible to have symptom D without having symptom B.

Part of the problem will be design of the card format on which the ailments and symptoms are recorded by the hospital.

5.4. Explain how the FORTRAN II and IV compilers set up storage locations where the following sequences of COMMON and EQUIVALENCE statements are used.

a)
```
COMMON        A,B,C
DIMENSION     S (3)
EQUIVALENCE   (B,S)
```
b)
```
COMMON        (A,B)
DOUBLE PRECISION (D)
DIMENSION C (2)
EQUIVALENCE (C (1), D), (B,C (2))
```
c)
```
COMMON        A, B, C
COMPLEX       Z1, Z2
DIMENSION     R (2)
EQUIVALENCE   (Z1, R(1)), (B, R(1))
```

5.5. Write a FORTRAN IV program that finds all prime numbers[2] between 1 and 100,000. There are 9,593 primes assuming that 1 is a prime number. Use tape unit number 3 as a scratch tape to store intermediate results. Print the answers 20 numbers per line, 50 lines per page.

Write a flow chart showing one box for each major operation on the program. Give a detailed analysis of each box.

Description of the Program

First, all odd numbers between 1 and 40,000 are scored in memory. All multiples of an odd number J are canceled, except J itself. The numbers left in that array are primes. In this way all primes between 1 and 40,000 are calculated. These primes are written on tape number 3.

Now, the first 67 primes are stored in the array NSAVE. The reason for this is that the prime number, 62 is the closest prime to the square root of 80,000. Next, the odd numbers between 40,000 and 80,000 are scored in core, and all numbers which are multiple of any prime less than $\sqrt{80{,}000}$ are canceled. The numbers left are primes, which are written on tape number 3. The same procedure is repeated, but

[2] A prime number is a number whose only factor is 1.

this time the odd numbers between 80,000 and 100,000 are divided by all primes less than $\sqrt{100,000}$. The prime number 67 is the closest prime to $\sqrt{100,000}$. The results are written on tape 3, this tape is rewound and the results are printed.

5.6. A company records its transactions on punched cards which also show the month in which the transactions took place. Information on the day, month, and year is punched in columns 75–80.

Write a program to sort the cards in ascending order by month and then print the information on the card and the date in which the transaction occurred (i.e., print in the new order). Allow the number of cards which can be entered to be quite large.

5.7. Assume that you have a subroutine written in FORTRAN IV which takes the derivative of a function and evaluates the resulting derivative at a given point.

Problem: Demonstrate the method by which a programmer can send one of many different functions to the subroutine, DERIV, and obtain numerical values in return. In other words, specify several different functions in the main program and then show the FORTRAN IV CALL statement and the first statement of the subroutine DERIV.

5.8. Using FORTRAN IV, is it much more difficult to return the resulting function (after differentiation) than to return the value as required in problem 5.7? How would the use of FORMAC alleviate both problems (Discuss)?

5.9. Given the following network:

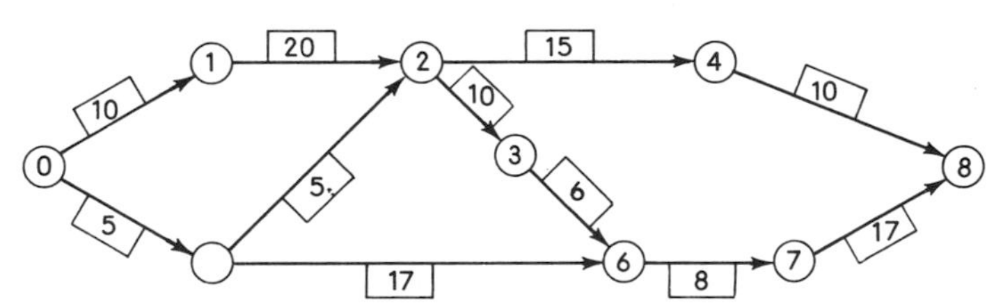

Write a FORTRAN IV program which will obtain the shortest path where the figures on the arrows are miles between the nodes. If it is impossible to reach one node from another node, place a very large mileage figure on the arrow between these two nodes; for example, (6) to (8). One way of expressing the above problem would be to write an array having nine rows and nine columns, where a_{ij} is the mileage from node i to node j; the diagonal elements should be very large to eliminate the possibility of going from node i to node i.

$$
\begin{array}{cccccc}
a_{11} & a_{12} & \cdots & a_{1j} & \cdots & a_{1n} \\
a_{21} & a_{22} & \cdots & a_{2j} & \cdots & a_{2n} \\
\cdot & \cdot & & \cdot & & \cdot \\
\cdot & \cdot & & \cdot & & \cdot \\
\cdot & \cdot & & \cdot & & \cdot \\
a_{i1} & a_{i2} & \cdots & a_{ij} & \cdots & a_{in} \\
\cdot & \cdot & & \cdot & & \cdot \\
\cdot & \cdot & & \cdot & & \cdot \\
\cdot & \cdot & & \cdot & & \cdot \\
a_{nj} & a_{n2} & \cdots & a_{nj} & \cdots & a_{nn}
\end{array}
$$

Now, to solve the above problem, one could examine all possible routes and take the one with the lowest total sum of miles; however, this would require a considerable amount of time.

Instead of considering all possible routes (including the impossible ones), construct a truth table, such as the following:

	0	1	2	3	4	5	6	7	8
0	F	T	F	F	F	T	F	F	F
1	F	F	T	F	F	F	F	F	F
2	F	F	F	T	T	F	F	F	F
3	F	F	F	F	F	F	T	F	F
4	F	F	F	F	F	F	F	F	T
5	F	F	T	F	F	F	T	F	F
6	F	F	F	F	F	F	F	T	F
7	F	F	F	F	F	F	F	F	T
8	F	F	F	F	F	F	F	F	F

A T represents a possible path from node x to node y if we use the nomenclature, a_{xy}; a_{yx} represents a possible path from y to x. The idea is to start at row 1 column 8 and go down column 8 until a "T" is found.

Record the number in location (k, 8) of the matrix of values; continue down column 8 until another T is encountered and record the number in the corresponding location of the matrix of values. Continue this process until there are no more T values in column 8.

Thus far, we have recorded all possible paths to node 8. For each of the T values, in this case rows 4 and 7, trace back for possible paths eventually leading to node 8.

Going one step further, we can examine column 7 to see that only row 6 contains a T value; implying that node 7 may only be reached from node 6. Therefore, we have a path from node 6 to node 8 at a total mileage of $a_{67}+a_{78}=8+17 = 25$.

An examination of column 4 reveals only one T value, that being in row 2. Thus, a second possible path to node 8 is via nodes 2 and 4 at a total mileage of $a_{24}+a_{48} = 15+10 = 25$.

To show the technique, consider the possible paths to node 6 by examining column 6; the two possibilities are node 3 and node 5. The total mileage from node 3 to node 8 is the mileage from node 3 to node 6, a_{36}, plus the mileage from node 6 to node 8, a_{68}; total mileage is $a_{36}+a_{68} = 6+25 = 31$.

Node 3 may only be reached from node 2, a distance of 10 miles. At this point we can decide which path from node 2 to node 8 is the shortest; compare the path 2, 4, 8, a total of 25 miles with the path 2,3,6,7,8, a total of 41 miles. Therefore, if we are at node 2 we will take the path 2, 4, 8.

Continue in this manner until the optimal solution has been reached.

The program should handle up to 10 nodes.[3]

5.10. For some of the programs given in Chapters 2, 3, and 4, modify the input/output statements so that these programs may now be processed by the FORTRAN IV compiler. Make all other necessary changes, such as double-precision and complex numbers, interaction between COMMON and EQUIVALENCE statements, utilization of SENSE SWITCHES and SENSE LIGHTS, and handling of logical instructions.

Can these programs be improved through the use of FORTRAN IV?

---

[3] For a method of handling the above problem with recursive functions and tables; see R. E. Bellman and S. E. Dreyfus, *Applications of Dynamic Programming* (Princeton, N.J.: Princeton University Press.)

6. Introduction to Numerical Methods

6.1. Approximate and Direct Methods

Many mathematical problems are either too difficult to lend themselves. to a direct answer or can be answered directly only with a great deal of work. To illustrate a direct answer to a problem, consider the problem of finding a root of the equation:

$$x^2 + 3\,x + 2 = 0\,,$$

the familiar quadratic formula gives:

$$x = \frac{-3 \pm \sqrt{9-8}}{2} = \frac{-3+1}{2} = -1$$

and

$$\frac{-3-1}{2} = -2\,.$$

One root is -1 and the other root is -2. The above problem is an example of a problem which can be solved directly; i.e., there is no approximation involved in obtaining the answer. However, someone may now ask: "If the above problem is to be solved by a digital computer, how does the computer take the square root of the coefficients, $b^2 - 4ac$, where b is the coefficient of the variable raised to the first power, a is the coefficient of the variable raised to second power, and c is the coefficient of the variable raised to the zero power (the constant term)." One obvious way to evaluate the square root of some number h, is to take the logarithm to the base 10. For the above example,

$$\sqrt{b^2 - 4ac} = \sqrt{1};$$
$$\text{Let} \qquad Y = \sqrt{b^2 - 4ac}$$
$$= \sqrt{1}$$

take logarithms of both sides to get:

$$\log Y = \tfrac{1}{2} \log 1$$
$$= \tfrac{1}{2} (0)$$
$$= 0$$

because the log of 1 equals 0—Now $Y = 1$, because 1 is the antilogarithm of 0.

Every high school mathematics student knows that the logarithm, to the base 10, of the number 1 is 0, so the problem was trivial; however, instead of the problem being to find the root of the equation $x^2 + 3x + 2 = 0$, consider the problem of finding the roots of the equation $x^2 + 5x - 2 = 0$. In this case $a = 1$, $b = 5$, and $c = -2$; therefore the quantity $b^2 - 4ac = 25 - 8 = 17$. To solve for the roots of the quadratic equation via the quadratic formula,

$$\frac{-b \pm \sqrt{b^2 - 4ac},}{2a}$$

one must first evaluate the square root of 17 (of course, the square root of 17 will be an unending decimal because 17 is an irrational number—the reader must realize that since the computer carries only a finite number of decimal places, the number will have to cut off at some point—like the number $\sqrt{2}$ would have to be cut off at 1.414 if each storage position could contain four decimal digits).

Let $Y = \sqrt{b^2 - 4ac} = \sqrt{17}$. Taking logarithms of both sides of the equation yields:

$$\log Y = \tfrac{1}{2} \log 17$$
$$= \tfrac{1}{2} (1.2304)$$
$$\log Y = .6152$$
$$\therefore Y = 4.123$$

From the above examples, one can see that to obtain the roots of a quadratic equation by the direct method involving the quadratic formula, one should be able to take the square root of a number or the logarithm of a number.[1] If the programmer desires to use logarithms, he faces two choices: (1) Read a table of logarithms into the machine and write a routine by which the computer can look up the logarithm of a number and, given the

[1] Not strictly true; odd-integer method does not require it but is time consuming.

logarithm of a number, find the number. A simple version of such a program might be the following:

```
      READ(5,7)(A(I),I=1,5000)
    7 FORMAT (10F8.4)
```

Here the computer is instructed to read the logarithms of 5,000 numbers from tape unit 5; presumably, these logarithms (to some base, say, 10) were taken out of table in some book and placed on the tape. To find the logarithm of a number, say, N, the program would be

$$\text{ALLQ} = \text{A (N)}$$

If some base other than the one in the table were needed, the table value must be multiplied by some conversion factor. Given the logarithm of some number N, the process of locating the number entails a time-consuming search through the table and in all likelihood would also necessitate the use of linear interpolation between values in the table. (2) The second possibility would be to read a table of square roots of numbers into the computer. In both cases a great deal of internal memory space is wasted in addition to the time to look up the values. Other problems to be considered are the size of the table and the desired accuracy; some applications might require the logarithm accurate to 5 places while another application might require the logarithm accurate to 15 places—to satisfy all requirements one might need a table of logarithms accurate to 20 places, again using up more core space than necessary if one could vary the accuracy.

Fortunately, there are methods available utilizing computers which can quickly generate the logarithm of a number to as many places as is desired while taking up very little computer memory space. These methods will be discussed later; in the meantime consider the square root of a number; say the number is N.

$$x^2 - N = 0; x^2 = N; x = \sqrt{N}$$

To solve this problem we will now introduce a method which can be used to find a real root of a polynomial with real coefficients (the method will find complex roots if the polynomial possesses complex coefficients). A root occurs where the graph of $f(x)$ crosses the X-axis; i.e., where $f(x) = 0$. A first guess at the root is at $x = a$; this guess might have come from a prior knowledge of the problem or from a graphical examination. From this preliminary graph of the function, we can say that the root lies between, say 3 and 4, because the sign of $f(x)$ changes in this range (Fig. 6–2); it can be proved that if the function, $f(x)$, is continuous in the interval a to b and the sign of $f(x)$ changes from a to b, there exists at least one root in the interval (since it is possible to have a function of the type shown in Figure 6–3 there may exist more than one root in the interval). In this case, a could have the value 3. Notice (Fig. 6–1) that the distance on the X-axis between

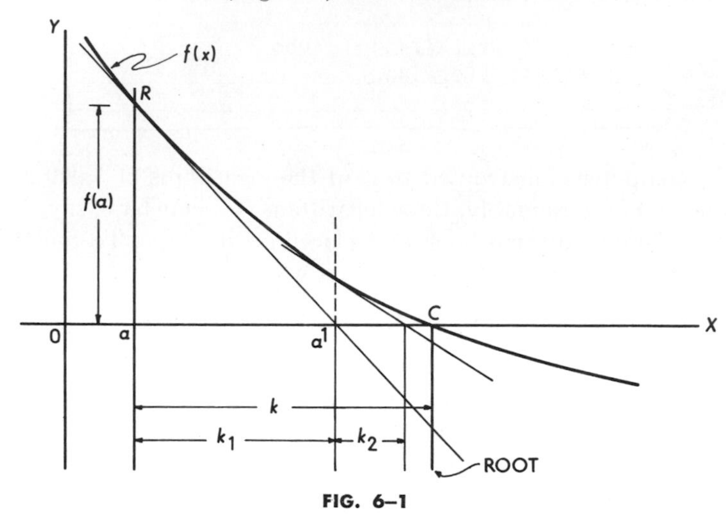

FIG. 6–1

$x = a$ and the point at which $f(x)$ crosses the X-axis (C), is denoted by the letter k; therefore, if r is one root of $f(x)$, $r = a + k$. Draw the tangent to the curve at a; the tangent crosses the X-axis at a^1. The tangent of the angle aa^1R is $Ra/aa^1 = f(a)/aa^1$. The tangent of the angle ca^1R is therefore

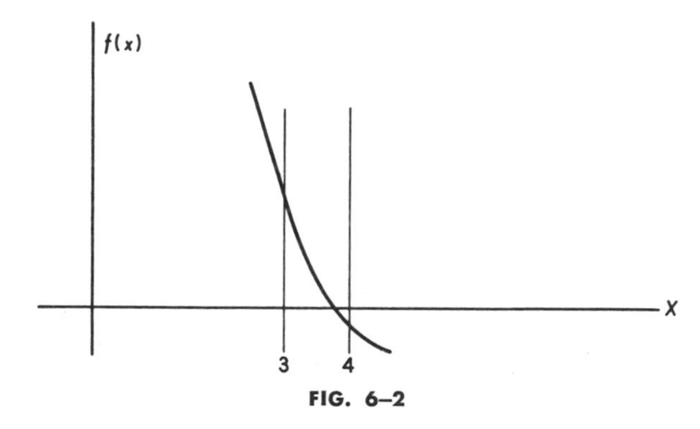

FIG. 6–2

$-f(a)/aa^1$ since $\angle ca^1R = 180° - \angle aa^1R$. However, the tangent of the angle ca^1R is also equal to the value of the first derivative of the function, $f(x)$, at the point $x = a$. Consequently, if $f'(x)$ denotes the derivative of $f(x)$,

$$f'(a) = \frac{-f(a)}{aa^1} \quad \text{or} \quad aa^1 = \frac{-f(a)}{f'(a)}$$

If we denote aa^1 by k_1, then $a^1 = k_1 + a$. Now the same procedure can be repeated using a^1 as an approximation to the root r. In other words, use a^1 to get k_2; then $k_1 + k_2$ is the second approximation to k, the real error in the first approximation of r. We then obtain $a^2 = a^1 + k_2$, the second approximation of r.

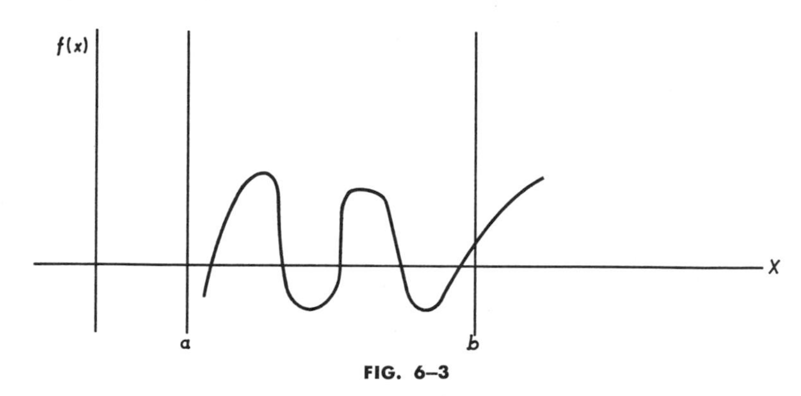

FIG. 6–3

In general, $a^{n+1} = k_n + a^n$, where a^{n+1} is x_{n+1}, or the $n + 1$ st approximation to a root of the equation, $f(x) = 0$; a_n is x_n, or the nth approximation to a root of the equation $f(x) = 0$; and $k_n = \dfrac{f(a_n)}{f'(a_n)}$. By continuing the method, one may get very close (approach C as a limit) to the point *C;* no matter how long the process continues; i.e., no matter how large n becomes, $k_n \neq k$. The methods of tangents (Newton's Method) fails if the graph of the function is parallel to the X = axis at $x = a$.

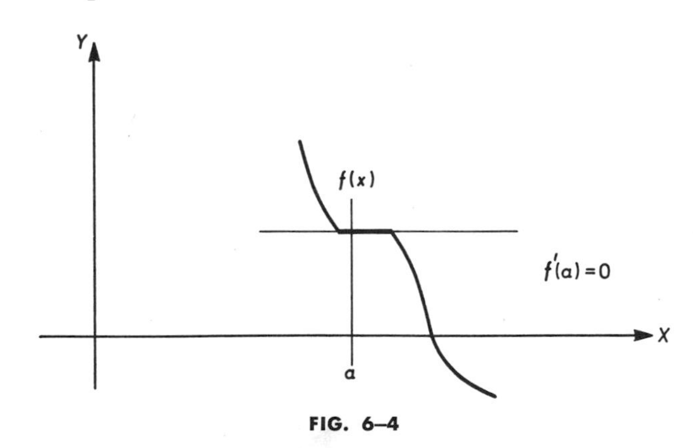

FIG. 6–4

This will occur when the first derivative of the function with respect to x at a is zero causing $\dfrac{f(x)}{f'(x)}$ to be indeterminate at $x = a$. Another cause of trouble would be a function whose graph looked like the following:

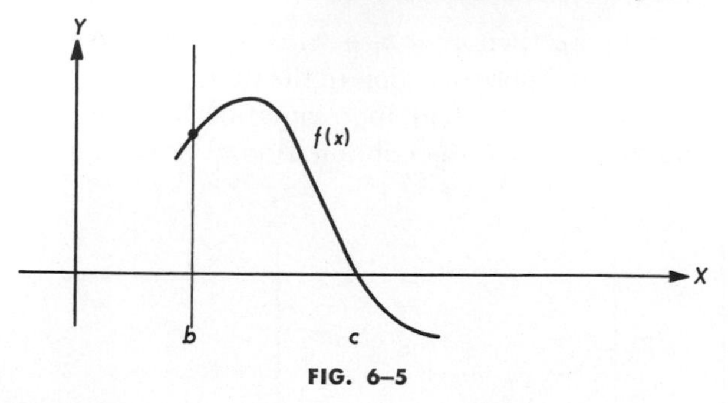

FIG. 6–5

An initial approximation of $x = b$ would cause the method to be divergent instead of converging to the root of the function at $x = c$.

Let us now apply this method to find the square root of N, or to find a root of the equation,

$$f(x) = x^2 - N = 0 .$$
$$f(a_n) = a_n^2 - N$$
$$f'(x)_{a_n} = (2x)_{a_n} = 2a_n$$
$$x_{n+1} = x_n - \frac{f(a_n)}{f'(a_n)} \text{ becomes}$$
$$x_{n+1} = x_n - \frac{(a_n^2 - N)}{2a_n}$$

Now

$$a_n = x_n \text{ so}$$
$$x_{n+1} = x_n - \frac{x_n^2 - N}{2x_n}$$
$$x_{n+1} = \frac{2x_n^2 - x_n^2 + N}{2x_n}$$
$$= \frac{x_n^2 + N}{2x_n}$$
$$= \tfrac{1}{2}(x_n + Nx_n^{-1})$$

Denoting the starting value (obtained from prior knowledge or graphical means) as x_0, one may obtain the next approximation through the use of the general formula:

$$x_1 = \frac{x_0^2 + N}{2x_0}$$

A program will be written to illustrate this method, but first the reader may benefit by considering this approximation to the root in steps via a graph. The graphs of the two functions, $f_1(x) = x$, and $f_2(x) = \frac{x^2 + N}{2x}$, intersect

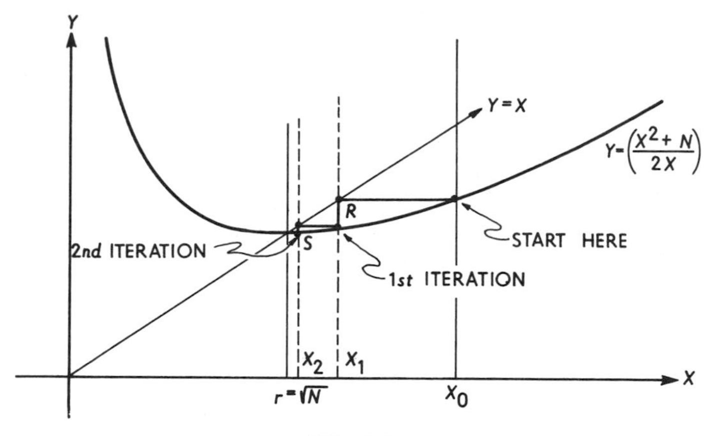

FIG. 6–6

at the point $x = r$ which is the square root of N; the reader may actually equate $f_1(x)$ and $f_2(x)$ and see that the root of the function $x^2 - N = 0$ actually lies at the intersection of $f_1(x)$ and $f_2(x)$.

$$x = \frac{x^2 + N}{2x},$$

$$2x^2 = x^2 + N,$$

$$2x^2 - x^2 = x^2 = N,$$

$$\text{or } x = \sqrt{N}$$

Letting x_0 be the initial approximation to the root, $r = N$,

$$x_1 = \frac{x_0{}^2 + N}{2x_0},$$

this is the first step or iteration to the point R on the graph and consists of moving to the function $y = x$ and substitution of the new value of x into the function

$$y = \frac{(x^2 + N)}{(2x)}$$

Then

$$x_2 = \frac{x_1{}^2 + N}{2x_1},$$

provides the second step to the point S on the graph (Fig. 6–6) and consists of moving to the function $y = x$ and substitution into the function

$$y = \frac{(x^2 + N)}{(2x)}.$$

The process should continue until the difference between the nth approximation and the $(n-1)$st approximation is less in absolute value than some preset tolerance. It can be simply proved by mathematical analysis that for any $N>0$ and for $x_0>0$ (keeping in mind that the choice for a starting approximation depends on the graph of the function in the sense that better proximity of the starting value to the root is needed if the graph contains a point of inflection—see previous discussion on exceptions to conversion for Newton's Method), the sequence of approximations $x_0, x_1, \ldots, x_n$ converges to the true root in the limit. Even if the starting approximation is to the left of the root, i.e., if $x_0<r$, $x_n>r$, for all n (except for $n=0$); consequently, the process is the same for $x_0<r$.

$$x_{n+1} = \tfrac{1}{2}\,(x_n + Nx_n^{-1}),$$

subtracting $\sqrt{N}$ from both sides:

$$x_{n+1} - \sqrt{N} = \tfrac{1}{2}\,(x_n + Nx_n^{-1}) - \sqrt{N}.$$

Now the right-hand side can be rewritten as:

$$\tfrac{1}{2}\,(x_n - \sqrt{N})^2\, x_n^{-1}$$

because upon expansion

$$\begin{aligned} \tfrac{1}{2}\,(x_n - \sqrt{N})^2\, x_n^{-1} &= \tfrac{1}{2}\,(x_n^2 - 2\sqrt{N}\,x_n + N)\,x_n^{-1}, \\ &= \tfrac{1}{2}\,(x_n - 2\sqrt{N} + Nx_n^{-1}), \\ &= \tfrac{1}{2}\,(x_n + Nx_n^{-1}) - \sqrt{N}, \\ \text{therefore } x_{n+1} - \sqrt{N} &= \tfrac{1}{2}\,(x_n - \sqrt{N})^2\, x_n^{-1}. \end{aligned}$$

If $x_n>0$, then the quantity $\tfrac{1}{2}\,(x_n - \sqrt{N})^2\, x_n^{-1}$ is greater than zero;

$$\frac{1\,(>0)}{2\,(>0)} \Rightarrow >0,$$

therefore, $x_{n+1}>\sqrt{N}$ as long as $x_n>0$ and x_0 may be less than $\sqrt{N}$.

Following is a flow chart and program for the calculation of the square root of N, where N>0:

FLOW CHART

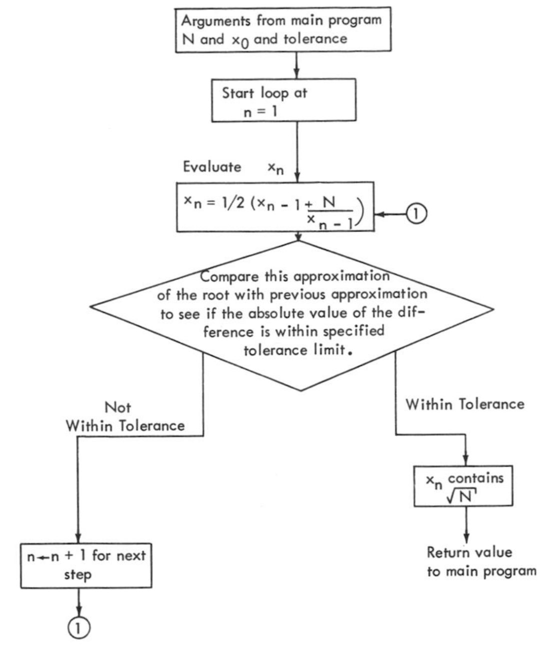
Arguments from main program
N and x0 and tolerance
Start loop at
n = 1
Evaluate xn
xn = 1/2 (xn - 1 + N / xn - 1)
1
Compare this approximation of the root with previous approximation to see if the absolute value of the difference is within specified tolerance limit.
Not Within Tolerance
Within Tolerance
xn contains √N
Return value to main program
n←n + 1 for next step
1

PROGRAM

```
C FOR COMMENT
STATEMENT NUMBER | Cont. | FORTRAN STATEMENT
      FUNCTION SQROT(A,XØ,T)
      IF (T) 1Ø,3Ø,3Ø
   3Ø SQROT=.5*(XØ+A/XØ)
      IF(ABS(SQROT-XØ)-T)1Ø,1Ø,2Ø
   2Ø XØ=SQROT
      GO TO 3Ø
   1Ø RETURN
      END
```

SQROT, a floating-point variable contains the result of the function. Notice the check on T (the tolerance); if $T<0$, control is returned to the main program.

It was pointed out in an earlier chapter that the FORTRAN IV compiler contains a square root routine among its mathematical routines; mathematical routines in FORTRAN IV are written as FORTRAN functions.

The square root routine contained in the FORTRAN IV compiler is written in much the same way as the above routine, SQROT; the routine in the compiler is called SQRT. Using this routine, the following program illustrates the direct calculation of the roots of a quadratic equation using the quadratic formula. In the program the emphasis is not only on the program coding but also on the important areas of documentation and internal testing of data.

DOCUMENTATION

Input

(Data is to be punched under format (3F 10.0), A, B, C.)

The last card of the group should contain the number 9999. in columns 1–10. The limits on the parameters A, B, and C are 1,000; a check is performed on each parameter to insure that the problem will run only with correct data. Incorrect data will cause an error message to be printed, and the next set of data will then be read into the computer. Checks are performed on each of the parameters, A, B, and C, to guard against division by zero as well as to provide a clearer output; for example, if $A = 0$, then the equation is a linear one:

$$Bx + C = 0$$

and $x = -B/C$. Of course, C is checked for a zero value; if $C = 0$, the only solution to the equation $Bx = 0$ is the trivial one, $x = 0$. A test was not included to test for nonnumeric characters placed in either A, B, or C fields by mistake; this would require reading all data under the A-type format and require decoding.

Output

For each equation to be solved, the parameters are printed and all roots including appropriate comments. The format E 10.3 was used in this case because each parameter in the sample problem has 3 significant figures. The FORTRAN IV

$$\underbrace{-\text{X.xxxE}-\text{XX}}_{10}$$

compiler utilized to run the sample problem reserves one place to the left of the decimal point in addition to the six places normally reserved for the scale factor, the decimal point, and the sign. The three significant figures appear to the right of the decimal point. Ten equations and their respective solutions will appear on each page of output. In addition to the parameters of the equation and the solution, the number of the equation is printed on the same line.

The total number of data cards read by the computer is printed at the bottom of the final page.

Method

The quadratic formula is used to solve the roots of quadratic equations. Roots are partitioned into classes by an examination of the discriminant; this simplifies solution of the problem by the computer and allows a better descriptive output.

The above material on input, output, and method, along with the flow chart shown in Figure 6–8 completes the formal documentation of the program. To provide an insight into the programming technique used in solving the problem, we will now go into further detail. Statements number 110 to 121 are all FORMAT statements which characterize the output. The variable I is used as an equation counter; i.e., I contains a value telling which equation is being processed by the computer. To limit the number of equations printed per page of output to 10, the

```
       K = 10
 1     IF (K - 10) 31, 32, 32
32     WRITE (6, 110)
       WRITE (6, 111)
       K = K - 10
```

printing device must be given some signal to skip to the next page and must also be provided with a heading for each page. A 1 punch in column 1 is the signal used to activate the skipping mechanism on the FORTRAN system on which the sample program was run. Here again, we must point out to the prospective programmer the dangers of not becoming acquainted with all the rules concerning the running of the FORTRAN compiler at that particular location; if the programmer inadvertently instructs the computer to punch out results starting in column 1, there is the possibility that one of the answers will have a 1 in column 1 and thereby not only cause an error because the first figure is lost, but also create an unsightly output containing one value per page. FORMAT statement 110 is used to create the 1 punch in column 1. The variable K is initialized at -10, and one is added to location K for every equation which is processed by the computer; when the value in location K reaches zero (i.e., when 10 equations have been processed), the printing device will skip to a new page and the heading will be printed at the top of the page. For an explanation of the remainder of the program, the student can match the numbers on the flow chart with their corresponding ISN numbers on the program. In the following program the student will notice that in the H code in some FORMAT statements not all the blanks have been included.

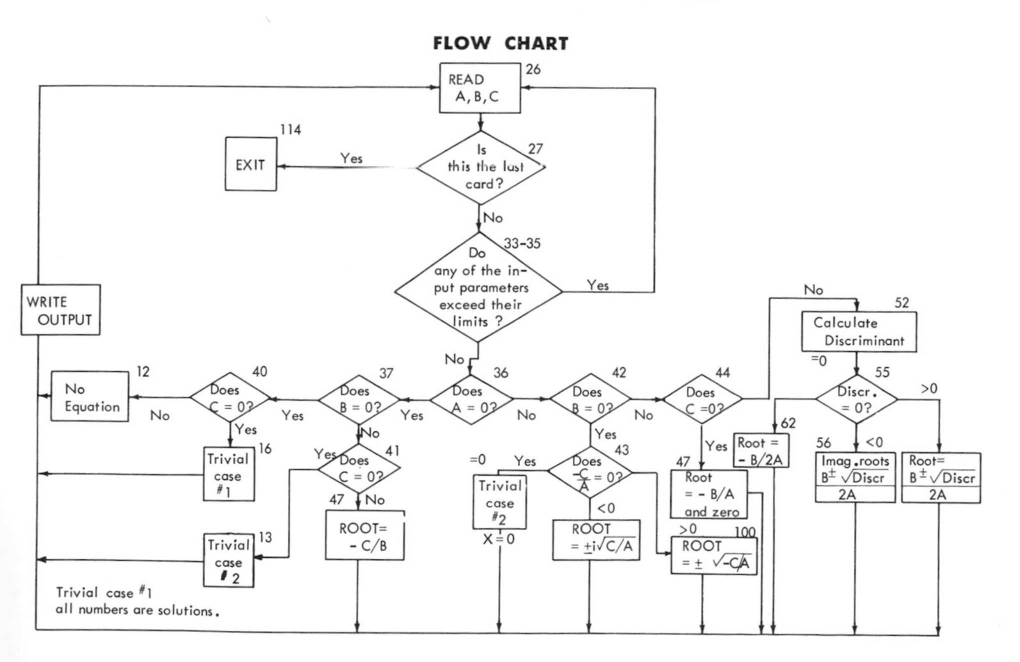

FORTRAN SOURCE LIST

```
ISN
     C                          QUADRATIC  EQUATION
  1   110 FORMAT (1H1)
  2   111 FORMAT(///,4H   EQN,5×,1HA,9×,1HB,9×,1HC,10×,15HCOMMENT + ROOTS,/)
  3   100 FORMAT(3F10.4)
  4   101 FORMAT(37×,46H QUADRATIC EQN. WITH A COMPLEX PAIR OF ROOTS ,/,
         140×,1H(,E10.3,1H,,EI0.3,3H),(,E10.3,1H,,E10.3,1H),/ )
  5   102 FORMAT(37×,47H QUADRATIC EQN. WITH TWO IDENTICAL REAL ROOTS ,
         1/, 40×, E10.3, / )
  6   103 FORMAT(37×,37H QUADRATIC EQN. WITH TWO REAL ROOTS ,/, 40×,
         12(E10.3, 1×),/ )
  7   104 FORMAT(37×,31H LINEAR EQN. WITH A REAL ROOT ,/,40×,E10.3,/)
 10   109 FORMAT(40×,78HQUARDATIC EQN. WITH TWO CONJUGATE IMAGINARY ROOTS, +
         1 OR – 1 TIMES BELOW VALUES,/,40×, 2(E10.3, 1×), /)
 11   105 FORMAT(37×, 32H INPUT DATA EXCEEDS LIMITS SET ,/)
 12   106 FORMAT(37×,18H NOT AN EQUATION ,/)
 13   107 FORMAT(37×,31H TRIVIAL CASE, ZERO ONLY ROOT ,/ )
 14   108 FORMAT(/,/,14,39H DATA CARDS READ. END OF PROGRAM )
 15   112 FORMAT(1×, 13, 3(1×, E10.3))
 16   243 FORMAT(40×, 39HTRIVIAL CASE, ALL NUMBERS ARE SOLUTIONS, / )
 17   121 FORMAT(40×,35HONE ROOT IS ZERO, OTHER GIVEN BELOW,/40×, E10.3,/)
 20       I = 0
 21       K = 10
 22   1   IF (K – 10) 31, 32, 32
 23   32  WRITE (6, 110)
 24       WRITE (6, 111)
 25       K = K – 10
 26   31  READ (5, 100) A, B, C
```

```
27          IF (A - 9999.) 2, 90, 2
30    2     I = I + 1
31          K = K + 1
32          WRITE (6, 112) I, A, B, C
33    3     IF(ABS(A) - 1000.) 4, 89, 89
34    4     IF(ABS(B) - 1000.) 5, 89, 89
35    5     IF(ABS(C) - 1000.) 6, 89, 89
36    6     IF(A) 10, 7, 10
37    7     IF(B) 9, 8, 9
40    8     IF(C) 87, 27, 87
41    9     IF(C) 85, 88, 85
42    10    IF(B) 12, 11, 12
43    11    IF(-C/A) 83, 88, 84
44    12    IF(C) 13, 59, 13
45    27    WRITE (6, 243)
46          GO TO 1
47    59    ROOT = -B/A
50          WRITE (6, 121) ROOT
51          GO TO 1
52    13    D = 2.0 * A
53          R = -B/D
54          DISCR = B * B - 4.0 * A * C
55          IF (DISCR) 79, 80, 81
56    79    AMAG = SQRT ( -DISCR) / D
57          AMAGN = - AMAG
60          WRITE ( 6, 101) R, AMAG, R, AMAGN
61          GO TO 1
62    80    WRITE(6, 102) R
63          GO TO 1
```

FORTRAN SOURCE LIST—*Continued*

```
 64   81   DMPR = SQRT(DISCR) / D
 65        R1 = R + DMPR
 66        R2 = R - DMPR
 67   60   WRITE (6, 103) R1, R2
 70        GO TO 1
 71   82   ROOT = - B/A
 72   61   WRITE (6, 104) ROOT
 73        GO TO 1
 74   83   AMAG = SQRT (C/A)
 75        AMAGN = -AMAG
 76        WRITE(6, 109) AMAG, AMAGN
 77        GO TO 1
100   84   R1 = SQRT (-C/A)
101        R2 = - R1
102        GO TO 60
103   85   ROOT = - C/B
104        GO TO 61
105   87   WRITE (6, 106)
106        GO TO 1
107   88   WRITE (6, 107)
110        GO TO 1
111   89   WRITE (6, 105)
112        GO TO 1
113   90   WRITE(6, 108) I
114   91   CALL EXIT
115        STOP
116        END
```

EQN	A	B	C	COMMENT + ROOTS
1	0.100E 01	0.100E 01	−0.100E 01	QUADRATIC EQN. WITH TWO REAL ROOTS 0.618E 00 −0.162E 01
2	0.100E 01	0.100E 01	0.100E 01	QUADRATIC EQN. WITH A COMPLEX PAIR OF ROOTS (−0.500E 00, 0.866E 00),(−0.500E 00,−0.866E 00)
3	0.100E 01	0.200E 01	0.100E 01	QUADRATIC EQN. WITH TWO IDENTICAL REAL ROOTS −0.100E 01
4	0.300E 01	0.200E 01	0.	ONE ROOT IS ZERO, OTHER GIVEN BELOW −0.667E 00
5	0.300E 01	−0.	0.200E 01	QUADRATIC EQN. WITH TWO CONJUGATE IMAGINARY ROOTS, + OR − I TIMES BELOW VALUES 0.816E 00 −0.816E 00
6	−0.	0.300E 01	0.200E 01	LINEAR EQN. WITH A REAL ROOT −0.667E 00
7	0.500E 01	−0.	−0.	TRIVIAL CASE, ZERO ONLY ROOT

FORTRAN SOURCE LIST—*Continued*

```
EQN       A            B            C          COMMENT + ROOTS

  8  -0.          0.500E 01  -0.
                                               TRIVIAL CASE, ZERO ONLY ROOT

  9  -0.         -0.           0.600E 01
                                               NOT AN EQUATION

 10  -0.         -0.          -0.
                                               TRIVIAL CASE, ALL NUMBERS ARE SOLUTIONS

 11   0.510E 01   0.370E 01    0.690E 01
                                               QUADRATIC EQN. WITH A COMPLEX PAIR OF ROOTS
                                               (-0.363E 00, 0.111E 01),(-0.363E 00,-0.111E 01)

 12   0.317E 02   0.523E 02   -0.740E 01
                                               QUADRATIC EQN. WITH TWO REAL ROOTS
                                                 0.131E 00 -0.178E 01


 12 DATA CARDS READ. END OF PROGRAM
```

6.2. Recurrence Relations

In the preceding chapter the reader was introduced to a method by which the square root of a number, N, could be approximated to any desired degree. When $N>0$, the sequence $\{x_n\}$ converges to $\sqrt{N}$;

$$\{x_{n+1}\} = \tfrac{1}{2}(x_n + Nx_n^{-1}) \text{ for } n = 0,1,2, \ldots$$

Before using the computer to evaluate the square root of a number by utilizing the above sequence, the analyst must be sure that the sequence does, in fact, converge to the square root of the number; otherwise, a great deal of computer time could be wasted with no results. The convergence of the above sequence to N can be proved directly or, since the above formula can be deduced by Newton's Method (see the last section), it is sufficient that the general requirements for convergence in Newton's Method apply in this case.

$$\left|\frac{f(a_n)\,f''(a_n)}{[f'(a_n)]^2}\right| < 1$$

implies convergence of the sequence $\{a_n\}$, where

$$a_{n+1} = a_n - \frac{f(a_n)}{f'(a_n)}$$

For the present case:

$$\begin{aligned} f(x) &= x^2 - N \\ f'(x) &= 2x \\ f''(x) &= 2 \end{aligned}$$

Therefore,

$$\begin{aligned} f(a_n) &= a_n^2 - N \\ f'(a_n) &= 2a_n \\ \text{and } f''(a_n) &= 2 \end{aligned}$$

Now

$$\left|\frac{f(a_n)\,f''(a_n)}{[f'(a_n)]^2}\right| < 1$$

implies

$$|f(a_n)\,f''(a_n)| < [f'(a_n)]^2$$

or

$$|(a_n^2 - N)(2)| < 4a_n^2$$

So the following must hold:

$$|a_n^2 - N| < 2a_n^2$$

Since $a_n^2 \leq N$ by definition, the above inequality must hold if $N > 0$.

Not only is it important to question whether or not a sequence converges to the correct value, but also to question the rate of convergence.

The above sequence converges to N in a quadratic manner; i.e., as the square of the difference between the approximate value and the true value. Let

$$\epsilon_n = x_n - N^{1/2} \tag{1}$$

be the error after the nth term of the sequence; we also may use the phrase, "after the nth iteration."

Then

$$\epsilon_{n+1} = x_{n+1} - N^{1/2} \tag{2}$$

is the error after the $(n + 1)$ st iteration.
Since

$$x_{n+1} = \tfrac{1}{2}(x_n + Nx_n^{-1}), \tag{3}$$

we have

$$\epsilon_{n+1} = \tfrac{1}{2}(x_n + Nx_n^{-1}) - N^{1/2}, \tag{4}$$

After expanding

$$\epsilon_{n+1} = \tfrac{1}{2}x_n + \frac{N}{2}x_n^{-1} - N^{1/2} \tag{5}$$

and multiplying by $2x_n$, we obtain

$$2x_n\epsilon_{n+1} = x_n^2 + N - 2x_nN^{1/2} \tag{6}$$

Notice that

$$\epsilon_n^2 = (x_n - N^{1/2})^2 = x_n^2 + N - 2x_nN^{1/2}. \tag{7}$$

Substituting (7) in (6),

$$2x_n\epsilon_{n+1} = \epsilon_n^2 \tag{8}$$

Therefore,

$$\epsilon_{n+1} = \tfrac{1}{2}\epsilon_n^2x_n^{-1} = C(\epsilon_n^2) \tag{9}$$

From (9) one can see that the error in the approximation decreases in a quadratic (by the square) manner.

When $0 \leqslant N \leqslant 1$ and $x_0 = 0$, $\{x_n\} \rightarrow N^{1/2}$ in a linear manner (as the first power of x);
where

$$x_{n+1} = x_n + \tfrac{1}{2}(N - x_n^2).$$

To see that the convergence is linear, again let

$$\epsilon_n = x_n - N^{1/2},$$

then

$$\epsilon_{n+1} = x_{n+1} - N^{1/2}.$$

Since

$$x_{n+1} = x_n + \tfrac{1}{2}(N - x_n^2),$$

we have

$$\epsilon_{n+1} = x_n + \tfrac{1}{2}(N - x_n^2) - N^{1/2};$$

or

$$\epsilon_{n+1} = \epsilon_n + \tfrac{1}{2}(N - x_n^2),$$

but

$$(N - x_n^2) = (N^{1/2} - x_n)(N^{1/2} + x_n).$$

Therefore,

$$\epsilon_{n+1} = \epsilon_n + \tfrac{1}{2}(-\epsilon_n)(N^{1/2} + x_n),$$

or

$$\epsilon_{n+1} = \epsilon_n (1 - \tfrac{1}{2}(N^{1/2} + x_n).$$

Both ϵ_{n+1} and ϵ_n appear to the first power illustrating that the convergence is slower. Because the error decreases as the square in the sequence which converges quadratically, the sequence

$$x_{n+1} = \tfrac{1}{2}(x_n + N x_n^{-1})$$

converges much faster than the sequence

$$x_{n+1} = x_n + \tfrac{1}{2}(N - x_n^2)$$

which converges linearly.

Newton's Method may be applied to the equation

$$N = \frac{1}{x} \quad \text{or} \quad f(x) = N - \frac{1}{x}$$

$$x_{n+1} = x_n - \frac{f(x_n)}{f'(x_n)} \quad \text{(Newton's Formula)}$$

$$x_{n+1} = x_n - \frac{N - \dfrac{1}{x_n}}{\dfrac{1}{x_n^2}}$$

Simplifying,

$$x_{n+1} = x_n - Nx_n^2 + x_n$$

or

$$x_{n+1} = 2x_n - Nx_n^2$$

and

$$x_{n+1} = x_n (2 - Nx_n)$$

Since $N = \frac{1}{x}$ is the same as $x = \frac{1}{N}$, the above sequence will converge quadratically to N^{-1} for suitable x_0 and $N > 0$. If division is not available on the computer, the above method can be used to calculate reciprocals and then carry out a multiplication.

In general, applying Newton's Method to the equation

$$N = \frac{1}{x^p};$$

$$f(x) = N - \frac{1}{x^p},$$

or

$$x_{n+1} = x_n - \frac{\left(N - \frac{1}{x_n^p}\right)}{\frac{p}{x_n^p} + 1}$$

$$x_{n+1} = x_n - \frac{f(x_n)}{f'(x_n)}$$

$$x_{n+1} = \frac{px_n - Nx_n^{p+1} + x_n}{p}$$

$$x_{n+1} = x_n (p - Nx_n^p + 1) / p,$$

in which the sequence $\{x_n\}$, converges to the reciprocal of the pth power of N.

Graphically the quadratic convergence to N^{-1} can be shown as in Figure 6–7.

An approximate relation which converges cubically (to the third power of ϵ_n to $N^{1/2}$ is

$$x_{n+1} = \frac{x_n^3 + 3Nx_n}{3x_n^2 + N}$$

and the relation

$$x_{n+1} = x_n [3(1 - Nx_n) + (Nx_n)^2]$$

has cubic convergence to N^{-1} when $0 < x_0 < 2 N^{-1}$.

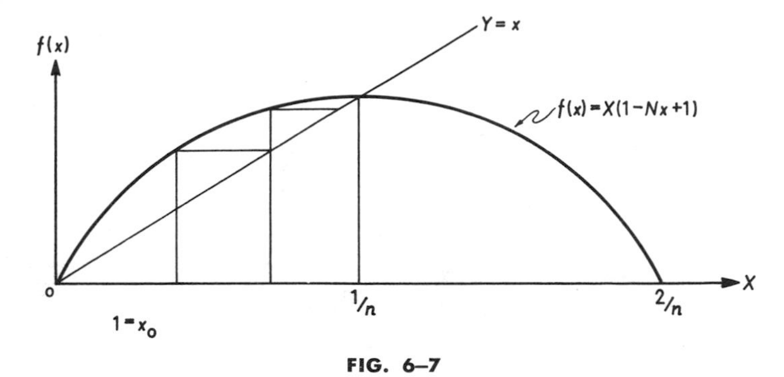

FIG. 6–7

It is also possible to generate the elementary transcendental functions by these methods. One result in this direction is the following:

Given: $x_0 > 0$ and $y_0 > 0$ and set

$$x_{n+1} = \tfrac{1}{2}\,(x_n + y_n)\,,$$
$$y_{n+1} = \sqrt{x_{n+1} \cdot y_n}$$

Then

$\lim_{n \to \infty} x_n$ and $\lim_{n \to \infty} y_n$ are equal. Now, if $x_0 = \cos\theta$ and $y_0 = 1$, then

$$\lim_{n \to \infty} x_n = \lim_{n \to \infty} y_n = (\sin\theta)\,/\,\theta$$

Thus far the approximate methods all had one thing in common, namely, the present value is used to generate the next value; such a type of relationship is called a recurrence relation. Even when a program does not require the use of a recurrence relation, it may be more efficient to convert the program into one utilizing a recurrence relation; although this is not possible in all cases. Following is an example of a program which can be considerably improved (quicker and uses less memory space) by transforming the method of solution into a recurrence relation.

Problem: Evaluate

$$\sum_{m=0}^{\infty} \binom{n}{m} \binom{n-m}{k-m} t^m\,,$$

a summation occurring in probability theory. Binomial coefficients of the form $\binom{a}{b}$ were discussed in earlier chapters; they are defined as

$$\binom{a}{b} = \frac{a!}{b!\,(a-b)!}\,;$$

where $b > a$ or $a < 0$ implies $\binom{a}{b} \equiv 0$, and $0!$ is defined to be 1. All of the fol-

```
C FOR COMMENT
STATEMENT NUMBER | Cont. | FORTRAN STATEMENT
      FUNCTION FACT(I)
      FACT=1
      IF(I.LE.1)RETURN
      DO 1Ø J=2,I
   1Ø FACT=FACT*FLOAT(J)
      RETURN
      END
```

lowing programs will use the FORTRAN function subprogram, FACT(I). Notice that instead of floating the fixed-point variable J by some statement of the form R = J, which would lead to the following sequence of instructions.

```
C FOR COMMENT
STATEMENT NUMBER | Cont. | FORTRAN STATEMENT
      DO 1Ø J=2,I
      R=J
   1Ø FACT=FACT*R
```

the FORTRAN IV built-in function, FLOAT (argument), was used to float the contents of location J.

One program which would evaluate the above summation is the following:

Input:

Parameters N, K, and T are accepted from tape unit 5 in this manner:

N and K; up to 5-place integers (I − FORMAT)—
T; up to 10-digit floating point

NOTE: Most computer centers require data to come into the computer via tape because it is so much faster than punched cards; the idea is to solve the problem on the fast, expensive computer and leave the time-consuming job to a cheaper computer designed to handle the moving and transportation of data. A typical setup might be to have the cheaper computer read the data from cards and place it on tape, then to use the above tape READ statement. On cards the data would look like the illustration at the top of page 255.

Locations N and K are checked for the following conditions:

Is $K > N$?
Is $K < 0$?

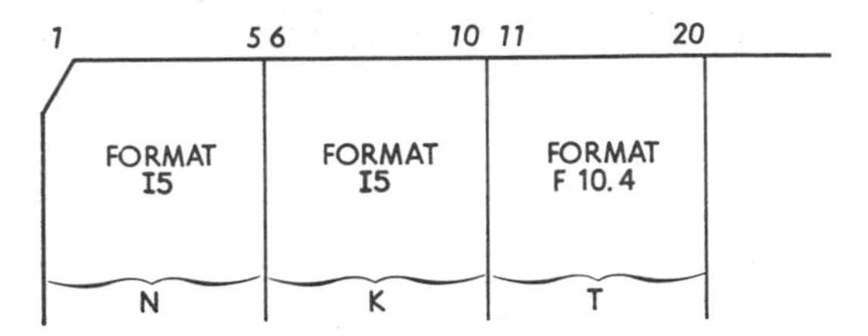

If the answer to either is yes, the computation is completed at that point. Another possible check would be to see if T was in some desired range; for example, is $T > 0$?

Output:

Both the input parameters and the results are written on tape unit 6 under the following format

5	4	5	4	10	15	15
N	BLANK	K	BLANK	T	BLANK	RESULT
						±0.xxxxxxxxE±xx

Again the tape would be printed on some smaller computer to print the above output.

METHOD

$$\binom{N}{M}\binom{N-M}{K-M} = \frac{N!}{M!\,(N-M)!}\cdot\frac{(N-M)!}{(K-M)!\,(N-M-K+M)!}$$

$$= \frac{N!}{M!\,(K-M)!\,(N-K)!}$$

when

$$M = 0\,,$$

$$\frac{N!}{M!\,(K-M)!\,(N-K)!} = \frac{N!}{K!\,(N-K)!}$$

In addition to the test for $K > N$ or $K < 0$, a test for $K = 0$ is included in the program. If $K = 0$, the statement IF (K·GT·N·OR·K·LE·0) GO TO 30 sends control to statement 30; at that time the location ANS is set equal to 1 because when

$$K = 0,\ M = 0 \text{ then } \binom{N}{M}\binom{N-M}{K-M} t^M = \binom{N}{0}\binom{N}{0} t^0 = (1)\,(1)\,(1) = 1\,.$$

After the last set of parameters has been run (i.e., the function is evaluated once for each set of parameters) a message informs the user that the com-

FLOW CHART

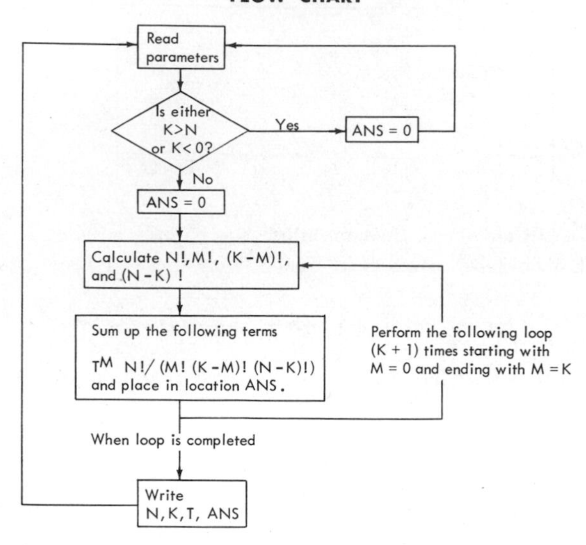

PROGRAM

```
C FOR COMMENT
STATEMENT NUMBER | Cont. | FORTRAN STATEMENT
   99 READ(5,1)N,K,T
    1 FORMAT(2I5,F1Ø.4)
      ANS=Ø
      IF(K.GT.N.OR.K.LE.Ø)GO TO 3Ø
      L2=K+1
      DO 1Ø L1=1,L2
      M=L1-1
   1Ø ANS=ANS+T**M*FACT(N)/(FACT(M)*FACT(K-M)*FACT(N-K))
      GO TO 2Ø
   3Ø IF(K.EQ.Ø) ANS=1.
   2Ø WRITE(6,2)N,K,T,ANS
    2 FORMAT(I5,4XI5,4XF1Ø.4,15XE15.8)
      GO TO 99
      END
```

puter has reached the end of the input list on tape unit 5; therefore, processing is terminated. In the above program one loop served to sum all terms as the index M varied from 0 to K. Another possible program would have the first term calculated outside the loop; then, the loop would include all terms as the index M varied from 1 to K. Whether one method is preferable to the other depends on the application. If the first term had not been included in the loop, the following program would suffice.

```
C FOR COMMENT
STATEMENT NUMBER | FORTRAN STATEMENT
   99 READ(5,1)N,K,T
    1 FORMAT(2I5,F10.4)
      IF(K.GT.N.OR.K.LE.0)GO TO 50)
      TPOW=1
      ANS=FACT(N)/FACT(K)*FACT(N-K)
      DO 10 M=1,K
      TPOW=TPOW*T
   10 ANS=ANS+TPOW*FACT(N)/FACT(M)*FACT(K-M)*FACT(N-K))
      GO TO 20
   50 ANS=0
      IF(K.EQ.0)ANS=1
   20 WRITE(6,2)N,K,T,ANS
    2 FORMAT(I5,4XI5,4XF10.4,15XE15.8)
      GO TO 99
      END
```

Another interesting feature of the above program is the simple recurrence relation used to calculate the term, T^M, as opposed to the previous program. Before, T^M was calculated each time for M = 0, . . . , K. Remember, when the exponent is a fixed-point variable, the FORTRAN compiler calculates T^K as

$$\underbrace{T \cdot T \cdot T \cdot \ldots T}_{\text{K times}}$$

Therefore, to calculate T^4 as T·T·T·T· is wasteful of time if the value of T^3 is already known. If T^3 is known, it is better to calculate T^4 as $T^3 \cdot T$. In the above program T^M is calculated as part of the DO loop. Entering the loop TPOW equals 1 which is the same as T^0; then TPOW = TPOW * T places the values T^1 in location TPOW. In this way TPOW contains T^i and T^{i+1} is calculated with the statement TPOW = TPOW * T.

In the definition of the function,

$$\sum_{M=0}^{\infty} \binom{N}{M} \binom{N-M}{K-M} T^M,$$

notice that the index M varies from 0 to infinity. Of course, it is not possible to have the computer execute a DO loop an infinite number of times; fortunately, it is not necessary to vary M from zero to infinity to evaluate the above function. When $M > K$, the term $\binom{N-M}{K-M}$, becomes zero by definition, since $(K-M) < 0$. Therefore, it is unnecessary to have the index

M exceed K since the terms for which $M > K$ are zero and add nothing to the sum.

Instead of evaluating $\binom{a}{b}$ as $\frac{a!}{b!\,(a-b)!}$, one could factor out the common terms:

$$\frac{a \cdot (a-1) \cdot (a-2) \cdots (a-b+1) \cdot \cancel{(a-b)} \cdots \cancel{(1)}}{b!\,\cancel{(a-b)} \cdot \cancel{(a-b-1)} \cdots \cancel{(1)}} = \frac{(a) \cdot (a-1) \cdots (a-b+1)}{b!}.$$

Using this simplification, and if instead of using the factorial subprogram FACT, another subprogram like the following was available, one could reduce the length of computation time.

```
      FUNCTION FACT1 (L1, L2)
      FACT 1 = 1
      L3 = L1 - L2 + 1
      DO 10 K = L 3, L1
 10   FACT1 = FACT1 * FLOAT (K)
      RETURN
      END
```

The limits on the loop run from L1−L2+1 to L1, so the calculation becomes (L1−L2+1)·(L1−L2+2)···(L1−L2+L2), which is the desired product in the numerator. Now ANS = FACT (N) /(FACT (K) * FACT (N−K)) could be written ANS = FACT1 (N, K) / FACT (K) and statement 10 could be rewritten as ANS = ANS + TPOW * FACT1 (N,K) /(FACT (M) * FACT (K−M) * FACT (K)).

Another possibility would be the use of a binomial coefficient subprogram instead of the factorial subprogram; a program of this nature has been given in an earlier chapter. Using such a subprogram, say BINOM (I, J), N = BINOM (I, J) would give the result of $\binom{I}{J}$.

The above simplification could also be utilized in case the function BINOM was used in place of FACT because

$$\binom{a}{b} = \binom{a}{a-b}$$

since

$$\binom{a}{a-b} = \frac{a!}{(a-b)!\,(a-a+b)!} = \frac{a!}{(a-b)!\,b!}$$

Therefore, N = BINOM (I, I−J) is equivalent to N = BINOM (I, J).

Even though the original program has already seen some improvement, the largest improvement comes in defining the function itself in as a recurrence relation.

$$\binom{N}{M-1}\binom{N-(M-1)}{K-(M-1)} = \binom{N}{M-1}\binom{N-M+1}{K-M+1}$$

$$= \frac{N!}{(M-1)!\,(N-M+1)!}\;\frac{(N-M+1)!}{(K-M+1)!\,(N-M+1-K+M-1)} \quad (1)$$

$$= \frac{N!}{(M-1)!\,(N-M+1)!}\;\frac{(N-M+1)!}{(K-M+1)!\,(N-K)!}$$

$$= \frac{N!}{(M-1)!\,(K-M+1)!\,(N-K)!}$$

$$\binom{N}{M}\binom{N-M}{K-M} = \frac{N!}{(N-K)!}\;\frac{1}{M!\,(K-M)\,!}$$

$$= \frac{N!}{(N-K)!}\;\frac{1}{M\,(M-1)!}\cdot\frac{K-M+1}{(K-M+1)!} \quad (2)$$

This was demonstrated earlier.

The last equality is due to the fact that

$$M! = M\,(M-1)! \text{ and } \frac{1}{(K-M)!} = \frac{K-M+1}{(K-M+1)!}$$

because

$$(K-M+1)! = (K-M+1)\cdot(K-M)\cdot(K-M-1)\cdots(1)$$
$$= (K-M+1)\,(K-M)!$$

From (1) and (2) one can see that (2) can be calculated from (1) by multiplying by $\frac{K-M+1}{M}$.

$$\binom{N}{M}\binom{N-M}{K-M} = \frac{N!}{(M-1)!\,(N-K)!\,(K-M+1)!}\cdot\frac{K-M+1}{M}$$

$$= \frac{K-M+1}{M}\cdot\binom{N}{M-1}\binom{N-(M-1)}{K-(M-1)}.$$

Now the Mth term can be calculated from the $(M-1)$st term without calculating all the factorials for each iteration; this results in a great saving in calculation time on the computer. For this method, the associated program follows:

```
C FOR COMMENT
STATEMENT
 NUMBER   Cont.  FORTRAN STATEMENT
   99     READ(5,1)N,K,T
    1     FORMAT(2I5,F10.4)
          IF(K.GT.N.OR.K.LE.0)GO TO 50
          COEF=FACT(N)/(FACT(N-K)*FACT(K))
          ANS=COEF
          DO 10 M=1,K
          COEF=COEF*T**M*FLOAT(K-M+1)/FLOAT(M)
   10     ANS=ANS+COEF
          GO TO 20
   50     ANS=0
          IF(K.EQ.0)ANS=1
   20     WRITE(6,1)N,K,T,ANS
    2     FORMAT(I5,4XI5,4XF10.4,15XE15.8)
          GO TO 99
          END
```

All the recursive relations explained thus far have been programmed in FORTRAN in an iterative or recurrent manner; i.e.; using a DO Loop which utilizes the present value of the function to calculate the next value of the function. For some years there has been a good deal of controversy as to whether or not all recursive functions can be handled as recurrence relations. If there was a recursive function which could not be programmed in a recurrent manner, the following procedure would be required. Suppose that a process is required to be repeated a certain variable number of times in a certain variable number of nested loops. An example (to be explained in greater detail in the next chapter) which might utilize this technique is the evaluation of a determinant by successively reducing the order of the determinant by cofactors until the determinant is of order 2. If the original determinant was of order 10, the procedure would be as shown in Figure 6–8.

All determinants of order 2 are solved by a simple routine, and the values thus obtained must be used to calculate (this procedure will be explained in detail in the next chapter) the higher-order determinants until the original determinant has been evaluated.

For the evaluation of determinants in the above manner, the number of nested loops must be two less than the order of the original determinant. If the order of the original determinant is n, then $(n-2)$ loops are required. Letting I_n denote the determinant of order $n-1$

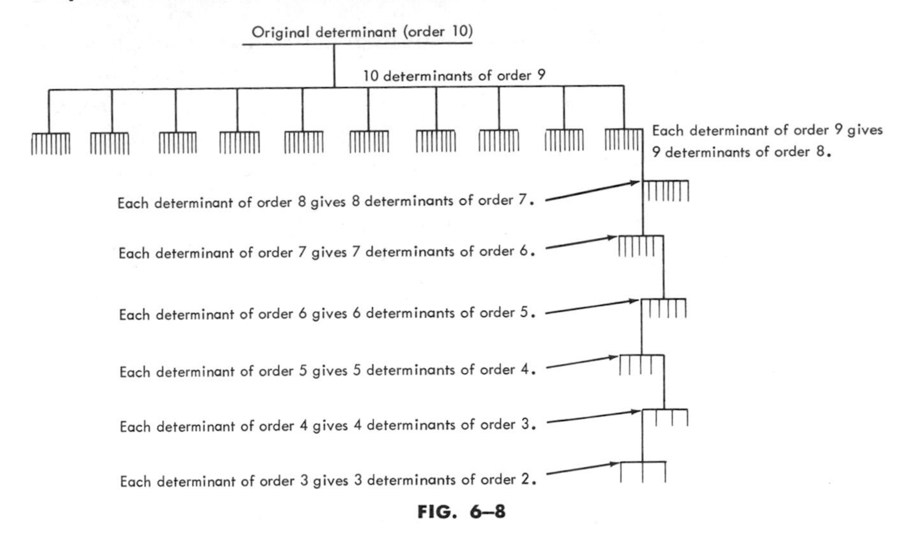

FIG. 6–8

Loop $1 - I_n \rightarrow$ DO n times (n determinants of order $n-1$)
Loop $2 - I_{n-1} \rightarrow$ DO $(n-1)$ times
Loop $3 - I_{n-2} \rightarrow$ DO $(n-2)$ times
. .
. .
. .
Loop $(n-2)$ – $I_3 \rightarrow$ DO (3) times (at this point a routine is called three times to evaluate a 2nd order determinant)

Here both the number of variables and the number of nested loops are variable. In order to solve this type of problem, we must write an iterative routine which iterates itself. This entire procedure is very similar to the method used previously in this chapter to evaluate functions in an iterative manner.

To illustrate the procedure:

$$T_0 = 0$$
$$T_k = C_k + T_{k-1}$$
$$T = T_n$$

where T_i denotes the ith term in a sequence of n terms and I represents the value of the function which has been expressed recursively as a function of n terms. Now if P is a part of a certain program and P is composed of $(N-2)$ loops, we can say P is a function of $I_n, I_{n-1}, I_{n-2}, \ldots, I_3$.

Then, we could write the following:

$$S_0 = P\,(I_2)$$
$$S_k = C_k + P\,(I_{k-1})$$
$$S = S_{n-2}$$

where, in applying the procedure to the determinant, S_k is the kth loop and S is the value of the original determinant. To program the above problem it is necessary to use an array to replace the set of loop variables; also, this array, the variable giving the number of loops, and the procedure itself (here called P), must be defined outside of the routine which will call itself.

Write the procedure, P, as an arithmetic statement function, a FORTRAN FUNCTION, or FORTRAN SUBROUTINE. Reserve an array, say I, which has as its maximum size the maximum size of the determinant minus 2. The arguments to be sent to the routine which will call itself are the name of the function (remember that in FORTRAN IV names of functions may be used as arguments in other functions provided they appear in an EXTERNAL statement—see Chapter 5), the array I, the dimension of the array I, and the variable giving the number of the iteration. The kth storage location in the array I contains the upper limit of the loop needed to specify the number of times the routine must be used in order to evaluate S_k, or the kth iteration of the routine which calls itself.

```
      SUBROUTINE CITSF (I, J, P, K)   (K is the number of the iteration of
                                         the routine CITSF which must
                                         call itself)
      DIMENSION I(J)                  (in a subroutine the DIMENSION
                                         may be variable if it is fixed in
                                         the calling program)
      EXTERNAL P
      M = I (K)
      DO 20 L = 1, M
   20 Execute P (K), M times.
      RETURN
      END
```

FORTRAN does not permit a subroutine to call itself directly, and therefore a special procedure is necessary if FORTRAN is to be used to program recursively.[2] The procedure is not specified here because it has been proved mathematically[3] that every recursive function can be programmed as a recurrence relation; i.e., as was done earlier in this chapter without the need of calling itself.

The reader may now ask why do we consider recursive programming (having a routine call itself) if it is not needed for numerical solutions. In symbol manipulation (symbolic logic), such as that needed for language definition, recursive programming is necessary. The example given here is probably the worst numerical method to solve a determinant, as the reader will learn in the next chapter.

---

[2] For the method see James A. Ayer, "Recursive Programming in FORTRAN," *Communications of the ACM*, Vol. VI, No. 11 (November, 1963).

[3] See H. Gordon Rice, "Recursion and Iteration," *Communications of the ACM*, Vol. VIII, No. 2 (February, 1965).

6.3. Other Approximate Methods

Recurrence relations, such as those derived from application of Newton's Method, are not the only approximate methods for digital computers. Cecil Hastings, in his book *Approximations for Digital Computers*,[4] uses polynomials to approximate many useful functions without using iterative procedures. Following is Hastings' approximation to the sine of x; for a recurrence relation (say, one derived from application of Taylor's series) to yield the same accuracy would require more computation time.

Hasting Approximation–sin $\frac{\pi}{2}X$ for the range $-1 \leq X \leq 1$:

$$\sin \frac{\pi}{2} X = C_1X + C_3X^3 + C_5X^5$$

$$C_1 = 1.5706268$$
$$C_3 = -.6432292$$
$$C_5 = .0727102$$

Using the above approximation function results in an error of less than $\pm$ .0001. In the same range, the following approximation function results in an error of less than $\pm$ .000001.

$$\sin \frac{\pi}{2} X = C_1X + C_3X^3 + C_5X^5 + C_7X^7$$

$$C_1 = 1.570794852$$
$$C_3 = -.645920978$$
$$C_5 = .079487663$$
$$C_7 = -.004362476$$

A recurrence relation can be derived from the application of Taylor's Series to the sine function.

Taylor's Series—If $f(x)$ possesses derivatives of all orders in an interval including $x = a$, it can be represented in that interval as:

$$f(x) = f(a) + f'(a)(x-a) + \frac{f''(a)}{2!}(x-a)^2 + \ldots + \frac{f^{(n)}(a)}{n!}(x-a)^n + \ldots,$$

for those values of x for which the individual terms of the sum go to 0 in the limit as n goes to infinity. For:

$$f(x) = \sin x,$$
$$f'(x) = \cos x,$$
$$f''(x) = -\sin x,$$

[4] Cecil Hastings, Jr., *Approximations for Digital Computers* (Princeton, N.J.: Princeton University Press, 1955), pp. 138–39.

$$f'''(x) = -\cos x,$$
$$f^{\text{IV}}(x) = \sin x,$$
$$\vdots$$

therefore,

$$f(x) = \sin(x) = \sin(a) + \cos(a)(x-a) - \sin\frac{(a)(x-a)^2}{2!} - \frac{\cos(a)(x-a)^3}{3!} + - \ldots \quad (1)$$

If we take a equal to zero, (1) becomes:

$$f(x) = \sin(0) + \cos(0)(x) - \sin(0)\frac{(x)^2}{2!} - \cos(0)\frac{x^3}{3!} + \sin(0)\frac{(x)^4}{4!} + - \ldots,$$

since

$$\sin(0) = 0 \text{ and } \cos(0) = 1.$$

$$f(x) = x - \frac{x^3}{3!} + \frac{x^5}{5!} - \frac{x^7}{7!} + \frac{x^9}{9!} - + \ldots \quad (2)$$

The general term in (2) is:

$$\frac{(-1)^n x^{2n+1}}{(2n+1)!} \text{ for } n = 0, 1, 2, \ldots$$

To compute $f(x)$ through a recurrent relation, notice that the nth term,

$$\frac{(-1)^n x^{2n+1}}{(2n+1)!}$$

can be computed from the $(n-1)$st term,

$$\frac{(-1)^{n-1} x^{2(n-1)+1}}{(2(n-1)+1)!},$$

by multiplying the $(n-1)$st term by

$$\frac{-x^2}{(2n)(2n+1)}$$

Equation (2) illustrates the use of an infinite series to evaluate a function. Because it is impossible to evaluate an infinite amount of terms, and because even if this were possible it would be useless, since each computer location can only contain a finite number of places (limiting the accuracy to the length of the storage location), the series is cut off after a certain number of terms. In a series like (2), i.e., one in which the sign of each term is different from the previous term (alternating signs), the error in cutting off the series at the kth term is equal to or less than the value of the kth term (assuming $|U_{n+s}| \leq |U_n|$ and $\lim_{n \to \infty} U_n = 0$). For example, if (2) was cut off after the fourth term, the error will be equal to or less than

$$e = \frac{x^9}{9!}$$

The value for $f(x)$ will then be

$$x - \frac{x^3}{3!} + \frac{x^5}{5!} - \frac{x^7}{7!}$$

within an error, e.

The calculation of the errors involved with approximate calculations are often the most difficult part of numerical methods and numerical analysis; because the author assumes only a good high school mathematics background, this book will not delve into the area of error analysis. To learn more about error analysis in numerical methods, the student can consult the references given at the back of the book.

6.4. Relaxation

Not all approximation techniques may be used for computer solution of problems. Relaxation methods usually are more applicable by manual calculation than computer calculation because of the many decisions involved and because each problem may require a small modification in the technique. Computers are ideally suited to perform the same calculations many times; manual calculation is needed for problems which require little calculation for each answer and which require a modification of the calculating procedure for each answer. To illustrate the relaxation method, we shall look at the problem of simultaneous linear equations (a topic which will be discussed in much greater detail in the next chapter).

Given:

$$\begin{aligned} x - 2y &= 25 \\ 4x - 2y &= 40 \end{aligned}$$

Solve for x and y. If we write,

$$\begin{aligned} R_1 &= 25 - x + 2y \\ R_2 &= 40 - 4x + 2y, \end{aligned}$$

when $R_1 = R_2 = 0$, x and y will be the correct solution to the above two simultaneous linear equations. It may not be possible to reduce R_1 and R_2

to exactly 0 in a finite number of steps, but in most cases the user may reduce R_1 and R_2 to as close to zero as he likes if he tries enough approximations; reduction of R_1 and R_2 to numbers with very small absolute values results in successively more accurate evaluation of x and y. If the way in which the equations first appear does not yield values for R_1 and R_2 which approach zero (i.e., the values either diverge or oscillate), there may be some transformation which, when applied to the original equations yield equations which are solvable by relation methods. In the given example an initial guess of $x = 0$ and $y = 0$ (for lack of better information) yields $R_1 = 25$ and $R_2 = 40$.

If y is decreased by 15 units, i.e., $\Delta y = -15$, then $R_1 = 25 - 0 + 2 (-15) = -5$ and $R_2 = 40 - 0 + 2 (-15) = 10$. Notice that R_1 has been reduced to less than zero instead of exactly to zero; it is said that the first constraint has been overrelaxed. When $R_1 = 0$, the first constraint is said to be in a relaxed condition. Many times it is quicker to reach the solution if one of the constraints is overrelaxed; but the degree of overrelaxation is more of an art than a science. The condition of the coefficients (in the first equation the coefficient of x is 1 and of y is -2; in the second equation the coefficient of x is 4 and of y is -2) certainly should be related to the degree of overrelaxation (the degree of negativity of R_1 or R_2, depending on whichever equation is being overrelaxed); but there is no direct relation which can be specified.

After the first step, the two equations are:

$$R_1 = -5 - x + 2y$$
$$R_2 = 10 - 4x + 2y$$

so that if $x = 0$, $y = 0$, $R_1 = -5$ and $R_2 = 10$.

As the second step set $\Delta x = 5$; this step yields $R_1 = -10$ and $R_2 = -10$. The two equations then become:

$$R_1 = -10 - x + 2y$$
$$R_2 = -10 - 4x + 2y$$

so $R_1 = -10$ and $R_2 = -10$. An obvious final step would be to set $\Delta y = 5$. This results in $R_1 = 0$ and $R_2 = 0$.

$$x = 0+5 = 5; y = 0+(-15)+5 = -10$$

To illustrate the fact that the condition of the coefficients affect the method of solution, the student should try to apply overrelaxation to the following set of equations:

$$x + 5y = 75$$
$$4x - 2y = 102$$

There are many ways to apply relaxation techniques and many possible transformations; this fact, in addition to the unexplained relation between the coefficients and the amount of overrelaxation needed in each case, makes relaxation techniques difficult to use for computer calculation. It is not meant to imply that relaxation methods are not powerful techniques; in many complicated mathematical problems, overrelaxation may be the fastest way to solve the problem.

6.5. Monte Carlo Methods

6.5.1. Probability

Monte Carlo is another approximation technique which becomes feasible through the use of digital computers. Essentially, Monte Carlo methods depend on transforming a direct mathematical problem (such as taking the integral of a function) into a probabalistic problem; the computer is used to generate these probabilities by simulating the circumstances into which the problem is imbedded. Consider the problem of finding the area under the curve, $f(x) = ax^3 + bx^2 + cx + d$, in the region from $x = 0$ to $x = 4$.

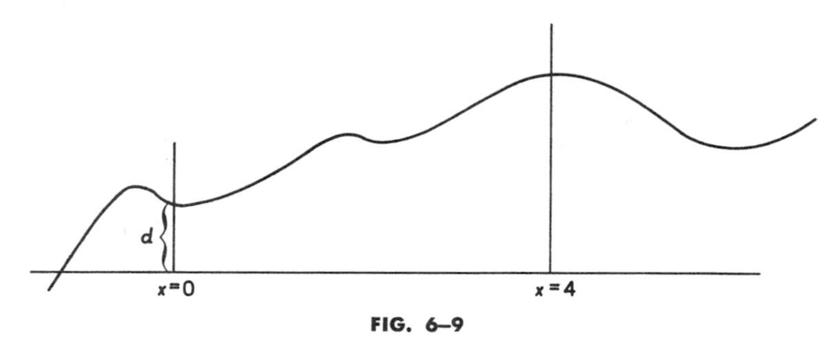

FIG. 6–9

If one could find the ratio of area under the curve to some known area, then the area under the curve could be derived by multiplying the known area by the ratio.

To illustrate the above example, one might consider another similar problem, that of estimating the number of red and black balls in a large box. Suppose there exists a large box (large enough to contain so many balls that it would not be feasible to count all of the balls) and that all of these balls have been thoroughly mixed; by thoroughly mixed, we imply that if

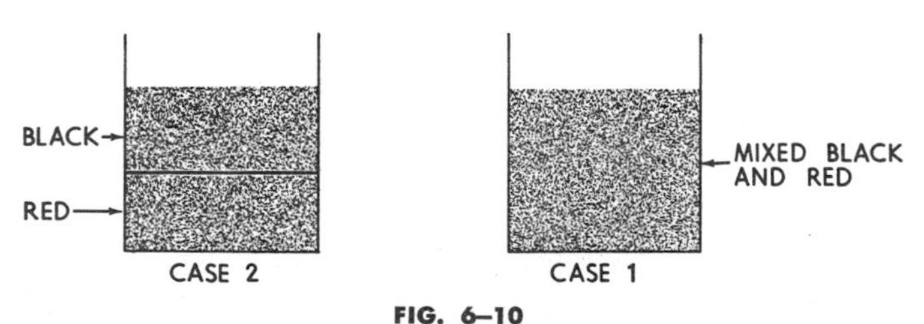

FIG. 6–10

there were the same number of red balls as black balls, a person would be equally likely to draw a black ball as a red ball. Instead of mixing the balls, the experiment could be set up by first dumping the red balls in the box and then the black balls (so all the black balls would be on top). For each of the cases mentioned, (i.e., the case of the thoroughly mixed balls and the case of black on top, red on bottom), the following two questions are important:

1. What is the chance of a blindfolded person picking a red ball in either case?
2. If the blindfolded person draws 10 balls from the box, what can be said about the distribution of red and black balls in the box (that is, the total number of red balls compared with the total number of black balls) in either case?

QUESTION 1

Case 1

Since the number of red balls is the same as the number of black balls, the chances of picking a red ball is 1 out of 2 or 50 percent.

Case 2

Obviously the chance of picking up a red ball is zero. A more interesting question for case 2 would be the following: If a person has no knowledge of the method in which the experiment was conducted (the way in which the balls were dumped into the box), what answer would he give to the previous question 1? With no knowledge of the experiment, the answer must be "a 50 percent chance for either type of ball, since there are two types of balls."

QUESTION 2

Case 1

When the balls have been thoroughly mixed, the total number of red balls and the total number of black balls can be estimated from the sample. For a sample consisting of 6 red balls and 4 black balls out of a total of 10,000 balls, a logical estimate given this information is (6/10) (10,000) = 6,000 red balls and 4,000 black balls.

Questions regarding the size and number of samples needed in order to be correct in your estimate or to be 95 percent sure you are correct (given a sample, it is desirable to know in what percentage of cases using this sample the estimate made from the sample will be correct), lie in the realm of statistics and will not be investigated further in this book. However, the student has probably come to the correct qualitative conclusion that a larger sample would yield more accurate results.

Case 2

A sample of 10 balls drawn from the box yields 10 black balls; following the procedure for estimation which was explained in the above paragraph, one would estimate that the box contains all black balls—an observation which is as far as is possible from the truth.

Returning to the problem of finding the area under the function, $f(x) = ax^3+bx^2+cx+d$, one can see it is the second question in the above example which affects the procedure needed to solve this problem. We wish to enclose the desired unknown area in a figure whose area is known and then draw a sample of elements from each of the figures in order to establish the ratio of the size of the unknown figure to the size of the known figure. Imagine a box shaped like the region enclosed by the curves $x = 0$, $x = 4$, $y = 0$, and $y = ax^3+bx^2+cx+d$; the height of this box will only permit the balls to be stacked one deep (Figure 6–11[*a*]). Imagine another box

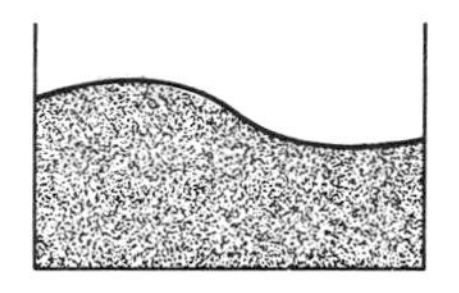

FIG. 6–11(a)

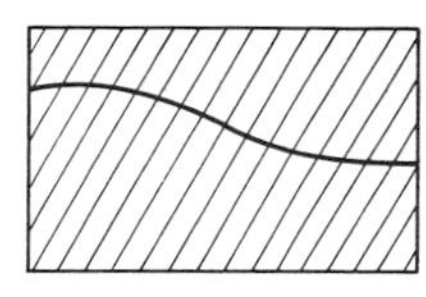

FIG. 6–11(b)

shaped like the region enclosed by the lines $x = 0$, $x = 4$, $y = 0$, and $y = d+k$ (when $x = 0$, $f(x) = d$ and $k > 0$); again the height of the box will only permit the balls to be stacked one deep (see Figure 6–11[b]). If the two boxes of balls are marked to indicate in which box they originate and are then dumped into one large box and mixed thoroughly, the problem becomes very similar to that in the previous example. A sample is drawn from the large box, and the area of Figure 6–11(a) is estimated from the ratio of balls from the box in Figure 6–11(a) to the balls from Figure 6–11(b) and the area of Figure 6–11(b). Notice that the balls in Figure 6–11(a) are also included in Figure 6–11(b); therefore, it would be possible to use only the box in Figure 6–11(b) to supply the balls if the balls under the curve were marked in one way and the balls enclosed in the area between $f(x)$ and the line $y = d+k$ were marked in another way. To increase

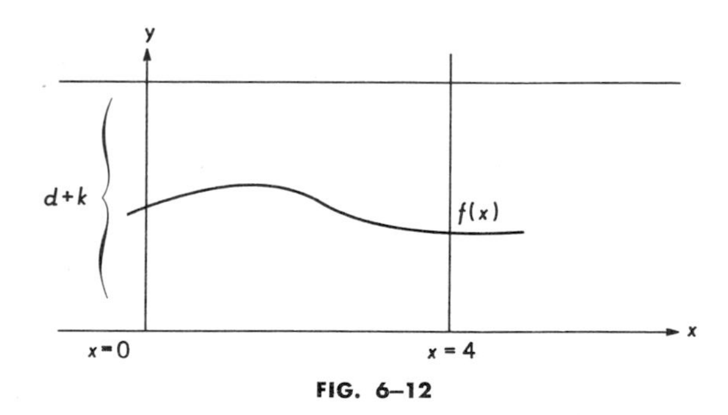

FIG. 6–12

the accuracy of the approximation, one must reduce the size of the balls and increase the size of the sample beyond that which is feasible by manual methods. Instead of filling the areas with balls, one could choose points from Figure 6–12 in such a way that each point in the area enclosed by the lines $x = 0$, $x = 4$, $y = 0$, and $y = d+k$ had an equal chance of being selected (this is equivalent to a thorough mixing of the balls in the previous example). The ratio of the number of points selected from the area under the function to the total area under the rectangle multiplied by the area under the rectangle will be the estimate of the area under the function. We have stressed the need for obtaining a large sample and the need for each element of the sample to have equal chance of being included in the sample. Fortunately, the digital computer can help us meet these needs through a random number generator and the inherent speed built into the computer.

6.6. Random Number Generators

Many methods are available which utilize computers to generate random numbers but most are not popular because they either require too much time or create a sequence of numbers whose behavior has not been satisfactorily demonstrated by tests. Statistical tests which validate the randomness of the generated numbers may be found in statistics books as well as in computational journals and have been a subject of concentrated study for some time.

The most popular class of random number generators starts with an initial number and repeatedly multiplies it by some given number, each time retaining only the least significant half of the digits. There are three advantages to this method.

1. A great many random numbers may be generated without repeating the numbers.
2. The method is fast; requiring only one multiplication per number (also only two storage locations are required—one for the random numbers and one for the multiplier).
3. The program may be written entirely in FORTRAN because there is no need for symbol manipulations (see earlier chapters for details on symbol manipulation).

One formula in this category of random number generators is

$$r_i = Pr_{i-1} \mod m^n \text{ for } i = 2^5$$

where P is the multiplier, m is the base of the number system for which the computer is designed (binary, decimal, etc.), and n is length of the storage location in the machine (assuming a fixed-length storage location). Suppose a computer is designed to store and do calculations to the base 2 and has a five-digit storage length. Say, $r_1 = 10101$ and $P = 10011$, then $r_2 = Pr_1 = 111111111(110001111) \mod 2^5 = 1111$.

[5] B. A. Galler, *The Language of Computers: An Introduction* (Ann Arbor: University of Michigan Press, 1961).

```
       10101
       10011
       -----
       10101
      10101
     00000
    00000
   10101
   ---------
   111111111
```

The function, mod (x,y) divides x by y and gives as result, the remainder from the division. When the divisor is a number which is 1 greater than the largest number a storage location can hold, the mod function serves to cut off the left half of the number. In the above example, the divisor is 2^5, or 100000, a number which is 1 greater than the largest number which a storage location in the machine can hold—the largest number is 11111.

```
              1100
100000√110001111
       100000
       ------
        100011
        100000
        ------
          1111
```

The remainder is 1111.

In the hypothetical machine mentioned above, there can be only 2^5 different representations; that is, even the best choice of P and r can yield only 32 random numbers before the sequence repeats. A sequence which has a short period (the period of a sequence is the amount of different numbers which appear before the sequence starts over again) definitely cannot be used for generating random numbers for the following reason: Suppose each point on a line should have an equal chance of being selected:

Because there are a great many points on the line, there must be a random number representing every point (theoretically). If only 32 points could be represented, there would be a much greater chance that one of these 32 would be selected rather than any of the others (in fact, the other points have no chance of being selected).

For the random generator,

$$r_i = Pr_{i-1} \mod m^n \text{ for } i \geq 2,$$

where m is the base of the internal number system and n is the length of each storage location, a good choice of parameters is $P = 5^{15}$ and $r_1 = 2^{35} - 1$ when $m = 2$ and $n = 36$.[6] For this choice, the period of the resulting se-

[6] M. L. Juncosa, *Random Number Generation on the BRI High-Speed Computing Machines* (Report No. 855, Ballistics Research Laboratory; Aberdeen, Md.).

quence of random numbers is 2^{33}, or about 8.5 million numbers can be generated without repetition.

As the reader will soon learn, applications utilizing random numbers sometimes require that these numbers possess a property other than that each possible number has an equal chance of making an appearance (that is, the application may require random numbers for some probability distribution other than the uniform distribution). Random numbers possessing the property that each number has an equal chance of appearing are called uniform random numbers or random numbers drawn from a uniform probability distribution. We shall try to utilize uniform random numbers in our efforts to generate random numbers from other probability distributions. Because the uniform random number generator will be used as a part of a general random number generator, it is advantageous to write it as an arithmetic statement function to be included as part of the general random number generator; the general random number generator can then be written as a FORTRAN FUNCTION.

FLOW CHART—General Random Number Generator

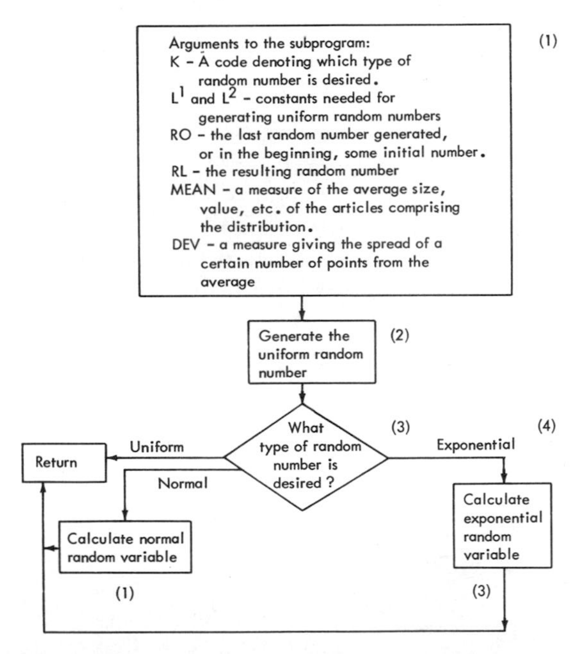

To generate the uniform random variable, the following arithmetic statement function would suffice:

$$RO = MOD\ (RO * L1,\ L2)$$

where:

$$L1 = 5 ** 15$$
$$L2 = 2 ** 35$$

RO is a fixed-point variable, and the computer has a 36-bit binary storage location. The MOD function is an open subroutine which is written into the FORTRAN IV compiler. In its general form, MOD (Arg 1, Arg 2), both arguments must be integer, and the result is integer. AMOD, the floating-point counterpart of MOD is also available in the FORTRAN IV compiler. For purposes of generating random numbers, the largest possible storage space (a full 36 binary bits unless double precision is used; but double precision would require too much time per random number) is needed; therefore, it is desirable to use fixed-point numbers. Remember, the scale factor for floating-point numbers requires some space.

MOD (Arg_1, Arg_2) is defined as $Arg_2 - [Arg_1 / Arg_2]\, Arg_2$, when $[Y]$ is the integral part of Y. As previously mentioned, it is desirable to generate uniform random numbers in the range 0 to 1; it is then easy to scale these numbers to the required range for a particular application. To scale the fixed-point result, R0 to the range 0 to 1, we write

RL = FLOAT (RO) / FLOAT (L2);

a statement using a FORTRAN IV BUILT-IN FUNCTION which floats a constant stored in a fixed-point location. The complete arithmetic statement function is then

UNIF (M) = FLOAT (MOD (M*L1,L2))/FLOAT (L2).

Generation of random numbers is only one part of the Monte Carlo procedure. A second step is the relation of the random numbers, drawn by the method given above, to the physical process. It is desirable to use the speed of the computer to let the analyst "watch" the physical process actually occurring; then it will be easy to give an answer to the problem. In other words, if the analyst knows enough about the physical process to state the chances of something happening and if, after specifying the chances of all the individual events, he can specify how these events are related to each other, then the analyst can solve the problem when he observes each of the individual events. However, it may not be possible to observe the events, either because of the expense involved, the time involved, or some similar reason. Therefore, the speed of the computer is used to generate random numbers; these random numbers are then used to take a sample from the set of points comprising each event. This process is called simulation.

For the example of calculating the area under the curve, consider the following steps:

1. What are the chances of a point occurring, either under the curve or under the rectangle enclosing the curve? The answer is that each point has an equal

chance of occurring; a statement on the probability distribution of the variable.

2. After "watching" a large number of points fall in the rectangle, multiply the ratio of the points under the curve to those which fell outside the curve but under the rectangle by the area of the rectangle. Step 2 utilizes the knowledge of the relation of this entire area to the area of the curve.

Before giving a program to solve for area under the curve, it is necessary to explore some of the difficulties introduced to the Monte Carlo methods when probability distributions occur other than the one in which all points have an equal chance of occurrence. One complexity introduced to the problem is that of the continuous probability distribution as opposed to the discrete probability distribution. Using the random number generator, $F_k = Pr_{k-1}$, mod m^n, it is only possible to generate a finite number of numbers; i.e., a maximum of 8½ million. Since each number has an equal chance of being generated, the chance of any one number being selected is 1/8,500,000 (if there are 8.5 million different numbers before the sequence of random numbers is repeated). Letting x be a variable which can take on each of k different numbers or values, then

$$f(x) = \frac{1}{k} \qquad x = 1, \ldots, k$$

gives the chance of generating any value—$f(x)$ is called the probability density function. Before utilizing the random numbers to solve the problem of finding the area under the curve, it should be pointed out that there are many more points under the curve and the rectangle than one could possibly hope to generate.[7] The limited supply of random numbers means that not every point under the rectangle does actually have an equal chance of being selected. Fortunately, each point does not need to be represented in order to solve the problem (the problem will be solved later in this section); to consider all points under the curve, one would have to use the integral calculus.

A probability density function in which the variable x can take on an infinite number of values is called a continuous distribution; the subject will be covered briefly here because many practical problems revolve around variables which may have any of an infinite number of values.

For a variable X which can take on any value between 0 and k, the chance of each point occurring should be $1/k$. However, instead of k points in this interval, theoretically there are infinitely many points in the interval. By the definition of probability, the probability of all points in the interval must sum to 1, a fact which is impossible when one adds up $1/k$ an infinite number of times. Therefore, theoretically the probability of each

[7] Actually, a denumerable amount of points. See, for example, A. M. Mood and F. A. Graybill, *Introduction to the Theory of Statistics* (New York: McGraw-Hill Book Co., 1963).

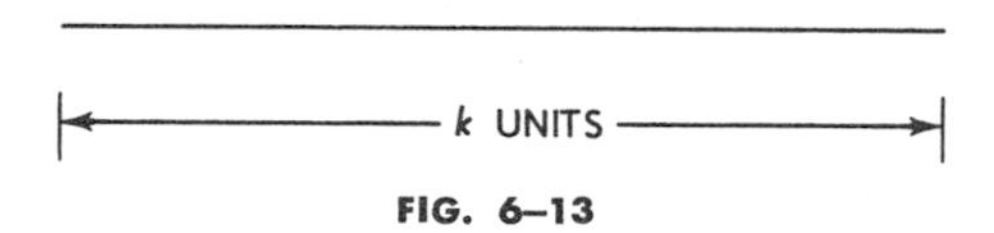

FIG. 6–13

point occurring must be zero. To avoid the problem of zero probability, we introduce the concept of probability density. In the case of each point in the interval 0 to k, the probability density can be pictured as when $f(x)$ gives the probability density for some value of the variable x. A probability density function which is constant over the interval is known as a uniform probability density.

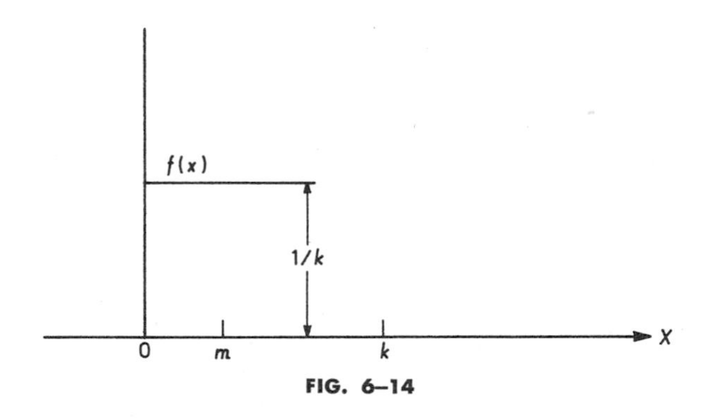

FIG. 6–14

As the probability, or chance of occurrence of any point in the interval 0 to k is 0, we must consider another way of discussing probability. Instead of asking about the chances of any one point, one could ask about the chances of obtaining a value equal to or less than some given value. For example, in Figure 6–14, one may ask about the chances of drawing a number whose value is equal to or less than m; i.e. $P\{x \leqslant m\}$. Letting all the values the variable x can assume in the interval 0 to k comprise the entire set of possible values, then the chance of drawing a value in that part of the set (subset) containing all values of x which are less than or equal to m is $P\{x \leqslant m\}$.

For the variable x, which can take on any value in a range and not just a limited or discrete number of values in this range (continuous variable), the function $P(M) = P(x \text{ is included in the event } M) = P\{x \leqslant m\}$, where the event M contains all values of x which are equal to or less than m, equals $\int_M f(x)\,dx$ where $f(x)$ is the probability density function. In this example the event M can be specified by a knowledge of the point m, so one may also write $P(m) = \int_M f(x)\,dx$.

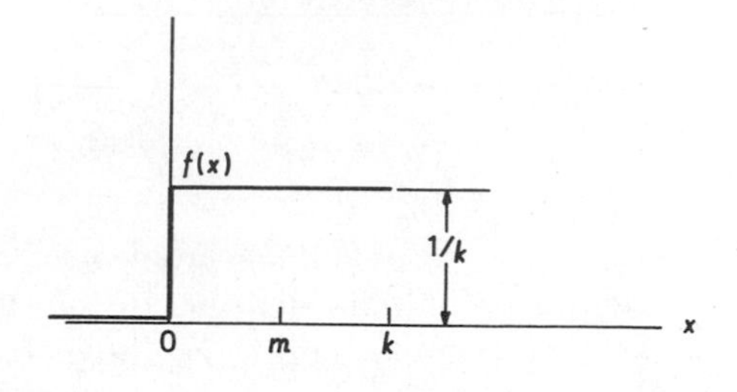

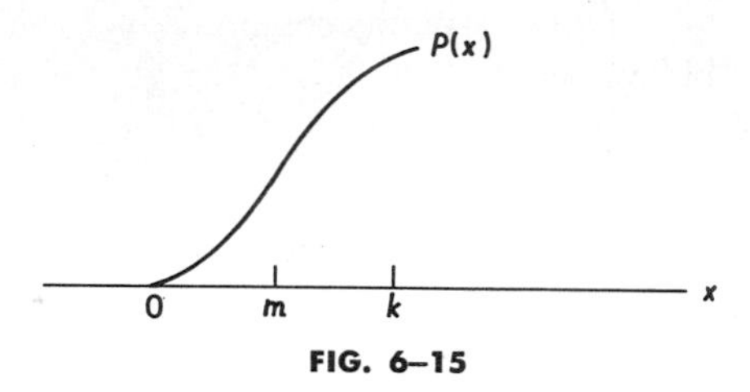

FIG. 6–15

Uniform density function $f(x)$

$$P(x) = \int f(x)\, dx = \int_0^k f(x)\, dx$$

Over the entire set of possible values

$$= \int_0^k \frac{1}{k}\, dx = \frac{1}{k}\int_0^k dx = \frac{1}{k}\Big[x\Big]_0^k$$

$$= 1$$

$P(x)$ is called the cumulative distribution function. To find the probability that a value of x is included in the event M, calculate $P(m)$ as:

$$P(m) = \int_0^m f(x)\, dx = \frac{1}{k}\Big[x\Big]_0^m = \frac{m}{k}$$

If instead of using the continuous uniform distribution, one had used the uniform distribution which contained only k points (the discrete uniform distribution), the probability of drawing a value of x in the event M would be

$$m\left(\frac{1}{k}\right) = \frac{1}{k}$$

when the event M consists of all values of x which are equal to or less than m. For this reason the analyst can use the generated random numbers directly to represent points in the area under the rectangle or the curve.

Many natural and "real-world" events do not follow a uniform probability density. Consider the arrivals of a train—it seems likely that most arrivals will be very close to the scheduled time, i.e., either a little early or a little late; however, a few arrivals are likely to be a few hours late due to some unforeseen occurrence. Assume that due to some scheduling mistakes there will also be some very early arrivals (admittedly a somewhat far-fetched assumption included to illustrate a point). The train arrival process would lead to the probability density function shown in Figure 6–16. (x is said to be normally distributed if $n(x) = \frac{1}{\sqrt{2\pi}\sigma} e^{-(x-\mu)^2/2\sigma^2}$ $-\infty < x < \infty$; σ and μ are the parameters)

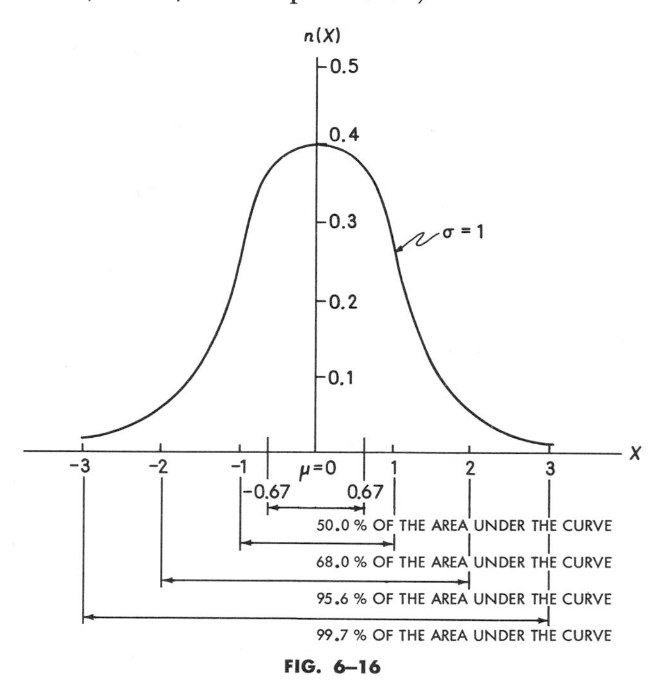

FIG. 6–16

The probability density given in Figure 6–16 is called the normal density function; it is a continuous probability distribution. Theoretically, a train could arrive at 1:00000000001 or 1:00000000000000005 or 12:59210100-000151; in reality, it is only possible to measure the time as accurately as is allowed by the measuring instrument, namely the watch—which means, at the very most, to the tenth of a second. The normal density function has two parameters which describe the location of the center of the bell-shaped curve and the width of the curve; these are the mean and the standard deviation. By definition, the mean of a normal distribution is:

$$\mu = \int_{-\infty}^{\infty} x f(x)\, dx ,$$

and the standard deviation is:

$$\sigma = \sqrt{\int_{-\infty}^{\infty} (x - \mu)^2 f(x)\, dx}$$

The normal density function is

$$f(x) = \frac{1}{\sqrt{2\pi}\,\sigma} e^{-(x-\mu)^2/2\sigma^2} \qquad -\infty < x < \infty$$

For the normal density function, 50 percent of the area under the curve falls between $\pm$ 0.67 standard deviations from the mean, 68.3 percent of all values will be within $\pm$ 1 standard deviation from the mean, 95.6 percent of all values will be within $\pm$ 2 standard deviations from the mean, and 99.7 percent of the values will be within ± 3 standard deviations from the mean.

To get the cumulative normal distribution, take the integral of $f(x),dx$'

$$P(x) = \int_{-\infty}^{\infty} f(x)\, dx = \frac{1}{\sqrt{2\pi}\,\sigma} \int_{-\infty}^{\infty} e^{-(x-\mu)^2/2\sigma^2}\, dx\,.$$

This function is tabulated in simpler form in many statistical texts.[8]

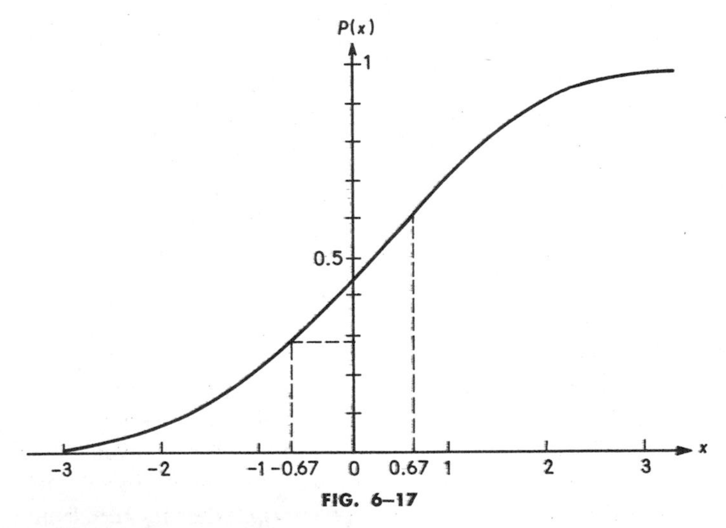

FIG. 6–17

By definition $P(x)$ must be in the range of 0 to 1; therefore, we can use the generated random numbers for $P(x)$. Since the object of our process is to find a random value of a variable possessing a normal probability density,

[8] See Mood and Graybill, *op. cit.*

we wish to find x, given the value, $P(x)$. In other words, we are given:

$$P(x) = r$$

where r is the uniformly generated random variable. Providing there is an inverse function, $P^{-1}(x)$, the inverse function can be applied to the above equation giving:

$$P^{-1}P(x) = P^{-1}(r)$$

or

$$x = P^{-1}(r)$$

One way to obtain the value of x is to use the random number as a location on the $P(x)$ axis and then move on a horizontal projection to the curve, $P(x)$, and then project vertically to the x-axis; the intersection gives the value of x for a corresponding r or $P(x)$. (Figure 6–18).

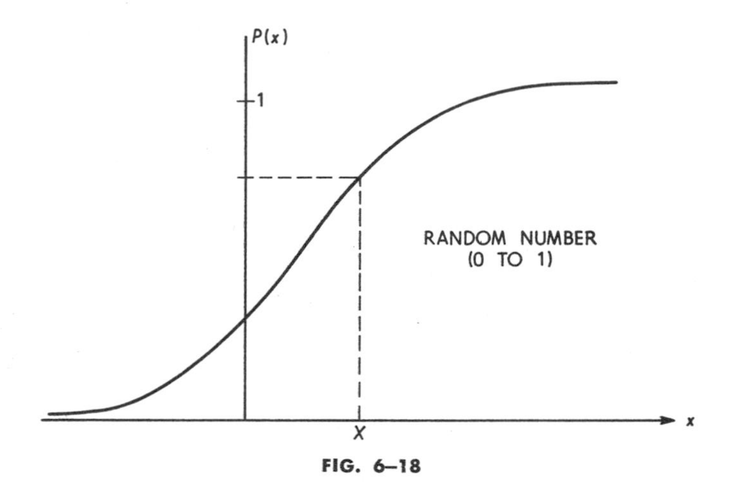

FIG. 6–18

This method will work for most cumulative probability distributions, whether the cumulative probability distribution comes from a discrete or continuous density function. If the density function is discrete, the process of converting to the cumulative distribution is very simple. For the discrete density function shown in Figure 6–19, the cumulative probability distribution is as indicated in Figure 6–20.

Although the method described above for finding random values will work for variables possessing many probability density functions, it is too slow and requires too much memory space to plot and look-up values on the computer to be of practical value.

Any probability density function for a continuous variable x can be transformed to the uniform density function; thus, another method of generating random values from many probability density functions is first

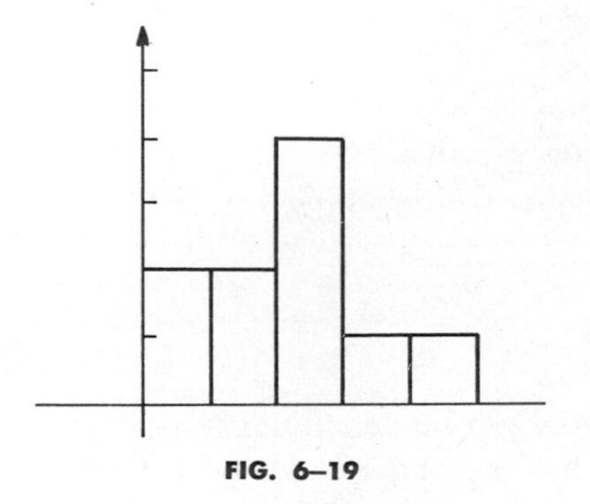

Prob. of $\{x = 1\}$ is .2
Prob. of $\{x = 2\}$ is .2
Prob. of $\{x = 3\}$ is .4
Prob. of $\{x = 4\}$ is .1
Prob. of $\{x = 5\}$ is .2

FIG. 6–19

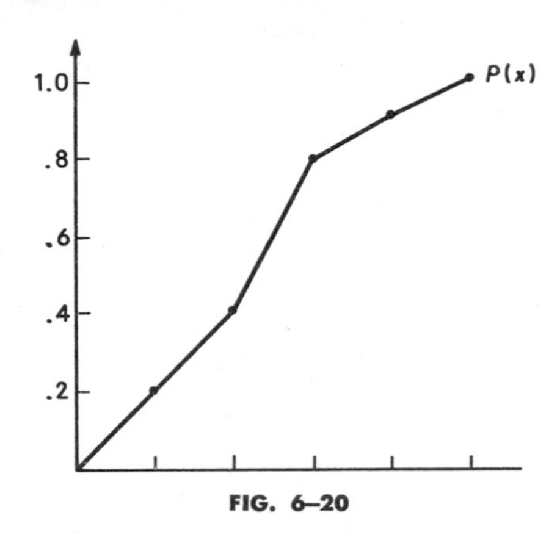

FIG. 6–20

to generate a uniformly distributed random number and transform it to a value from the desired distribution; essentially, this method is the mathematical equivalent of the graphical method mentioned earlier.

One such transformation[9] which results in random drawings from the normal probability distribution is the following:

$$P = \mu + \sigma\left\{ \text{sign } (r - .5)\left[v - \frac{a_0 + a_1 v + a_2 v^2}{1 + b_1 v + b_2 v^2 + b_3 v^3} \right] \right\}$$

where $v = \sqrt{-2 \log_e .5\ (1 - |1 - 2r|)}$, r is a uniformly distributed random number, $a_0 = 2.515517$, $a_1 = .802853$, $a_2 = .010328$, $b_1 = 1.432788$, $b_2 = .189269$, $b_3 = .001308$, and sign $(t) = +1$ if $t \geqslant 0$, and sign $(t) = -1$ if $t < 0$.

Another distribution which occurs in the "real world" is the following:

[9] Juncosa, *op. cit.*

Suppose we have the type of process in which the variable x represents the time from a given starting point and the probability that the event continues on after a time $(x + h)$ if the event is going on at time x is independent of the past duration of the event; this is true if and only if the probability density function that the event lasts for longer than x time units is $f(x) = e^{-\lambda x}$, where λ is a constant characterizing the event. The above density function is called the exponential distribution and is typical of the length of telephone conversations and waiting lines for counters and machines. For $\lambda = 1$,

$$r = P(m) = \int_0^m e^{-x}\,dx$$

is the cumulative distribution, and $m^0 = -\ln r$.

Besides direct transformations there are other techniques which are faster; for example, it can be proved that the average of a large number of uniform random variables yields a normal density. If $x_1, x_2, \ldots, x_n$ are a number of uniform random numbers, then

$$\frac{x_1 + x_2 + \ldots + x_n}{n}$$

yields a normal random variable; for practical purposes, about 12 random values are needed to yield one normal random variable. Another method, claimed to be the fastest yet devised, is given by MacLaren, Marsaglia, and Bray for normal random variables[10] and for exponentially distributed random numbers.[11] The method in each case combines three approximating functions and utilizes about 500 constants. If there was an unlimited amount of storage space, the fastest method for generating normal or exponential random variables would be to generate a uniform random variable and use it as an address where the corresponding value for the normal or exponential distribution would be stored; however, this method could require about 8.5 million storage locations.

To add to the personal library of the reader, following is a typical random number generator which can return a sample from either the uniform distribution, the normal distribution, or the exponential distribution. The flow chart presented earlier will be repeated here.

Notice that the arithmetic statement function for generating uniformly distributed random numbers between 0 and 1 is split into three statements, only one of which is an arithmetic statement function; namely,

---

[10] In *Communications of the ACM*, January, 1964.

[11] *Ibid.*, May, 1964.

```
UNIF (M) = MOD (M * L1, L2)
      RO = UNIF (RO)
```

and

```
      RL = FLOAT (RO) / FLOAT (L2)
```

instead of

```
UNIF (M) = FLOAT (MOD (M*L1, L2)) / FLOAT (L2)
```

The advantage of breaking up the function definition is that now the location which carries r_k as input to the random number generator also carries r_{k+1} (the new random number) before it is scaled down to the region 0 to 1. In this way the routine may be used in recurrent fashion without a great deal of manipulation in the calling program. Before using the preceding subprogram, the programmer may want to include input tests, but it should be pointed out that speed is essential here because of the great number of times the subroutine will be used to solve a problem.

Now that the programmer has use of a subroutine which can generate random values, he can apply the Monte Carlo method to solve for the area under the curve in the original example. To solve the problem we must be

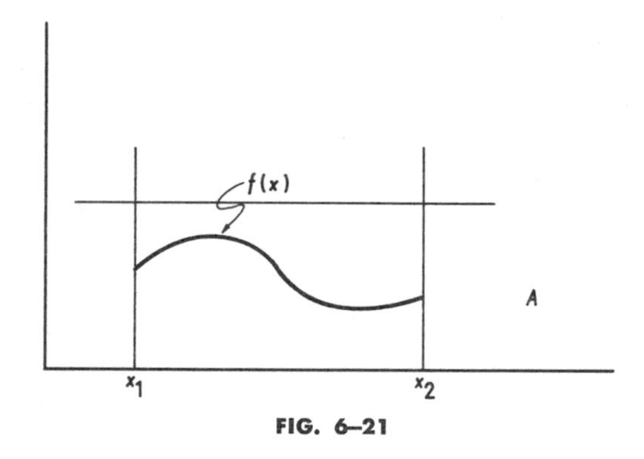

FIG. 6–21

able to say whether a random point that falls inside the rectangle (x_2-x_1), A, also falls inside or outside the curve, $f(x)$. Therefore, the programmer must be able to give the computer a method of calculating or describing $f(x)$. If the computer could convert the curve to mathematical form through some electronic device, the program could calculate areas of graphs whose functions were unknown. Unfortunately, this type of equipment is not readily available and is usually more difficult to program. Without this equipment, the computer must be able to calculate the function at any point to be able to indicate whether or not the random points fall under the curve. Functions such as log, exponential, square root, sin, cos, and arctangent are

FLOW CHART—General Random Number Generator

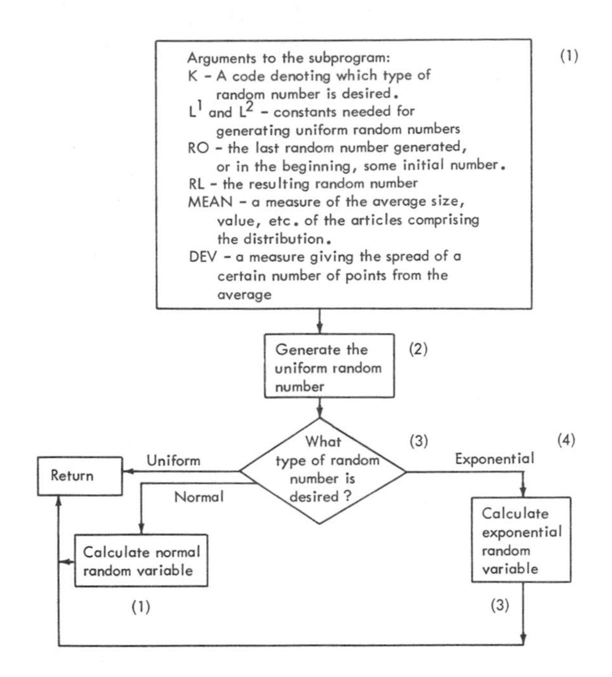

FORTRAN IV PROGRAM—General Random Number Generator

```
C FOR COMMENT
STATEMENT NUMBER | Cont. | FORTRAN STATEMENT
      SUBROUTINE RAND(K,L1,L2,RØ,RL,MEAN,DEV)                              (1)
      INTEGER RØ
C     FOLLOWING IS THE FUNCTION DEFINITION FOR
C     UNIFORM RANDOM NUMBERS
      UNIF(M)=MOD(M*L1,L2)                                                 (2)
C     FOLLOWING IS THE FUNCTION DEFINITION FOR THE SIGN FUNCTION
      SN(X)=X-.5
      RØ=UNIF(RØ)
      RL=FLOAT(RØ)/FLOAT(L2)                                               }
      IF(K.EQ.1)GO TO 2                                                    }(3)
      GO TO (3,4),K                                                        }
    3 Y=1                                                                  }
      IF(SN(RL).LT.Ø.) Y=-1.                                               }
      V=SQRT(-2.*ALOG(.5*(1.-ABS(1.-2.*RL))))                              }(5)
      RL=FLOAT(MEAN)+DEV*Y*(V-(2.515517+.8Ø2853*V                          }
     1+.Ø1Ø328*V**2)/(1.+1.432788*V+.189269*V**2+.ØØ13Ø8*V**3))            }
      RETURN
    4 RL=-ALOG(RL)                                                         (4)
    2 RETURN                                                               (6)
      END
```

already provided by the FORTRAN IV compiler; as for other functions, the programmer must write these as FORTRAN FUNCTIONS. The function in the original example is a polynomial; a typical subprogram to evaluate polynomials will be given in the next section and will be of the form

FUNCTION FUN (X)

Assuming this function to be available to the programmer, he may now write a program which utilizes a Monte Carlo method to solve for the area under the curve.

FLOW CHART—for Monte Carlo Integration Routine

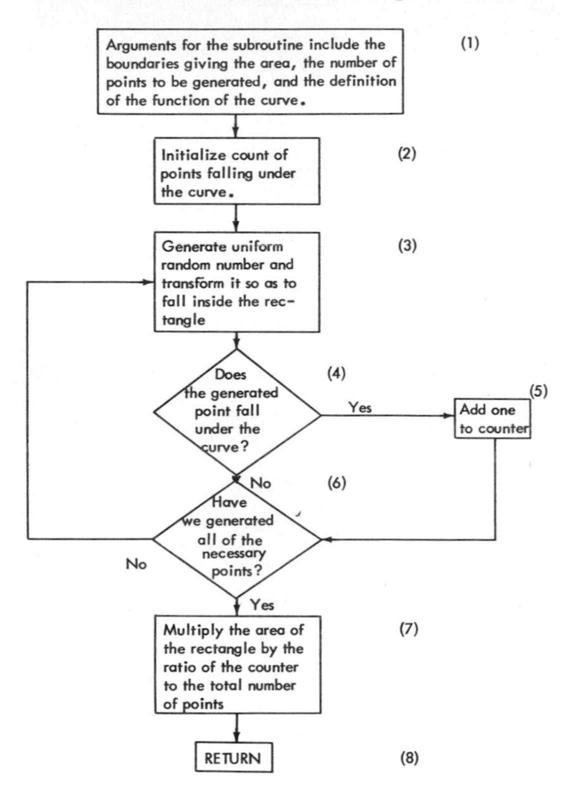

SUBPROGRAM—Calculation of Area by Monte Carlo Method

```
C FOR COMMENT
STATEMENT
 NUMBER   Cont.   FORTRAN STATEMENT
1     5   6  7

             SUBROUTINE INTMC(X1, X2, A, N, FUN, AREA)          (1)
             NCNT=Ø                                              (2)
             K=1
             K1=2**35-1
             L2=2**35
             L1=5**15
             DO 1Ø I=1,N
             CALL RAND(K,L1,L2,K1,R,M,D)                         (3)
             X=(X2-X1)*R+X1
             Y=A*R
       1Ø    IF(Y.LE.FUN(X))NCNT=NCNT+1                          (4),(5),(6)
             AREA=FLOAT(NCNT)/FLOAT(N)*(X2-X1)*A                 (7)
             RETURN                                              (8)
             END
```

Arguments X1 and X2 give the segment along the abscissa; the bounds on the ordinate being $y = 0$ to $y = A$. Because FUN is the name of a FORTRAN FUNCTION subprogram, it must appear in an EXTERNAL statement in the calling program. In the beginning, the location K1 contains r_0, the initial number for the random number generator; after the first random number has been generated by the RAND subroutine, this random number (before scaling; it is still in fixed-point mode) goes to location K1 so as to be in position for input to obtain the next random number. Locations L2 and L1 are the parameters for the random number generator and must be sent to RAND to give the analyst a choice of the sequence of random numbers being generated by RAND. M and D are dummy variables in the CALL statement; since RAND calls for seven arguments, M and D are included. These last two arguments would be utilized only if normally distributed random values were desired and not uniformly distributed random values. In statement 10 the random value of Y is compared to the value of the function at that point; this value being FUN (X), since the coordinates of the random point are (x, y), where x and y are uniformly distributed random numbers scaled to fall under the area $x = x_1$ to $x = x_2$ and $y = 0$ to $y = A$. Location AREA contains the resulting value for the area under the curve. Intuitively, the larger the value of N, the more accurate is the result; this can be shown to be true.

Monte Carlo methods can be applied successfully to many practical problems in science and business. Let us say that a large food store wants to check the average time in line for a customer, the percentage of customers who must wait longer than seven minutes with the present counter facilities and the average number in line; also, the store wants to know the effect of adding a new counter or a bag wrapper at each counter. Assume the present set up is the following:

The customer may go to any counter and he may switch to another counter if that line is going faster. The customers arrive at the counter area in a normal distribution with mean of three minutes and a standard deviation of one minute (actually, the distribution of arrivals is closer to some modification of the Poisson distribution, than the normal[12]) and counter number 1 gives service according to the exponential distribution with $\lambda = 2$ minutes, counter number 2 gives service according to the exponential distribution with $\lambda = 2.5$ minutes, and counter number 2 gives service according to the exponential distribution with $\lambda = 1.8$ minutes. To arrive at these distributions, the store would have to keep data on these events over some period of time. Now the computer can be used to generate this type of operation for a year or two with very little trouble. Each day is started with no one coming to the counter area; then normal random numbers are generated in RAND with $\mu = 3$ minutes and $\sigma = 1$ minute—each arrival being recorded on a sheet and the first arrival being sent to one of the three counters. It will be assumed that the customer does not know which is the faster counter; then each third day the first customer will go to a different counter. When the customer arrives at a particular counter, a service time is drawn at random from RAND (we here assume that RAND can generate random numbers from exponential distributions with λ other than 1—to do this, λ would have to be included as an argument to RAND) with the λ for that particular counter. In this way, a record can be kept of how many customers are in each line at any time of the day, the time each customer spent in line, and the percentage of customers who had to be kept in line longer than seven minutes.

Using the above method, the store manager can also "test" other facilities, such as more counters, faster counters, and more personnel; this is called simulation. Certainly, it is better to spend an hour or two of computer time than it is to make a costly change utilizing only the present data

[12] See W. Feller, *Introduction to Probability and its Applications* (Princeton, N.J.: Princeton University Press, 1959).

for the decision and then, through practical experience, find out that the change was wrong. In other words, through Monte Carlo methods, the businessman may try many different possibilities without actually making the changes.

6.7. Other Introductory Computer Problems

In the present section the reader will be introduced to three common programming areas: areas which have either arisen in previous examples or which will appear in methods given in Chapters 7 and 8, in addition to many other problems arising in mathematics and business.

6.7.1 Evaluation of Polynomials

For a polynomial of the form

$$P = a_0x^n + a_1x^{n-1} + \ldots + a_{n-1}x^1 + a_n,$$

given a value for x, find P. To put the problem into a recurrent or iterative form we can use the following factorization:

Start with the constant a_0,	a_0
Multiply by x and add a_1	$a_1 + a_0x$
Multiply by x and add a_2	$\begin{cases} x\ (a_1 + a_0x)\ a_2 \\ \text{or } a_2 + a_1x + a_0x^2 \end{cases}$
Multiply by x and add a_3	$\begin{cases} x\ (a_2 + a_1x + a_0x^2) + a_3 \\ \text{or } a_3 + a_2x + a_1x^2 + a_0x^3 \end{cases}$
⋮	
Multiply by x and add a_n	$\begin{cases} x\ (a_{n-1} + a_{n-2}x + a_{n-3}x^2 \\ + \ldots + a_0x^{n-1}) + a_n \\ \text{or } a_n + a_{n-1}x + a_{n-2}x^2 \\ + \ldots + a_1x^{n-1} + a_0x^n \end{cases}$

For $n = 4$, we get

$$(x\ (x\ (x\ (x\ (a_0) + a_1) + a_2) + a_3) + a_4)$$

The coefficient of x^n, i.e. a_0, must not be zero; if a_0 is zero, the degree of the polynomial is not n, but at most $(n-1)$. Notice that a test for a zero degree polynomial must be specified because a zero degree polynomial is a constant; in this case a_0.

FLOW CHART—Polynomial Evaluation Routine

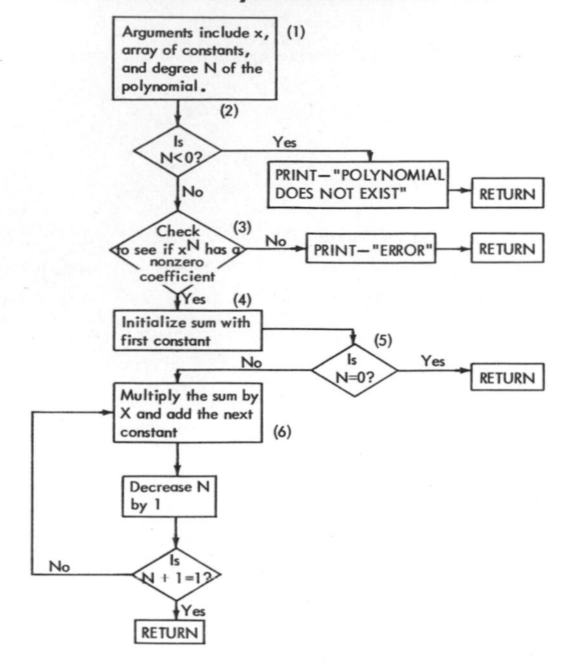

Routine for Evaluating Polynomials

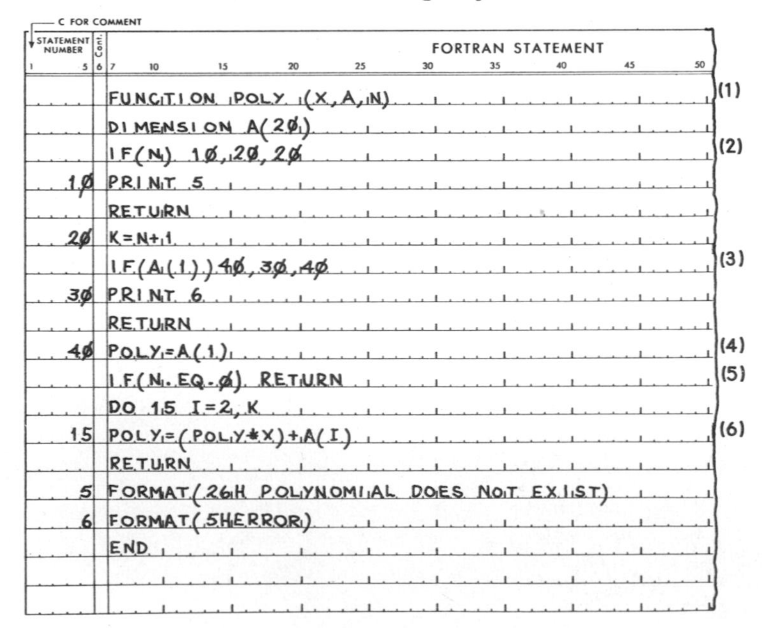

```
C FOR COMMENT
STATEMENT NUMBER | Cont. | FORTRAN STATEMENT

      FUNCTION POLY (X,A,N)                                  (1)
      DIMENSION A(20)
      IF(N) 10,20,20                                         (2)
   10 PRINT 5
      RETURN
   20 K=N+1
      IF(A(1))40,30,40                                       (3)
   30 PRINT 6
      RETURN
   40 POLY=A(1)                                              (4)
      IF(N.EQ.0) RETURN                                      (5)
      DO 15 I=2,K
   15 POLY=(POLY*X)+A(I)                                     (6)
      RETURN
    5 FORMAT(26H POLYNOMIAL DOES NOT EXIST)
    6 FORMAT(5HERROR)
      END
```

The FORTRAN compiler does not permit zero subscripts, therefore, the coefficient of x^n is a_1 not a_0. Poly $= a_1x^n + a_2x^{n-1} + \ldots + a_nx^1 + a_{n+1}$.

Polynomials occur so often in both science and business that it is not hard to demonstrate two other practical uses of the polynomial evaluation routine. Given a polynomial of degree n, $P_n(x)$, then we may write

$$P_n(x) = (x - \mathrm{r})Q_{n-1}(x) + R \tag{1}$$

where $Q_{n-1}(x)$ is a polynomial of degree $(n-1)$ or less.

$$P_n(x) = a_0x^n + a_1x^{n-1} + a_2x^{n-2} + \ldots + a_{n-1}x + a_n \tag{2}$$

and

$$Q_{n-1}(x) = b_0x^{n-1} + b_1x^{n-2} + \ldots + b_{n-2}x + b_{n-1} \tag{3}$$

If we multiply equation (3) by $(x-r)$ and add R, according to equation (1), the result should be $P_n(x)$. Now in order for two polynomials to be equal, the coefficients of each power of x must be equal. Utilizing this fact, the following set of equations hold:

$$\left.\begin{array}{ll}
a_0 = b_0 & \text{Coefficient of } x^n \\
a_1 = b_1 - rb_0 & \text{Coefficient of } x^{n-1} \\
a_2 = b_2 - rb_1 & \text{Coefficient of } x^{n-2} \\
\quad\vdots & \quad\vdots \\
a_{n-1} = b_{n-1} - rb_{n-2} & \text{Coefficient of } x^{n-(n-1)} = x \\
a_n = -rb_{n-1} + R & \text{Coefficient of } x^0
\end{array}\right\} \tag{4}$$

or

$$\left.\begin{array}{l}
b_0 = a_0 \\
b_1 = a_1 + rb_0 \\
b_2 = a_2 + rb_1 \\
\quad\vdots \\
b_{n-1} = a_{n-1} + rb_{n-2} \\
R = a_n + rb_{n-1}\,.
\end{array}\right\} \tag{5}$$

The last set of equations expresses the coefficients of the polynomial $Q_{n-1}(x)$ in terms of the coefficients of the polynomial $P_n(x)$. A simple way of deriving the coefficients of $Q_{n-1}(x)$ from the coefficients of $P_n(x)$ is called synthetic division. When the polynomial $\mathrm{P}_n(x)$ is divided by the polynomial $(x-r)$, the result should be $Q_{n-1}(x)$ and some remainder (see equation (1)). One form for writing down this division process is to specify the coefficients of $P_n(x)$ on the first line and the coefficients of $Q_{n-1}(x)$ on the third line; the second line is reserved for intermediate products—

Divisor

r $\quad a_0 \quad a_1 \quad a_2 \quad a_3 \ldots a_{n-1} \quad a_n$

To start the third line, revert to equations (5); since $b_0 = a_0$, write b_0 in the third line.

$$\begin{array}{r|cccccc} & a_0 & a_1 & a_2 & a_3 \ldots a_{n-1} & a_n \\ r & & & & & \\ \hline & b_0 & & & & \end{array}$$

Next, multiply the most recent entry in the third line by the divisor r and add to the next entry in line 1 to get the next entry in line 3; i.e. $b_1 = a_1\, rb_0$.

$$\begin{array}{r|cccccc} & a_0 & a_1 & a_2 & a_3 \ldots a_{n-1} & a_n \\ r & & rb_0 & & & \\ \hline & b_0 & b_1 & & & \end{array}$$

If we continue in this way, the coefficients of $Q_{n-1}(x)$ will emerge in the third line in an iterative type of calculation.

$$\begin{array}{r|cccccc} & a_0 & a_1 & a_2 & a_3 \ldots a_{n-1} & a_n \\ r & & rb_0 & rb_1 & rb_2 \quad rb_{n-2} & rb_{n-1} \\ \hline & b_0 & b_1 & b_2 & b_3 \ldots b_{n-1} & R=b_n \end{array}$$

By the Remainder Theorem, if r is a root of $P_n(x)$, then $R = 0$.

To divide the polynomial, $P_n(x)$, by $(x-r)$ the polynomial evaluating routine may be employed with a slight modification. The argument R, is the root, r, of the polynomial.

Routine for Evaluating Polynomials—Mod 1

```
C FOR COMMENT
STATEMENT
 NUMBER   Cont.   FORTRAN STATEMENT
      FUNCTION POLY(X,A,N,R)
      DIMENSION A(2Ø)
      COMMON B(2Ø)
      IF (N) 1Ø,2Ø,2Ø
   1Ø PRINT 5
      RETURN
   2Ø K=N+1
      IF(A(1))4Ø,3Ø,4Ø
   3Ø PRINT 6
      RETURN
   4Ø POLY=A(1)
      B(1)=A(1)
      IF (N.EQ.Ø) RETURN
      DO 15 I=2,K
      POLY=(POLY*X)+A(I)
   15 B(I)=A(I)+R*B(I-1)
      RETURN
    5 FORMAT(25HPOLYNOMIAL DOES NOT EXIST)
    6 FORMAT(5HERROR)
      END
```

The coefficients for the polynomial $Q_{n-1}(x)$ are formed in the B array; notice that as soon as the coefficient is formed it is placed in the B array; this is the only change in the routine. If r is a root of $P_n(x)$, then $b_n = R$ will be zero.

Another practical use of the polynomial evaluating routine is to calculate the slope of a polynomial at a particular point, say $x = 5$. If we differentiate the polynomial

$$P_n(x) = (x-r) \cdot Q_{n-1}(x) + R = xQ_{n-1}(x) - r\,Q_{n-1}(x) + R$$

with respect to x, we get

$$P'_n(x) = xQ'_{n-1}(x) - rQ'_{n-1}(x) + Q_{n-1}(x)$$

or

$$P'_n(x) = (x-r)\,Q'_{n-1}(x) + Q_{n-1}(x).$$

Evaluating

$$P'_n(x) \text{ at } x = r, \text{ we get}$$
$$P'_n(r) = Q_{n-1}(r)$$

But $Q_{n-1}(r)$ is the remainder from the process of dividing $Q_{n-1}(x)$ by $(x-r)$; as can be seen from the equation $Q_{n-1}(x) = (x-r)\,T_{n-2}(x) + R_1$; at $x = r$, $Q_{n-1}(r) = R_1$. Therefore:

$$Q_{n-1}(x) = b_0x^{n-1} + b_1x^{n-2} + b_2x^{n-3} + \ldots + b_{n-2}x^1 + b_{n-1}$$

$$\begin{array}{c|cccccc}
 & b_0 & b_1 & b_2 & b_3 \ldots & b_{n-2} & b_{n-1} \\
r & & & & & & \\
 & & c_0r & c_1r & c_2r \ldots & c_{n-3}r & c_{n-2}r \\
\hline
 & c_0 & c_1 & c_2 & c_3 \ldots & c_{n-2} & c_{n-1} = R_1
\end{array}$$

where

$$T_{n-2}(x) = c_0x^{n-2} + c_1x^{n-3} + c_2x^{n-4} + \ldots + c_{n-3}x^1 + c_{n-2}$$

Thus, to obtain the slope (derivative of the polynomial at the point or the ratio of the incremental increase [decrease] on the ordinate to the incremental increase [decrease] on the abscissa) at the point k, the analyst need only apply synthetic division by $(x-k)$ twice and the remainder after the second division gives the result. When the polynomial evaluating routine is available, the call would be the following:

Main Program

```
COMMON  Y (20)
READ 7, X, N
        ______
        ______
        ______
K = N + 1
READ 6, (A (J), J = 1, K)
R = POLY (X,A,N)
L = N - 1
T = POLY (X, Y, L)
SLOPE= Y(N)
        ______
        ______
        ______
```

Notice that the slope, which is $Q_{n-1}(r)$ or the remainder from the second synthetic division resides in location $Y(N)$ or it is the coefficient c_n.

Synthetic division and the polynomial evaluating routine may be used to provide another method of programming Newton's Method (actually the Newton-Raphson Method) for finding roots. The reader may recall that Newton's formula is

$$x^{(k+1)} = x^{(k)} - \frac{f(x)_{x=a_k}}{f'(x)_{x=a_k}};$$

$f(x)$ and $f'(x)$, both evaluated at the present value of the root, may be calculated by the polynomial evaluation routine; $f(x)_{x=a_k}$ is the remainder from dividing $P_n(x)$ by $(x-r)$ and $f'(x)$ is the remainder from dividing $Q_{n-1}(x)$ by $(x-r)$.

Routine for Calulating Real Roots of Polynomials by Newton's Method

```
      SUBROUTINE NEWT(X,A,N)
      DIMENSION A(2Ø)
      COMMON Y(2Ø)
      K=N+1
      IF(K-2Ø) 1Ø,1Ø,2Ø                                  (1)
   2Ø PRINT 15
   15 FORMAT(9HTOO LARGE)
      RETURN
      DO 3Ø I=1,1ØØ
   1Ø T=POLY(X,A,N)                                      (2)
      R=Y(K)
      L=N-1
      S=POLY(X,Y,L)                                      (3)
      U=Y(N)
      TEMP=X-R/U
      X=TEMP
   3Ø IF (TEMP.LE..ØØØØ5) RETURN
      PRINT 4Ø
   4Ø FORMAT (13HTOO MUCH TIME)
      RETURN
      END
```

A limit of 100 iterations was set in case the user has an equation which yields slow conversion to the root in question. An equation of the 20th degree is the largest which can be handled by the program; this is tested for in (1). Notice that the value (kth iteration) of the polynomial $P_n(x^{(k)})$ is placed in T and the value of the polynomial $Q_{n-1}(x^{(k)})$ is placed in S in (2) and (3) even though these values are not required by the calling program in this case. The above situation arises because the polynomial evaluation routine was written as a FORTRAN FUNCTION instead of a FORTRAN SUBROUTINE; remember, the FORTRAN FUNCTION may return only one value in the calling statement—the other values must be returned via the COMMON area. The COMMON area as an agent to transfer arguments and results between general routines has its limitation in that the user must not use a certain portion of the COMMON area for other purposes. In this case then, it appears a FORTRAN SUBROUTINE would have been better than a FORTRAN FUNCTION.

6.7.2. Plotting

For many purposes it is necessary to obtain auxiliary equipment in order to utilize a digital computer in plotting functions, grade lines (mining), engineering design, etc. However, in some cases it is possible to utilize a digital computer for plotting without auxiliary equipment other than a printer. As a production technique this method would be too slow, but for small scientific and business problems it may be feasible. The technique will be illustrated for polynomials.

Suppose we desire a plotting routine in which the printer can utilize 119 spaces (usually 120 spaces are available, but the first column may be used by the FORTRAN compiler to signal the printer) in a horizontal direction across the printed page and in which there are 60 possible printed lines along the breadth of the page. Clearly, the page must be planned in the sense that the routine must be given the range for the dependent variable, as well as for the independent variable. The programmer must decide which divisions along each axis should be marked (i.e., every fourth division, every fifth division, etc.).

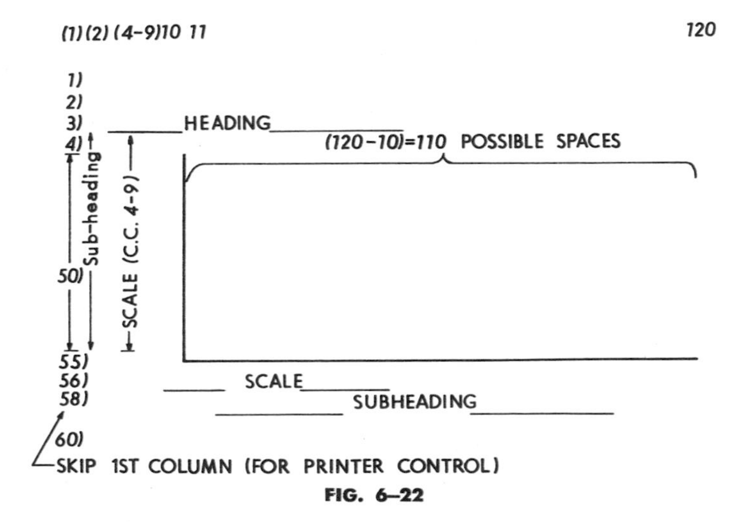

FIG. 6–22

Going down the page vertically:

Line 1–2	Blank
Line 3	Heading
Line 4	Blank
Line 5–54	Available for data points
Line 55	Periods marking the abscissa
Line 56	Scale for the independent variable
Line 57	Blank
Line 58	Heading for the independent variable
Line 59–60	blank

Going across the page horizontally:

Column 1	Required to be blank (printer control)
Column 2	Heading for the independent variable (much easier for the analyst to print this heading manually, but possible in FORTRAN)
Column 3	Blank
Column 4–9	Scale for the dependent variable
Column 10	Period marking the ordinate
Column 11–120	Available for data points

If the programmer writes the plotting routine by starting the plot with the independent variable at its lowest value and incrementing the independent variable, then the routine will be limited to decreasing functions unless the dependent variable is plotted on the x-axis and the independent variable on the y-axis; the reason is that the printer is not equipped to reverse the paper in the vertical direction. To write the routine with the axis in the usual direction (i.e., with dependent variable as the ordinate and the independent variable as the abscissa) would require a sorting of the dependent values into decreasing sequence thus considerably complicating the program.

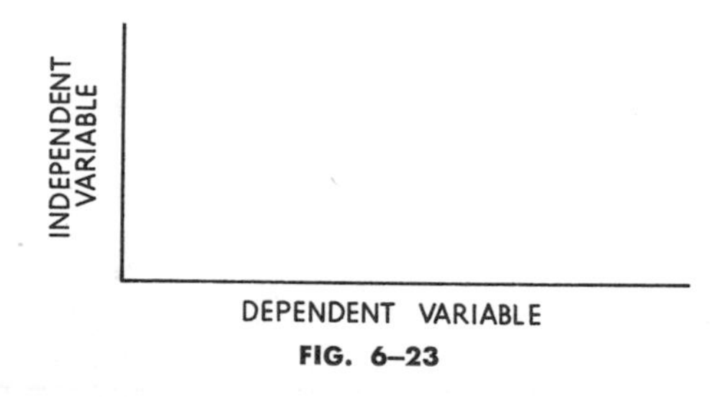

FIG. 6–23

The axes are to be indicated with periods. For the ordinate, each time a line is printed (every line) a period is brought out (see statement 3); for the abscissa, a period is brought out at each possible point in the desired line (see statement 5).

FLOW CHART

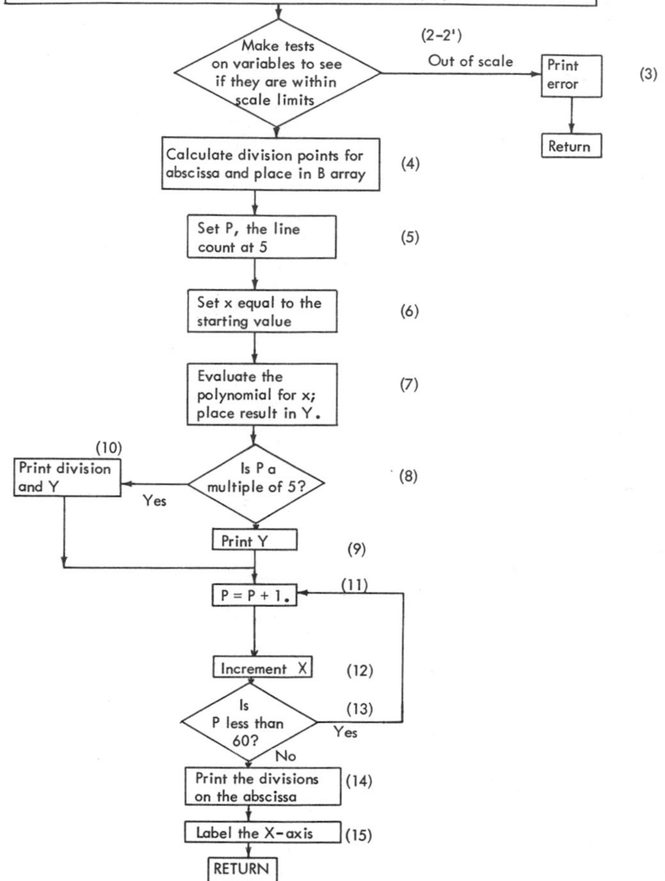
(1)
Arguments for the subprogram include the following: upper and lower bounds for the dependent variable — the starting value and the increment for the independent variable — headings — the coefficients and degree of the polynomial
Make tests on variables to see if they are within scale limits
(2-2')
Out of scale
Print error
(3)
Return
Calculate division points for abscissa and place in B array
(4)
Set P, the line count at 5
(5)
Set x equal to the starting value
(6)
Evaluate the polynomial for x; place result in Y.
(7)
(10)
Print division and Y
Yes
Is P a multiple of 5?
(8)
Print Y
(9)
P = P + 1.
(11)
Increment X
(12)
Is P less than 60?
(13)
Yes
No
Print the divisions on the abscissa
(14)
Label the X-axis
(15)
RETURN

Plotting Routine

```
      SUBROUTINE PLOT(INC,IBGN,Y1,Y2,A,N,HEAD1,HEAD2)                (1)
      COMMON D(2Ø)
      DIMENSION A(2Ø),B(1Ø),LINE(11Ø),HEAD1(15),HEAD2(15)
      REAL INC,IBGN
      DATA SPACE,PT/1H ,1H*
      IF(ABS(Y1).GE.1ØØØ.)GO TO 15                                   )
      IF(IBGN.GE.1ØØØ.OR.(IBGN.GE.1ØØ.AND.INC.GE.1ØØ).OR.(INC.GE.1ØØØ))  (2)
     1GO TO 15                                                       )
      B(1)=Y1
      Z=(ABS(Y1)+ABS(Y2))/1Ø.                                        )
      DO 1Ø I=2,1Ø                                                   (4)
   1Ø B(I)=B(I-1)+Z                                                  )
      IF(B(I).GE.1ØØØ.)GO TO 15                                      (2')
      WRITE(6,1)
      WRITE(6,2) HEAD1
      P=5                                                            (5)
      X=IBGN                                                         (6)
   5Ø Y=POLY(X,A,N)                                                  (7)
      DO 7 J=1,11Ø
```

```
    7 LINE(J)=SPACE
      K=Y/(ABS(Y1)+ABS(Y2))*11Ø.+.5
      LINE(K)=PT
      IF(AMOD(P,.5).EQ.0.)GO TO 90                   (8)
      WRITE(6,3) LINE                                (9)
      GO TO 8Ø
   9Ø WRITE(6,4) X,LINE                              (1Ø)
   8Ø P=P+1                                          (11)
      X=X+INC                                        (12)
      IF(P.LT.6Ø.)GO TO 5Ø                           (13)
      WRITE(6,5)
      WRITE(6,6)(B(I),I=1,1Ø)                        (14)
      WRITE(6,2) HEAD2                               (15)
    1 FORMAT(1H1)
    2 FORMAT(/15A6)
    3 FORMAT(9X1H.,11ØA1)
    4 FORMAT(3XF6.2,1H.,11ØA1)
    5 FORMAT(9X,111(1H.))
    6 FORMAT(7XF6.2,9(4XF6.2))
```

```
   15 WRITE(6,7)                                     (3)
    7 FORMAT(5HERROR)
      RETURN
      END
```

A DATA statement allows data to be placed in the routine without having to use a READ statement; to place a READ statement in a subroutine would reduce its generality. To calculate the point on the line where the value of the polynomial falls, we must remember that there are only a limited number of places where the point may fall; namely 110 places. Therefore, a value which is returned from the polynomial evaluating routine must be scaled down to a number between 0 and 1, then placed in the range 0 to 110, and finally rounded to an integer between 0 and 110; all three requirements are accomplished via the statement,

```
K = Y / (ABS (Y1)+ABS (Y2)) * 110. + .5
```

The entire array, LINE, is supplied with blanks, and then an asterisk is sent into the kth place in order to indicate the plotted value. After each line has been written on tape (latter to printed off-line), the entire LINE array is resupplied with blanks; a more efficient method would be to simply change the one asterisk back to a blank before sending in the next asterisk; the reader may try this procedure. To add to this program, the student may generate unequal spacing along the vertical axis, plot parametric equations, and introduce other complications.

DESCRIPTION OF THE ROUTINE

Note again that a space is reserved in the COMMON area even though the D array is not used because of the COMMON statement in the POLY routine. Coefficients for the polynomial are in the A array, and its degree is in location N. Locations Y1 and Y2 contain the lower and upper values for y; locations IBGN and INC contain the starting point and increment for the independent variable. Both the heading for the graph itself and the label for the abscissa permit the use of 90 alphameric characters (15 words of 6 alphameric characters each) via the use of the arrays HEAD 1 and HEAD 2.

It was decided to allocate the six spaces for divisional marking along either axis; therefore, tests must be included to see that the starting and ending values or the starting values and the increments are not larger than three figures to the left of the decimal point and one to right of the decimal point—F6.2 implies ± xxx.x. To avoid being caught by these tests, the variables may have to be scaled before reaching the plotting routine.

The statements comprising group (4) in the routine create the divisional markings for the abscissa. Notice that it is possible to have 11 divisional points each at 10 spaces apart; however, to simplify the labeling of the axis, only the first 10 out of the 11 are to be labeled. Labeling starts at Y1 and goes in increments of Z, where Z = (ABS (Y1)+ABS (Y2))/10.; labeling of only 10 divisions avoids the rounding problem in labeling (the student should try a different number of divisions if he does not see the difficulty).

Count of printing lines starts at 5 and goes to 60 instead of 1 to 55 to facilitate the labeling of each fifth line via the FORTRAN IV BUILT-IN FUNCTION, AMOD. The present count will yield no remainder when divided by 5 if P, the line count, is a multiple of five; testing the remainder for zero can then be used to signal the division labeling as well as for plotting the value for that line. Starting with the value 5, allows a divisional printing for the first line; another possibility would be to start at 0, but not at 1 if it is desired to mark the first division.

6.7.3. Permutations

Index a set of n things with the integer numbers; that is, represent these n things by the letters $a_i, i = 1; \ldots, 10$, or $a_1, a_2, \ldots, a_n$, where i, the index, ranges over the integers from 1 to n. Once each of the n things can be identified by its index, the n things may be arranged in different order. One such ordering is $a_1, a_2, a_3, \ldots, a_n$; these items are said to be in natural order or in the natural ordering of their index integers. Obviously, the above ordering of the integers $(1, 2, \ldots, n)$ is not the only possible ordering; another is 2, 1, 3, 4,5, if n equals 5. To ask how many orderings there are of the n integers is the same as asking the number of ways in which someone can pick n different balls out of a box without replacing a ball once it has been removed.

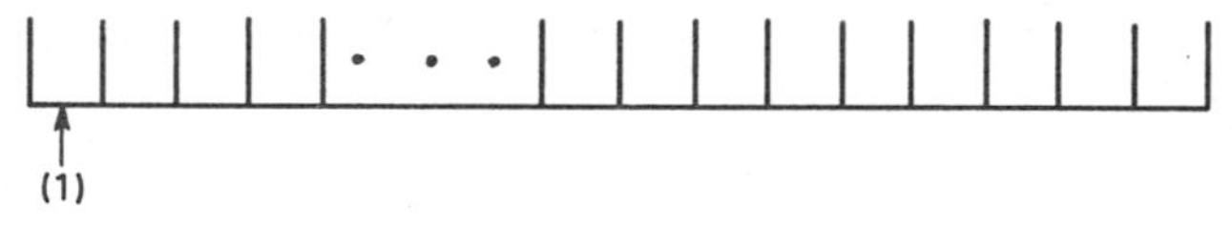

FIG. 6–24

There are n ways of picking the first element since there are originally n elements in the box. When the first element is removed from the box, there are $(n-1)$ elements remaining in the box; therefore, there are $(n-1)$ ways picking out the second element. Continuing in the above manner, after $(n-1)$ elements have been chosen, there remains only one way to choose the last element. When we multiply together all the possible ways of choosing each element, we have the total number of ways in which n labeled elements can be drawn from a box without replacement; that number is $(n) \cdot (n-1) \cdot (n-2) \ldots (2) \cdot (1) = n!$; i.e., n factorial.

Each ordering of the integers is called a permutation or reordering from the natural order; the natural order may be thought of as a permutation of itself. Because the number of permutations of the n integers rises rapidly with the number n, it is not feasible to list manually all possible permutations in order to obtain each ordering without repeating a previous ordering. The reader should convince himself that this is true by letting n equal 4 and then, starting with the natural order, trying to obtain the 24 possible orderings by rearranging the four integers. The computer can be used to list all possible permutations by "brute force" in a method simulating the way the student would have ordered them manually (this method will be illustrated in the next chapter). However, many solutions to statistical and mathematical problems depend on listing all the possible permutations in an "orderly" way; by an "orderly" way we mean an ordering of the permutations by the integers so that by referring to the integer m we can obtain the mth out of a total of $n!$ ($m<n!$) permutations. In other words, we wish to set up a one-to-one correspondence between the set of integers 1 to $n!$ and the $n!$ permutations; given an integer we can obtain a particular permutation, and given a particular permutation, we can obtain the integer index or rank of that permutation. If we can set up this correspondence, we can generate random permutations for certain problems which require Monte Carlo procedures for solution by generating uniform random integers from 1 to n. To set up an orderly listing of the permutations we first introduce the following representation of a number:

$$b_1\,(n-1)!+b_2\,(n-2)!+b_3\,(n-3)!+\ \dots\ +b_{n-2}\,(2)!+b_{n-1}\,(1)!+b_n$$

where the b_i, $i = 1, \dots, n$, are integers and $0\leqslant b_i\leqslant (n-1)$.

For the number 4, the following representations are possible:

$b_{n-2} = 2,$	$b_i = 0$ all other i
$b_{n-1} = 4$	$b_i = 0$ all other i
$b_{n-2} = 1,\ b_{n-1} = 2,$	$b_i = 0$ all other i
$b_{n-2} = 1,\ b_{n-1} = 1,\ b_n = 1,$	$b_i = 0$ all other i
$b_n = 4$	$b_i = 0$ all other i

and other ways which the student can write out.

The above representation is not useful to us unless we can generate a unique number of the form

$$b_1(n-1)!+b_2(n-2)!+\ \dots\ +b_{n-2}(2)!+b_{n-1}(1)!+b_n$$

for each integer from 0 to $n!-1$; this procedure is necessary for the generation of a unique permutation from an integer in the range of 0 to $(n!-1)$ or 1 to $n!$. A further restriction, namely, that $b_j\leqslant n-j$ is necessary and sufficient to obtain a one to one correspondence between the new numbers and the integers. For example, now the number 4 can be represented only as $b_{n-2} = 2$ and $b_i = 0$ for all other i. Now $b_{n-1} = 4$ will not work because $j = n-1$ and $b_{n-(n-1)}$ or $b_1\leqslant 1$; but here $b_1 = 4$ so $b_1\leqslant 1$. Also $b_{n-2} = 1$, $b_{n-1} = 1$, and $b_n = 1$ will not work because when $j = n$, $b_j = b_n\leqslant n-n = 0$ so b_n must be zero; but here $b_n = 1$.

To satisfy himself the student should show that none of the other ways specified earlier for the number 4 will work. Notice that the numbers $b_1(n-1)!+b_2(n-2)!+\dots+b_{n-2}(2)!+b_{n-1}(1)!+b_n$ where $0\leqslant b_j\leqslant n-j$, b_i are integer, depend only on the sequence of b's, $\{b\}$. Therefore, we have a one to one correspondence between the set of $n!$ integers 0 to $(n! - 1)$ and the $n!$ sequences $b_1, b_2, \dots, b_n$ (the b's may be permuted in $n!$ ways). A one to one correspondence between these two sets implies that a functional relation exists, such that $F\,(I) = B_I$, and also the inverse relation $F^{-1}\,(B_I) = I$

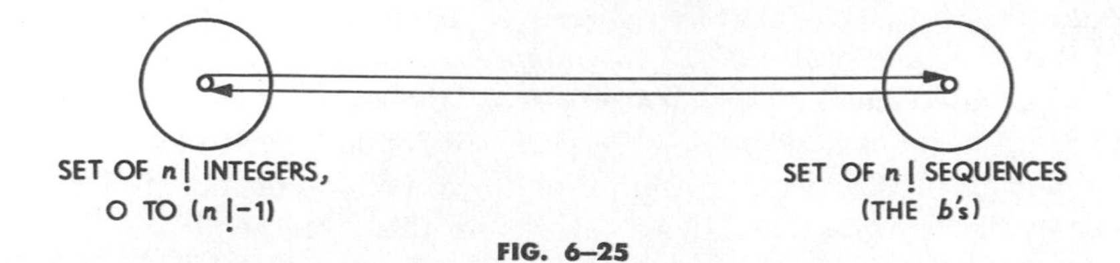

FIG. 6–25

exists. One way to calculate the b sequences from the integers is the following:

$$
\begin{aligned}
I \div (n-1)! &= b_1 + \text{REM }(1)\\
\text{REM }(1) \div (n-2)! &= b_2 + \text{REM }(2)\\
\text{REM }(2) \div (n-3)! &= b_3 + \text{REM }(3)\\
&\vdots\\
\text{REM }(n-2) \div (1)! &= b_{n-1} + \text{REM }(n-1)\\
\text{REM }(n-1) \div (0)! &= b_n + 0
\end{aligned}
$$

where I is the integer, and REM (j) is the remainder from the division of I by $(n-j)!$. By the remainder theorem this process is unique. As an example, suppose $n = 5$ and $I = 77$ (77 was picked randomly out of the range 0 to 119 since $5! = 120$), then

$$
\begin{aligned}
77 \div (4)! &= 77 \div 24 = 3+5\\
5 \div (3)! &= 5 \div 6 = 0+5\\
5 \div (2)! &= 5 \div 2 = 2+1\\
1 \div (1)! &= 1 \div 1 = 1+0\\
0 \div (0)! &= 0 \div 1 = 0+0
\end{aligned}
$$

where $0! \equiv 1$ and $\{b\} = 3, 0,2, 1,0$; i.e., $b_1 = 3$, $b_2 = 0_1$ $b_3 = 2$, $b_4 = 1$, and $b_5 = 0$. Using the inverse function, given that $\{b\} = 3,0,2,1,0$; calculate I.

$$
\begin{aligned}
I &= b_1\,(4)! + b_2\,(3)! + b_3\,(2)! + b_4\,(1)! + b_5\,(0)\,!\\
&= 3\,(4)! + 0\,(3)! + 2(2)! + 1(1)! + 0\,(0)!\\
&= 72 \quad + \quad 0 \quad + \quad 4 \quad + \quad 1 \quad + \quad 0\\
&= 77
\end{aligned}
$$

$\{b\}$ is called the factorial sequence. Now, we seek to generate the permutation of the integers from the factorial sequence. Notice that the factorial sequence itself cannot serve as the permutation of the integers from 1 to n because b_i may equal b_j, where $i \neq j$, as can be seen from the above example in which $b_2 = b_5 = 0$.

Starting with the factorial sequence one can "look-up" the permutation sequence from the natural sequence. Take the b sequence and add 1 to each term since any b_i may be zero and zero cannot be used as an index in a look-up procedure. Using the $\{b\}$ from the above example:

$\{b\} = 3, 0, 2, 1, 0$	
$\{b+1\} = 4, 1, 3, 2, 1$	Add 1 to each b_i
$\{n\} = 1, 2, 3, 4, 5$	Write the natural sequence
$\{p\} = 4$	Form the permutation sequence, $\{p\}$, by using the $\{b + 1\}$ as a dictionary: The first term of $\{b + 1\}$ is 4 so take the fourth member of $\{n\}$ and write it down; crossing it out from $\{n\}$. Next take the first term of those terms remaining in $\{n\}$ and put it in $\{p\}$: Continue in this manner.

$\{n\} =$ ~~1~~, $2, 3, 5$
$\{p\} = 4, 1$
$\{n\} = 2, 3,$ ~~5~~
$\{p\} = 4, 1, 5$
$\{n\} = 2,$ ~~3~~
$\{p\} = 4, 1, 5, 3$
$\{n\} =$ ~~2~~
$\{p\} = 4, 1, 5, 3, 2.$

Thus, the 78th permutation out of a total of 120 permutations of the 5 integers 1, 2, 3, 4, 5 is 4, 1, 5, 3, 2.

It is easy to regenerate $\{b\}$ from $\{p\}$ by the following procedure: Compare p_1 with all following p_i; write down the number of integers which are less than p_1 which follow p_1—in this case 1, 3, and 2 are less than p_1 so $b_1 = 3$. Do the same for p_2 to get $b_2 = 0$ since 5, 3, and 2 are larger than 1. Continuing in this way $b_3 = 2$, $b_4 = 1$, and $b_5 = 0$; $\{b\} = 3, 0, 2, 1, 0$.

Using this method, an analyst can generate any of the $n!$ permutations with a storage requirement of only the factorial sequence for that permutation, the natural sequence, and the permutation itself. However, if it is needed to generate all the possible permutations for some number n, this method is relatively inefficient because it does not use any information provided by the last permutation; each permutation is generated independently.

The next method utilizes the most recent permutation to create the next permutation; but it requires more storage than the first method.

The routine furnishes a permutation given a number I, from 0 to N!–1. Instead of calling a factorial routine in to give each factorial, the generation of the factorials is incorporated in the subroutine to avoid unnecessary use of the calling sequence. The statement K (I1) = I / NFAC (IJ) gives b_{I1}, the (I1) st term of the b sequence (here it is placed in the k array); then, I = I– NFAC (IJ) * K (I1) gives the remainder from the division of I by NFAC (IJ). By placing the remainder in location I, the next division of I by NFAC (IJ) will produce the next term in the b sequence; therefore, we get a recurrence relationship.

Generation of the permutation sequence from the natural sequence via the factorial sequence is the most complicated part of the routine. The vari-

FLOW CHART—Permutation Generating Routine

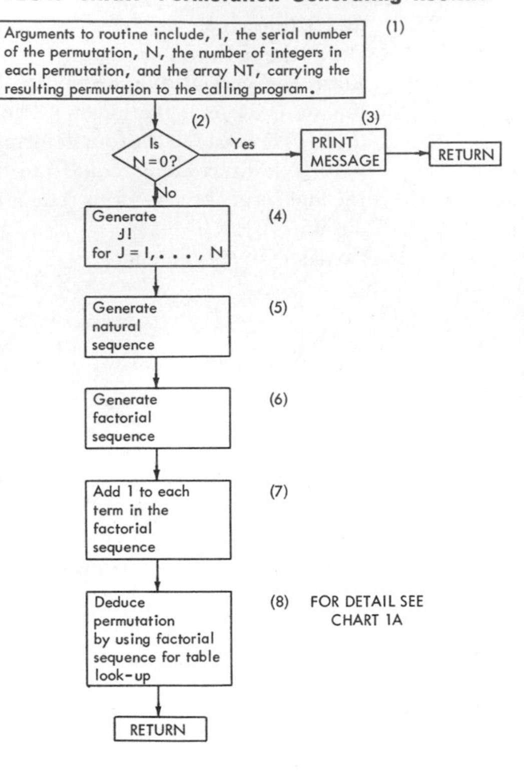
Arguments to routine include, I, the serial number of the permutation, N, the number of integers in each permutation, and the array NT, carrying the resulting permutation to the calling program.
(1)
(2)
Is N=0?
Yes
(3)
PRINT MESSAGE
RETURN
No
Generate J! for J = I, . . . , N
(4)
Generate natural sequence
(5)
Generate factorial sequence
(6)
Add 1 to each term in the factorial sequence
(7)
Deduce permutation by using factorial sequence for table look-up
(8) FOR DETAIL SEE CHART 1A
RETURN

Details of Deducing Permutation Sequence from Natural Sequence

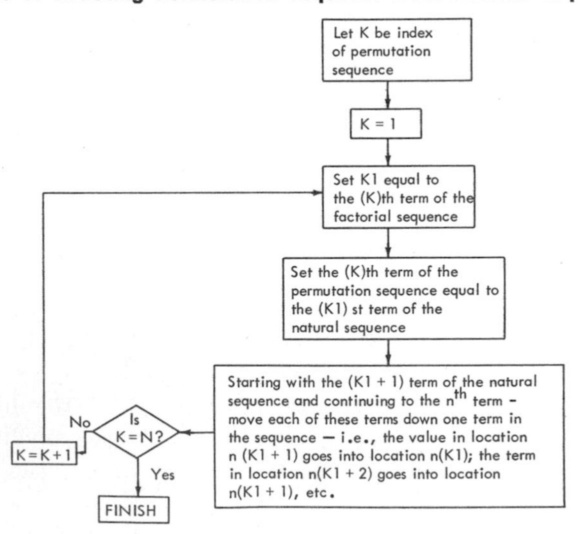
Let K be index of permutation sequence
K = 1
Set K1 equal to the (K)th term of the factorial sequence
Set the (K)th term of the permutation sequence equal to the (K1) st term of the natural sequence
Starting with the (K1 + 1) term of the natural sequence and continuing to the nth term - move each of these terms down one term in the sequence — i.e., the value in location n (K1 + 1) goes into location n(K1); the term in location n(K1 + 2) goes into location n(K1 + 1), etc.
Is K=N?
No
K=K+1
Yes
FINISH

Routine to Generate the Permutation with Rank I, from an Orderly List of N! Permutations

```
      SUBROUTINE PERM(I,N,NT)
      DIMENSION NFAC(20),NATT(20),NT(20),K(20)                  (1)
      IF(N)36,36,37                                             (2)
   36 WRITE(6,87)                                               (3)
   87 FORMAT(9HERROR-N=0)
      RETURN
   37 NFAC(1)=1                                                 (4)
      DO 82 J12=2,N
   82 NFAC(J12)=NFAC(J12-1)*J12
C         BY FIRST CALCULATING THE FACTORIAL SEQUENCE, AND THEN
C         DERIVING THE PERMUTATION SEQUENCE
      DO 4 I1=1,N                                               (5)
    4 NATT(I1)=I1
      DO 20 I1=1,N                                              (6)
      IJ=N-I1+1                                                 &
      K(I1)=I/NFAC(IJ)                                          (7)
      I=I-NFAC(IJ)*K(I1)
   20 K(I1)=K(I1)+1
C         THE FOLLOWING LOOP FORMS THE MAPPING OF THE FACTORIAL
C         SEQUENCE PLUS 1 ONTO THE NATURAL SEQUENCE,THUS PRODUCING
C         THE PERMUTATION SEQUENCE
      DO 40 I2=1,N                                              (8)
      K1=K(I2)
      NT(I2)=NATT(K1)
      K1P=K1+1
      N1=N-I2+1
      IF(K1P-N1)6,6,40
    6 DO 440 I3=K1P,N1
      K1=I3-1
  440 NATT(K1)=NATT(I3)
   40 CONTINUE
      RETURN
      END
```

able I2 is used as the index of the factorial sequence (actually after 1 has been added to each term of the factorial sequence) as well as the index for the permutation sequence. The variable K1 is set equal to the (I2) term of the factorial sequence and then K1 serves as the index for the table look-up of the natural sequence; that is, the (K1) st term of the natural sequence becomes the (I2) term of the permutation sequence. For this process to function correctly for all terms of the permutation sequence, some way must be devised to skip the terms in the natural sequence which have already been used for the permutation sequence. If the factorial sequence is 4, 1, 3, 2, 1 after the addition of 1 to each term, then with I2 = 1, K1 becomes 4. The fourth term in the natural sequence is 4, so the (I2) term or the 1st term of the permutation sequence is 4. Now I2 = 2, so K1 = 1; but now the natural sequence is no longer 1,2,3,4,5, but 1,2,3,5. The 1st term is I in either case giving a permutation sequence of 4,1. The natural sequence becomes 2,3,~~5~~; I2 = 3 and K1 becomes 3. Now the third term in the permutation sequence becomes 5, showing the need for crossing out previously used members of the natural sequence. The easiest way to handle the problem of crossing out the used members of the sequence is to move every number which lies to the right of the crossed-out term one place to the left.

1, 2, 3, ~~4~~, 5
1, 2, 3, 5, 5

At the end, the natural sequence will become 5, 5, 5, 5, 5; however, this fact is not involved in the solution of the problem (the reader should satisfy himself that this is true). The instructions

```
6    DO 440 I3 = K1P, N1
     K1 = I3 - 1
440  NATT (K1) = NATT(I3)
```

accomplish the shifting of the natural sequence.

First, let us rewrite the method of expressing a number in the form

$$C_1\, 1! + C_2 2! + \ldots + C_{n-1}\,(n-1)!,\ 0 \leqslant c_i \leqslant i$$

for integer i from 1 to $(n!-1)$. The reader should be able to see that this representation is the reverse of

$$b_1\,(n-1)! + b_2\,(n-2)! + \ldots + b_{n-1}\,(1)! + b_n;$$

where b_i are integers from 0 to $(n-1)$ and $b_j \leqslant n-j$. In each case there are only $(n-1)$ elements necessary for the permutation of n numbers, $0,1,2,\ldots,(n-1)$ since $b_n = 0$.

A method, developed by M.B.Wells,[13] generates each permutation from

---

[13] M. B. Wells, "Generation of Permutation by Transposition," *Math. Comp.*, Vol. XV (1961),192–195.

the last permutation by interchanging just two numbers. Each integer k $(k \leqslant n)$ has a one-to-one correspondence with a $\{c\} = (c_1, c_2, c_3, \ldots, c_{n-1})$. We may think of the c sequence as a reservation of $(n-1)$ places in memory.

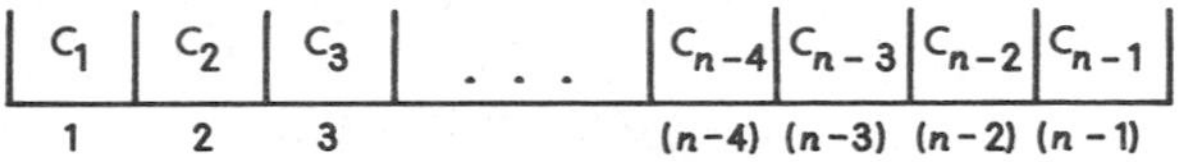

c_1	c_2	c_3	. . .	c_{n-4}	c_{n-3}	c_{n-2}	c_{n-1}
1	2	3		$(n-4)$	$(n-3)$	$(n-2)$	$(n-1)$

FIG. 6–26

Let i, where the range of i is from 1 to $(n-1)$ and the i are integers, be the addresses of the $(n-1)$ storage locations and let the $\{c\}$ be the contents of these storage locations; therefore, c_i is the contents of the ith storage location. Now define h, a function depending on k (the number or ranking of the permutation in the orderly list of $n!$ permutations), as the first i such that $c_i \neq i$; i.e., $h = h\,(k) \equiv$ first i such that $c_i \neq i$. To obtain h, one must first calculate the factorial sequence, $\{c\}$: Then, compare c_1 to 1; if $c_1 \neq 1$, $h = 1$. If, $c_1 =$ I, compare c_2 to 2 and $h = 2$ if $c_2 \neq 2$. Continue this process until h takes on a value.

In the same way as the i's were used as addresses for elements of the factorial sequence, the h's are used as addresses for the permutations. If each permutation is written as $d_0, d_1, d_2, \ldots, d_{n-1}$ requiring n places in memory, then h will vary from 0 to $(n-1)$.

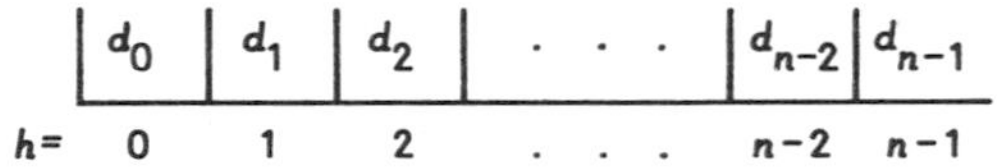

	d_0	d_1	d_2	. . .	d_{n-2}	d_{n-1}
$h=$	0	1	2	. . .	$n-2$	$n-1$

FIG. 6–27

To obtain the $(k+1)$ st permutation from the kth permutation the following rules must hold:

1. Interchange the marks in place h and $h-1$ if h is odd *or* if h is even and $c_{h+1} < 2$.
2. Otherwise interchange the marks in places h and $h-c_{h+1}$.

In the above calculations the address identifying an element to be modified may become negative; if this is true, assume the negative location to be the 0 location.

Illustrating the above method for the case of $n = 5$. The numbers are 0, 1, 2, 3, 4. For $k = 0$, or the 0th permutation, to calculate h we need the actorial sequence:

$$\begin{aligned} k \div (n-1)! &= 0 \div 4! = 0 \div 24 = c_4 + R = 0+0 \\ \text{Rem} \div (n-2)! &= 0 \div 3! = 0 \div 6 = c_3 + R = 0+0 \\ \text{Rem} \div (n-3)! &= 0 \div 2! = 0 \div 2 = c_2 + R = 0+0 \\ \text{Rem} \div (n-4)! &= 0 \div 1! = 0 \div 1 = c_1 + R = 0+0 \\ &\text{or } 0, 0, 0, 0 \equiv c_1, c_2, c_3, c_4 \end{aligned}$$

To calculate h compare c_1 with 1; since $c_1 = 0$, $c_1 \neq 1$—therefore, $h = h(0) = 1$. Because h is odd, rule 1 leads to the $(k+1)$ st permutation 1, 0, 2, 3, 4; the interchange of the contents of the 0th and the first place.

For the next calculation, $k = 1$; the factorial sequence becomes

$$\begin{aligned} 1 \div 4! &= 0+1 \\ 1 \div 3! &= 0+1 \\ 1 \div 2! &= 0+1 \\ 1 \div 1! &= 1+0 \end{aligned}$$

giving the factorial sequence 1,0,0,0. Now $c_1 = 1$, $h \neq 0$; but $c_2 \neq 2$, $c_2 = 0$ —therefore, $h = h\ (1) = 2$. Since h is even we must check to see if $c_{h+1} < 2$; here c_{h+1} is c_3 and is equal to 0 which is less than 2 so rule (1) holds. The new permutation is therefore

$$1,\ 2,\ 0,\ 3,\ 4$$

since the first and second marks had to be interchanged.

In the application of rule 1, it is conceivable that c_{h+1} could refer to c_n, which is not explicitly calculated; however, c_n must be zero as we showed by the previous form for the factorial sequence.

FLOW CHART—Wells's Method

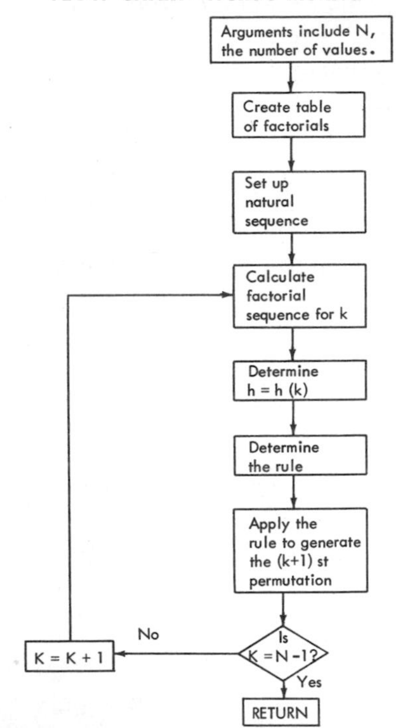

Routine to Calculate Permutations—Wells's Method

```
SUBROUTINE WELLS (N)
DIMENSION NFAC (7), NPER (9), NA (8)
NM1 = N – 1
NFAC (1) = 1.
```

```
      DO 400 1 = 2, N
  400 NFAC (I) = NFAC (I - 1)*I
      NFACM1 = NFAC (N) - 1
C
C        SET UP NATURAL NUMBER SEQUENCE WITH A SMALL VARIATION
C        FROM THE METHOD IN THAT WE SET UP THE ACTUAL NATURAL
C        NUMBER SEQUENCE RATHER THAN THE SEQUENCE MINUS ONE...
C        THE REASON FOR THIS IS FOUND IN THE CALCULATIONS BELOW...
C
      DO 100 I = 1, N
  100 NPER (I) = I
      NPER (N + 1) = 0
      NPER (N + 2) = NPER (N + 1)
      NA (N) = 0
      NA (N + 1) = NA (N)
      DO 10 M = 1, NFACM1
      MR = M - 1
C
C        CALCULATE THE FACTORIAL SEQUENCE
C
      DO 2 I = 1, NM1
      NN = N - I
      NA (NN) = MR/NFAC (NN)
    2 MR = MR - NFAC (NN) * NA (NN)
C
C        FIND FIRST I SUCH THAT I IS UNEQUAL TO A (I)
C        IN OTHER WORDS CALCULATE H
C
      DO 5 I = 1,NM1
      IF (I - NA (I))4,5,4
    5 CONTINUE
      NH = N
      GO TO 6
    4 NH = I
C
C        DETERMINE NEW PERMUTATION VIA ONE OF THE GIVEN RULES
C
    6 IF (MOD (NH, 2)) 7,9,7
    7 NTEMP = NPER (NH + 1)
      NPER (NH + 1) = NPER (NH)
      NPER (NH) = NTEMP
      GO TO 10
    9 IF (NA (NH + 1) - 2) 7,11,11
   11 NTEMP = NPER (NH + 1)
      NT = NH - NA(NH + 1) + 1
      IF (NT - 1) 21, 21, 20
   21 NT = 1
```

```
20 NPER (NH + 1) = NPER (NT)
   NPER (NT) = NTEMP
10 WRITE(6,87)(NPER (K1), K1 = 1, N)
87 FORMAT(7 (3XI6))
   RETURN
   END
```

The above routine writes all the permutations on tape; it may be more useful to send all permutations back to the main program, maybe via COMMON storage. In order to generate random permutations, the main program must have recourse to all the permutations using Wells's Method; the reader can change the program to accomplish this purpose.

The above method for giving an orderly list of permutations requires that the last permutation must be kept in storage to generate the new one, which in itself does not require a great deal of storage space. But, let us say we wish to generate a random permutation; after generating a random number for k, the kth permutation cannot be generated by the last method unless the computer has access to the $(k-1)$st permutation. Therefore, in reality, all $n!$ permutations must be stored within the computer.

Random permutations are used in statistical sampling theory; for example, latin square designs. In the next chapter a listing of all the possible permutations for a number n will be shown to be useful in evaluating a determinant.

6.7.4. Sorting

Most industrial computer applications and many scientific problems revolve around the ordering of the data. In this section a simple way of arranging a group of numbers in ascending order is presented to demonstrate an example program for this important problem area. In Chapter 8, a more sophisticated method with accompanying program will be presented to demonstrate the wide variety of approaches to the general sorting and classifying problem.

The following example will illustrate the procedure.

Given sequence: 4 3 1 5 2

Arrange them in ascending order.

Method—Compare the first number with the second and interchange them if the second number is smaller than the first (in other words, out of order). Now compare the first number with the third number and again interchange them if they are out of the desired order. Repeat the process until the first number has been compared with the last number.

Compare the first and second numbers—interchange them

4 3 1 5 2

3 4 1 5 2

Compare the first and third numbers—interchange them	1	4	3	5	2
Compare the first and the fourth numbers—do not interchange them	1	4	3	5	2
Compare the first and the fifth numbers—do not interchange them	1	4	3	5	2
Repeat the same procedure starting with the second element	1	4	3	5	2
	1	3	4	5	2
	1	3	4	5	2
	1	2	4	5	3
Now start with the third element—	1	2	4	5	3
	1	2	4	5	3
	1	2	3	5	4
Now start with the fourth element—	1	2	3	5	4
Desired order—	1	2	3	4	5

Notice that the limit on the outside loop must be $(N - 1)$ and not N be-because at the time $1 = N$, then $J = N+1$ and $A\ (N+1)$ will have no value; it is undefined. Also the starting value of the inner loop is the starting point of the outer loop plus one, as required by the given method.

FLOW CHART—Sorting Program

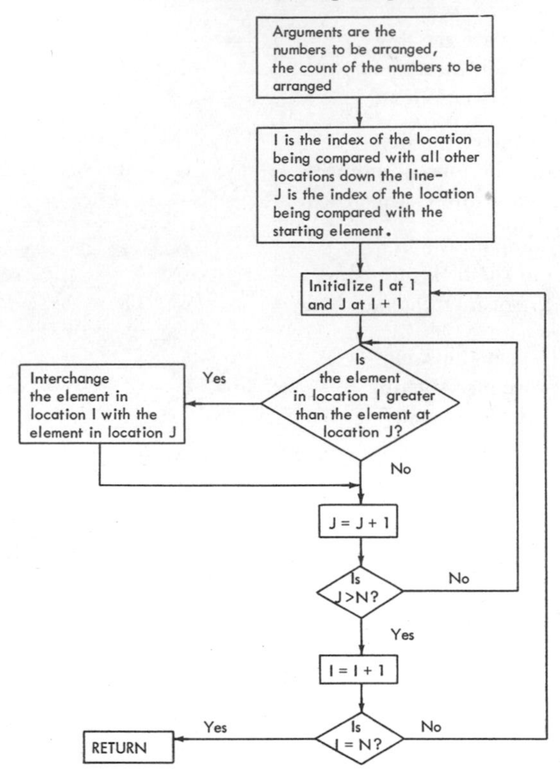

Arguments are the numbers to be arranged, the count of the numbers to be arranged
I is the index of the location being compared with all other locations down the line- J is the index of the location being compared with the starting element.
Initialize I at 1 and J at I + 1
Is the element in location I greater than the element at location J?
Yes
Interchange the element in location I with the element in location J
No
J = J + 1
Is J>N?
No
Yes
I = I + 1
Is I = N?
Yes
No
RETURN

FORTRAN PROGRAM—Sorting

```
C FOR COMMENT
STATEMENT NUMBER | Cont. | FORTRAN STATEMENT

      SUBROUTINE SRT(A,N)
      DIMENSION A(100)
      IF(N.GT.100)GO TO 40
      IF(N.LE.0)GO TO 40
      K=N-1
      DO 20 I=1,K
      L=I+1
      DO 20 J=L,N
      IF(A(J)-A(I))10,10,20
   10 TEMP=A(I)
      A(I)=A(J)
      A(J)=TEMP
   20 CONTINUE
      RETURN
   40 WRITE(6,1)
    1 FORMAT(5HERROR)
      RETURN
      END
```

Problems

6.1. Referring back to problem 4.11, we are given the following additional information:

Price of an item = \$1.18
Overhead = \$2,500 per year
Total income is net income + overhead
Inventory cost = \$0.50/unit/month
Penalty cost = \$4/item

(The cost attributed to loss of sale, goodwill, etc., which occurs if a unit of the item cannot be delivered to the customer at that time).

a) Assume that demand for the item is distributed uniformly in the interval $\bar{x} \pm .4\bar{x}$, where $\bar{x}$ is the mean sales. Also assume that the sales take place at the end of the month so that all production in a certain month can go toward satisfying the demand in that month.

Maximize total income over a 24-month period by generating sales in a Monte Carlo fashion and trying different rates of production.

b) Repeat the above procedure using a normal distribution for demand with a standard deviation of 0.4 units.

6.2. In an earlier chapter a subprogram was given for the calculation of binomial coefficients, called BINOM. If one needs only certain binomial coefficients, then the most efficient way to write a program would be to call a subprogram, such as BINOM. However, if one will need to use most of the binomial coefficients within a certain range or to refer to some of them more than once, it is more efficient to generate all the binomial coefficients over the range and store them in memory.

Write a FORTRAN program which will calculate the binomial coefficients of the form $\binom{n}{r}$, for a given ranges of n and r, in a recurrent manner.

Hint: Use the formula $\binom{n+1}{r} = \binom{n}{r} + \binom{n}{r-1}$

for $0<r<n$

6.3. Write a FORTRAN program which will find the sum of the kth powers of the first n natural numbers. Define

$$S_k = 1^k + 2^k + 3^k + \ldots + n^k$$
$$S_0 = n$$

Use the fact that $(n+1)^{k+1} - 1 = (k+1)S_k + \binom{k+1}{2} S_{k-1} + \ldots + S_0$. K and n are the parameters.

6.4.

Problem

Let F be a real-valued function, defined and continuous on the interval $[A,B]$ with sgn $F(A) \neq$ sgn $F(B)$.[14] Compute X so that, for some zero Z of F in $[A,B]$,

[14] The sign or signum function is defined:

$$\text{sgn } T = \begin{cases} -1 \; ; T < 0 \\ 0 \; ; T = 0 \\ +1 \; ; T > 0 \end{cases}$$

$$|X-Z| \leqslant \text{ERROR, a positive constant} \tag{1}$$

Analysis

Since sgn $F(A) \neq$ sgn $F(B)$, the continuity of F on $[A,B]$ implies (by an intermediate value theorem) the existence of at least one Z in $[A,B]$ such that $F(Z) = 0$. To approximate Z, compute

$$X \leftarrow (A+B)/2 \tag{2}$$

Now, either sgn $F(X) \neq$ sgn $F(B)$ or sgn $F(X) \neq$ sgn $F(A)$. In the first case redefine

$$A \leftarrow X \tag{3}$$

and in the second case,

$$B \leftarrow X \tag{4}$$

In either case we obtain a new interval, half as long as the original one, and to which the first sentence of this paragraph applies equally as well. After K repetitions of this procedure, both Z and X lie in an interval $[A,B]$ with length 2^{-K} times the length of the one originally given. Clearly, when K is large enough,

$$|B-A| \leqslant \text{ERROR} \tag{5}$$

will hold, implying (1).

The word "iteration" is commonly used in two senses. First, an iteration is a cyclic process for solving a problem, usually by successive approximation; then, an iteration is any particular cycle of such a process. When the approximate solution is sufficiently accurate, the iteration is said to converge. The iteration discussed in the preceding paragraph, the "Bisection Algorithm," converges when (1) is satisfied. Since it implies (1), (5) is an adequate test for the convergence of this iteration. The strength of the Bisection Algorithm is its certainty; its weakness is its inefficiency. To find a zero of F in the unit interval with an error not exceeding 10^{-6} will require 20 iterations and hence 20 evaluations of F. This situation may be improved by the use of an iteration function of the form

$$G(X) = X-F(X)H(X) \tag{6}$$

where $0 < H(Z) < \infty$. It can be shown that if G is a continuous function, satisfying a contractive Lipschitz condition and mapping $[A,B]$ into itself, there exists a unique zero Z of F in $[A,B]$, and the substitution

$$X \leftarrow G(X) \tag{7}$$

generates a sequence which converges to Z.[15] If F has a derivative DF defined on $[A,B]$ we may take

$$H(X) = 1/DF(X) \tag{8}$$

in which case $G(X)$ is called the Newton iteration function. Otherwise we may choose

$$H(X) = (B-A)/(F(B)-F(A)) \tag{9}$$

[15] Cf. J. F. Traub, *Iterative Methods for the Solution of Equations* (New York: Prentice-Hall, Inc., 1964), chap. i.

under which $G(X)$ defines the Regula Falsi iteration function. It is assumed here that at each iteration the interval $[A,B]$ is redefined as in the sentence after (2). Even if this is done, (5) will not always be a satisfactory convergence test for an iteration defined by (7) rather than (2). For example, X might always replace B, so that the length of $[A,B]$ will never be less than the distance from A to Z, which remains unchanged. The following convergence test overcomes this difficulty:

$$|F(X)| \leq C \cdot \text{ERROR} \tag{10}$$

where C is a positive constant such that

$$C|P-Q| \leq |F(P)-F(Q)| \text{ for all } P, Q \text{ in } [A,B] \tag{11}$$

In other words C is a positive lower bound on the absolute value of every difference quotient of F over $[A,B]$. Clearly (10) and (11) imply (1), for X and Z are in $[A,B]$ and $F(Z) = 0$, so by (11)

$$C|X-Z| \leq |F(X)-F(Z)| \leq |F(X)| \tag{12}$$

Now apply (10), cancel C and (1) follows. To facilitate computation of C we note that (11) is equivalent to

$$C \leq |DF(P)| \text{ for all } P \text{ in } [A,B] \tag{13}$$

assuming that the derivative DF is defined on $[A,B]$. If a positive C satisfying (11) or (13) cannot be found, set $C = 0$. Now (10) implies $F(X) = 0$ which means that X is precisely a zero of F. It must be stressed, however, that in this case and in case C or ERROR is chosen unrealistically small, (10) may never in practice be satisfied due to the round off error generated in computing F(X). Even using the Bisection Algorithm, (5) may never hold if ERROR is chosen smaller than the limit of machine significance.

Program

Write a FORTRAN program to solve the stated problem, utilizing some form of (7) and redefining the interval at each iteration as indicated after (2). Should (7) produce an iterate X falling outside of the current interval, redefine X using (2). Employ both (5) and (10) as convergence tests, terminating the iteration if either one is satisfied. A complete set of input data should contain values for C, ERROR, A, B and X, an initial approximation to Z, while $F(X)$ and (if used) $DF(X)$ should be defined by arithmetic statement functions. Immediately after being input, C, ERROR, A, B and X should be output as an "echo," which exhibits the input data while providing a statement of the problem being solved, including the formula for the particular $F(X)$ being used. Next, the input data should be checked, outputting the message,

IMPROPER INPUT DATA

and skipping to the next set if any of the following conditions exist:

$$C < 0$$
$$\text{ERROR} < 10^{-7} \cdot \max\{|A|, |B|\}$$
$$\text{sgn}\, F(A) = \text{sgn}\, F(B)$$

After a convergence test is passed, clearly labeled values for X, the final iterate, and K, the number of iterations required, should be output. The program should then proceed to the next set of input data.

Test Data

For preliminary testing purposes take $F(X)$ to be any function whose roots you know, preferably a made-up polynomial with several integer roots. Then it will be easy to determine appropriate values for C, A, B, and X. At this stage the use of relatively large values for ERROR will enable you to run more sets of data within the time limit. When you have sufficient confidence in your program, test it with the function

$$F(X) = 2.*\text{ATAN}(X)-1./X+1.570796328$$

and the input data below.

C	*ERROR*	*A*	*B*	*X*
.65	1.E−06	−2.	−1.	−1.5
5.6	1.E−06	.1	.5	.3

6.5.

Problem

Given a real polynomial of degree $N > 2$

$$P(X) = P_1X^N + P_2X^{N-1} + \ldots + P_NX + P_{N+1}$$

and $N - 1$ real numbers

$$R_1 < R_2 < \ldots < R_{N-1}, \tag{1}$$

such that the sign of P alternates at these points, i.e.

$$\text{sgn } P(R_K) = -\text{sgn } P(R_{K-1}) \neq 0;\ K = 2,3, \ldots ,N-1, \tag{2}$$

find all the zeros of P.

Analysis

It must be admitted that this problem lacks generality. In fact, (1) and (2) imply that P has at least $N - 2$ real zeros, and thus at most two complex zeros; but, even so, a program which solves this problem should be useful.

In theory the problem presents no new difficulties, since problem **6.4** provides a means of finding one real zero Z_K in each of the $N - 2$ intervals $[R_K,R_{K+1}]$; $K = 1, 2, \ldots ,N-2$. Now, the product

$$(X - Z_1)(X - Z_2) \ldots (X - Z_{N-2}) \tag{3}$$

is a factor of $P(X)$, and the other factor must be a polynomial of degree 2, which can be treated using a quadratic equation solver, producing the remaining two zeros of P.

There are, however, some practical difficulties to be overcome. We will find it best to represent polynomials, for computer programming purposes, by only the array of their coefficients. Thus the polynomial P will be represented by the vector $(P_1,P_2, \ldots ,P_{N+1})$. You will see immediately that, while addition and subtraction of polynomials reduce to vector addition and subtraction, multiplication and division entail some complications, particularly division. Fortunately, the only division we are concerned with is by the product in (3), and this may be thought of as $N - 2$ successive divisions by linear factors. The division algorithm for a polynomial of degree M

$$Q(X) = Q_1X^M + Q_2X^{M-1} + \ldots + Q_MX + Q_{M+1} \tag{4}$$

divided by the linear factor $X - Y$ may be written as

$$Q(X) = Q'(X)(X - Y) + Q'_{M+1}, \tag{5}$$

where the quotient

$$Q'(X) = Q'_1X^{M-1} + Q'_2X^{M-2} + \ldots + Q'_M \tag{6}$$

is a polynomial of degree $M-1$, and the remainder Q'_{M+1} is a constant. Since (5) is true for arbitrary X, we may expand (5) using (4) and (6), and then equate coefficients of like powers of X, obtaining after a little manipulation

$$\begin{aligned} Q'_1 &= Q_1 \\ Q'_J &= Q_J + Q'_{J-1}Y;\ J = 2,3,\ldots,M+1. \end{aligned} \tag{7}$$

This is seen to be a recursion formula for computing the coefficients of the quotient polynomial when $J = 1,2,\ldots,M$, and the remainder when $J = M + 1$. The algorithm in (7) is commonly known as "synthetic division." For computational purposes we will not be concerned with saving the values of the Q_J, so we let them be "clobbered" by the Q'_J. In short, we will drop the primes altogether and replace equality by substitution, rewriting (7) as

$$Q_J \leftarrow Q_J + Q_{J-1}Y;\ J = 2,3,\ldots,M+1 \tag{8}$$

Corresponding to (8) is the FORTRAN SUBROUTINE subprogram shown below.

```
      SUBROUTINE SYNDIV(NQ,Q,Y)                    (9)
      DIMENSION Q(NQ)
      DO 1 J=2,NQ
    1 Q(J)=Q(J)+Q(J-1)*Y
      RETURN
      END
```

Here NQ stands for the number of coefficients of Q, i.e., the degree of Q plus one. A FORTRAN segment which would use SYNDIV to perform the division of $P(X)$ by the product in (3) could be written

```
      ...                                          (10)
      KMAX=NP-3
      ...
      DO 4 K=1,KMAX
    4 CALL SYNDIV(NP-K+1,P,Z(K))
```

where NP is the number of coefficients of P. At the end of this procedure the desired 2nd degree quotient polynomial will be

$$P_1X^2 + P_2X + P_3 \tag{11}$$

The algorithm (8) can be put to other valuable uses. To see this consider the Taylor series expansion of $Q(X)$ about an arbitrary real Y

$$Q(X) = Q(Y) + \sum_{J=1}^{M} \frac{Q^{(J)}(Y)}{J!}(X - Y)^J, \tag{12}$$

where $Q_{(J)}(Y)$ represents the Jth derivative of Q evaluated at Y. This series is finite because all derivatives of Q with order greater than M are identically zero. It is clear from (12) that when $Q(X)$ is divided by $X - Y$ the remainder is $Q(Y)$ while the quotient is a polynomial of degree $M-1$, which, when divided by $X - Y$, yields a remainder of $Q^{(1)}(Y)/1!$ and a quotient of degree $M-2$, which itself may be divided by $X - Y$, and so forth. M repetitions of this process will thus yield a sequence of remainders

$$Q(Y), \frac{Q^{(1)}(Y)}{1!}, \frac{Q^{(2)}(Y)}{2!}, \ldots, \frac{Q^{(M)}(Y)}{M!} \tag{13}$$

In terms of synthetic division, all this amounts to is applying (8) once for each $K = 1,2, \ldots ,M$, but letting $J = 1,2, \ldots ,M+2-K$ at each step. When this is done the sequence

$$Q_{M+1}, E_M, Q_{M-1}, \ldots, Q_1 \tag{14}$$

will correspond exactly to (13). An application of this is seen in the following FORTRAN segment, which uses SYNDIV to evaluate $P(X)$ and $P^{(1)}(X)$ for use in the Newton iteration function, where X is being thought of as the current approximation to a zero of P.

```
      . . .
      DO 20 J=1,NP
20    O(J)=P(J)
      CALL SYNDIV(NP,OX)
      . . .
      CALL SYNDIV(NP-1,O,X)
      . . .
      X=X-O(NP)/O(NP-1)
      . . .
```

Here it was necessary to introduce the auxiliary array O in order to save the given coefficients of P for subsequent iterations.

We conclude this section with the observation that synthetic division entails less computation than any other means of evaluating a polynomial. It amounts to writing the polynomial in "nested" form

$$P(X) = (\ldots (P_1X + P_2)X + \ldots + P_N)X + P_{N+1}.$$

Program

Write a quadratic equation solver in subroutine form; i.e.,

```
SUBROUTINE QUADEQ(A,B,C)
```

which finds and outputs the roots of the equation

$$AX^2 + BX + C = 0.$$

Eliminate the input routine and modify your program from problem **6.4** so that it uses SYNDIV to effect all function and (if any) derivative evaluations. Also add any needed RETURN statements and the first statement

```
FUNCTION ZERO(NP,P,A,B,C,ERROR,X)
```

which locates, outputs and returns as the value of ZERO an approximate zero (in the interval $[A,B]$ with error not exceeding ERROR) of the polynomial P with NP coefficients, where C is a lower bound on the absolute value of the derivative of P over $[A,B]$, and X is an initial approximation to this zero.

The main program for this assignment should do the following:

1) Input and echo NP and $P(J)$; $J=1,2,\ldots,NP$.
2) Set KMAX=NP−3; then input and echo values for $A(K),B(K),C(K)$, ERROR $(K),X(K)$; $K=1,2,\ldots,$KMAX.
3) If the intervals $]A(K),B(K)[$; $K=1,2,\ldots,$KMAX are not disjoint write the message

   "INTERVALS NOT DISJOINT"

   and go to 1) above. Otherwise proceed to 4).
4) For $K=1,2,\ldots,$KMAX set
   Z(K)=ZERO(NP,P,A(K),B(K),C(K),ERROR(K),X(K))
5) Perform the division of $P(X)$ by the product in (3) as shown at (10).
6) Execute the statement

   CALL QUADEQ(P(1),P(2),P(3))
7) GO TO 1).

In the input data $[A(K),B(K)]$ should be the smallest subinterval of $[R_K,R_{K+1}]$ (see (1)) that the student can find, such that P changes sign at its endpoints. This is so that $C(K)$, a lower bound for the absolute value of the derivative of P over $[A(K),B(K)]$, can be determined as large as possible to reduce the number of iterations needed. In (3) one need only check that the intervals are disjoint, since the FUNCTION subprogram ZERO supposedly checks the validity of its own arguments. If it is desired that all the $Z(K)$ be accurate to the same number n of significant figures, and the $X(K)$ are reasonably good initial approximations, then one may set

$$\mathrm{ERROR(K)} \doteq |\mathrm{X(K)}|\cdot 10^{-n}$$

with good results. It would be unwise to take $n > 7$, however, since only eight decimal significant figures are stored internally.

Test Data

The sign of the polynomial

$$X^6 + 5X^5 + 2X^4 - 13X^3 - 11X^2 - 8X + 6$$

alternates at the points

$$-4,\ -3,\ -1,\ 1,\ 2$$

Find all of its zeros accurate to six significant figures.

6.6. Use Monte Carlo methods to evaluate the following integral:

$$\int_2^6 \ln x \, dx$$

Compare the answer with that obtained by using the FORTRAN IV log subroutine.

7. Arrays and Matrix Methods

7.1. Determinants

All of the simple properties of determinants can be shown through the use of permutations; in Chapter 6 some time was spent on permutations, so those properties covered there will be mentioned only briefly here. Suppose we have given a certain ordering of the integers from 1 to 7, say, 1, 2, 3, 4, 5, 6, 7; if we transpose two of these numbers, say, 2 and 6, we obtain a permutation of the above ordering: namely, 1, 6, 3, 4, 5, 2, 7. Now, define an inversion to be any pair of numbers which are out of the natural order. In the above sequence, the number of possible inversions is $\binom{7}{2} = \frac{7!}{5!2!} =$ 21; the number of ways of picking 2 things out of 7. Although there are 21 possible inversions, only 7 inversions are present in the sequence 1, 6, 3, 4, 5, 2, 7; namely, 6–3, 6–4, 6–5, 6–2, 3–2, 4–2, and 5–2. A permutation is defined to be even if the number of inversions is even; it is defined to be odd if the number of inversions is odd. Using this definition, the permutation 1,6,3,4,5,2,7 is odd.

A determinant is a property defined on a square array of numbers namely:

$$\begin{matrix} a_{11} & a_{12} & a_{13} & \cdots & a_{1n} \\ a_{21} & a_{22} & a_{23} & \cdots & a_{2n} \\ \cdot & \cdot & \cdot & \cdots & \cdot \\ \cdot & \cdot & \cdot & \cdots & \cdot \\ \cdot & \cdot & \cdot & \cdots & \cdot \end{matrix}$$

The first subscript denotes the row and the second subscript denoted the column.

$a_{n1} \quad a_{n2} \quad a_{n3} \cdots a_{nn}$ There are n rows and n columns in and nxn or an array of order n.

nxn Array A

$$\text{Determinant of} \qquad A = \sum \pm (a_{1i}a_{2j}a_{3k} \ldots a_{ns}) .$$

Overall permutations of the second subscript

The above definition can be interpreted as follows: go down the rows in the natural sequence—i.e., start at the first row, then the second, etc. In each row choose one element from each column; the sequence of choices from the columns can be pictured as a permutation of n numbers, the column subscripts. For each permutation of the column subscripts we obtain n elements. These n elements are multiplied together to form a product. Since there are $n!$ permutations of a sequence of n numbers, there will be $n!$ products. These products are then summed together under the following rule:

1. Add the product to the total if the product was formed from an even permutation of the columns.
2. Subtract the product from the total if the permutation of the columns forming the product was odd.

In the array of order two,

$$\begin{matrix} a_{11} & a_{12} \\ a_{21} & a_{22} \end{matrix}$$

the determinant is calculated as the sum of the two products, $a_{11}a_{22}$ and $a_{12}a_{21}$. The permutation of the second subscripts in the product $a_{11}a_{22}$ is even because they are in the natural order—1,2. The permutation of the second subscripts in the product $a_{12}a_{21}$ is odd because there is one inversion in the sequence 2,1. Therefore, the product $a_{12}a_{21}$ must be subtracted from the product $a_{11}a_{22}$. The determinant of the array, A, is $a_{11}a_{22}-a_{12}a_{21}$.

If two numbers, in a sequence of n numbers, are interchanged, the permutation of the original sequence is changed from even to odd or from odd to even.

$$1, 2, \ldots, j, \ldots, k, \ldots, n.$$

Interchange j and k—to find the effect on the permutation, it is necessary to find the number of inversions created by the interchange of the two numbers. A simple way of describing the process is to break up the entire process into two steps:

1. If we imagine each number sitting in a location, we may move all numbers from 1 to $(j-1)$ one location to the left—no inversions are caused by this step.

$$1,2, \ldots, j-1, \quad , j, \ldots, k, \ldots, n$$

Now move the number k to the vacant spot between $(j-1)$ and j; in this process k moves over $(k-j)$ numbers creating $(k-j)$ inversions from the original sequence:

$$1, 2, \ldots, j-1, k, j, \ldots, k-1, \quad , k+1, \ldots, n$$

2. Then move j to the vacated place between $(k-1)$ and $(k+1)$; this creates another $(k-j-1)$ inversions from the original sequence. The total number of inversions is $(k-j) + (k-j+1) = 2(k-j) + 1$, which is an odd number. Therefore, if the original sequence contained an odd number of inversions, the new sequence contains an even number of inversions; and, if the original sequence contained an even number of inversions, the new sequence contains an odd number of inversions.

$$|A| = \begin{vmatrix} a_{11} & a_{12} & \cdots & a_{1n} \\ a_{21} & a_{22} & \cdots & a_{2n} \\ \cdot & \cdot & & \cdot \\ \cdot & \cdot & & \cdot \\ \cdot & \cdot & & \cdot \\ a_{n1} & a_{n2} & \cdots & a_{nn} \end{vmatrix}$$

Determinant

A determinant, signified by $|A|$ undergoes a change of sign when two columns are interchanged because of the above procedure. In each product the second subscripts on two of the elements are interchanged, causing a changing in the nature of the permutation; this is the same as multiplying the product by -1. Since each product is multiplied by -1, the -1 may be factored out of all the products in the sum. Thus, if the original determinant had value $|A|$, the new determinant has value $-|A|$. In the same way, if every element in a column is multiplied by a scaler λ, then the entire determinant is multiplied by λ, since each product contains one element which was multiplied by λ. If all the elements in a determinant, which has n rows and n columns, are multiplied by λ, then the determinant is multiplied by λ.

Denoting a typical element of a determinant by a_{ij}, if the subscripts were turned around so that each a_{ij} became a_{ji}, the array, in effect, would be turned over the main diagonal, or transposed.

Array A

$$\begin{matrix} a_{11} & a_{12} & a_{13} & \cdots & a_{1n} \\ a_{21} & a_{22} & a_{23} & \cdots & a_{2n} \\ a_{31} & a_{32} & a_{33} & \cdots & a_{3n} \\ \cdot & \cdot & \cdot & & \cdot \\ \cdot & \cdot & \cdot & & \cdot \\ \cdot & \cdot & \cdot & & \cdot \\ a_{n1} & a_{n2} & a_{n3} & \cdots & a_{nn} \end{matrix}$$

Transpose of Array $A = A^T$

$$\begin{matrix} a_{11} & a_{21} & a_{31} & \cdots & a_{n1} \\ a_{12} & a_{22} & a_{32} & \cdots & a_{n2} \\ a_{13} & a_{23} & a_{33} & \cdots & a_{n3} \\ \cdot & \cdot & \cdot & & \cdot \\ \cdot & \cdot & \cdot & & \cdot \\ \cdot & \cdot & \cdot & & \cdot \\ a_{1n} & a_{2n} & a_{3n} & \cdots & a_{nn} \end{matrix}$$

If the value of the determinant is $|A|$, then the determinant of the transpose $|A^T|$ also is $|A|$. In other words, $|A| = |A^T|$. The determinant of the transposed array is defined as:

$$\sum (\pm)\ (a_{i1}\ a_{j2}\ a_{k3} \ldots a_{sn})$$

Sum taken
over all possible
permutations
of the first
subscript

or moving the column number in natural sequence, try all permutations of the rows. It is easily seen that the definitions for $|A|$ and $|A^T|$ are the same; therefore, they are equal (both have the same number of products and each product contains the same elements). Since $|A^T| = |A|$, all the properties defined for the columns (i.e., interchanging, multiplying by a scaler, etc.) also hold for the rows of A; this is true because the columns of A^T are the rows of A.

If all the elements in a row or column of A are zero, then $|A| = 0$ because each product will contain a zero.

Another way of evaluating determinants utilizes cofactors. If the ith row and the jth column of an array are crossed out, the remaining $(n-1)$ by $(n-1)$ array is called a subarray.

$$\begin{array}{ccccccc}
a_{11} & a_{.2} & a_{13} & \ldots & a_{1j} & \ldots & a_{1n} \\
a_{21} & a_{22} & a_{23} & \ldots & a_{2j} & \ldots & a_{2n} \\
a_{i1} & a_{i2} & a_{i3} & \ldots & a_{ij} & \ldots & a_{in} \\
a_{n1} & a_{n2} & a_{n3} & \ldots & a_{nj} & \ldots & a_{nn}
\end{array}$$

Subarray of Order (*n*-1)

The determinant of this subarray is called the minor of the element a_{ij}. The cofactor is defined as the minor multiplied by $(-1)^{i+j}$—denoted by A_{ij}, if a_{ij} is the pivot element; that is, the element on the intersection of the row and column which has been crossed out. It can be proved by mathematical induction that:

$$\sum_i a_{ij}\ A_{ij} = \sum_j a_{ij}\ A_{ij} = |A|$$

or, if the array is expanded by cofactors of any row or column, the result will be the determinant of the array.

The following example illustrates both the cofactor method and the evaluation of the determinant by definition. A 3 by 3 determinant is expanded into 3 (2×2) determinants, which are then evaluated by definition.

$$\begin{vmatrix} 2 & 1 & 0 \\ 0 & -1 & 1 \\ 1 & 0 & 3 \end{vmatrix}$$

Expand by cofactors of the second row to get:

$$(0)\,(-1)^{2+1} \begin{vmatrix} 1 & 0 \\ 0 & 3 \end{vmatrix} + (-1)\,(-1)^{2+2} \begin{vmatrix} 2 & 0 \\ 1 & 3 \end{vmatrix} + (1)\,(-1)^{2+3} \begin{vmatrix} 2 & 1 \\ 1 & 0 \end{vmatrix}$$

First cross out column 1 and row 2, then column 2 and row 2, and finally column 3 and row 2. A (2×2) determinant is calculated as $(a_{11}a_{22} - a_{21}a_{12})$ because the first product is the natural permutation of the second subscripts (added, since the natural order is an even permutation) and the second product uses the permutation 2,1, which contains 1 inversion and therefore, is odd; it must be subtracted from the total. To evaluate the sum of the three determinants:

$$0 - (6) - (-1) = -5$$

consider a simplification of the following determinants:

$$\begin{vmatrix} \lambda_1 a_{11} + \lambda_2 a_{31} & \lambda_1 a_{12} + \lambda_2 a_{32} & \lambda_1 a_{13} + \lambda_2 a_{33} \\ a_{21} & a_{22} & a_{23} \\ a_{31} & a_{32} & a_{33} \end{vmatrix}$$

If this determinant is expanded by elements of the first row, we obtain:

$$(\lambda_1 a_{11} + \lambda_2\, a_{31})\, A_{11} + (\lambda_1 a_{12} + \lambda_2\, a_{32})\, A_{12} + (\lambda_1 a_{13} + \lambda_2\, a_{33})\, A_{13},$$

or

$$\lambda_1\, a_{11}\, A_{11} + \lambda_2\, a_{31}\, A_{11} + \lambda_1 a_{12}\, A_{12} + \lambda_2 a_{32}\, A_{12} + \lambda_1 a_{13} A_{13} + \lambda_2 a_{33}\, A_{13},$$

combining like terms,

$$(\lambda_1\, a_{11}\, A_{11} + \lambda_1 a_{12}\, A_{12} + \lambda_1 a_{13}\, A_{13}) + (\lambda_2 a_{31} A_{11} + \lambda_2 a_{32}\, A_{12} + \lambda_2 a_{33}\, A_{13})$$

or

$$\lambda_1\, |A| + \lambda_2\, |A_0|\ ;$$

$$\text{where } |A_0| = \begin{vmatrix} a_{31} & a_{32} & a_{33} \\ a_{21} & a_{22} & a_{23} \\ a_{31} & a_{32} & a_{33} \end{vmatrix} \text{ and } |A| = \begin{vmatrix} a_{11} & a_{12} & a_{13} \\ a_{21} & a_{22} & a_{23} \\ a_{31} & a_{32} & a_{33} \end{vmatrix}$$

A determinant with two identical rows or columns has a value of zero because if we interchange the two equal rows, we get the negative of the original value; and yet both determinants must be equal since they have the same elements—

$$|A| = -\,|A| \text{ only holds for } |A| = 0.$$

Going back to the simplified example, $|A_0| = 0$. Therefore, letting $\lambda_1 = 1$, we have deduced the important property that the addition, element by element, of a multiple of one row to another row does not change the value of the determinant (although this has been proved for the 3×3 case, it is not hard to extend the deduction to the general case).

7.1.1. Evaluation of a Determinant by Definition

Two difficult problems arise when someone tries to evaluate manually a determinant by definition; first, it is difficult to generate all possible permutations of the second subscript without repetition; second, it is difficult to count the number of inversions in each permutation in order to tell if the permutation is even or odd. Either of the methods for generating an orderly list of permutations presented in Chapter 6 will provide a computer solution of the first difficulty; however, we shall show later that the table look-up method may be made more efficient. Now, let us return to the factorial sequence $b_1, b_2, \ldots, b_{n-1}, b_n$; where $b_j \leqslant (n-j)$ and $b_n = 0$, say that $n = 5$; then the factorial sequence for $I = 37$ is 1,2,0,1,0 as $b_1, b_2, \ldots, b_{n-1}, b_n$; where $b_j \leqslant (n-j)$ and $b_n = 0$, say that $n = 5$, then the factorial sequence for $I = 37$ is 1,2,0,1,0, as the student can verify for himself; the permutation sequence is 2,4,1,5,3. To obtain the number of inversions in any sequence of numbers, we can start with the first number and compare it with all the following numbers; count 1 for each following number which is less than the first number. Follow the same procedure for the second number, the third number, until the $(n-1)$st number. At the end of this procedure, the total count should give the number of inversions because it gives a count of the pairs of numbers in the sequence which are out of the natural order. Writing the individual counts for each number down as a sequence, we obtain the sequence 1,2,0,1,0, which, as was already shown to be true in Chapter 6, is the original factorial sequence. Therefore, a sum of the terms of the factorial sequence gives the total number of inversions for the permutation.

Before presenting the entire routine for evaluating a determinant by definition using the table look-up method, the reader should reconsider that method. The most time-consuming part of either method are the divisions necessary to obtain the factorial sequence; if the permutation sequence could be calculated directly from the number of the permutation, the program would be much quicker. Of course, if the factorial sequence is not calculated, then the number of inversions must be obtained directly from the permutation by the method of counting the number of values following each value which are out of the natural sequence (as explained earlier). In the following pages are programs illustrating both the method using the factorial sequence and the direct calculations.

EXHIBIT: CALCULATION OF DETERMINANTS BY DEFINITION—METHOD 1

Description of the Problem

The determinant of the array is found in the following way: Given the size n (number of rows or columns), and the array itself, it follows that there are $n!$ permutations of the row and column components of the array, satisfying the essential condition that only one element per row and column be picked per permutation. The problem is to find all possible permutations (in this case, the column index) and use them accordingly.

A factorial sequence $\{b\}$ is found in the following way: Since there are $n!$ permutations, I will vary from 0 to $(n! - 1)$, each I producing a permutation of n integers; n divisions are performed:

$$\begin{aligned} I/(n-1)! &= J_1+R_1 \\ R_1/(n-2)! &= J_2+R_2 \\ R_2/(n-3)! &= J_2+R_3 \\ &\cdot \\ &\cdot \\ &\cdot \\ R_{n-1}/0! &= J_n+R_n \end{aligned}$$

The sequence $J_1, J_2, J_3, \ldots, J_n$ represents the factorial sequence { }. $\sum_{i=1}^{n} J_i$ being an even integer implies the sign of the factor in the determinant [$(I + 1)$st permutation] is positive. $\sum_{i=1}^{n} J_i$ being an odd integer implies a negative sign.

As a result of the above calculations, we produce another sequence:

$$J_1+1, J_2+1, J_3+1, \ldots, J_n+1 = \{b'\} = b'_1, b'_2, b'_3, \ldots, b'_n.$$

Then form a mapping of $\{b'\}$ onto the natural sequence,

$$1, 2, 3, \ldots, n;$$

the b_i th element being mapped onto the "unmapped" natural sequence component in the (b'_i) th position, omitting all previously mapped components. The resulting sequence serves as the column indices for our n matrix elements to be multiplied together as the $(I + 1)$st term in our determinant evaluation. The process is repeated until $I = n! - 1$.

Input Information Required

Card Number	*Format*	*Column*	*Contents*
1	I6	6	N
2 thru $(n+1)$	E11.5	1–11	$B_{j,1}$
or in general terms;		12–22	$B_{j,2}$

card j of the matrix (meaning row j). . . .

E11.5 . . .

$B_{j,n}$

Multiple problems can be run by stacking cards of the type above.

Possible Output

1. Input array
2. Determinant

FLOW CHART for Calculation of Determinants of Order 2 thru 7

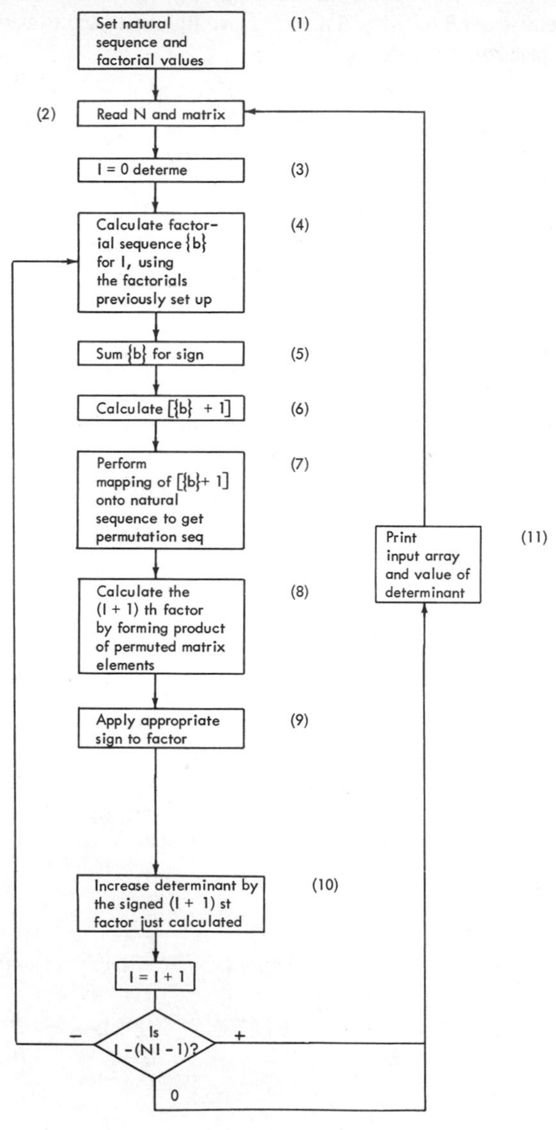

Program to Calculate Determinants of Arrays of Order 2 through 7

```
C
      DIMENSION NFAC(8),NAT(7),NATT(7),NT(7),B(7,7),K(7)

      NFAC(1) = 1                              }
      NFAC(2) = NFAC(1)                        }
      NFAC(3) = 2                              }  Set up factorial values            (1)
      DO 2 I1 = 4,8                            }
    2 NFAC(I1) = NFAC(I1 - 1) * (I1 - 1)       }
  100 READ (5,1000) N                          }
 1000 FORMAT(I6)                               }
C                                              }
C        READ IN THE ARRAY, ONE ROW PER CARD   }  Read in ARRAY and N, giving        (2)
C                                              }  the number of rows and
      DO 3 I1 = 1,N                            }  columns in the array.
    3 READ (5,2000) (B(I1,I2),I2=1,N)          }
 2000 FORMAT(7E11.5)                           }
      DETERM = 0.0                             }
      NOI = NFAC(N+1)                                                           }
C                                                                               }  Initialize location
C        THE FOLLOWING LOOP CALCULATES ALL OF THE PERMUTATIONS                  }  which will hold result
C        BY FIRST CALCULATING THE FACTORIAL SEQUENCE, AND THEN                  }  and the index which
C        DERIVING THE PERMUTATION SEQUENCE                                      }  will indicate which permutation   (3)
C                                                                               }  is to be generated
      DO 53 IR = 1,NOI                                                          }
      DO 4 I1 = 1,N      }
      NT(I1) = I1        }  Set up natural sequence
    4 NATT(I1) = I1      }
```

Program to Calculate Determinants of Arrays of Order 2 through 7—Continued

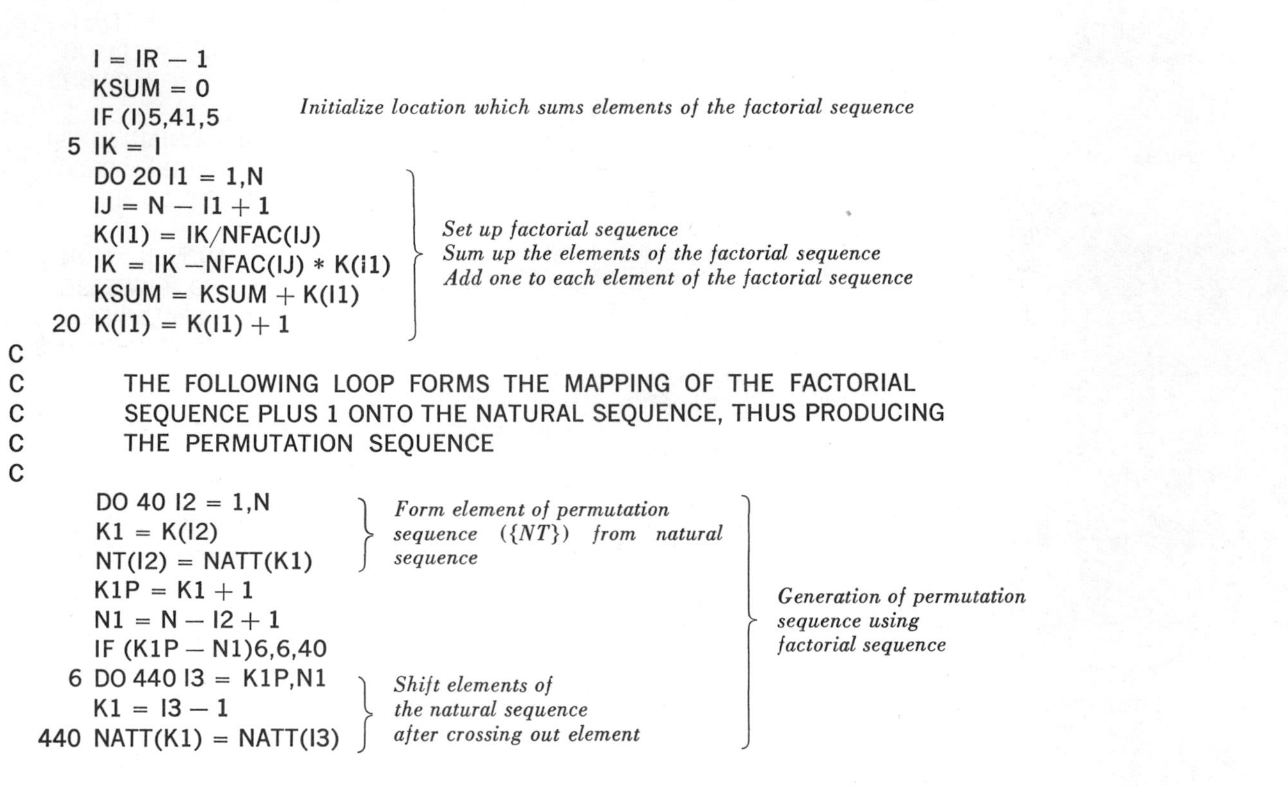

```
      I = IR - 1
      KSUM = 0                 Initialize location which sums elements of the factorial sequence
      IF (I)5,41,5
    5 IK = I
      DO 20 I1 = 1,N                  }
      IJ = N - I1 + 1                 }
      K(I1) = IK/NFAC(IJ)             }  Set up factorial sequence                              (4)
      IK = IK -NFAC(IJ) * K(I1)       }  Sum up the elements of the factorial sequence          (5)
      KSUM = KSUM + K(I1)             }  Add one to each element of the factorial sequence      (6)
   20 K(I1) = K(I1) + 1               }
C
C        THE FOLLOWING LOOP FORMS THE MAPPING OF THE FACTORIAL
C        SEQUENCE PLUS 1 ONTO THE NATURAL SEQUENCE, THUS PRODUCING
C        THE PERMUTATION SEQUENCE
C
      DO 40 I2 = 1,N          }  Form element of permutation         }
      K1 = K(I2)              }  sequence ({NT}) from natural        }
      NT(I2) = NATT(K1)       }  sequence                            }
      K1P = K1 + 1                                                   }  Generation of permutation   (7)
      N1 = N - I2 + 1                                                }  sequence using
      IF (K1P - N1)6,6,40                                            }  factorial sequence
    6 DO 440 I3 = K1P,N1      }  Shift elements of                   }
      K1 = I3 - 1             }  the natural sequence                }
  440 NATT(K1) = NATT(I3)     }  after crossing out element          }
```

```
   40 CONTINUE
   41 FACTOR = 1.0

      DO 51 I1 = 1,N                 ) Calculate the (IR - 1)st product
      I2 = NT(I1)                    } by multiplying the elements specified by        (8)
   51 FACTOR = FACTOR * B(I1,I2)     ) the permutation sequence
      IF (MOD(KSUM,2))52,53,52       ) Check to see if number of inversions is
   52 FACTOR = -FACTOR               } even or odd and apply the necessary sign
   53 DETERM = DETERM + FACTOR       ) to the product and add to result                (9), (10)
      WRITE (6,3000)
 3000 FORMAT(////10X,12HINPUT ARRAY/)
      DO 54 I1 = 1,N                             )
   54 WRITE (6,4000) (B(I1,I2),I2=1,N)           }
 4000 FORMAT(7E17.8)                             } Print Input Array                   (11)
      WRITE (6,5000) DETERM                      } And Value of Determinant
 5000 FORMAT(/10X,14HDETERMINANT=E15.8)          )
      GO TO 100
      END
```

```
          INPUT MATRIX

 0.10000000E 01   0.                 0.15000000E 01    0.21000000E 01
 0.12000000E 01  -0.21000000E 01     0.25000000E 01    0.
 0.              -0.12000000E 01     0.31000000E 01   -0.14000000E 01
-0.31000000E 01   0.22000000E 01     0.                0.23000000E 01

          DETERMINANT = -0.34531699E 02
```

Most of the table look-up method has already been discussed in the present chapter and the preceding chapter; however, a permutation sequence is generated for each number I (I goes from 1 to N). If we denote the permutation sequence as $nk_1, nk_2, \ldots, nk_n$, then the column of the array to be used is addressed by the numbers in the $\{nk\}$.

$$\begin{matrix} a_{11} & a_{12} & a_{13} & a_{14} \\ a_{21} & a_{22} & a_{23} & a_{24} \\ a_{31} & a_{32} & a_{33} & a_{34} \\ a_{41} & a_{42} & a_{43} & a_{44} \end{matrix}$$

Let the numbers in the sequence $\{nk\}$ be $\{3, 1, 4, 2\}$; then the elements to be multiplied to give the 18th ($I = 17$, the reader should check this) out of a total of 24 permutations possible when $n = 4$, are $a_{1,(nk_1)}\ a_{2,(nk_2)}\ a_{3,(nk_3)}\ a_{4,(nk_4)}$.

To avoid the division steps necessary to generate the factorial sequence, the second method introduces a truth table which keeps count of which permutations have already been generated so that no permutations are repeated.

Outline

1. Data read under F8.0; ten coefficients maximum for the determinant of a 10×10 matrix. The value of N is first card read in under I2 FORMAT. N is tested to verify the correct dimension.
2. Data read, and printed, DET function called.
3. Output printed under E 12.5 with comments.

```
      DIMENSION A(10,10)
 10   ISET = 1
  1   READ (5,101) N
101   FORMAT(12)
 39   DO 40 IA = 1,N
 40   READ(5,102) (A(IA,JA),JA=1,N)
102   FORMAT(10F8.0)
      WRITE(6,103)ISET,N,N
103   FORMAT(6H1 SET ,13,3X,13,3H BY .13,12H DETERMINANT )
      DO 50 IC=1,N
 50   WRITE (6,104) (A(IC,JC),JC=1,N)
104   FORMAT(10(IX,E11.4))
      V = DET(A,N)
      WRITE(6,105) V
105   FORMAT(33H THE VALUE OF THE DETERMINANT IS ,E12.5)
      ISET = ISET + 1
      GO TO 1
      END
```

FLOW CHART

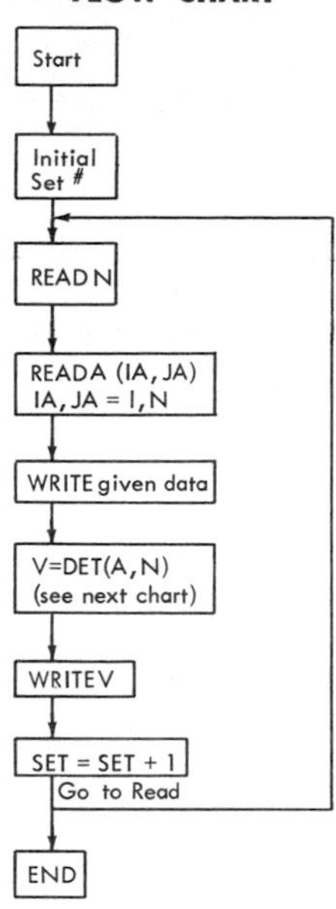

DET *Function*

1. Data input under call statement for problem; V = DET(A,N).
2. A truth table is used to check against using any number more than once in any permutation. Initially the table is zeroed out; i.e., FALSE.

   The first permutation is the natural sequence.

   The first part of the program calculates the permutations, next the inversions, next the value of the product under consideration—then repeats the procedure.

   The permutations are generated by starting with the natural sequence and increasing the value at each position to N. Move to the left checking truth table each time.

   When $S(1) = N$ and no values can be increased, the last permutation has occurred.

   The inversion count simply subtracts the terms from each other, checking for reversal of sign.
3. The value of the determinant is returned.

FUNCTION DET (A,N)

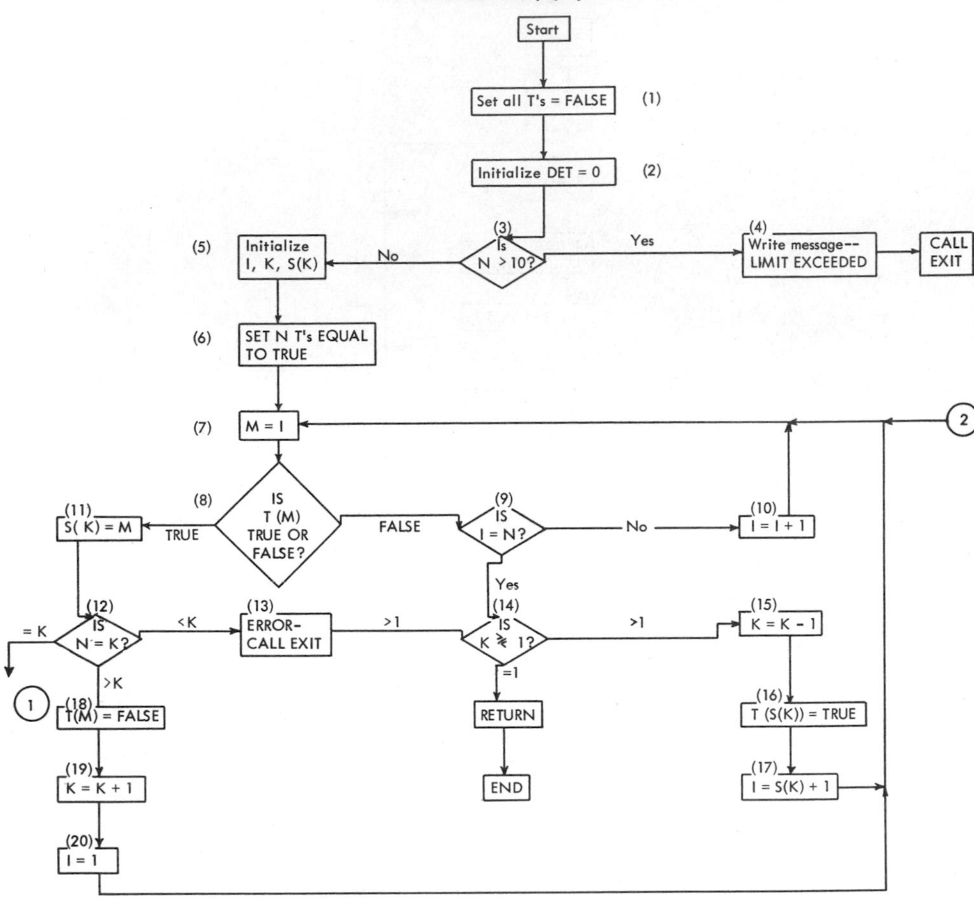


```
      FUNCTION DET(A,N)
      DIMENSION A(10,10)
      INTEGER S(10)
      LOGICAL T(10)
      DO 800 ICH=1,10
800   T(ICH) = .FALSE.
      DET =0.
      IF(N-10) 39,39,22
 22   WRITE(6,23) N
 23   FORMAT(27H1 DIMENSION LIMIT 10,N = ,13)
199   CALL EXIT
```

FUNCTION DET (A,N)—*Continued*

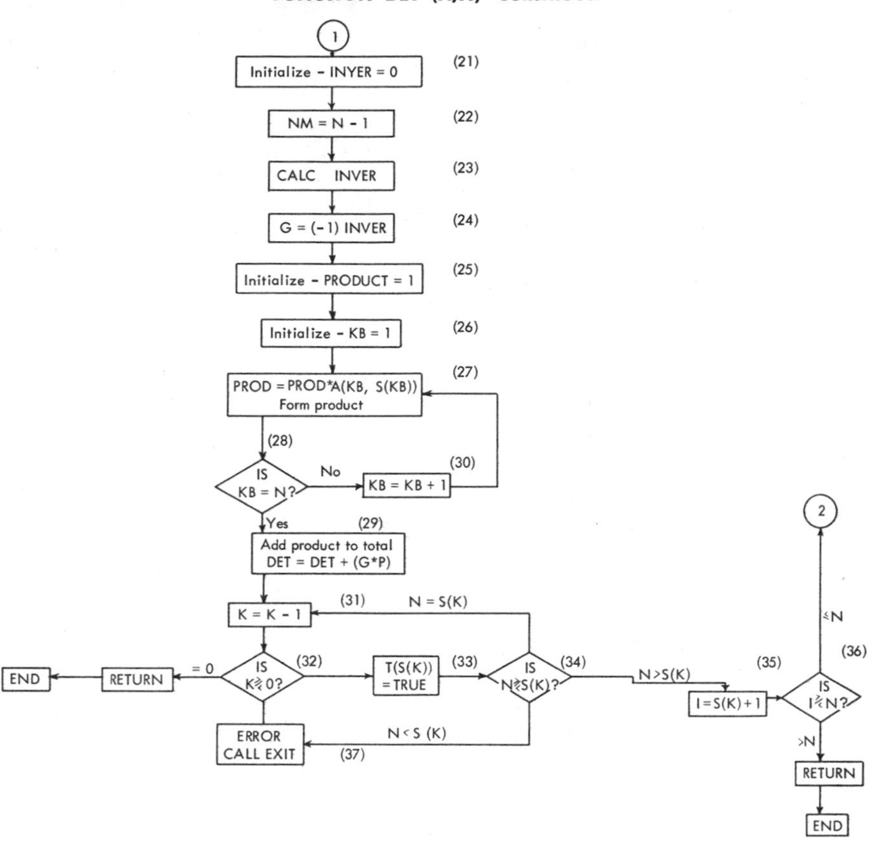


```
 39   I = 1
      K = 1
      S(K) = 1
      DO 2 J=1,N
  2   T(J) = . TRUE.
  3   DO 4 M=I,N
  4   IF(T(M)) GO TO 15
 11   IF(K—1) 12,20,14
 12   WRITE(6,103)
103   FORMAT(22H ERROR AT STATEMENT 11 )
200   CALL EXIT
```

```
 14  K=K-1
     IDUM= S(K)
     T(IDUM) =.TRUE.
     I = S(K) + 1
     GO TO 3
 15  S(K) = M
 16  IF(N-K) 13,6,5
 13  WRITE(6,104)
104  FORMAT(22H ERROR AT STATEMENT 16 )
201  CALL EXIT
  5  T(M) =.FALSE.
     K=K+1
     I=1
     GO TO 3
  6  INVER = 0
     NM = N-1
     DO 301 IB=1,NM
     MA = IB+ 1
     DO 301 JB = MA,N
     IF(S(JB)-S(IB)) 302,303,301
302  INVER=INVER +1
301  CONTINUE
303  G = (-1.) ** (INVER + 2)
     P= 1.
     DO 304 KB = 1,N
     KA= S(KB)
304  P = P * A(KB,KA)
     DET = DET + (G*P)
  7  K=K-1
700  IF(K) 702,20,701
702  WRITE(6,620)
620  FORMAT(24H ERROR AT STATEMENT 700
     CALL EXIT
701  IDUM = S(K)
     T(IDUM) =.TRUE.
 17  IF(N-S(K))216,7,8
216  WRITE(6,105)
105  FORMAT(22H ERROR AT STATEMENT 17 )
202  CALL EXIT
  8  I= S(K) + 1
     IF(N-I) 20,3,3
 20  RETURN
     END
```

```
SET    1        4 BY   4  DETERMINANT
0.1000E 01     0.                0.1500E 01    0.2100E 01
0.1200E 01   -0.2100E 01        0.2500E 01    0.
```

```
 0.            -0.1200E 01   0.3100E 01  -0.1400E 01
-0.3100E 01     0.2200E 01   0.                0.2300E 01
THE VALUE OF THE DETERMINANT IS -0.34532E 02
```

To illustrate the function which evaluated the determinant, consider the case where $n = 4$. The logical array, T, is used as a set of switches showing which permutations have been included in the total. This array is first initialized by setting all possible locations in the array to FALSE; in the given program, T consists of 10 logical variables. After initializing the location which will contain the value of the determinant and checking to see if the size of the array is too large for the program, the following indices are initialized:

I—the index for the T array.
K—the index for the permutation sequence.
{S}—the permutation sequence.

Then the first N (in this case, 4) locations of the T array are reinitialized, and they are set to TRUE (the reason for reinitializing will become clearer later).

T (1)	T (2)	T (3)	T (4)	T (5)	. . .	T (10)
T	T	T	T	F	. . .	F

K = 1, S(K) ≡ S(1) = 1, I = 1 where T ≡ TRUE and
F ≡ FALSE

Since I= 1, M= I so M = 1. T(M) = T (1) =TRUE; therefore, after executing statement number 4, control is transferred to statement number 15. Now S(K)≡ S(1) = M = 1; because N is greater than K (4>1), control is then transferred to statement number 5—causing T (1) to be set equal to FALSE. K is increased by 1 and I is reset to 1; then control is transferred back to statement 3. Notice that the loop is reinitialized at I or 1. I= 1, M = I = 1. Because T (M) ≡ T(1) = FALSE, M is increased by 1 to 2 and since M does not equal N, the loop is repeated. Now T(M)≡ T (2) = T so control is transferred to statement number 15; S(K) ≡ S (2) ≡ M = 2. Because N is greater than K (4>2), we go to statement number 5 and T (M) ≡ T(2) = FALSE, K = 3, I= 1. Then transfer to statement number 3—again the loop consisting of statements number 3 and 4 is entered. Because T (1) = T (2) = FALSE, the loop is repeated twice; when M = 3, T (3) = FALSE, so again control is transferred to statement number 15. There, S(K) = S (3) = M = 3 and since N is still greater than K (4>3), we go to statement 5. Now T(3) is set equal to FALSE and K = 4, I = 1, and control is transferred back to statement number 3. After 3 repetitions of the loop T(4) = TRUE, so the same procedure is repeated with S (4) set equal to 4; but now N = K = 4 so control is transferred to statement number 6.

The number of inversions must be derived from the permutation sequence itself since there is no factorial sequence; the procedure is to count all numbers following each number which are less than that number or out of the natural order. The location INVER is used to count the number of inversions. Notice that the loop compares all elements following the element in question with the element in question; the element in question is moved from element 1 to element $(n-1)$. The number of inversions determines the sign of the product which is formed in location P by taking the first subscript in the natural order and using the elements in the permutation sequence as the second subscript. The product is then added to the total with the correct sign.

K is then reduced by 1 to 4. Because K does not yet equal zero, control is transferred to statement number 701—IDUM = S(K) ≡ S(3) = 3. At this point, T(1) = FALSE, T(2) = FALSE, T(3) = FALSE, T(4) = TRUE. T(IDUM) = T(S(K)) ≡ T(3) is set to TRUE. Because N(N=4) is greater than S(K) ≡ S(3) = 3 control is transferred to statement number 8; I = S(K) + 1 = 3 + 1 = 4, so N = I and control is transferred back to statement number 3. With I = 4, M = 4 = N and T(M) = T(4) = TRUE, the loop transfers control to statement number 15.S(K) ≡ S(3) = M = 4, and N is greater than K (4>3), so control goes to statement number 5; where T(M) ≡ T(4) is set to FALSE, K is increased by 1 to 4, I is set to 1 and control is transferred back to statement number 3.

After two tries through the loop (T(1) = FALSE, T(2) = FALSE), control is transferred to statement number 15 where S(K) ≡ S(4) = 3. Now since N = K = 4, the next statement to be executed is statement number 6; the permutation sequence is now 1,2,4,3. After calculating the sign and the product, and adding the product into the total, the next permutation is generated by the program.

It is left for the student to generate the remaining 22 permutations, the next permutation being 1,3,2,4.

7.1.2. Evaluation of a Determinant by Reduction to Triangular Form

Consider a special type of array, namely:

$$\begin{array}{ccccc}
a_{11} & a_{12} & a_{13} & \cdots & a_{1n} \\
0 & a_{22} & a_{23} & \cdots & a_{2n} \\
0 & 0 & a_{33} & \cdots & a_{3n} \\
\cdot & \cdot & 0 & \cdot & \cdot \\
\cdot & \cdot & \cdot & \cdot & \cdot \\
\cdot & \cdot & \cdot & \cdot & \cdot \\
0 & 0 & 0 & \cdots & a_{nn}
\end{array}$$

where all the elements below the main diagonal are zero; the determinant of such an array is much easier to evaluate than a general array (one in which each element may take on any value within some range determined by the computer, zero or nonzero). Expanding the determinant of the above array by cofactors of the first column, we get

$$a_{11} \cdot A_{11} + 0 \cdot A_{21} + 0 \cdot A_{31} + \ldots + 0 \cdot A_{n1} = a_{11} \cdot A_{11} .$$

Notice that the cofactor A_{11} is of the same form

$$\begin{matrix} a_{22} & a_{23} & a_{24} & \cdots & a_{2n} \\ 0 & a_{33} & a_{34} & \cdots & a_{3n} \\ 0 & 0 & a_{44} & \cdots & a_{4n} \\ \cdot & \cdot & \cdot & \cdot & \cdot \\ \cdot & \cdot & \cdot & \cdot & \cdot \\ \cdot & \cdot & \cdot & \cdot & \cdot \\ 0 & 0 & 0 & \cdots & a_{nn} \end{matrix}$$

as the original determinant. Again expand by cofactors of the second column to give

$$a_{11} \left(a_{22} \cdot A_{22} + a_{32} \cdot A_{32} + a_{42} \cdot A_{42} + \ldots + a_{n2} \cdot A_{n2} \right) ;$$

but because

$$a_{32} = a_{42} = \ldots = a_{n2} = 0,$$
$$|A| = a_{11} \cdot a_{22} \cdot A_{22}.$$

Continuing in this way we arrive at the following:

$$|A| = a_{11} \cdot a_{22} \cdot a_{33} \ldots a_{nn},$$

or simply multiplying the elements down the main diagonal. The signs of the cofactors ($(-1)^{i+j}$) are all positive since the only cofactors to be evaluated are those along the main diagonal.

If a general determinant can be transformed into an equivalent triangular form without too much trouble, the method might prove to be an efficient one for computer evaluation. First, the element a_{21} must be reduced to zero;

$$\begin{matrix} a_{11} & a_{12} & a_{13} & \cdots & a_{1n} \\ a_{21} & a_{22} & a_{23} & \cdots & a_{2n} \\ \cdot & \cdot & \cdot & \cdots & \cdot \\ \cdot & \cdot & \cdot & \cdots & \cdot \\ \cdot & \cdot & \cdot & \cdots & \cdot \\ a_{n1} & a_{n2} & a_{n3} & \cdots & a_{nn} \end{matrix}$$

a_{21} can be reduced to zero by subtracting a_{21}, but this procedure is not one of the available transformations we can use with determinants. Earlier we saw that it was possible to add a multiple of one row to another row without changing the value of the determinant; in order to subtract a_{21} from a_{21}, we could use the ratio

$$(-a_{21}/a_{11})$$

as a multiplier of the first row and then subtract it from the second row. In this way, the new element a_{21} equals the old element a_{21} minus the product of (a_{21}/a_{11}) and the element a_{11}.

If we represent the transformed elements with primes, we have

$$a'_{21} = a_{21} - (a_{21}/a_{11})\, a_{11} = 0$$

All the remaining elements in the second row are transformed in the following way:

$$a'_{2j} = a_{2j} - (a_{21}/a_{11})\, a_{ij} \text{ for } j = 2, \ldots, n.$$

Next, a_{31} must be reduced to zero; again to reduce a_{31} to zero it is necessary to subtract a_{31}. Again, we might try to add a multiple of row 1; namely, $(-a_{31}/a_{11})$ to get

$$a'_{31} = a_{31}\, (-a_{31}/a_{11})a_{11} = 0$$

All remaining elements in the third row become

$$a'_{3j} = a_{3j} - (a_{31}/a_{11})a_{ij} \text{ for } j = 2, \ldots, \text{n}$$

An interesting question involves the use of row 2, instead of row 1, as the row which must be multiplied by a scalar and added to row 3. Note that the procedure by which an element is reduced to zero, $a'_{21} = a_{21} - (a_{21}/a_{11})\, a_{11}$ requires a multiplication and an addition; it would be much simpler to just set a'_{21} equal to zero. However, an even easier procedure would be to ignore a_{21}. Following this procedure, any attempt to evaluate the determinant through expansion by minors will give the wrong result; but, we must keep in mind that at the end of the complete reduction process, one need only multiply the elements down the main diagonal. Then there will be no error in ignoring the elements which should be zero. The complete reduction process can take place without reference to these elements which are assumed to be zero; the analyst must be careful to avoid these elements—in the example, the use of row 2 instead of row 1 would result in a miscalculation because $a'_{3j} = a_{3j} - (a_{31}/a_{21})$ uses a_{21} which should be zero and is not; even if a_{21} was zero, division by zero is not permitted.

In the same way, a_{41} may be reduced to zero by adding to row 4 a multiple of row 1; the multiplier being the ratio $(-a_{41}/a_{11})$. Continue in this way until all elements in the first column below a_{11} are reduced to zero to give a determinant of the form

$$\begin{array}{ccccc}
a_{11} & a_{12} & a_{13} & \cdots & a_{1n} \\
0 & a'_{22} & a'_{23} & \cdots & a'_{2n} \\
0 & a'_{32} & a'_{33} & \cdots & a'_{3n} \\
\cdot & \cdot & \cdot & \cdots & \cdot \\
\cdot & \cdot & \cdot & \cdots & \cdot \\
\cdot & \cdot & \cdot & \cdots & \cdot \\
0 & a'_{m} & a'_{n3} & \cdots & a'_{nn}
\end{array}$$

To reduce the determinant further, it is necessary to reduce a'_{32} to zero; this can be done by adding to row 2 a multiple of row 1; the necessary multiple being $(- a'_{32}/a'_{22})$—

$$a''_{32} = a'_{32} - (a'_{32}/a'_{22})a'_{22} = 0$$

Again, all remaining elements in row 3 become

$$a''_{3j} = a'_{3j} - (a'_{23}/a'_{22})a_{2j} \text{ where } j = 3, \ldots, n.$$

To use row 1 as the row which should be multiplied by the scalar and added to row 3 would result in an error because $a''_{31} = a'_{31} - (a'_{32}/a_{12})a_{11} \neq 0$ even if a'_{31} is zero since a'_{32} does not necessarily equal zero and $a_{11} \neq 0$. When row 2 is used

$$a''_{31} = a'_{31} - (a'_{32}/a_{22})a'_{21}$$

Now a''_{31} can be assumed to be zero, because a'_{31} was assumed to be zero and a'_{21} was assumed to be zero. Again, the easiest procedure will be to assume a''_{32} to be zero and ignore a''_{32} from this point on. For the remaining elements in the third row,

$$a''_{3j} = a'_{3j} - (a'_{32}/a'_{22})a'_{2j} \text{ for } j = 3, \ldots, n$$

To reduce a''_{42} to zero, a scalar multiple of row 2 is added to row 4, that scalar being $(-a'_{42}/a'_{22})$. The element a''_{42} is ignored and the remaining elements in the fourth row are

$$a''_{4j} = a'_{4j} - (a'_{42}/a'_{22})a'_{2j} \text{ for } j = 3, \ldots, n$$

Continue in this way until all elements in the second column below a'_{22} are reduced to zero (at least assumed that way); the resulting determinant is

$$\begin{array}{ccccc}
a_{11} & a_{12} & a_{13} & \cdots & a_{1n} \\
a''_{21} & a''_{22} & a''_{23} & \cdots & a''_{2n} \\
a''_{31} & a''_{32} & a''_{33} & \cdots & a''_{3n} \\
\cdot & \cdot & \cdot & & \cdot \\
\cdot & \cdot & \cdot & & \cdot \\
\cdot & \cdot & \cdot & & \cdot \\
a''_{n1} & a''_{n2} & a''_{n3} & \cdots & a''_{nn}
\end{array}$$

where $a''_{21}, a''_{31}, \ldots, a''_{n1}, a''_{32}, a''_{42}, \ldots, a''_{n2}$ are zero. By our method of improving computer efficiency, these elements are not actually set to zero but simply ignored from this point on to the completion of the process.

The above procedure must be continued for columns 3, . . . , $(n-1)$. Following is a flow chart and a subprogram for evaluation of a determinant by reduction to triangular form.

FLOW CHART—Determinant by Triangularization

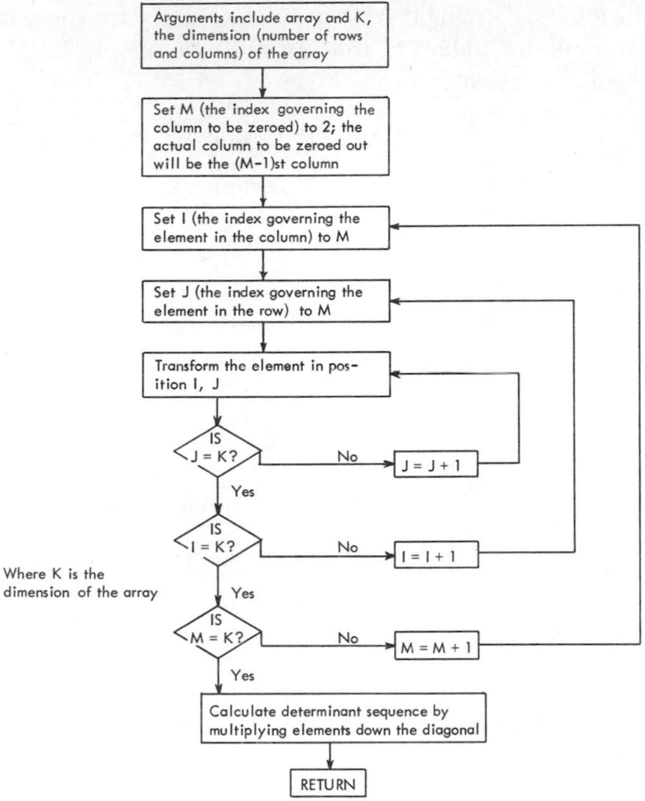

Notice that the J loop starts at M, so if the first column is being zeroed out, elements in the column 2 to column K are transformed; the J loop moves across the row. Also, the I loop starts at M, so if the first column is being zeroed out, only row 2 to row K are transformed; the I loop moves down the rows. For M = 2, the elements in column 1, from element 2 through element K are zeroed out; actually, by starting the I and J indices at M and by starting M at 2, the elements in the first column below a_{11} are ignored and not zeroed out. The index M is always one ahead of the column being zeroed out, so that when M = K the (K−1)st column is being zeroed out. Therefore, the above procedure applies throughout the reduction process.

SUBPROGRAM—Evaluation of a Determinant by Triangularization

```
      FUNCTION DET(A,K)
      DIMENSION A(1Ø,1Ø)
      DO 7 M=2,K
      DO 7 I=M,K
      DO 7 J=M,K
    7 A(I,J)=A(I,J)-A(M-1,J)*A(I,M-1)/A(M-1,M-1)
      DET=1.Ø
      DO 8 I=1,K
    8 DET=DET*A(I,I)
      RETURN
      END
```

The loop including statement number 8 multiplies the elements down the main diagonal.

Two improvements should be made to this routine as it is written above. First, the reader should note the ratio, A(I,M−1) / A(M−1,M−1) does not depend on the index J, and yet it is written in the J loop, the innermost loop. Because the innermost loop is the loop which is most often executed by the computer, any instruction which can be moved out of the inner loop to an outer loop will result in a more efficient program. If the innermost loop (the J loop) is executed 10 times for each iteration of the next outer loop (the I loop), the ratio A(I,M−1) / A(M−1,M−1), is calculated 10 times instead of once. Because the I loop may be executed 10 times for each iteration of the outermost loop (the M loop), which itself may be executed 10 times, the number of wasted calculations is very considerable.

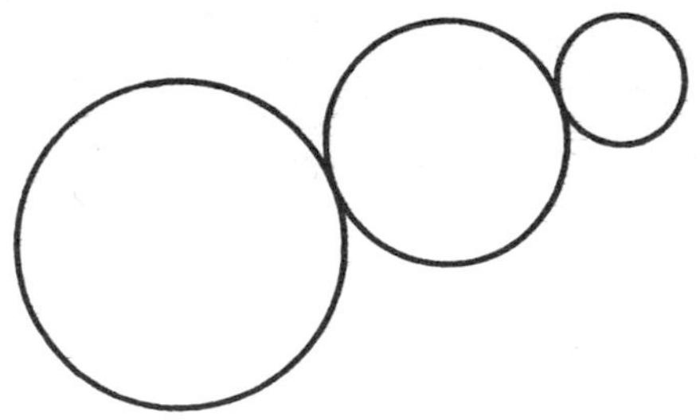

FIG. 7–1

Due to the "gear-like" behavior of a nest of DO loops, the innermost loop goes through 1,000 iterations as compared to 100 iterations of the middle loop; therefore, the ratio will be calculated 900 times more than are necessary to solve the problem. The ratio cannot be moved beyond the middle loop because the ratio depends on the index I, as well as M. Thus, to improve the efficiency of the program, the ratio will be moved to the middle loop.

```
      FUNCTION DET(A,K)
      DIMENSION A(10,10)
      DO 7 M=2,K
      DO 7 I=M,K
      R=A(I,M-1)/A(M-1,M-1)
      DO 7 J=M,K
    7 A(I,J)=A(I,J)-A(M-1,J)*R
      DET=1.0
      DO 8 I=1,K
    8 DET=DET*A(I,I)
      RETURN
      END
```

The above program is not general in the sense that all elements which will serve as pivot elements in the reduction process are assumed to be nonzero. If an element serving as a pivot is zero, the computer will be stopped due to division by zero; it is possible that the FORTRAN compiler (remember, not all FORTRAN compilers work exactly the same) will substitute an arbitrarily large constant and continue instead of stopping at this point.

To make the program entirely general in nature, a zero-test routine needs to be included in the program.

1st Pivot Element → a_{11}

$$\begin{matrix} \boxed{a_{11}} & a_{12} & a_{13} & a_{14} & \cdots & a_{1n} \\ a_{21} & a_{22} & a_{23} & a_{24} & \cdots & a_{2n} \\ \vdots & \vdots & \vdots & \vdots & & \vdots \\ a_{n1} & a_{n2} & a_{n3} & a_{n4} & & a_{nn} \end{matrix}$$

There are two ways of handling the zero-test procedure; first, the pivot element is tested for zero. If the pivot element is zero, either the first and second columns are to be interchanged and then the new pivot element can be tested. In the second method the element in the pivot row and the second column is tested for zero—if it is zero, the next element in the pivot row should be tested. if it is not zero, then the first and second column should be interchanged. This decision is strictly a probabilistic one—if the analyst expects a great deal of zeros, it is better to test before interchanging; but, if the analyst expects only a few zero elements, it is better to interchange the columns and then test for zero. For our purposes we shall assume a great propensity for zeros and therefore test before interchanging columns; remember, an interchange of columns leads to a change in the sign of the determinant. If all elements to the right (that is, all elements with a

```
      FUNCTION DET(A,K)
      DIMENSION A(1Ø,1Ø)
      IF(K-1Ø) 21,21,31
   31 WRITE(6,1Ø1)
  1Ø1 FORMAT(19HDIMENSION TOO LARGE)
      RETURN
   21 Z=1.
      DO 7 M=2,K
      IF(A(M-1,M-1).NE.Ø.) GO TO 5Ø
      DO 3Ø I1=M,K
   3Ø IF(A(M-1,I1).NE.Ø.)GO TO 4Ø
      DET=Ø
      RETURN
   4Ø I3=M-1
      DO 2Ø I2=I3,K
      TEMP=A(I2,I3)
      A(I2,I3)=A(I2,I1)
   2Ø A(I2,I1)=TEMP
      Z=Z*(-1.)
```

```
   5Ø DO7I=M,K
      R=A(I,M-1)/A(M-1,M-1)
      DO 7 J=M,K
    7 A(I,J)=A(I,J)-A(M-1,J)*R
      DET=1.Ø
      DO8I=1,K
    8 DET=DET*A(I,I)
      DET=DET*Z
      RETURN
      END
```

larger second subscript) of the pivot element are zero (of course, in addition to the pivot element being zero), the determinant is zero. Notice that the zero test must be performed on the pivot element between the M loop and the I loop because the ratio is used in the I loop. Location Z is initialized at 1 and is multiplied by −1 every time it is necessary to interchange columns; in this way, the final value of the determinant can be multiplied by Z to give the correct value (an even number of column interchanges leads to Z being 1, while an odd number of column interchanges leads to Z being −1).

The pivotal elements are tested for zero separately from the other elements in the pivotal row; if the pivotal element is not zero, control is transferred to statement number 50 to start the reduction process for that column. On the other hand, if the pivotal element is zero, the loop

```
    DO  30  I 1 = M, K
30  IF (A (M-1, I1) . NE. O.)GO TO 40
```

tests the elements in the pivotal row to the right of the pivotal element for a nonzero element. If this loop is completed without branching out (all elements to the right of the pivotal element are zero), the value of the determinant is set to zero and control is transferred to the calling program. A nonzero element causes a branch to statement number 40 for the process of interchanging the pivotal column—the (M − 1)st column—and the column possessing the nonzero element in the pivotal row—this is the (I1)st column because an unnatural exit leaves the index I1 intact. It is not necessary to test the elements in the pivotal row to the left of the pivotal element because these elements have already been zeroed out (actually, these elements are probably not zero but have been "assumed" to be zero and ignored—this has been previously explained).

In the loop ending with statement number 20, the two columns are interchanged; the student should notice that the row index, I2, governing the row index of the elements to be interchanged starts at (M−1) or I3, which is the pivotal row. In other words, elements above the pivotal row need not be interchanged because the elements above the diagonal need not be used to reduce elements below the pivotal row during the remainder of the reduction process.

Notice that the multiplication by Z is not included in the loop ending at statement number 8 because this might lead to an error, and even if it did not lead to an error, it would be inefficient because it is only necessary to carry out the multiplication by Z one time and not k times.

Both of the methods presented in this section for evaluation of determinants can be classified as direct and not approximate methods. For a determinant with a certain percentage of zero elements "evaluation by definition" is faster than "reduction to triangular form"; if the percentage of zeros is below a certain critical level (depending on the size of the determinant), the latter method is more efficient.

7.2. Matrix Operations

Earlier in this chapter the reader was introduced to an array of numbers, this array (defined to have the same number of rows and columns) can be called a matrix. We will define a matrix to be an array of elements such that each column has the same number of elements. Also each row has the same number of elements; however, it is not necessary that the number of rows and columns in the array be the same (that is, the matrix need not be a square array).

$$\begin{array}{cccc} 1 & 5 & 7 & 2 \\ & 2 & 1 & 3 \\ & & 4 & 6 \\ & & 5 & 1 \end{array}$$

The above array is not a matrix because not all columns have the same number of elements

$$\begin{array}{cccc} 1 & 5 & 7 & 2 \\ & 2 & 1 & 3 \\ & & 4 & 6 \\ & & & 3 \end{array}$$

Again, the above array is not a matrix for the same reason.

$$\begin{array}{cccc} 1 & 5 & 7 & 2 \\ 0 & 2 & 1 & 3 \\ 0 & 0 & 4 & 6 \\ 0 & 0 & 0 & 3 \end{array}$$

This is a matrix; it is a special type called a triangular matrix. It should be noted that the number of columns and the number of rows of a matrix need not be equal.

$$\begin{array}{cccc} 2 & 1 & 7 & 3 \\ 4 & -5 & 0 & 6 \end{array}$$

The above array is a matrix which has two rows and four columns.

A matrix does not possess a single value; the elements of a matrix may represent many different quantities, such as units of a vitamin per pound of ingredient, some quantity of money, etc. Although a matrix itself does not possess a single value, properties may be defined on matrices which do possess a single value. For example, the determinant of a matrix (we defined this property only for square matrices) may be evaluated by either of the methods given in the previous section. Another property is the trace of a matrix; the trace of a matrix is defined to be the sum of the elements along the main diagonal.

In order to use matrices to solve problems, we must be able to perform mathematical operations with matrices; similar to the algebra of real numbers, there is an algebra of matrices (it is not implied that the two algebras are exactly the same).

Addition of two matrices is defined to be the addition of corresponding elements. If a_{ij} is a typical element of matrix A, and if b_{ij} is a typical element of matrix B, then a typical element of matrix C is defined as $c_{ij} = a_{ij}+b_{ij}$, where matrix C is sum of matrices A and B.

$$\overset{A}{\begin{bmatrix} 1 & 3 & 5 \\ 2 & 6 & 1 \\ 3 & 8 & 2 \\ 1 & 5 & -1 \end{bmatrix}} + \overset{B}{\begin{bmatrix} 2 & 0 & 1 \\ 3 & 0 & -5 \\ 1 & 1 & 2 \\ 0 & 5 & -3 \end{bmatrix}} = \overset{C}{\begin{bmatrix} 3 & 3 & 3 \\ 5 & 5 & -4 \\ 4 & 9 & 4 \\ 1 & 10 & -4 \end{bmatrix}}$$

Notice that matrices A and B must be of the same size in order to be summable; and then matrix C is the same size as both matrix A and matrix B.

Define the multiplication of the matrix A by a scalar, say k, as multiplication of each of the elements of the matrix A by k.

$$\overset{A}{\begin{bmatrix} 2 & 1 \\ 1 & 5 \\ 3 & -7 \\ 4 & 2 \end{bmatrix}} \quad \overset{kA}{\begin{bmatrix} 4 & 2 \\ 2 & 10 \\ 6 & -14 \\ 8 & 4 \end{bmatrix}} \quad \textit{where } k = 2$$

With these two definitions, matrix subtraction is simply $A+kB$, where $k = -1$.

$$\overset{A}{\begin{bmatrix} 1 & 2 \\ -1 & 1 \\ 3 & 0 \end{bmatrix}} \overset{B}{\begin{bmatrix} 0 & 1 \\ 1 & 0 \\ 2 & -1 \end{bmatrix}}, \quad \overset{A}{\begin{bmatrix} 1 & 2 \\ -1 & 1 \\ 3 & 0 \end{bmatrix}} + \overset{(-1)B}{\begin{bmatrix} 0 & -1 \\ -1 & 0 \\ -2 & 1 \end{bmatrix}} \overset{=C}{= \begin{bmatrix} 1 & 1 \\ -2 & 1 \\ 1 & 1 \end{bmatrix}}$$

Addition of matrices is both commutative and associative; that is,

$$A+B = B+A$$

and

$$A+(B+C) = (A+B)+C$$

Multiplication of matrices is defined in the following way: for the product $A \cdot B = C$, the element in row i and column j of the matrix C is formed by multiplication of row i of matrix A by column j of matrix B.

$$[a_{i1}, a_{i2}, a_{i3}, a_{i4}, \ldots, a_{in}] \cdot \begin{bmatrix} b_{ij} \\ b_{2j} \\ b_{3j} \\ b_{4j} \\ \cdot \\ \cdot \\ \cdot \\ b_{nj} \end{bmatrix} = c_{ij}$$

The product is

$$(a_{i1} \cdot b_{ij}) + (a_{i2} \cdot b_{2j}) + (a_{i3} \cdot b_{3j}) + (a_{i4} \cdot b_{4j}) + \ldots + (a_{in} \cdot b_{nj}) = c_{ij};$$

or

$$c_{ij} = \sum_{k=1}^{n} a_{ik} \cdot b_{kj};\ i = 1, \ldots, m \text{ and } j = 1, \ldots, \mathrm{I}$$

where there are m rows in the matrix A and l columns in the matrix B. Notice that to follow the definition of matrix multiplication, the number of columns in the matrix A must be the same as the number of rows in the matrix B; in the above example, this number is n.

$$\overset{A}{\begin{bmatrix} 1 & 3 & 2 & 5 \\ 0 & -1 & 2 & -1 \\ 1 & 3 & 0 & 2 \end{bmatrix}} \cdot \overset{B}{\begin{bmatrix} 3 & 0 \\ -1 & 2 \\ 2 & 1 \\ 0 & 6 \end{bmatrix}} = \overset{C}{\begin{bmatrix} 4 & 38 \\ 5 & -6 \\ 0 & 18 \end{bmatrix}}$$

$$\begin{aligned}
c_{11} &= (1)(3)+(3)(-1)+(2)(2)+(5)(0) = 4 \\
c_{21} &= (0)(3)+(-1)(-1)+(2)(2)+(-1)(0) = 5 \\
c_{31} &= (1)(3)+(3)(-1)+(0)(2)+(2)(0) = 0 \\
c_{12} &= (1)(0)+(3)(2)+(2)(1)+(5)(6) = 38 \\
c_{22} &= (0)(0)+(-1)(2)+(2)(1)+(-1)(6) = -6 \\
c_{32} &= (1)(0)+(3)(2)+(0)(1)+(2)(6) = 18
\end{aligned}$$

Notice that there are four columns in matrix A and four rows in matrix B; if this were not true, it would not be possible to multiply the two matrices together. Matrix C has three rows, the same as matrix A; and matrix C has two columns, the same as matrix B. Matrix multiplication is associative, but not commutative; that is

$$A \cdot (B \cdot C) = (A \cdot B) \cdot C$$

But $A \cdot B \neq B \cdot A$; in fact, even if it is possible to multiply $A \cdot B$, it may not be possible to multiply $B \cdot A$ because of their respective sizes. Only when A and B are square is it possible for both $A \cdot B$ and $B \cdot A$ to exist; and even then, they are not necessarily equal to each other. A program for matrix multiplication was given earlier and it is repeated here.

```
      SUBROUTINE  MATMLY (A, B, C, N, L, M)
      DIMENSION  A (10,10), B (10,10), C (10, 10)
      DO  20  J = 1, L
      DO  20  I = 1, M
      C (I,J) = 0
      DO  20  K = 1, N
   20 C (I,J) = C(I,J)+A(I,K) * B (K,J)
      RETURN
      END
```

Given a matrix, *A;* if the matrix is "turned over the main diagonal" (this is the same as interchanging the subscripts), the new matrix is called *A*—transpose symbolized as A^T.

$$A = \begin{bmatrix} a_{11} & a_{12} & a_{13} & a_{14} \\ a_{21} & a_{22} & a_{23} & a_{24} \\ a_{31} & a_{32} & a_{33} & a_{34} \end{bmatrix} \qquad A^T = \begin{bmatrix} a_{11} & a_{21} & a_{31} \\ a_{12} & a_{22} & a_{32} \\ a_{13} & a_{23} & a_{33} \\ a_{14} & a_{24} & a_{34} \end{bmatrix}$$

If A is, *Then A^T is*

$$\begin{bmatrix} 1 & 2 & -1 & 6 \\ 0 & 3 & 1 & -5 \\ 2 & 0 & 3 & -2 \end{bmatrix} \qquad \begin{bmatrix} 1 & 0 & 2 \\ 2 & 3 & 0 \\ -1 & 1 & 3 \\ 6 & -5 & -2 \end{bmatrix}$$

Some special matrices which will be needed in discussions of matrix operations are the null matrix, a matrix consisting of all zeros, and the identity matrix, a square matrix with ones down the diagonal and zeros elsewhere.

$$\begin{bmatrix} 0 & 0 & 0 & 0 \\ 0 & 0 & 0 & 0 \end{bmatrix} \qquad \begin{bmatrix} 1 & 0 & 0 & 0 \\ 0 & 1 & 0 & 0 \\ 0 & 0 & 1 & 0 \\ 0 & 0 & 0 & 1 \end{bmatrix}$$

Null Matrix $\equiv 0$ *Identity Matrix* $\equiv I_n$ *where n is the dimension*

$$A + 0 = 0 + A = 0$$

if the addition can take place.

$$A * 0 = 0$$

if the multiplication can take place.

Now, we define a matrix K, such that, A * K = K * A = I; K will be called the matrix inverse of A and will be denoted by A^{-1}. Not every matrix has an inverse; of course, A and A^{-1} must both be square matrices.

Let us return for a moment to review determinants and consider the expansion of a determinant by minors of row i using the cofactors of row j; that is $\Sigma a_{ij} A_{kj}$. The evaluation of

$$\begin{vmatrix} 1 & 0 & 2 \\ 0 & 1 & -1 \\ 1 & 3 & 0 \end{vmatrix} = 1 ,$$

as we can see using expansion by minors of row 1;

$$1 \begin{vmatrix} 1 & -1 \\ 3 & 0 \end{vmatrix} - 0 \begin{vmatrix} 0 & -1 \\ 1 & 0 \end{vmatrix} + 2 \begin{vmatrix} 0 & 1 \\ 1 & 3 \end{vmatrix}$$

However, if it is expanded by row 1 using the cofactors of row 2, the result is zero;

$$1 \begin{vmatrix} 0 & 2 \\ 3 & 0 \end{vmatrix} - 0 \begin{vmatrix} 1 & 2 \\ 1 & 0 \end{vmatrix} + 2 \begin{vmatrix} 1 & 0 \\ 1 & 3 \end{vmatrix}$$

To show that this is, in general, true, is left as an exercise for the reader. Another way of mathematically stating the above is

$$\sum_j a_{ij} A_{kj} = |A| \delta_{ik} \qquad \text{where } \delta_{ik} = 1 \text{ if } i = k, \text{ otherwise } \delta_{ik} = 0 \tag{7.1}$$

If we write the above equation,

$$\sum_j a_{ij}\, a_{jk}{}^{+} = |A| \delta_{ik} , \tag{7.2}$$

the reader should see the resemblance between this equation and the equation-defining matrix multiplication; also $a_{jk}{}^{+} = A_{kj}$. Interpretation of equation (7.1) as a matrix equation results in the matrix equation,

$$A\, A^{+} = |A|\, I . \tag{7.3}$$

In equation 7.2, a_{ij} is a typical element of the matrix A, A^{+} is a matrix whose elements are the cofactors of the matrix A with the indices interchanged (in other words, the transpose of the matrix of cofactors), $|A|$ is a scaler in terms of matrices (it is a single value), and δ_{ik} is the identity matrix because only the elements down the diagonal are nonzero and equal to 1. The matrix A^{+} is called the adjoint matrix of A.

When the above equation is divided by $|A|$, $A\left(\frac{A^{+}}{|A|}\right) = I$; but, from the definition of the matrix inverse, $\left(\frac{A^{+}}{|A|}\right) = A^{-1}$. Therefore, we have not only proved that if a matrix has a nonzero determinant, then it has an inverse (we have not proved the converse, although it is true in finite-dimensional vector spaces) but have also come up with a method of calculating the inverse. Unfortunately, this method is not very efficient for computer solution; however, it does lend itself to a not-too-difficult program. Following are two ways in which the computer is used to calculate the inverse of a matrix by the adjoint method.

Before giving two computer programs, an example worked manually is offered to further illustrate the method.

Calculate the inverse of the matrix:

$$A = \begin{bmatrix} 1 & 2 & 0 \\ -1 & 1 & 3 \\ 0 & 1 & -1 \end{bmatrix}$$

Expanding by elements of the first row, we have

$$|A| = 1\begin{vmatrix} 1 & 3 \\ 1 & -1 \end{vmatrix} - 2\begin{vmatrix} -1 & 3 \\ 0 & -1 \end{vmatrix} + 0\begin{vmatrix} -1 & 1 \\ 0 & 1 \end{vmatrix} = -4 - 2 + 0 = -6\,.$$

Now calculate the nine cofactors—

$$A_{11} = \begin{vmatrix} 1 & 3 \\ 1 & -1 \end{vmatrix} = -4$$

$$A_{12} = \begin{vmatrix} -1 & 3 \\ 0 & -1 \end{vmatrix} = -1\,(1) = -1$$

$$A_{13} = \begin{vmatrix} -1 & 1 \\ 0 & 1 \end{vmatrix} = 1\,(-1) = -1$$

$$A_{21} = \begin{vmatrix} 2 & 0 \\ 1 & -1 \end{vmatrix} = (-1)\,(-2) = 2$$

$$A_{22} = \begin{vmatrix} 1 & 0 \\ 0 & -1 \end{vmatrix} = -1$$

$$A_{23} = \begin{vmatrix} 1 & 0 \\ -1 & 3 \end{vmatrix} = (-1)\,(3) = -3$$

$$A_{31} = \begin{vmatrix} 2 & 0 \\ 1 & 3 \end{vmatrix} = 6$$

$$A_{32} = \begin{vmatrix} 1 & 0 \\ -1 & 3 \end{vmatrix} = (-1)\,3 = -3$$

$$A_{33} = \begin{vmatrix} 1 & 2 \\ -1 & 1 \end{vmatrix} = 3 = 3$$

$$A^{+} = \begin{bmatrix} A_{11} & A_{21} & A_{31} \\ A_{12} & A_{22} & A_{32} \\ A_{13} & A_{23} & A_{33} \end{bmatrix};$$

$$A^{-1} = \frac{A^+}{A} = \frac{1}{6}A^+ = -\frac{1}{6}\begin{bmatrix} -4 & 2 & 6 \\ -1 & -1 & -3 \\ -1 & -1 & 3 \end{bmatrix} = \begin{bmatrix} 4/6 & -2/6 & -1 \\ 1/6 & 1/6 & 3/6 \\ 1/6 & 1/6 & -3/6 \end{bmatrix}$$

Then by matrix multiplication

$$\begin{bmatrix} 4/6 & -2/6 & -1 \\ 1/6 & 1/6 & 3/6 \\ 1/6 & 1/6 & -3/6 \end{bmatrix} \quad \begin{bmatrix} 1 & 2 & 0 \\ -1 & 1 & 3 \\ 0 & 1 & -1 \end{bmatrix} = \begin{bmatrix} 1 & 0 & 0 \\ 0 & 1 & 0 \\ 0 & 0 & 1 \end{bmatrix}$$

7.2.1. Calculation of the Inverse by Using the Adjoint Matrix

The necessity of placing the matrix in two arrays (duplication) depends on the type of routine used to calculate the determinant. If the triangularization routine is chosen, the matrix must be placed in two different arrays because during the process of triangularization the original matrix is destroyed. Therefore, the matrix appears in both the working array, C, and

FLOW CHART—Matrix Inverse by Adjoint Method

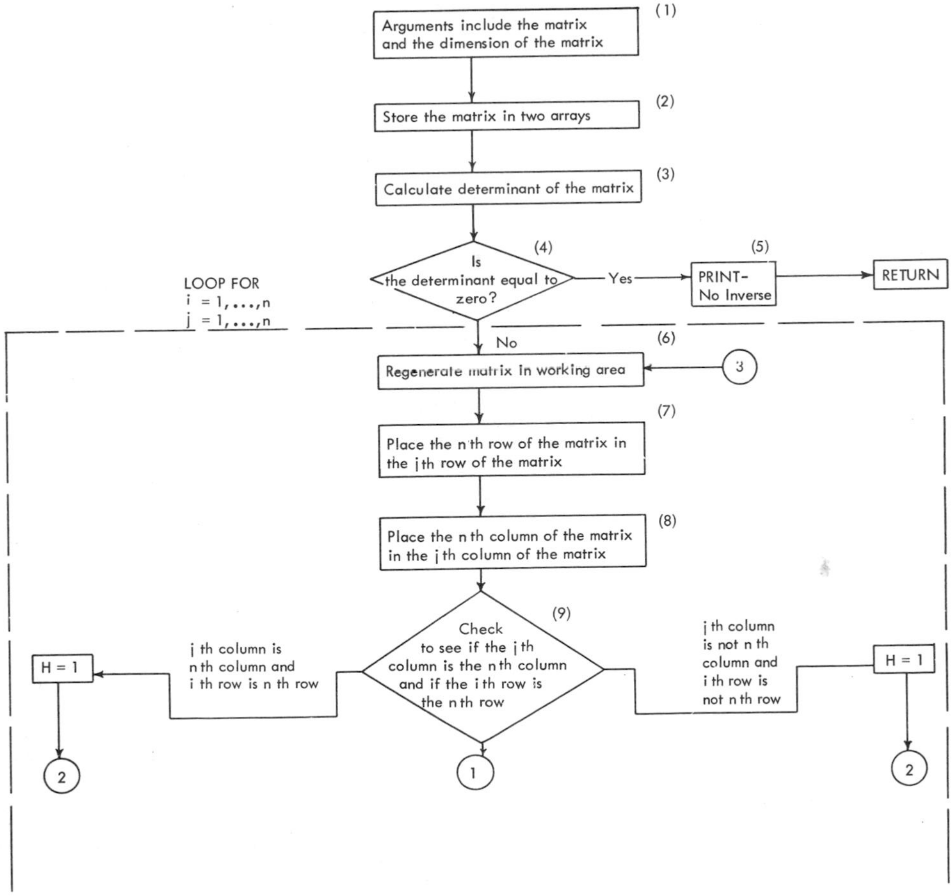

(1) Arguments include the matrix and the dimension of the matrix

(2) Store the matrix in two arrays

(3) Calculate determinant of the matrix

(4) Is the determinant equal to zero? — Yes → (5) PRINT—No Inverse → RETURN

LOOP FOR
i = 1,...,n
j = 1,...,n

No

(6) Regenerate matrix in working area ← 3

(7) Place the n th row of the matrix in the j th row of the matrix

(8) Place the n th column of the matrix in the j th column of the matrix

(9) Check to see if the j th column is the n th column and if the i th row is the n th row

j th column is n th column and i th row is n th row → H = 1 → 2

j th column is not n th column and i th row is not n th row → H = 1 → 2

→ 1

FLOW CHART—*Continued*

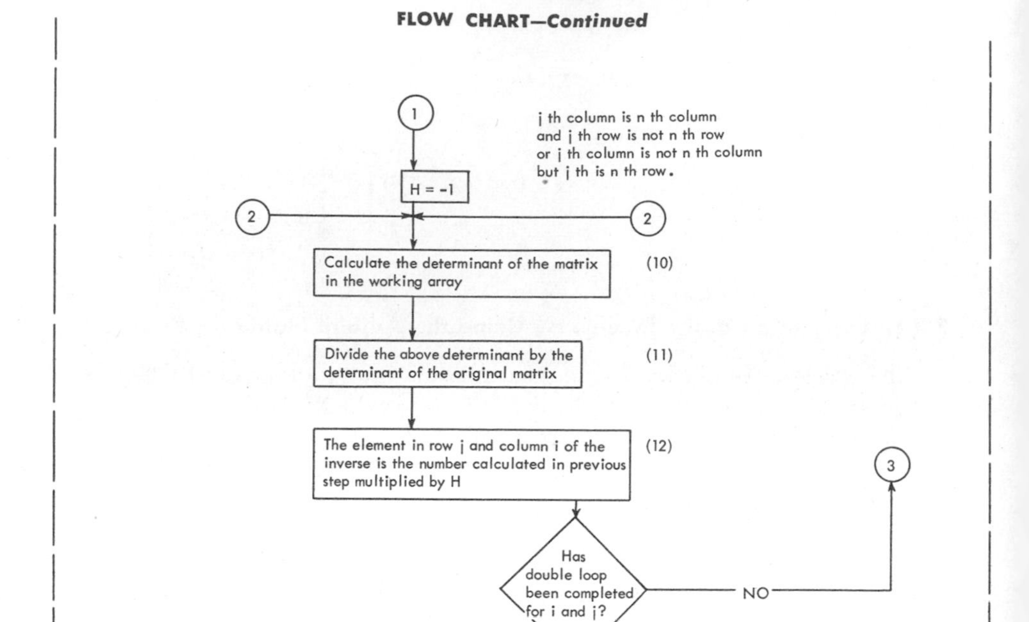

the original array, B. However, if the determinant is evaluated by definition, the original matrix is not destroyed in the calculation of the determinant.

Even if the working array, C, is not needed in the calculation of the determinant it will be needed to regenerate the matrix after the interchange of the ith row with the nth row and the jth column with the nth column. The regeneration of the original matrix in the working array takes place in the double loop ending with statement number 17.

Only one other point needs to be explained in the program; that is the way in which the value of H is decided upon. Remember that an interchange of two columns of a determinant (no matter which two columns) leads to a change in the sign of the determinant; the same holds true for an interchange of rows. Therefore, if both two columns are interchanged *and* two rows are interchanged, there will be no change in sign of the determinant because $(-1) \cdot (-1) = 1$. Also, if neither two columns nor two rows are interchanged, there will be no change in the sign of the determinant. However, if either two columns or two rows are interchanged, but not both, the sign of the determinant will be changed. Now when $I = N$ in the loop ending with statement number 18, two rows will not be interchanged; and

SUBPROGRAM—Method Matrix Inverse by Adjoint Method

```
      SUBROUTINE INVERS (A,B,C,N)                                  (1)
      DIMENSION A(10,10),B(10,10),C(10,10)
      DO 20 I=1,N                                                  (2)
      DO 20 J=1,N
   20 C(I,J)=B(I,J)
      E=DET(C,N)                                                   (3)
      IF(E) 14,12,14                                               (4)
   12 WRITE(6,13)                                                  (5)
   13 FORMAT(5X,32H THE GIVEN MATRIX HAS NO INVERSE)
      RETURN
   14 M=N-1
      DO 16 I=1,N
      DO 16 J=1,N
      DO 17 K=1,N                                                  (6)
      DO 17 L=1,N
   17 C(K,L)=B(K,L)
      H=1
      DO 18 L=1,N                                                  (7)
   18 C(I,L)=C(N,L)
```

```
      DO 19 K=1,N                                                  (7)
   19 C(K,J)=C(K,N)                                                (8)
      IF (.NOT.(N.EQ.J.AND.N.EQ.I.OR.N.NE.J.AND.N.NE.I)), H=-1     (9)
   16 A(J,I)=DET(C,M)/E*H                                          (10),(11),(12)
      RETURN
      END
```

when J = N in the loop ending with statement number 19, two columns will not be interchanged. When I ≠ N, there will be an interchange of two rows and when J ≠ N, there will be an interchange of two columns.

The logic of the above decision may be incorporated in one FORTRAN IV LOGICAL IF statement:

IF (·NOT·(N·EQ·J·AND·N·EQ·I·OR·N·NE·J·AND·N·NE·I))H = −1

A≡N·EQ·J
B≡N·EQ·I
C≡N·NE·J
D≡N·NE·I

J	I	A	B	A·AND·B	C	D	C·AND·D	A·AND·B·OR·C·AND·D	·NOT·E
= N	= N	T	T	T	F	F	F	T	F
≠ N	≠ N	F	F	F	T	T	T	T	F
= N	≠ N	T	F	F	F	T	F	F	T
≠ N	= N	F	T	F	T	F	F	F	T

Notice that the entire logical expression is TRUE only if there will be a change in sign; in this case H is to set equal to -1 and then an element of the inverse is calculated. The logical expression will be FALSE if there will be no change in sign; in this case the statement, H= -1, is not executed and then an element of the inverse is calculated. Since H had been set to 1 in the statement following statement number 17 and has not been changed, the multiplying factor is 1. A closer examination of moving column n to column j and row n to row i may be interesting.

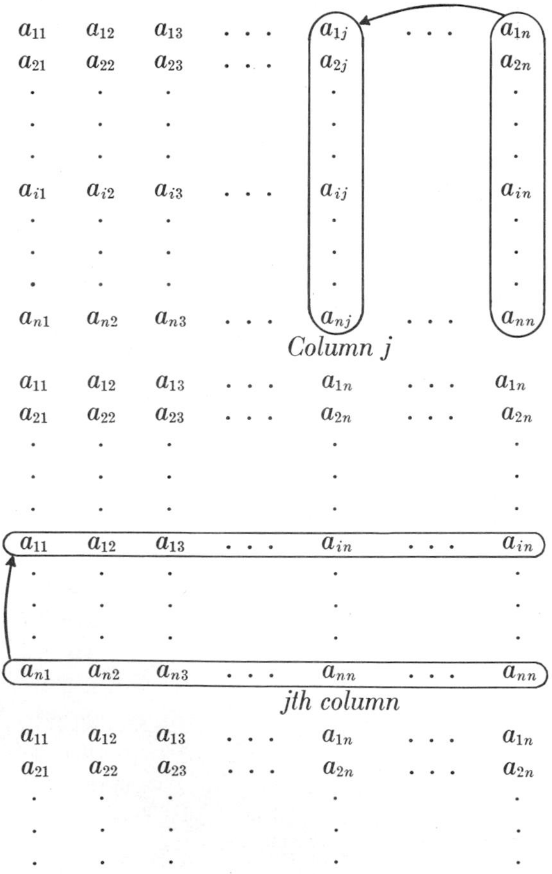

$$
\begin{array}{cccccccc}
a_{11} & a_{12} & a_{13} & \cdots & a_{1j} & \cdots & a_{1n} \\
a_{21} & a_{22} & a_{23} & \cdots & a_{2j} & & a_{2n} \\
\cdot & \cdot & \cdot & & \cdot & & \cdot \\
\cdot & \cdot & \cdot & & \cdot & & \cdot \\
\cdot & \cdot & \cdot & & \cdot & & \cdot \\
a_{i1} & a_{i2} & a_{i3} & \cdots & a_{ij} & & a_{in} \\
\cdot & \cdot & \cdot & & \cdot & & \cdot \\
\cdot & \cdot & \cdot & & \cdot & & \cdot \\
\cdot & \cdot & \cdot & & \cdot & & \cdot \\
a_{n1} & a_{n2} & a_{n3} & \cdots & a_{nj} & \cdots & a_{nn}
\end{array}
$$

Column j

STEP 1)

$$
\begin{array}{ccccccc}
a_{11} & a_{12} & a_{13} & \cdots & a_{1n} & \cdots & a_{1n} \\
a_{21} & a_{22} & a_{23} & \cdots & a_{2n} & \cdots & a_{2n} \\
\cdot & \cdot & \cdot & & \cdot & & \cdot \\
\cdot & \cdot & \cdot & & \cdot & & \cdot \\
\cdot & \cdot & \cdot & & \cdot & & \cdot \\
a_{i1} & a_{i2} & a_{i3} & \cdots & a_{in} & \cdots & a_{in} \\
\cdot & \cdot & \cdot & & \cdot & & \cdot \\
\cdot & \cdot & \cdot & & \cdot & & \cdot \\
\cdot & \cdot & \cdot & & \cdot & & \cdot \\
a_{n1} & a_{n2} & a_{n3} & \cdots & a_{nn} & \cdots & a_{nn}
\end{array}
$$

The matrix now has two columns the same; column n and column j

jth column

STEP 2)

$$
\begin{array}{ccccccc}
a_{11} & a_{12} & a_{13} & \cdots & a_{1n} & \cdots & a_{1n} \\
a_{21} & a_{22} & a_{23} & \cdots & a_{2n} & \cdots & a_{2n} \\
\cdot & \cdot & \cdot & & \cdot & & \cdot \\
\cdot & \cdot & \cdot & & \cdot & & \cdot \\
\cdot & \cdot & \cdot & & \cdot & & \cdot
\end{array}
$$

The matrix now has two rows the same; row n and row i.

$$
\begin{array}{llllllll}
ith\ row & a_{n1} & a_{n2} & a_{n3} & & a_{nn} & \cdots & a_{nn} \\
 & \cdot & \cdot & \cdot & & \cdot & & \cdot \\
 & \cdot & \cdot & \cdot & & \cdot & & \cdot \\
 & \cdot & \cdot & \cdot & & \cdot & & \cdot \\
 & a_{n1} & a_{n2} & a_{n3} & & a_{nn} & & a_{nn}
\end{array}
$$

Note that the element a_{nn} appears four times in the matrix. At first glance this may appear to be an error, but it should be kept in mind that we are interested in the cofactor of the element a^{ij}, which is now the element a_{nn} because it is at the intersection of row i and column j.

$$
\begin{array}{lllllll}
a_{11} & a_{12} & a_{13} & \cdots & a_{in} & \cdots & a_{in} \\
a_{21} & a_{22} & a_{23} & \cdots & a_{2n} & \cdots & a_{2n} \\
\cdot & \cdot & \cdot & & \cdot & & \cdot \\
\cdot & \cdot & \cdot & & \cdot & & \cdot \\
\cdot & \cdot & \cdot & & \cdot & & \cdot \\
a_{n1} & a_{n2} & a_{n3} & \cdots & a_{nn} & \cdots & a_{nn} \\
\cdot & \cdot & \cdot & & \cdot & & \cdot \\
\cdot & \cdot & \cdot & & \cdot & & \cdot \\
\cdot & \cdot & \cdot & & \cdot & & \cdot \\
a_{n1} & a_{n2} & a_{n3} & \cdots & a_{nn} & \cdots & a_{nn}
\end{array}
$$

The cofactor of the element at the intersection of row i and column j is:

$$
\begin{array}{lllllllll}
a_{11} & a_{12} & a_{13} & \cdots & a_{1,j-1} & a_{1,j+1} & \cdots & a_{in} \\
a_{21} & a_{22} & a_{23} & \cdots & a_{2,j-1} & a_{1,j+1} & \cdots & a_{2n} \\
\cdot & \cdot & \cdot & & \cdot & \cdot & & \cdot \\
\cdot & \cdot & \cdot & & \cdot & \cdot & & \cdot \\
\cdot & \cdot & \cdot & & \cdot & \cdot & & \cdot \\
a_{i-1,1} & a_{i-1,2} & a_{i-1,3} & \cdots & a_{i-1,j-1} & a_{i-1,j+1} & \cdots & a_{i-1,n} \\
a_{i+1,1} & a_{i+1,2} & a_{i+1,3} & \cdots & a_{i+1,j-1} & a_{i+1,j+1} & \cdots & a_{i+1,n} \\
\cdot & \cdot & \cdot & & \cdot & \cdot & & \cdot \\
\cdot & \cdot & \cdot & & \cdot & \cdot & & \cdot \\
\cdot & \cdot & \cdot & & \cdot & \cdot & & \cdot \\
a_{n1} & a_{n2} & a_{n3} & \cdots & a_{n,j-1} & a_{n,j+1} & \cdots & a_{n,n}
\end{array}
\qquad (1)
$$

This is the correct cofactor for the element a_{ij}. However, if the cofactor were to be formed by crossing off the ith row and jth column, we would have to consider the factor $(-1)^{i+j}$. The advantage of method 1 is that row n and column n are crossed off and not row i and column j.

$$
\begin{array}{lcccccccc}
 & & & & & j\text{th column} & & & \\
 & a_{11} & a_{12} & a_{13} & \cdots & a_{1n} & \cdots & a_{1,n-1} & \\
 & a_{21} & a_{22} & a_{23} & \cdots & a_{2n} & \cdots & a_{2,n-1} & \\
 & \vdots & \vdots & \vdots & & \vdots & & \vdots & \\
i\text{th row} & a_{n1} & a_{n2} & a_{n3} & \cdots & a_{nn} & \cdots & a_{n,n-1} & \qquad (2) \\
 & \vdots & \vdots & \vdots & & \vdots & & \vdots & \\
 & a_{n-1,1} & a_{n-1,2} & a_{n-1,3} & \cdots & a_{n-1,n} & \cdots & a_{n-1,n-1} &
\end{array}
$$

Now (2) is the same as (1) except for an interchange of rows i and n and an interchange of columns j and n; the elements are the same. Since the sign changes due to these interchanges have already been accounted for, (2) is also the correct cofactor. But (2) is the cofactor of a_{nn} in the determinant of dimension n; therefore, the factor is now $(-1)^{n+n}$ or $(-1)^{2n}$. The number $2n$ is always an even number; thus, the factor $(-1)^{i+j}$ need not be considered when using this method.

A more direct method of obtaining the inverse of a given matrix is to calculate the cofactor of each element of the matrix including its sign (by evaluating $(-1)^{i+j}$) and placing this cofactor in the adjoint matrix (remembering to reverse the subscripts so as to give the transpose of the matrix of cofactors.

To set up the submatrix the following possibilities must be considered:

1. If the element in original matrix is to the left and above the element

Original Matrix

$$
\begin{array}{cc|cc}
a_{11} & a_{12} & a_{13} & a_{14} \\
a_{21} & a_{22} & a_{23} & a_{24} \\
\hline
a_{31} & a_{32} & \textcircled{a_{33}} & a_{34} \\
a_{41} & a_{42} & a_{43} & a_{44}
\end{array}
$$

Submatrix

$$
\begin{array}{cc}
a_{11} & a_{12} \\
a_{21} & a_{22}
\end{array}
$$

whose cofactor is being calculated, the relative position of the element in the submatrix does not change. Let a_{33} be the element whose cofactor is to be calculated; hereafter, this element will be called the pivot element. The elements in positions a_{11}, a_{12}, a_{21}, and a_{22} will also be in positions a_{11}, a_{12}, a_{21}, and a_{22} of the submatrix.

2. Elements in the original matrix which lie in rows above the pivot row and columns to the right of the pivot column are shifted one position to the left in the same row; thus, the elements in positions a_{14} and a_{24} go to positions a_{13} and a_{23}, respectively.

3. Elements in the original matrix which lie below the pivot row and to the left of the pivot column are to be moved up one position in the same column; thus, the elements in positions a_{41} and a_{42} go to positions a_{31} and a_{32}, respectively.

4. Elements in the original matrix which lie both below and to the right of the pivot element must be moved one space to the left and one space up; thus the element in position a_{44} goes to position a_{33}. The four movements are:

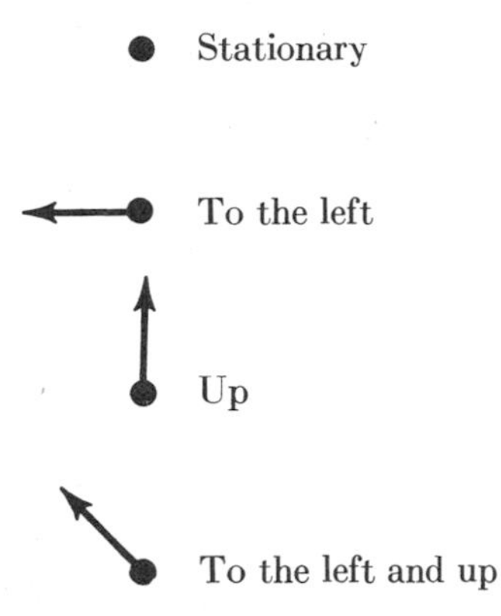

Elements in the pivotal row and pivotal column are ignored. Instructions for setting up the submatrix are contained in the double loop ending with statement number 10.

Using this straightforward method, the determinant of the submatrix

FLOW CHART—Matrix Inverse by Adjoint Method 2

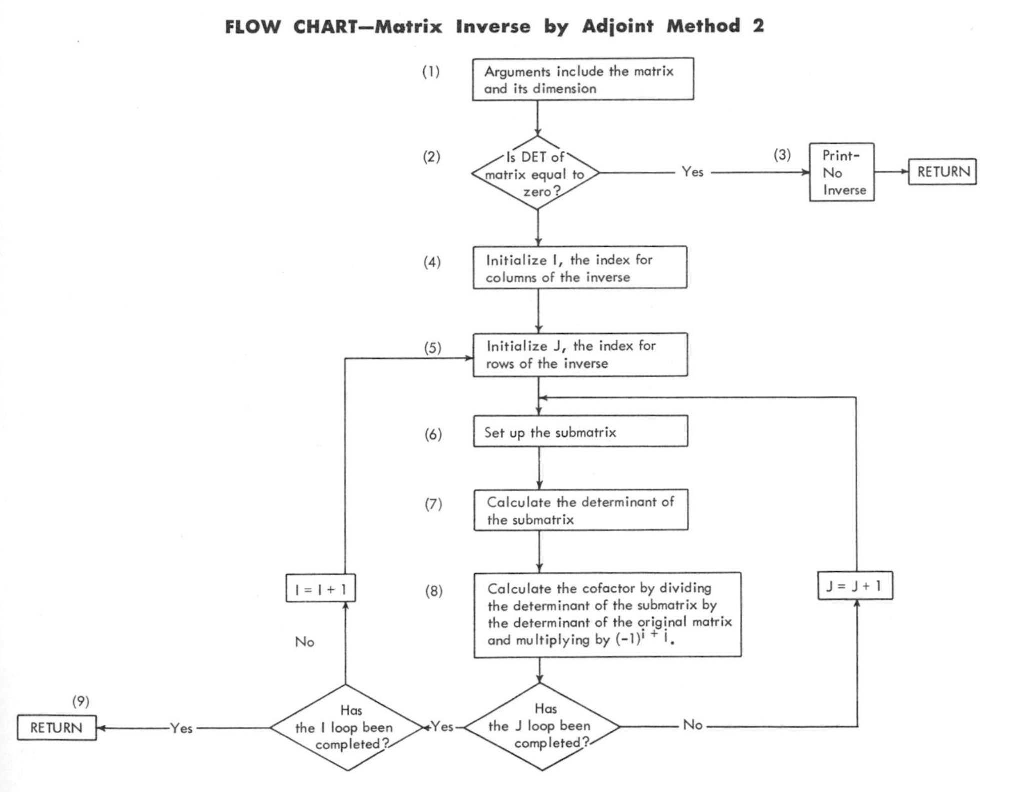

Detailed Chart of the Process of Setting Up the Submatrix

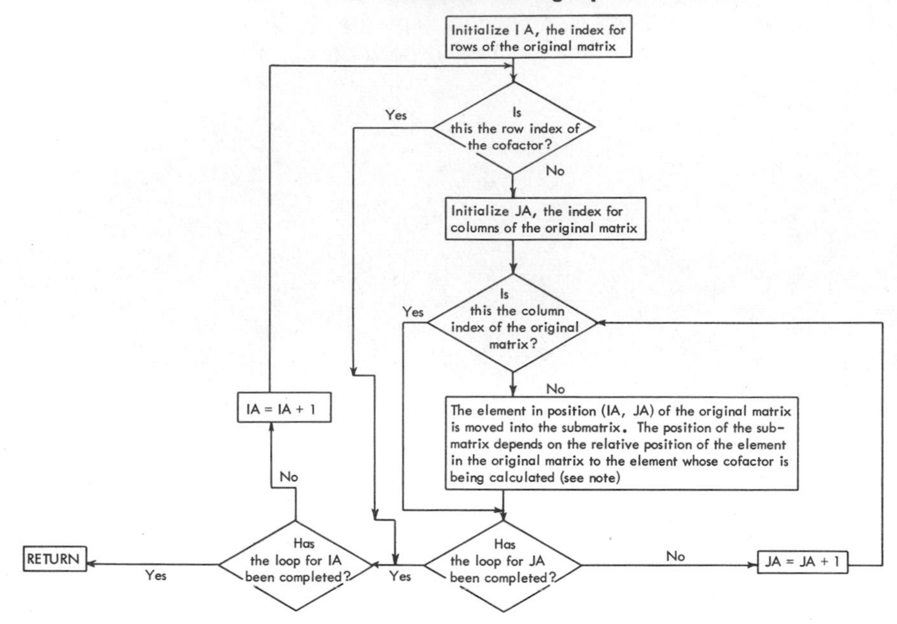

must be multiplied by $(-1)^{i+j}$ to give the cofactor of the element in the (i,j) the position of the determinant of the original matrix.

Following is a sample problem utilizing the method of cofactors to calculate the inverse of a given matrix; the program is written as a main program.

SUBPROGRAM—Matrix Inverse by Method 2

```
C FOR COMMENT
STATEMENT NUMBER | Cont. | FORTRAN STATEMENT

      SUBROUTINE INVERS(BA,NA,COF)                               (1)
      DIMENSION A(10,10),BA(10,10),COF(10,10)
      AMAG=DET(BA,NA)                                            (2)
      IF(AMAG) 4,200,4                                           (3)
  200 WRITE(6,70)
   70 FORMAT(10HNO INVERSE)
      RETURN
    4 N=NA-1
    5 DO 20 I=1,NA                                               (4)
    6 DO 20 J=1,NA                                               (5)
    7 IB=0
      DO 10 IA=1,NA
      IF(IA-I) 8,10,8
    8 IB=IB+1
      JB=0                                                       (6)
      DO 10 JA=1,NA
      IF(JA-J) 9,10,9
    9 JB=JB+1
      A(IB,JB)=BA(IA,JA)
```

SUBPROGRAM—*Continued*

```
C FOR COMMENT
STATEMENT NUMBER | FORTRAN STATEMENT
   10 CONTINUE
   20 COF(J,I)=((-I.)**(I+J))*(DET(A,N)/AMAG)           (7) & (8)
      RETURN                                            (9)
      END
```

SAMPLE PROBLEM

Given Matrix

0.1000E 01	0.	0.1500E 01	0.2100E 01
0.1200E 01	−0.2100E 01	0.2500E 01	0.
0.	−0.1200E 01	0.3100E 01	−0.1400E 01
−0.3100E 01	0.2200E 01	0.	0.2300E 01

Inverse Matrix

0.4568E−00	−0.4286E−00	0.1247E−00	−0.3412E−00
0.5620E 00	−0.9794E 00	0.5179E 00	−0.1978E−00
0.2528E−00	−0.2170E−00	0.3752E−00	−0.2433E−02
0.7810E−01	0.3591E−00	−0.3274E−00	0.1642E−00

FORTRAN SOURCE LIST

```
C FOR COMMENT
STATEMENT NUMBER | FORTRAN STATEMENT
      DIMENSION A(10,10,),BA(10,10),COF(10,10),C(10,10)
      ISET=1
    1 WRITE(6,100)
      READ(5,101) NA
  100 FORMAT(1H1,20X,16HMATRIX INVERSION,/)
  101 FORMAT(I2)
  102 FORMAT(10F8.0)
    2 DO 3 I=1,NA
    3 READ(5,102) (BA(I,J),J=1,NA)
      AMAG=DET(BA,NA)
      IF(AMAG) 4,200,4
  200 CALL EXIT
    4 N=NA-1
    5 DO 20 I=1,NA
    6 DO 20 J=1,NA
    7 IB=0
      DO 10 IA=1,NA
      IF(IA-I) 8,10,8
```

FORTRAN SOURCE LIST—*Continued*

```
    8 IB=IB+1
      JB=Ø
      DO 1Ø JA=1,NA
      IF(JA-J) 9,1Ø,9
    9 JB=JB+1
      A(IB,JB)=BA(IA,JA)
   1Ø CONTINUE
   2Ø COF(J,I)=((-1.)**(I+J))*(DET(A,N)/AMAG)
      WRITE(6,1Ø3)
  1Ø3 FORMAT(/,15H GIVEN MATRIX ,/)
      DO 3Ø I=1,NA
   3Ø WRITE(6,1Ø4) (BA(I,J),J=1,NA)
  1Ø4 FORMAT(1Ø(1X,E11.4))
      WRITE(6,1Ø5)
  1Ø5 FORMAT(/,16H INVERSE MATRIX ,/)
      DO 5Ø I=1,NA
      DO 5Ø J=1,NA
      C(I,J)=Ø.
      DO 5Ø K=1,NA
```

```
   5Ø C(I,J)=C(I,J)+(COF(I,K) * BA(K,J))
      DO 6Ø I=1,NA
   6Ø WRITE(6,1Ø4) (C(I,J),J=1,NA)
      ISET=ISET+1
      GO TO 1
      END
```

7.2.2. Matrix Inversion by Reduction

Another method for inversion of matrices revolves around reduction to a special form. The reduction is in some ways similar to the reduction of a determinant to triangular form. To reduce a determinant to triangular form we used the following properties—

1. Addition of a scalar multiple of one row to another row does not change the value of the determinant.
2. An interchange of two rows or two columns causes a change in the sign of the determinant.

The first property alone can be used to reduce the determinant to triangular form if and only if as the reduction procedure progresses, no pivot element has the value zero. Anytime a pivot element is zero, the second property must be used in order to bring a nonzero element to the pivot position.

Instead of operating directly on the matrix in the way reduction operations are performed on the determinant, the following elementary operations are performed on the matrix by multiplication using elementary matrices (an identity matrix which has been changed by elementary operations).

1. The interchange of two rows.
2. Multiplication of a row by a scalar.
3. Addition of a multiple of one row to another row.

To interchange two rows of a matrix, premultiply the matrix by an elementary matrix of the same dimension; to interchange row i and row j of the matrix, row i and row j of the identity should be interchanged. To interchange row 1 and row 3, multiply by the identity of the same dimension (i.e., 3) with rows 1 and 3 interchanged.

$$\begin{bmatrix} 0 & 0 & 1 \\ 0 & 1 & 0 \\ 1 & 0 & 0 \end{bmatrix} \begin{bmatrix} 2 & 1 & 6 \\ 3 & 1 & 4 \\ 0 & -1 & 1 \end{bmatrix} = \begin{bmatrix} 0 & -1 & 1 \\ 3 & 1 & 4 \\ 2 & 1 & 6 \end{bmatrix}$$

To multiply row 2 by the scalar k, premultiply by the identity matrix with the second row multiplied by k.

$$\begin{bmatrix} 1 & 0 & 0 \\ 0 & 1 & k \\ 0 & 0 & 1 \end{bmatrix} \begin{bmatrix} 2 & 1 & 0 \\ 0 & 3 & -1 \\ 1 & 0 & 5 \end{bmatrix} = \begin{bmatrix} 2 & 1 & 0 \\ 0 & 3k & -k \\ 1 & 0 & 5 \end{bmatrix}$$

To add k times row 3 to row 2, multiply by the identity matrix altered so that the new second row is equal to k times the third row added to the original second row.

$$\begin{bmatrix} 1 & 0 & 0 \\ 0 & 1 & k \\ 0 & 0 & 1 \end{bmatrix} \begin{bmatrix} 3 & 0 & -1 \\ 0 & 1 & 2 \\ 1 & 2 & 3 \end{bmatrix} = \begin{bmatrix} 3 & 0 & -1 \\ k & 1+2k & 2+3k \\ 1 & 2 & 3 \end{bmatrix}$$

Notice that the above elementary operations were performed on the original matrix by premultiplying (that is multiplying on the left) by a particular elementary matrix. Elementary column operations take place by postmultiplying (that is, by multiplying on the right) by an elementary matrix obtained by performing the desired operations on the columns of the identity matrix of the appropriate size.

In Chapter 6 it was demonstrated that a general determinant could be reduced to triangular form using addition of a multiple of one row to another row and the interchange of two rows (in the case of a zero pivot element).

$$\begin{bmatrix} a_{11} & a_{12} & a_{13} & \cdot & \cdot & \cdots & \cdot & a_{1n} \\ 0 & a_{22} & a_{23} & \cdot & \cdot & \cdots & \cdot & a_{2n} \\ 0 & 0 & a_{33} & \cdot & \cdot & \cdots & \cdot & a_{3n} \\ 0 & 0 & 0 & a_{44} & & \cdots & \cdot & a_{4n} \\ \cdot & \cdot & \cdot & \cdot & \cdot & & \cdot & \cdot \\ \cdot & \cdot & \cdot & \cdot & \cdot & & \cdot & \cdot \\ \cdot & \cdot & \cdot & \cdot & \cdot & & \cdot & \cdot \\ 0 & 0 & 0 & 0 & 0 & \cdots & 0 & a_{nn} \end{bmatrix}$$

The matrix can be further reduced to the form of an identity matrix; for this purpose the following procedure may be used: multiply the nth row by the scalar, $1/a_{nn}$; the new nth row is 0 0 . . . 0 1—then add $(-1/a_{n-1,n})$ times the nth row to the $(n-1)$st row; the new $(n-1)$st row then becomes 0 0 . . . 0 $a_{n-1,n-1}$ 0—now multiply the $(n-1)$st row by the scalar, $(1/a_{n-1,n-1})$ to give the final $(n-1)$st row 0 0 . . . 0 1 0.

Continuation of this process will lead to the identity matrix if there are no zero pivot elements; if a zero element occurs on a pivot point, the rows can be interchanged. Therefore, through the use of the three elementary operations, a general matrix may be reduced to the identity matrix in a finite number of steps. If $E_1, E_2, \ldots, E_n$ are elementary matrices, then we have shown that $E_n \ldots E_3E_2E_1A = I$, where first we have E_1A, then the result is premultiplied by E_2, etc. However, because of the associative property of matrix multiplication, we can first multiply together all of the elementary matrices and then take the product of this resulting matrix with A. Let $E_nE_{n-1} \ldots E_2E = E$; then $EA = I$; but then, $E = A^{-1}$.

If both A and I are located in the computer and the same elementary operations are performed on both A and I at the same time, then at the same time that the original A becomes I, the original I becomes E.

$$\begin{matrix} A & & I \\ \underbrace{EA} & & \underbrace{EI} \\ I & & E \end{matrix}$$

For computational purposes, it is not necessary to carry out the matrix multiplication of the original matrix by an elementary matrix in order to perform an elementary operation on the original matrix; it is sufficient to simply perform the elementary operation on the original matrix in the same way as elementary operations are performed on the determinant. The elementary matrices were introduced because each elementary matrix represents a way in which to transform the original matrix, and this transformation takes place through the matrix multiplication of the original matrix by the elementary matrix. After the transformation, the original matrix has a different meaning from that it had in its original form; in other words, the mathematical meaning has been changed by the operation.

From the above discussion the reader may get the impression that a computer program for matrix inversion by reduction is very similar to a program for triangularization of a determinant; this is true. In addition to the zero test, the program must include a routine which reduces the matrix from the triangular form to the identity form. An example will illustrate the procedure.

Given the matrix A, $\begin{bmatrix} 1 & 2 & 0 \\ -1 & 1 & 3 \\ 0 & 1 & -1 \end{bmatrix}$ obtain its inverse.

$$\overset{A}{\begin{bmatrix} 1 & 2 & 0 \\ -1 & 1 & 3 \\ 0 & 1 & -1 \end{bmatrix}} \qquad \overset{I}{\begin{bmatrix} 1 & 0 & 0 \\ 0 & 1 & 0 \\ 0 & 0 & 1 \end{bmatrix}}$$

Operations—add a scalar multiple of row 1 to row 2; namely, subtract $\left(\frac{-1}{1}\right)$ times row 1 from row 2 giving

$$\begin{bmatrix} 1 & 2 & 0 \\ 0 & 3 & 3 \\ 0 & 1 & -1 \end{bmatrix} \qquad \begin{bmatrix} 1 & 0 & 0 \\ 1 & 1 & 0 \\ 0 & 0 & 1 \end{bmatrix}$$

Now, subtract $\left(\frac{0}{1}\right)$ times row 1 from row 3 to get the same A as above since the scalar is zero. To reduce the element a_{23} to zero, subtract (1/3) times row 2 from row 3 to get

$$\begin{bmatrix} 1 & 2 & 0 \\ 0 & 3 & 3 \\ 0 & 0 & -2 \end{bmatrix} \qquad \begin{bmatrix} 1 & 0 & 0 \\ 1 & 1 & 0 \\ -1/3 & -1/3 & 1 \end{bmatrix}$$

Multiply row 3 by (−1/2).

$$\begin{bmatrix} 1 & 2 & 0 \\ 0 & 3 & 3 \\ 0 & 0 & 1 \end{bmatrix} \qquad \begin{bmatrix} 1 & 0 & 0 \\ 1 & 1 & 0 \\ 1/6 & 1/6 & -1/2 \end{bmatrix}$$

Substract 3 times row 3 from row 2.

$$\begin{bmatrix} 1 & 2 & 0 \\ 0 & 3 & 0 \\ 0 & 0 & 1 \end{bmatrix} \qquad \begin{bmatrix} 1 & 0 & 0 \\ 3/6 & 3/6 & 3/2 \\ 1/6 & 1/6 & -1/2 \end{bmatrix}$$

Multiply row 2 by the scalar, 1/3.

$$\begin{bmatrix} 1 & 2 & 0 \\ 0 & 1 & 0 \\ 0 & 0 & 1 \end{bmatrix} \qquad \begin{bmatrix} 1 & 0 & 0 \\ 1/6 & 1/6 & 3/6 \\ 1/6 & 1/6 & -3/6 \end{bmatrix}$$

Substract 2 times row 2 from row 1.

$$\begin{bmatrix} 1 & 0 & 0 \\ 0 & 1 & 0 \\ 0 & 0 & 1 \end{bmatrix} \qquad \begin{bmatrix} 4/6 & -2/6 & -1 \\ 1/6 & 1/6 & 3/6 \\ 1/6 & 1/6 & -3/6 \end{bmatrix}$$

The inverse is then the matrix which appears on the right. To prove this, multiply the matrix on the right by the original matrix A; the identity matrix will result.

$$\begin{bmatrix} 4/6 & -2/6 & -1 \\ 1/6 & 1/6 & 3/6 \\ 1/6 & 1/6 & -3/6 \end{bmatrix} \cdot \begin{bmatrix} 1 & 2 & 0 \\ -1 & 1 & 3 \\ 0 & 1 & -1 \end{bmatrix} = \begin{bmatrix} 1 & 0 & 0 \\ 0 & 1 & 0 \\ 0 & 0 & 1 \end{bmatrix}$$

In this example, no zero elements turned up at the pivot positions. If a zero element had turned up at the pivot position, an interchange of rows or columns would have been necessary. Because the matrix on the right must be changed in the same way as the original matrix, the true inverse would not have appeared on the right when the identity matrix appeared on the left. If column j and column k in the original matrix were interchanged in the calculations, row j and row k must be interchanged in the inverse; this statement is always true. For example, if in the matrix given earlier

$$\begin{bmatrix} 1 & 2 & 0 \\ -1 & 1 & 3 \\ 0 & 1 & -1 \end{bmatrix} \text{ whose inverse was calculated to be } \begin{bmatrix} 4/6 & -2/6 & -1 \\ 1/6 & 1/6 & 3/6 \\ 1/6 & 1/6 & -3/6 \end{bmatrix}$$

the first and the third columns are interchanged to give

$$\begin{bmatrix} 0 & 2 & 1 \\ 3 & 1 & -1 \\ -1 & 1 & 0 \end{bmatrix} \text{ then the inverse would be } \begin{bmatrix} 1/6 & 1/6 & -3/6 \\ 1/6 & 1/6 & 3/6 \\ 4/6 & -2/6 & -1 \end{bmatrix}$$

The reader should verify the above example by actually calculating the new inverse. To accomplish the interchange of rows in the inverse, the program must have an index telling which columns in the original matrix were interchanged in the process of obtaining the identity matrix on the left; this procedure will be emphasized in the following program.

Before writing the program, let us compare the proposed program with the program for evaluating a determinant by triangularization; the triangularization program was given earlier in this chapter. By the same method used there, a matrix can be reduced to triangular form.

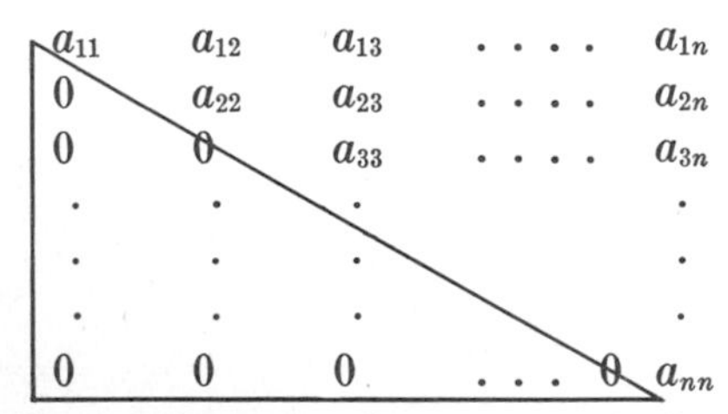

As stated in the earlier section, the elements in the lower triangle are only "assumed" to be zero; it was shown that the procedure of "assuming" the elements to be zero without actually setting them to zero had no effect on the result of the determinant if we multiplied the elements down the diagonal at the end of the procedure and attempted no intermediate evaluation. The same procedure can be used in calculating the inverse by the method of reduction if such assumptions do not affect the operations on the identity matrix, I. To see this, consider the problem of finding the inverse

$$A = \begin{bmatrix} a_{11} & a_{12} & a_{13} \\ a_{21} & a_{22} & a_{23} \\ a_{31} & a_{32} & a_{33} \end{bmatrix} \qquad I = \begin{bmatrix} 1 & 0 & 0 \\ 0 & 1 & 0 \\ 0 & 0 & 1 \end{bmatrix}$$

of A, a general matrix with 3 rows and 3 columns.

Operation 1—subtract (a_{21}/a_{11}) times the first row from the second row—the element a_{21} goes to zero—

Operation 2—subtract (a_{31}/a_{11}) times the first row from the third row—the element a_{31} goes to zero—

$$A \quad \begin{matrix} a_{11} & a_{12} & a_{13} \\ 0 & b_{22} & b_{23} \\ 0 & b_{32} & b_{33} \end{matrix} \qquad I \quad \begin{matrix} 1 & 0 & 0 \\ -a_{21}/a_{11} & 1 & 0 \\ -a_{31}/a_{11} & 0 & 1 \end{matrix}$$

Operation 3—subtract (b_{23}/b_{22}) times row 2 from row 3—the element b_{32} goes to zero.

$$A = \begin{bmatrix} a_{11} & a_{12} & a_{13} \\ 0 & b_{22} & b_{23} \\ 0 & 0 & c_{33} \end{bmatrix} \qquad I = \begin{bmatrix} 1 & 0 & 0 \\ -\dfrac{a_{21}}{a_{11}} & 1 & 0 \\ r & -\dfrac{b_{32}}{b_{22}} & 1 \end{bmatrix}$$

where

$$r = -a_{31}/a_{11} - (b_{32}/b_{22})(-a_{21}/a_{11})$$

Thus far there is no need to use the elements in row 2, column 1; row 3, column 1; and row 3, column 2.

Operation 4—multiply row 3 by the scalar $1/c_{33}$.
Operation 5—subtract b_{23} times row 3 from row 2.
Operation 6—multiply row 2 by $1/b_{22}$.

$$A = \begin{bmatrix} a_{11} & a_{12} & a_{13} \\ 0 & 1 & 0 \\ 0 & 0 & 1 \end{bmatrix} \qquad I = \begin{bmatrix} 1 & 0 & 0 \\ z/b_{22} & t/b_{22} & (-b_{23}/c_{33}).(1/b_{22}) \\ r/c_{33} & s/c_{33} & 1/c_{33} \end{bmatrix}$$

where

$$s = -b_{32}/b_{22}$$
$$t = 1 + \frac{b_{23}.b_{32}}{b_{22}.c_{33}}$$
$$z = -a_{21}/a_{11} - (r.b_{23}/c_{33})$$

Operation 7—subtract a_{13} times row 3 from row 1.

Operation 8—subtract a_{12} times row 2 from row 1.
Operation 9—multiply row 1 by the scalar $(1/a_{11})$.

$$\overset{A}{\begin{bmatrix} 1 & 0 & 0 \\ 0 & 1 & 0 \\ 0 & 0 & 1 \end{bmatrix}} \qquad \overset{I}{\begin{bmatrix} d_{11} & d_{12} & d_{13} \\ d_{21} & d_{22} & d_{23} \\ d_{31} & d_{32} & d_{33} \end{bmatrix}}$$

where

$$d_{11} = \frac{1 - \dfrac{a_{12}.z}{b_{22}} - \dfrac{a_{13}.r}{c_{33}}}{a_{11}}$$

$$a_{12} = \frac{0 - \dfrac{a_{12}(t)}{b_{22}} - \dfrac{a_{13}.s}{c_{33}}}{a_{11}}$$

$$d_{13} = \frac{0 - \dfrac{a_{12}(-b_{23})}{c_{33}.b_{22}} - \dfrac{a_{13}}{c_{13}}}{a_{11}}$$

$$\begin{aligned} d_{21} &= z/b_{22} & d_{31} &= r/c_{33} \\ d_{22} &= t/b_{22} & d_{32} &= s/c_{33} \\ d_{23} &= (-b_{23}/c_{33}) \cdot (1/b_{22}) & d_{33} &= 1/c_{33} \end{aligned}$$

Notice that operations 4 through 9 do not require the use of the elements in row 2, column 1; row 3, column 1; and row 3, column 2. After operation 4, the element in row 3, column 3 is no longer needed; it can be assumed to be 1—operation 5 can still be performed as "subtract b_{23} from the element in row 2, column 3" because $(b_{23}) \cdot (1) = b_{23}$ and $(b_{23}) \cdot (0) = 0$. After operation 6 the elements in row 2; column 2 and row 2, column 3 are not needed;

GENERAL FLOW CHART—Matrix Inversion by Reduction

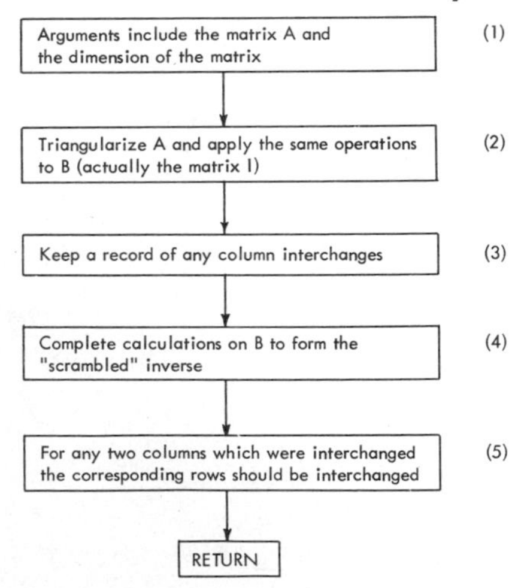

etc. The reasoning is the same as above. It should now be clear that the only operations needed on the original matrix A are the same as those required for triangularization of a determinant; the same elements may be "assumed" to zero instead of actually being set to zero.

Although the number of operations performed on A can be minimized in the above way, all operations must be performed on I; no elements of I may take on "assumed" values—they must be calculated because every element of the original matrix I is transformed into an element of the inverse matrix, A^{-1}.

The one-dimensional array IREC, with dimension one less than the dimension of the matrix A to be inverted is sufficient to keep track of the column interchange if we regard column 1 as position 1 in the array, col-

DETAILED FLOW CHART—Blocks 2 and 3

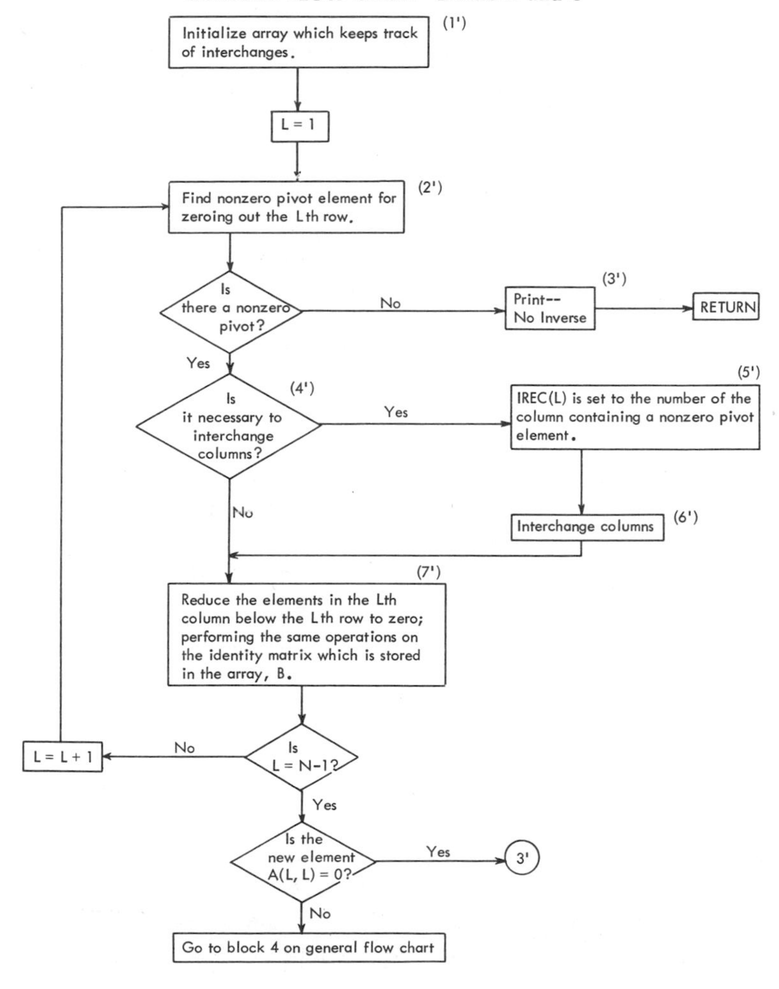

SUBPROGRAM—Matrix Inversion by Reduction

```
C FOR COMMENT
STATEMENT NUMBER | Cont. | FORTRAN STATEMENT

      SUBROUTINE INVERS(A, K, B)                          (1)
      DIMENSION A(10,10), IREC(9), B(10,10)
      IF(K-10) 21,21,31
   31 WRITE (6,101)
  101 FORMAT(19HDIMENSION TOO LARGE)
      RETURN
   21 DO 70 I=1,K                                         (1')
   70 IREC(I)=0
      DO 77 I=1,K
      DO 77 J=1,K
   77 B(I,J)=0
      DO 78 I=1,K
   78 B(I,I)=1
      DO 17 M=2,K
      IF(A(M-1,M-1).NE.0.)GO TO 50
      DO 30 I1=M,K                                        (2')
   30 IF(A(M-1,I1).NE.0.)GO TO 40
   87 WRITE (6,102)
  102 FORMAT(19HTHERE IS NO INVERSE)                      (3)
```

```
C FOR COMMENT
STATEMENT NUMBER | Cont. | FORTRAN STATEMENT

      RETURN
   40 I3=M-1
      DO 20 I2=I3,K                                       (4)
      TEMP=A(I2,I3)                                       (5)
      A(I2,I3)=A(I2,I1)                                   &
   20 A(I2,I1)=TEMP                                       (6)
      IREC(I3)=I1
   50 DO 17 I=M,K
      R=A(I,M-1)/A(M-1,M-1)
      DO 7 J=M,K
    7 A(I,J)=A(I,J)-A(M-1,J)*R                            (7')
      I12=M-1
      DO 8 J=1,I12
    8 A(I,J)=0.
      DO 17 J=1,K
   17 B(I,J)=B(I,J)-B(M-1,J)*R
      IF(A(K,K).EQ.0.)GO TO 87
      K5=K-1                                              (4)
      DO 27 K1=1,K5
```

umn 2 as position 2 in the array, etc., and column $(k - 1)$ as the $(k - 1)$st position of the array. In the loop ending with statement number 70, all positions in the array are set to zero. In the loop ending with statement number 30, a column with a nonzero pivot element is chosen, and the index of

SUBPROGRAM—*Continued*

```
C FOR COMMENT
STATEMENT NUMBER | Cont. | FORTRAN STATEMENT

      L=K-K1+1                                    ⎫
      DO 61 I9=1,L                                ⎪
   61 B(L,I9)=B(L,I9)/A(L,L)                      ⎪
      DO 27 N6=K1,K5                              ⎪
      L2=K-N6                                     ⎬ (4)
      DO 27 L1=1,K                                ⎪
   27 B(L2,L1)=B(L2,L1) - A(L,L1)*A(L2,L)         ⎪
      DO 37 L4=1,K                                ⎪
   37 B(1,L4)=B(1,L4)/A(1,1)                      ⎭
      DO 47 K2=1,K5                               ⎫
      IF(IREC(K2).NE.0) GO TO 3ØØ                 ⎪
   47 CONTINUE                                    ⎪
      GO TO 9Ø                                    ⎪
  3ØØ K6=IREC(K2)                                 ⎬ (5)
      DO 57 K3=1,K5                               ⎪
      TEMP=B(K6,K3)                               ⎪
      B(K6,K3)=B(K2,K3)                           ⎪
   57 B(K2,K3)=TEMP                               ⎭
      GO TO 47
   90 RETURN
      END
```

this column is in location I1. The statement IREC (I3) = I1, places the index of the column with the nonzero pivot element in the position I3 of the array; but, I3 is the index of the column which is being reduced. Because the columns are being reduced in natural sequence (i.e., 1,2,3, . . . ,$k-1$),I3 also represents the index of the array I3. For example suppose $a_{11} = 0, a_{12} = 0$, and $a_{13} \neq 0$; now I3 = 1 and I1=3. By looking at the first position in the array IREC, one can see that column 1 and column 3 were inter-

IREC(1) . . . IREC(8) IREC(9)

1	2	3	4	5	6	7	8	9

3
1

changed. When the pivot element of the column being reduced is not zero, column interchange is not necessary. For this case, the logic of the program passes to statement number 50 and does not utilize IREC. Since all positions of IREC were set to zero, a zero in position 2 of IREC denotes the fact that column 2 was reduced without the need for interchanging columns because the pivot element was not zero.

If all elements in the pivot row are zero (natural exit from the loop ending with statement number 30), the matrix has no inverse because the determinant of the matrix is zero (why?).

At the end of the group of statements marked (7)′, the original matrix has been reduced to triangular form, and the same operations have been performed on the identity. In the group of statements marked (4), the original matrix is reduced to the identity matrix; the same operations performed on the matrix located in area B result in A^{-1}. Note that in this second group of statements, it is necessary to start at row N and go back to row 1. Because the index in a DO loop is incremented and not decremented (i.e., the index m_1, is increased and not decreased by the increment m_3, until $m_1+m_3>m_2$), the following device is used: the index m_1 of the DO loop (in this case K1) is incremented by 1 and then subtracted from N+1; therefore, when K1 = 1,L = K+1−K1 = K, and when K1 = K−1, the upper limit of the DO loop, L = K+1−K1 = K+1−(K − 1) = 2. Thus, by using L as an index, the programmer is able to use an index which can be decremented at each step. Notice that the calculations for row 1 are handled separately in the loop ending at statement number 37; this simplifies the logic of the program without sacrificing computer time.

Checking for the need to interchange rows of the matrix B (the "scrambled inverse") takes place in the group of statements marked (5). When the value in position K2 of the array, IREC, is zero, there is no need for an interchange of rows. On the other hand, if the value in position K2 of the array, IREC, has a value other than zero, it is necessary to interchange row K2 and the row whose number is in position K2 of the array, IREC.

7.3. Simultaneous Equations

A direct application of inversion of matrices is in the solution of simultaneous equations. Suppose we are given a problem of the following nature:

Find a set of values (if there is a set of values) representing an amount of each of five foods, such that some requirements on the amount of vitamins and energy obtained from these foods are met. Say that it is required to obtain b_1 units of vitamin 1, b_2 units of vitamin 2, b_3 units of vitamin 3, b_4 units of vitamin 4, and b_5 units of energy. We must also be given the units of each vitamin or energy which can be obtained from one unit of each food. Mathematically, the problem is a set of five linear equations (we assume here that the units of vitamin and energy from each of the foods combine in a linear way).

$$a_{11}x_1 + a_{12}x_2 + a_{13}x_3 + a_{14}x_4 + a_{15}x_5 = b_1$$
$$a_{21}x_1 + a_{22}x_2 + a_{23}x_3 + a_{24}x_4 + a_{25}x_5 = b_2$$

$$a_{31}x_1 + a_{32}x_2 + a_{33}x_3 + a_{34}x_4 + a_{35}x_5 = b_3$$
$$a_{41}x_1 + a_{42}x_2 + a_{43}x_3 + a_{44}x_4 + a_{45}x_5 = b_4$$
$$a_{51}x_1 + a_{52}x_2 + a_{53}x_3 + a_{54}x_4 + a_{55}x_5 = b_5$$

Here, a_{11} represents the units of vitamin 1 per unit of food 1, a_{12} is the units of vitamin 1 per unit of food 2, a_{15} is the units of vitamin 1 per unit of food 5, a_{21} is the units of vitamin 2 per unit of food 1, a_{25} is the units of vitamin 2 per unit of food 5, etc.; also, x_1 represents the number of units of food 1 which should be used, x_2 the number of units of food 2 which should be used, etc. If we let i represent the vitamin or energy and j represent the food, we can write the set of equations in the form,

$$\sum_{j=1}^{5} a_{ij}x_j = b_i \quad \text{for } i = 1, \ldots, 5.$$

Notice that the a_{ij} in the above equations may be written as the matrix A, the unknowns (the x's) may be written as the column vector X, and the requirements (the b's) may be written as the column vector b, where a column vector is a matrix with one column and n rows (here, $n = 5$).

To place the above problem into a more practical perpective, the equalities should be changed to inequalities ($\leq$) and each food should be given a cost. Then one could reasonably ask for those foods which meet all the necessary vitamin and energy requirements at the minimum; this type of problem occurs in the blending of feed ingredients for poultry, the blending of oil products, the blending of pigments for paint, etc. Professor George Stigler of the University of Chicago was the first to recognize the above problem for feed blending.

The problem

$$\sum_{j=1}^{5} a_{ij}x_j = b_i \quad \text{for } i = 1, \ldots, 5$$

can then be pictured as a special case of the above problem where the requirements must be met exactly and the costs of the foods are zero. A set of such equations may either have a single solution, an infinite number of solutions, or no solution.

Without going deeply into the mathematics of matrix algebra, we can say that there is at least one solution to the above set of equations if the vector B is a linear combination of the column vectors of which the matrix A is composed (column vector $a_1 = (a_{11}, a_{21}, \ldots, a_{51})$; where the vector y is a linear combination of the vectors z_1 and z_2 if y can be written as $y = \lambda_1 z_1 + \lambda_2 z_2$ and both λ_1 and λ_2 are not zero.

Assuming that b can be written as a linear combination of the columns of A, consider the case where the matrix A has an inverse. First note that if a matrix has an inverse, the inverse must be unique. To show uniqueness, assume that A has two inverses, F and G:

$$\begin{aligned} FAG &= F(AG) = F(I) = F \\ FAG &= (FA)G = I(G) = G \\ &\therefore F = G \end{aligned}$$

thus, F and G are the same.

Given that A has an inverse, then if we multiply the equation $AX = B$ on both sides by A^{-1}, we get $A^{-1}AX = A^{-1}B$ or $IX = A^{-1}B$ or $X = A^{-1}B$. Now since A^{-1} is unique, X is unique; this implies that there is only one solution to the set of equations $AX = B$, if A has an inverse.

With the programs given thus far in the book, the reader can very easily write a program to solve a system of simultaneous equations in the special case in which A, the matrix of coefficients has an inverse.

```
      DIMENSION A(10,10),X(10),B(10)
      READ(5,101)N
      IF(N-10) 30,30,15
15    WRITE(6,103)
      CALL EXIT
30    DO 20 I=1,N
20    READ(5,102)(A(I,J),J=1,N),B(I)
101   FORMAT(I3)
102   FORMAT(11F7.3)
103   FORMAT(19HDIMENSION TOO LARGE)
      CALL INVERS(A,N,C)
      DO 82 I=1,N
82    X(I)=0
      DO 177 I=1,N
      DO 177 J=1,N
177   X(I)=X(I)+C(I,J)*B(J)
      WRITE(6,105)
      WRITE(6,104) (X(I),I=1,N)
104   FORMAT(10X,E14.8)
```

```
105   FORMAT (10X8HSOLUTION)
      CALL EXIT
      END
```

A worthwhile test in this program would be to test for no solution; it is left to the student to determine the mathematics needed for this test and then to incorporate the test in the program.

7.3.1. Solution of Simultaneous Equations by Determinants

Another method for solving the set of simultaneous equations $AX = B$ when A has an inverse in the utilization of determinants. Following are the rules for this method:

To calculate x_1, it is necessary to calculate two determinants, $|A|$ and $|A_{b1}|$, where A is the original matrix of coefficients and A_{b1} is the original matrix of coefficients with the exception of column 1, which contains the column vector, b; divide the second determinant by the first determinant.

To calculate x_j, it is necessary to calculate two determinants, $|A|$ and $|A_{bj}|$, where A is the original matrix of coefficients and A_{bj} is the original matrix of coefficients with column j replaced by the column vector b; divide the second determinant by the first determinant.

This method is known as Cramer's Rule and is very easy to prove using the adjoint matrix.

$$AX = B$$
$$A^{-1}AX = A^{-1}B$$
$$X = A^{-1}B$$

but

$$A^{-1} = \frac{A^+}{|A|}$$

therefore $X = \frac{1}{|A|}(A^+B)$; in terms of elements,

$$x_k = \frac{1}{|A|}\sum_j A_{kj}b_j$$

$(A^+ B)$ is a matrix multiplication, and can be written as

$$\sum_{j=1}^{n} A_{kj}b_j\,,$$

where A^+ is the adjoint of the original matrix A; A_{kj} is the cofactor of element a_{kj} of the original matrix (remember, the adjoint matrix is composed of cofactors of the original matrix which have been transposed over the main diagonal). The reader should also recall the

$$\sum_{j=1}^{n} A_{kj}a_{kj} = |A|$$

is the rule for expansion of a determinant by cofactors. Therefore,

$$\sum_{j=1}^{n} A_{kj}b_j$$

implies that the vector B has replaced column k of the determinant of the original matrix; i.e.,

$$x_k = \frac{|A_{bk}|}{|A|}$$

Following are the flow chart and program to evaluate a set of simultaneous equations by Cramer's Rule. Y contains the vector B. It is assumed that the function used to calculate the determinant uses the method

FLOW CHART—Cramer's Rule

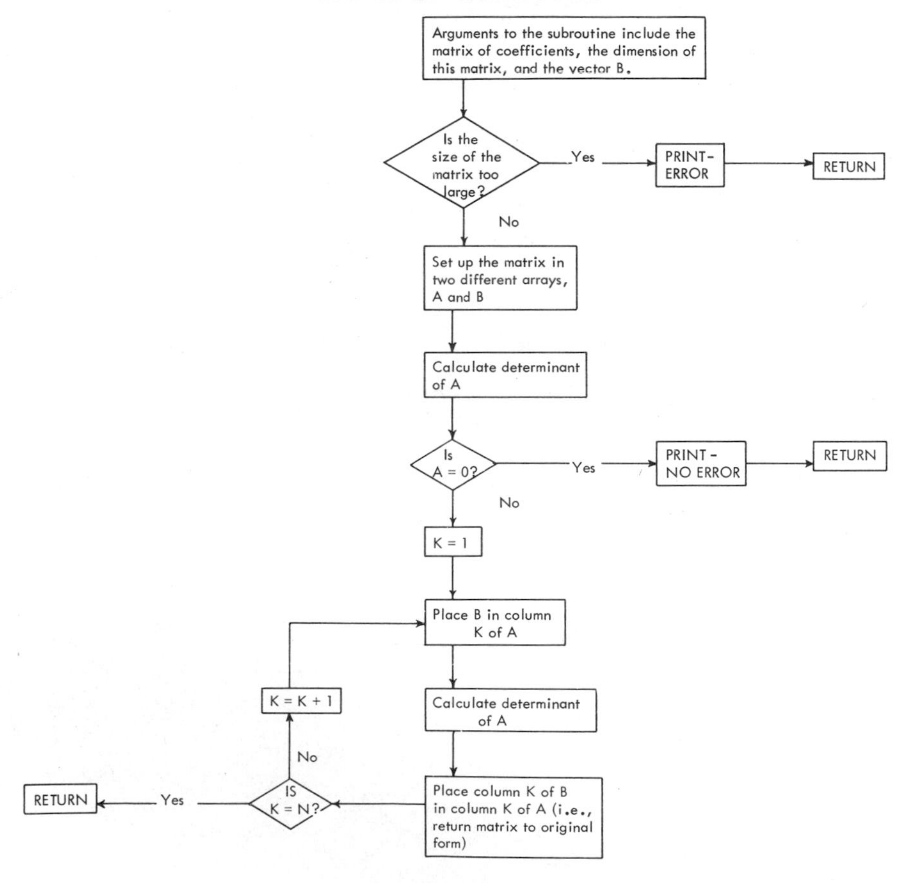

PROGRAM—Cramer's Rule

```
      SUBROUTINE CRAMER (A,Y,X,N)
      DIMENSION A(10,10),B(10,10),Y(10),X(10)
      IF (N-10) 10,10,20
   20 WRITE(6,101)
  101 FORMAT(19HDIMENSION TOO LARGE)
      RETURN
   10 DO 30 I=1,N
      DO 30 J=1,N
   30 B(I,J)=A(I,J)
      R=DET(A,N)
      IF(R.NE.0)GO TO 77
      WRITE(6,102)
  102 FORMAT(10HNO INVERSE)
      RETURN
   77 DO 47 K=1,N
      DO 37 J=1,N
   37 A(J,K)=Y(J)
      S=DET (A,N)
      X(K)=S/R
      DO 47 J=1,N
   47 A(J,K)=B(J,K)
      RETURN
      END
```

of definition, which does not destroy the matrix. If the triangularization method is used, the entire matrix A must be regenerated after the second RETURN statement and in the loop ending at statement number 47.

Each of the two methods offered in this section can solve a set of simultaneous equation only for the case in which the matrix of coefficients has an inverse. In general, the matrix of coefficients may have more columns than rows or even if the number of rows and columns are the same, one row of A may be a linear combination of the other rows of A. In either case A has no inverse; in the first case the matrix is not square and in the second case the determinant is zero. In the next section a method is offered in which a solution may be obtained (if there is one; the same criteria must be applied; i.e., B must be a linear combination of the columns of A) in the case where A has no inverse.

7.3.2. Solution of Simultaneous Linear Equations by Reduction of the Matrix of Coefficients

Consider a set of simultaneous linear equations in which the matrix of coefficients may not have an inverse.

$$\begin{array}{lr}
a_{11}\, x_1 + a_{12}\, x_2 + a_{13}\, x_3 + \ldots + a_{1n}\, x_n = b_1 & (1) \\
a_{21}\, x_1 + a_{22}\, x_2 + a_{23}\, x_3 + \ldots + a_{2n}\, x_n = b_2 & (2) \\
\cdot \quad \cdot \quad \cdot \quad \cdot \quad \cdot & \cdot \\
\cdot \quad \cdot \quad \cdot \quad \cdot \quad \cdot & \cdot \\
\cdot \quad \cdot \quad \cdot \quad \cdot \quad \cdot & \cdot \\
a_{n1}\, x_1 + a_{n2}\, x_2 + a_{n3}\, x_3 + \ldots + a_{nn}\, x_n = b_n & (n)
\end{array}$$

In equation (1), solve for x_1;

$$x_1 = \frac{b_1 - a_{12}x_2 - a_{13}x_3 - \ldots - a_{1n}\, x_n}{a_{11}}$$

or

$$x_1 = \frac{b_1}{a_{11}} - \frac{1}{a_{11}} \sum_{j=2}^{n} a_{1j}\, x_j$$

Now substitute this value of x_1 in equation 2 through equation n, thus eliminating x_1 from these equations. For example, equation (2) becomes:

$$a_{21}\left(\frac{b_1}{a_{11}} - \frac{a_{12}}{a_{11}}\, x_2 - \frac{a_{13}x_3}{a_{11}} - \ldots - \frac{a_{1n}x_n}{a_{11}}\right) + a_{22}\, x_2 + a_{23}\, x_3 + \ldots + a_{2n}\, x_n = b_2$$

and combining like terms the above equation becomes:

$$\left(a_{22} - \frac{(a_{21})(a_{12})}{a_{11}}\right) x_2 + \left(a_{23} - \frac{(a_{21})(a_{13})}{a_{11}}\right) x_3 + \ldots + \left(a_{2n} - \frac{(a_{21})(a_{1n})}{a_{11}}\right) x_n = b_2 - \frac{(b_1)(a_{21})}{(a_{11})}.$$

Notice that these coefficients are the same elements as those arising from the triangularization of a determinant and calculation of the inverse of a matrix by reduction. Equation (3) becomes.

$$a_{31}\left(\frac{b_1}{a_{11}} - \frac{a_{12}x_2}{a_{11}} - \frac{a_{13}\, x_3}{a_{11}} - \ldots - \frac{a_{1n}x_n}{a_{11}}\right) + a_{32}x_2 + a_{33}\, x_3 + \ldots + a_{3n}x_n = b_3$$

and combining like terms the above equation becomes:

$$\left(a_{32} - \frac{(a_{31})(a_{12})}{(a_{11})}\right) x_2 + \left(a_{33} - \frac{(a_{31})(a_{13})}{(a_{11})}\right) x_3$$
$$+ \ldots + \left(a_{3n} - \frac{(a_{31})(a_{1n})}{(a_{11})}\right) x_n = b_3 - \frac{(b_1)(a_{31})}{(a_{11})}$$

Again the coefficients are the same as those obtained when attempting to reduce a_{31} to zero in the triangularization process; namely, add a scalar multiple of row 1 to row 3—for a_{31}, the scalar multiple is $-(a_{31})$ so that

$$a'_{31} = a_{31} - \left(\frac{a_{31}}{a_{11}}\right) a_{11} = 0$$

Applying this reduction procedure to row 2 through row n, the following system emerges,

$$\begin{aligned} x_1 + c_{12}\, x_2 + c_{13}x_3 + \ldots + c_{1n}x_n &= d_1 \\ c_{22}\, x_2 + c_{23}x_3 + \ldots + c_{2n}x_n &= d_2 \\ c_{32}\, x_2 + c_{33}x_3 + \ldots + c_{3n}x_n &= d_3 \\ \vdots \qquad \vdots \qquad\qquad \vdots \quad &\quad \vdots \\ c_{n2}\, x_2 + c_{n3}x_3 + \ldots + c_{nn}x_n &= d_n \end{aligned}$$

where

$$c_{1j} = \frac{a_{1j}}{a_{11}} \quad \text{for } j = 2, \ldots, n \text{ and } d_1 = \frac{b_1}{a_{11}}$$

and

$$c_{ij} = a_{ij} - \frac{(a_{i1})}{(a_{11})}(a_{1j}) \quad \text{for } i = 2, \ldots, n \text{ and } j = 2, \ldots, n$$

and

$$d_i = b_i - b_i \frac{(a_{i1})}{(a_{11})} \quad \text{for } i = 2, \ldots, n.$$

For the next step, solve equation (2) for x_2 and substitute the resulting value in equation 3 through equation n, thus eliminating x_2 from these equations. To illustrate the procedure consider equation (3). First, equation (2) becomes:

$$x_2 = \frac{d_2}{c_{22}} - \frac{(c_{23})}{(c_{22})} x_3 - \frac{(c_{24})}{(c_{22})} x_4 - \ldots - \frac{(c_{2n})}{(c_{22})} x_n$$

and then equation (3) becomes

$$c_{32}\left(\frac{d_2}{c_{22}} - \frac{(c_{23})}{(c_{22})}x_3 - \frac{(c_{24})}{(c_{22})}x_4 - \ldots - \frac{(c_{2n})}{(c_{22})}x_n\right)$$
$$+ c_{33}x_3 + c_{34}x_4 + \ldots + c_{3n}x_n = d_3$$

Combining like terms, equation (3) becomes:

$$\left(c_{33} - \frac{(c_{32})(c_{23})}{(c_{22})}\right)x_3 + \left(c_{34} - \frac{(c_{32})(c_{24})}{(c_{22})}\right)x_4$$
$$+ \ldots + \left(c_{3n} - \frac{(c_{3n})(c_{2n})}{(c_{22})}\right)x_n = d_3 - \frac{(d_2)(c_{32})}{c_{22}}$$

Again the coefficients are the same as those arising from the reduction of a_{23} to zero in the triangularization of a determinant; that is, to reduce a_{23} to zero it is necessary to add a scalar multiple of row 2 to row 3—that scalar multiple being $-\frac{(a_{23})}{(a_{22})}$.

$$a'_{23} = a_{23} - \frac{(a_{23})}{(a_{22})}a_{22} = 0$$

Eliminating x_2 from equation (3) through equation (n) by the above reduction process gives the following set of equations:

$$\begin{aligned}
x_1 + r_{12}x_2 + r_{13}x_3 + \ldots + r_{1n}x_n &= s_1 \\
x_2 + r_{23}x_3 + \ldots + r_{2n}x_n &= s_2 \\
r_{33}x_3 + \ldots + r_{3n}x_n &= s_3 \\
\cdot \qquad\qquad \cdot &\quad \cdot \\
\cdot \qquad\qquad \cdot &\quad \cdot \\
\cdot \qquad\qquad \cdot &\quad \cdot \\
r_{n3}x_3 + \ldots + r_{nn}x_n &= s_n \;;
\end{aligned}$$

where

$$r_{1j} = c_{1j} \quad \text{for } j = 1, \ldots, n\,;\, s_1 = d_1\,;$$
$$r_{2j} = \frac{c_{2j}}{c_{22}} \quad \text{for } j = 2, \ldots, n\,;\, s_2 = \frac{d_2}{c_{22}}\,;$$
$$r_{ij} = c_{ij} - \left(\frac{c_{i2}}{c_{22}}\right)c_{2j} \quad \text{for } i = 3, \ldots, n, j = 3, \ldots, n$$

and

$$s_i = d_i - d_2\frac{(c_{i2})}{(c_{22})} \quad \text{for } i = 3, \ldots, n\,.$$

After $(n-1)$ steps in the reduction process (each step consists of eliminating one of the variables from the remaining equations), the set of equations becomes—

$$
\begin{aligned}
x_1 + z_{12}\, x_2 + z_{13}\, x_3 + \ldots + z_{1n}\, x_n &= y_1 \\
x_2 + z_{23}\, x_3 + \ldots + z_{2n}\, x_n &= y_2 \\
x_3 + \ldots + z_{3n}\, x_n &= y_3 \\
\vdots \quad & \quad \vdots \\
x_n &= y_n
\end{aligned}
$$

As a result of the $(n-1)$st step in the reduction process the last equation yields the value for x_n. To solve for x_{n-1}, it is only necessary to substitute the value obtained for x_n into the $(n-1)$st equation.

$$
\begin{aligned}
x_{n-1} + z_{n-1,n}(y_n) &= y_{n-1} \\
x_{n-1} + z_{n-1,n}\,(y_n) &= y_{n-1} \\
x_{n-1} &= y_{n-1} - z_{n-1,n}(y_n)
\end{aligned}
$$

It is not hard to see that this reverse substitution process is exactly the same process used to reduce the triangular matrix to the identity matrix in the reduction method for calculating the inverse matrix. From this discussion it should be obvious to the reader that the reduction process used to calculate the inverse matrix can be used to solve a system of simultaneous equations; the only difference is that instead of performing the same elementary operations on the identity as on the original matrix, now the same elementary operations must be performed on the column vector, B, as on the original matrix A. When the original matrix A has been reduced to the identity matrix, the original column vector, B, will have been reduced to the column vector X, which contains the solutions.

Before illustrating the flow chart and programs for solving a system of simultaneous equations by reduction, let us consider some examples:

$$
\begin{aligned}
3x_1 + x_2 + 2x_3 &= 2 & (1) \\
x_1 + 2x_2 + x_3 &= 1 & (2) \\
2x_1 + 4x_2 + 2x_3 &= 2 & (3)
\end{aligned}
$$

Solve for (x_1) in (1) to get

$$x_1 = 2/3 - 1/3\, x_2 - 2/3\, x_3$$

substituting this value in (2) and (3), the three equations become:

$$
\begin{aligned}
x_1 + 1/3\, x_2 + 2/3\, x_3 &= 2/3 & (4) \\
5/3\, x_2 + 1/3\, x_3 &= 1/3 & (5) \\
10/3\, x_2 + 2/3\, x_3 &= 2/3 & (6)
\end{aligned}
$$

Solve for x_2 in (5) to get:

$$x_2 = 1/5 - 1/5\, x_3$$

and substitute this value in equation (6) to get $0x_3 = 0$.

When all the coefficients in a row are zero, the row may be dropped from the set of equations, and the process of reduction may then be continued; this is a signal that the matrix of coefficients has no inverse. If row 3 is dropped from the set of equations, x_3 may take on any value; once x_3 has been assigned a value we can solve for x_1 and x_2 in terms of x_3. Assign a value of 0 to x_3, then from equation (5), $x_2 = 1/5$ and from equation (4), $x_1 = 3/5$. The student should substitute the values $x_1 = 3/5$, $x_2 = 1/5$, and $x_3 = 0$ back into equations (1), (2), and (3) to see if all the equations are indeed satisfied.

Another solution may be obtained by setting x_3 to 1. In this case, $x_1 = 0$ and $x_2 = 0$. Actually, there is a solution for every value of x_3; therefore the set of equations possesses infinitely many solutions.

The same problem could have been written as:

$$\begin{aligned} 3x_1 + x_2 + 2x_3 &= 2 \\ x_1 + 2x_2 + x_3 &= 1\,. \end{aligned}$$

Because there are 3 unknowns but only two requirements, one unknown may be set prior to solution and the other two unknowns solved in terms of the present unknown.

Notice that if the problem had been:

$$\begin{aligned} 3x_1 + x_2 + 2x_3 &= 2 \\ x_1 + 2x_2 + x_3 &= 1 \\ 2x_1 + 4x_2 + 2x_3 &= 3 \end{aligned}$$

there would have been no solution.

To carry out the calculations on the computer consider the following operations:

given:

$$\begin{aligned} [A]X &= [B] \\ [A^{-1}A]X &= [A^{-1}B] \\ [I]X &= [A^{-1}B] \end{aligned}$$

When sufficient elementary operations have been performed on A to obtain the identity matrix, the same elementary operations will have transformed the vector, B, to the vector, X.

When one or more rows develop all zero coefficients, the matrix A has no inverse; say row i has all zero coefficients, then row i can be ignored and the other variables can be solved in terms of x_i. The above program sets $x_i = 0$ instead of $x_i = 1$, $x_i = 2$, or $x_i = 3.7216$; this is arbitrary. The array SW, is used to denote whether or not the coefficients of a row are all zero. If the coefficients of row I are all zero, then SW(I) is set to 1; on the other hand, if the coefficients of row I are not all zero, then SW(I) equals zero because this array was initialized at 0 in the loop ending at statement number 26.

Notice that the system of equations is solved for $x(n)$ separately from the loop used to calculate x_i, $i = 1, \ldots, (n-1)$; the reason being that only one division is needed to solve for $x(n)$, while at least one multiplication and one subtraction are needed in addition to the one division—the logic is simplified by placing the calculation for $x(n)$ outside the loop.

The group of statements

```
      K6 = L + 1
47    DO 37 K2 = K6,K
37    B(L) = B(L) - A (L,K2) * X(K2)
      X(L) = B(L) / A(L,L)
```

FLOW CHART—Solution of Simultaneous Linear Equations by Reduction

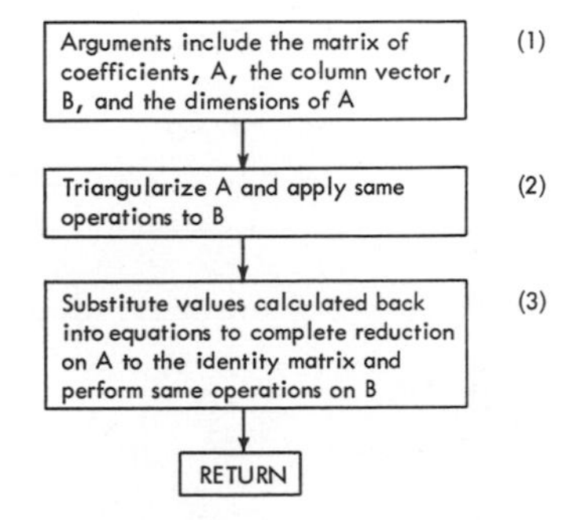
Arguments include the matrix of coefficients, A, the column vector, B, and the dimensions of A
(1)
Triangularize A and apply same operations to B
(2)
Substitute values calculated back into equations to complete reduction on A to the identity matrix and perform same operations on B
(3)
RETURN

DETAILED FLOW CHART—(3)

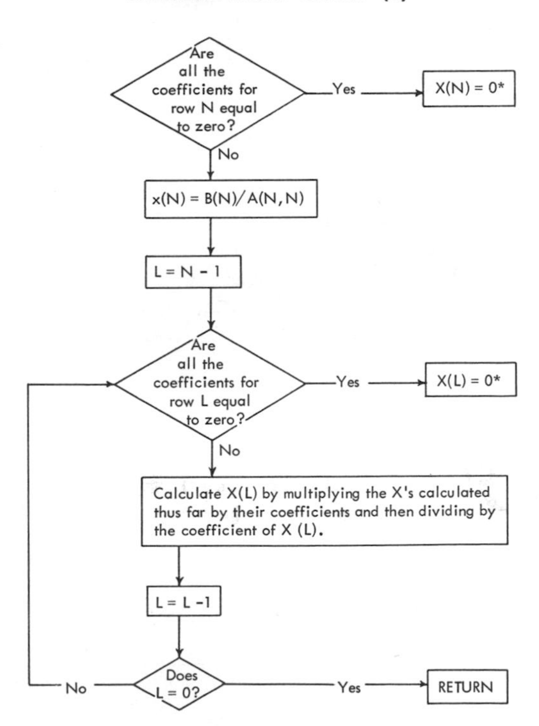
Are all the coefficients for row N equal to zero?
Yes
X(N) = 0*
No
x(N) = B(N)/A(N,N)
L = N - 1
Are all the coefficients for row L equal to zero?
Yes
X(L) = 0*
No
Calculate X(L) by multiplying the X's calculated thus far by their coefficients and then dividing by the coefficient of X (L).
L = L -1
Does L = 0?
No
Yes
RETURN

SUBPROGRAM—Solution of Simultaneous Linear Equations by Reduction

```
C FOR COMMENT
STATEMENT NUMBER | Cont. | FORTRAN STATEMENT
      SUBROUTINE SIMUL (A,B,N,X)                              (1)
      DIMENSION A(10,10),X(10),B(10),SW(10)
      IF (N-10) 21,21,31
   31 WRITE(6,101)
  101 FORMAT (19HDIMENSION TOO LARGE)
      RETURN
      DO 26 J5=1,N
   26 SW (J5)=0
      DO 18 M=2,N
      IF(A(M-1,M-1).NE.0.)GO TO 50                            (2)
      DO 30 I1=M,N
   30 IF(A(M-1,I1).NE.0.)GO TO 40
      SW(I1)=1
      GO TO 18
   40 I3=M-1
      DO 20 I2=I3,N
      TEMP=A(I2,I3)
      A(I2,I3)=A(I2,I1)
   20 A(I2,I1)=TEMP
```

```
C FOR COMMENT
STATEMENT NUMBER | Cont. | FORTRAN STATEMENT
   50 DO 17 I=M,N                                             (2)
      R=A(I,M-1)/A(M-1,M-1)
      DO 7 J=M,N
    7 A(I,J)=A(I,J)-A(M-1,J)*R
   17 B(I)=B(I)-B(M-1)*R
   18 CONTINUE
      IF(SW(N).EQ.0.)GO TO 27                                 (3)
      X(N)=0
      GO TO 28
   27 X(N)=B(N)/A(N,N)
   28 K5=N-1
      DO 38 K1=1,K5
      L=N-K1
      IF(SW(L).EQ.0.)GO TO 47
      X(L)=0
      GO TO 38
      K6=L+1
   47 DO 37 K2=K6,K
   37 B(L)=B(L)-A(L,K2)*X(K2)
```

SUBPROGRAM—Continued

```
C FOR COMMENT
STATEMENT NUMBER | Cont. | FORTRAN STATEMENT
      X(L)=B(L)/A(L,L)                               }(3)
   38 CONTINUE
      RETURN
      END
```

solves the system of linear equations for X(L) given X(L+1), X(L+2), . . . , X(N). To solve for X(N−2) given X(N−1) and X(N), the equation is:

$$B\ (N-2) = B(N-2) - A(N-2,N-1) * X(N-1) - A(N-2,N) * X(N),$$
$$X(N-2) = B(N-2)/A(N-2,N-2)$$

For this case, L = N−2, K6 = N−1 and K2 takes on the values (N−2) and (N−1).

Although the method of reduction (originated by Gauss) is general and straightforward to program, the speed of the method can be increased by utilizing the product form of the inverse; the accuracy can be increased by using the largest possible matrix entry for the pivot element (not necessarily starting with a_{11}) at each step and then eliminating the unknown corresponding to the vector containing the pivot element from the remaining equations. For example, in the coefficient matrix:

$$\begin{bmatrix} a_{11} & a_{12} & a_{13} \\ a_{21} & a_{22} & a_{23} \\ a_{31} & a_{32} & a_{33} \end{bmatrix} \begin{matrix} (1) \\ (2) \\ (3) \end{matrix}$$

Suppose the largest element turns out to be a_{22}; now equation (2) is solved for X_2 and then this value of X_2 is substituted in equation (1) and equation (3) to eliminate X_2 from these two equations. For the next step consider the elements a_{11}, a_{13}, a_{31}, and a_{33} for consideration as the new pivot element; if a_{31} is the largest of these four elements, then solve equation (3) for x_1 and substitute in equations (1) and (2). Equation (1) can then be solved for x_1 and this value used to calculate x_2 and x_3. Utilization of the largest element for the pivot reduces the loss in accuracy due to round-off error. In the appendix the reader will find this method utilized with the product form of the inverse to produce a very fast, accurate program for solution of simultaneous linear equations.

For very large systems of equations the loss in accuracy is so great as to nullify any reduction methods (even using double precision); in these cases the analyst is forced to use approximate methods which will give as much accuracy as necessary provided one is allowed enough computer time.

7.3.3. An Approximate Method of Solving a System of Simultaneous Equations

Consider the following system of simultaneous linear equations:

$$x_1 + 10x_2 + 2x_3 = 1 \quad (1)$$
$$x_1 - x_2 + 12x_3 = 2 \quad (2)$$
$$9x_1 + 2x_2 + 2x_3 = 1 \quad (3)$$

Make an initial guess for a starting solution; given no prior information about the above system, a convenient first solution is $x_1 = 0$, $x_2 = 0$, $x_3 = 0$. To calculate a first approximation to the true solution, solve equation (1) using $x_1 = 0$ and $x_3 = 0$; then from equation (2), calculate x_3 using the value calculated for x_2 and $x_1 = 0$; finally, calculate x_1 from equation (3) using the values calculated for x_2 and x_3.

$x_2 = 1/10$ from (1) with $x_1 = 0$ and $x_3 = 0$
$12x_3 = 2 - 0 + 1/10$ from (2) with $x_1 = 0$ and $x_2 = 1/10$,
or $x_3 = (21/10)/12 = 21/120$
$9x_1 + 2/10 + 42/120 = 1$ from (3) with $x_2 = 1/10$ and $x_3 = 21/120$
$9x_1 = 120/120 - 24/120 - 42/120 = 54/120$
$x_1 = 6/120 = 1/20$

Denoting the initial approximation to the true solution by $X^{(0)} = (x_1^{(0)}, x_2^{(0)}, x_3^{(0)}) = (0,0,0)$, then the first approximation may be denoted by $X^{(1)} = (x_1^{(1)}, x_2^{(1)}, x_3^{(1)}) = (1/20, 1/10, 21/120)$.

To calculate a second approximation $X^{(2)}$ to the true solution X, follow the same procedure as used for the first approximation; namely:

$$10x_2^{(2)} = 1 - x_1^{(1)} - 2x_3^{(1)} \quad \text{from (1)}$$

or

$$10x_2^{(2)} = 1 - 1/20 - 42/120$$

or

$$x_2^{(2)} = 3/50 = .06$$
$$12x_3^{(2)} = 2 - x_1^{(1)} + x_2^{(2)} \quad \text{from (2)}$$

or

$$12x_3^{(2)} = 2 - 1/20 + 3/50$$

or

$$x_3^{(2)} = 201/1200 = .167$$
$$9x_1^{(2)} = 1 - 2x_2^{(2)} - 2x_3^{(2)} \quad \text{from (3)}$$

or

$$9x_1^{(2)} = 1 - .120 - .334$$

or

$$x_1^{(2)} = .061$$

therefore, $X^{(2)} = (.061, .06, .167)$; the true solution is $X = (.0600, .0600, .1747)$.

Successive approximations are

Approximations	*1*	*2*	. . .	*True Value*
x_1	.05	.061	. . .	.0600
x_2	.10	.060	. . .	.0600
x_3	.175	.167	. . .	.1747

Why was equation (1) solved for x_2 instead of x_1? Why was equation (2) solved for x_3 instead of x_2? Why was equation (3) solved for x_1 instead of x_3? One answer might be—to increase the accuracy, in a way similar to choosing the largest matrix element for the pivot element.

Actually the reason for solving the equation in the order stated above is due to the need for a certain structure of the coefficients in order for the successive approximations to converge to the true solution. In general, the process of approximation given here can be expressed mathematically as:

$$\begin{aligned} a &= F_1(b,c) \\ b &= F_2(a,c) \\ c &= F_3(a,b) \end{aligned}$$

Where the variables are a, b, and c and F_1, F_2, and F_3 are some functional relationships. In other words, the method depends on expressing each variable as a function of the other variables. In addition to the need for the existence of this functional relationship, it can be proved[1] that

$$\left|\frac{\partial F_1}{\partial a}\right| + \left|\frac{\partial F_2}{\partial a}\right| + \left|\frac{\partial F_3}{\partial a}\right| < 1$$

where

$\dfrac{\partial F_1}{\partial a}$ is the derivative of F_1 with respect to a, etc., and

$$\left|\frac{\partial F_1}{\partial b}\right| + \left|\frac{\partial F_2}{\partial b}\right| + \left|\frac{\partial F_3}{\partial b}\right| < 1$$

and

$$\left|\frac{\partial F_1}{\partial c}\right| + \left|\frac{\partial F_2}{\partial c}\right| + \left|\frac{\partial F_3}{\partial c}\right| < 1$$

and

$\dfrac{\partial F_2}{\partial b}$ is the derivative of F_2 with respect to b, etc.

---

[1] See J. B. Scarborough, *Numerical Mathematical Analysis* (Baltimore: Johns Hopkins Press, 1962), pp. 209–11.

must hold if the successive approximations are to converge to the true solution; it is also true that the less the above sums are, the faster is the convergence to the true solution.

Applying these criteria for convergence to the previous example, if we let $a = x_1$, $b = x_2$, and $c = x_3$, equation (1) gives $a = F_1\ (b,c)$.

$$x_1 = 1 - 10x_2 - 2x_3 = F_1\ (x_2,\ x_3) = F_1\ (b,c)$$

$$\left|\frac{\partial F_1}{\partial a}\right| \equiv \left|\frac{\partial F_1}{\partial x_1}\right| = 0; \quad \left|\frac{\partial F_1}{\partial b}\right| = |-10| = 10; \quad \left|\frac{\partial F_1}{\partial c}\right| = |-2| = 2$$

Equation (2) gives $b = F_2\ (a,c)$;

$$x_2 = -2 + x_1 + 12x_3 = F_2\ (x_1,\ x_3) = F_2\ (a,c)$$

$$\left|\frac{\partial F_2}{\partial a}\right| = 1; \quad \left|\frac{\partial F_2}{\partial b}\right| = 0; \quad \left|\frac{\partial F_2}{\partial c}\right| = 12$$

And equation (3) gives $c = F_3\ (a,b)$;

$$x_3 = \frac{1}{2} - \frac{9}{2}x_1 - x_2 = F_3(x_1,x_2) = F_3(a,b)$$

$$\left|\frac{\partial F_3}{\partial a}\right| = \left|-\frac{9}{2}\right| = \frac{9}{2}; \quad \left|\frac{\partial F_3}{\partial b}\right| = |-1| = 1; \quad \left|\frac{\partial F_3}{\partial c}\right| = 0\,.$$

Thus,

$$\left|\frac{\partial F_1}{\partial a}\right| + \left|\frac{\partial F_2}{\partial a}\right| + \left|\frac{\partial F_3}{\partial a}\right| = 0 + 1 + \frac{9}{2} = \frac{11}{2} > 1$$

Therefore, the method of approximation will not converge to the solution; the successive approximations will either diverge or oscillate around the true solution. However, if the equations are solved in the order which was used in the example, we have the following: let $a = x_2$, $b = x_3$, and $c = x_1$, and let equation (1) give $a = F_1\ (b,c)$.

Now $x_2 = .1 - .1\ x_1 - .2\ x_3$, and $b = F_2\ (a,c)$.

$$x_3 = .167 - .0825x_1 + .0825x_2 \text{ and } c = F_3\ (a,b)$$
$$x_1 = .111 - .222x_2 - .222x_3$$

$$\left|\frac{\partial F_1}{\partial a}\right| = 0, \quad \left|\frac{\partial F_1}{\partial b}\right| = |-.2| = .2, \quad \left|\frac{\partial F_1}{\partial c}\right| = |-.1| = .1$$

$$\left|\frac{\partial F_2}{\partial a}\right| = |+.0825| = .0825, \quad \left|\frac{\partial F_2}{\partial b}\right| = 0, \quad \left|\frac{\partial F_2}{\partial c}\right| = |-.0825| = .0825$$

$$\left|\frac{\partial F_3}{\partial a}\right| = |-.222| = .222, \quad \left|\frac{\partial F_3}{\partial b}\right| = |-.222| = .222, \quad \left|\frac{\partial F_3}{\partial c}\right| = 0$$

Therefore,

$$\left|\frac{\partial F_1}{\partial a}\right| + \left|\frac{\partial F_2}{\partial a}\right| + \left|\frac{\partial F_3}{\partial a}\right| = 0 + .0825 + .222 = .1045 < 1\,,$$

$$\left|\frac{\partial F_1}{\partial b}\right| + \left|\frac{\partial F_2}{\partial b}\right| + \left|\frac{\partial F_3}{\partial b}\right| = .2 + 0 + .222 = .422 < 1\,,$$

and

$$\left|\frac{\partial F_1}{\partial c}\right| + \left|\frac{\partial F_2}{\partial c}\right| + \left|\frac{\partial F_3}{\partial c}\right| = .1 + .0825 + 0 = .1825 < 1\,.$$

It is obvious from the above example that the way in which the functions are written may be critical in the process of convergence. In the specific case of three simultaneous linear equations the requirements (i.e. that

$$\sum_{i=1}^{3} \left|\frac{\partial F_j}{\partial x_i}\right| < 1$$

for $j = 1,2,3$) can be satisfied if one coefficient in each equation is sufficiently larger than the other coefficient in that equation; moreover, in each equation the coefficient of a different variable must be the larger coefficient. For the above example, the coefficient of x_2 was the largest in equation (1), the coefficient of x_3 was the largest in equation (2), and the coefficient of x_1 was the largest in equation (3).

The general approximation process can be looked at in the following way:

$$\left.\begin{aligned} x_1^{(1)} &= F_1\,(x_2^{(0)}, x_3^{(0)}) \\ x_2^{(1)} &= F_2\,(x_1^{(1)}, x_3^{(0)}) \\ x_3^{(1)} &= F_3\,(x_1^{(1)}, x_2^{(1)}) \end{aligned}\right\} \text{1st approximation}$$

$$\left.\begin{aligned} x_1^{(2)} &= F_1\,(x_2^{(1)}, x_3^{(1)}) \\ x_2^{(2)} &= F_2\,(x_1^{(2)}, x_3^{(1)}) \\ x_3^{(2)} &= F_3\,(x_1^{(2)}, x_2^{(2)}) \end{aligned}\right\} \text{2nd approximation}$$

$$\vdots$$

$$\left.\begin{aligned} x_1^{(k+1)} &= F_1\,(x_2^{(k)}, x_3^{(k)}) \\ x_2^{(k+1)} &= F_2\,(x_1^{(k+1)}, x_3^{(k)}) \\ x_3^{(k+1)} &= F_3\,(x_1^{(k+1)}, x_2^{(k+1)}) \end{aligned}\right\} (k+1)\text{st approximation}$$

Notice once more that the latest possible approximation for each variable is used to calculate the other variables; to calculate $x_2^{(k+1)}$, $x_1^{(k+1)}$ has been calculated so it is used, but $x_3^{(k+1)}$ has not yet been calculated so $x_3^{(k)}$ is used.

The program for computer solution of simultaneous linear equations by the method of successive approximations is not difficult to write. For each equation it can either be assumed that the problem will be set up so that a_{11} is the largest coefficient in row 1, a_{22} the largest coefficient in row 2, and a_{33} the largest coefficient in row 3, or all coefficients in each equation can be tested for the largest and then the equation is solved for that variable associated with the largest coefficient; the latter method is the more general one. For the system $AX = B$, and assuming the largest coefficient to be in column j for row i, equation i is solved for x_j; that is,

$$x_j = \frac{b_j}{a_{jj}} - \frac{1}{a_{jj}} \sum_{\substack{l=1 \\ l \neq j}}^{n} a_{jl} x_l$$

Again, the latest approximations of the x_l are to be used. Notice the summation takes place over all the variables except x_j.

In the following program we shall assume that the equations have been arranged so that equation 1 can be solved for x_1, equation 2 for x_2, etc. Also, we shall assume that the necessary tests have been performed on the coefficients such that convergence to the true solution will be assured. It is left as an exercise for the reader to modify the program to handle the above situations and tests.

Earlier in this book we stated that in any approximate procedure, the desired accuracy must be specified, and a test must be included in the program so that the computer can stop when the approximate solutions have attained the desired accuracy. When each variable is required to have three significant figures, it is necessary to test two successive values of that variable; if the two successive values do not change in the three most significant figures, the desired accuracy has been attained. To obtain x_2 to three significant figures, the analyst can utilize the statement,

IF(ABS (X(2) − Y(2))· LT· .0005), GO TO 20,

where the (k)th approximation to $X(2)$ is located in $Y(2)$ and the $k + 1$st approximation to $X(2)$ is located in $X(2)$. To obtain three significant figures in $X(2)$, two successive approximations must differ by less than 5 in the fourth place. It can be stated that if a variable has attained the desired accuracy, further approximations cannot destroy the accuracy already attained (if the tests for convergence are met). With this in mind, the plan will be to check for the desired accuracy on x_1, and continue the approximations until the desired accuracy has been attained; then test x_2, but do not go back and test x_1, because it has already been calculated to the desired accuracy.

Notice that by sending the tolerance to the subprogram as an argument, the desired accuracy may be changed from one problem to the next problem giving a more general program.

FLOW CHART

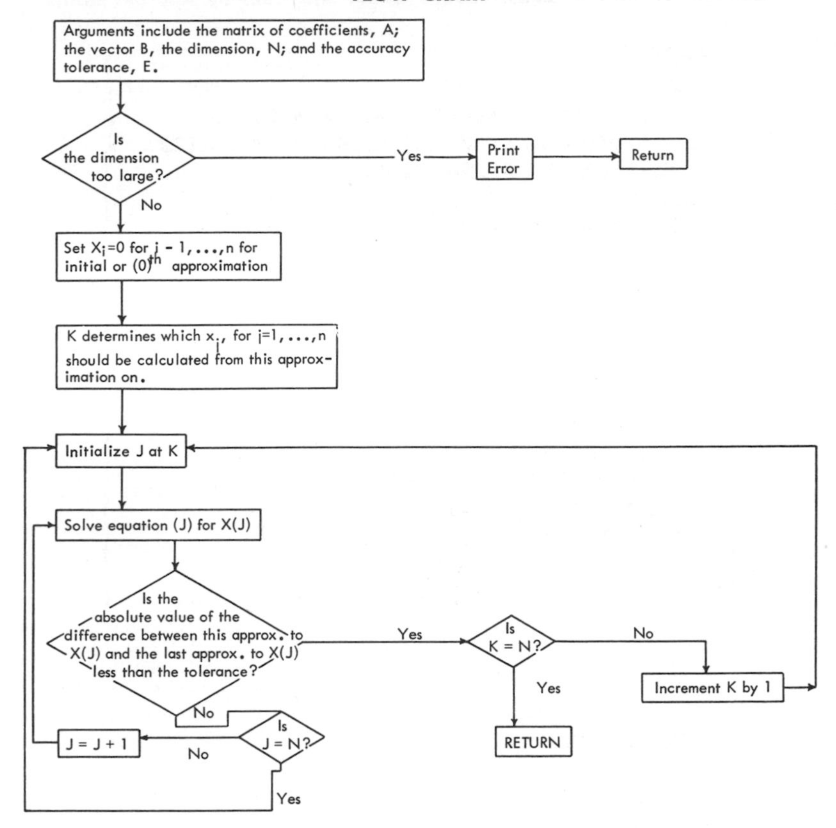

A variable index is needed for the starting index in the loop used to move from the calculation of one variable to the calculation of the next variable in the same step in the process of the approximation, that way it is not necessary to recalculate those variables which have already been found to be within the desired tolerance. An even more efficient means of checking to see which variables have been found to be within the desired tolerance is to check all the variables after each approximation; in all likelihood the rate of convergence will not be in the natural order; that is x_3 may converge faster then x_1. Therefore, it would be better to eliminate x_3 from further approximations before trying to eliminate x_1 from further approximations; before x_1 is found to fall within the desired tolerance limits, needless calculations will have been performed on x_3. As an exercise the student might try to incorporate this additional improvement into the program.

The use of the B array to hold the present approximation to the variable eliminates the need for additional storage space; this is the reason for writing the statements B(J) = B(J)/A(J,J) and X(J) = B(J) separately, instead of in one statement as X(J) = B(J)/A(J,J). Also note that the

PROGRAM—Solution of Simultaneous Linear Equations by Approximation

```
      SUBROUTINE APPSOL (X,A,B,N,E)
      DIMENSION X(10),A(10,10),B(10),K1(10)
      IF (N.LE.10) GO TO 15
      WRITE (6,127)
  127 FORMAT (19HDIMENSION TOO LARGE)
      CALL EXIT
   15 DO 17 I=1,N
      K1(I)=1
   17 X(I)=0.
   32 DO 50 J=1,N
      IF(K1(J).EQ.2) GO TO 50
      C=B(J)
      DO 20 L=1,N
      IF(L.EQ.J) GO TO 20
      C=C-A(J,L)*X(L)
   20 CONTINUE
      C=C/A(J,J)
      IF (ABS(C-X(J)).LT.E) K1(J)=2
      X(J)=C
   50 CONTINUE
      DO 40 K = 1,N
   40 IF(K1(K) .EQ.1) GO TO 32
      RETURN
      END
```

statement, B(J) = B(J)/A(J,J), is not included in the loop ending with statement number 20 because the index, L, of the loop is not involved in this statement. To include the statement, B(J) = B(J)/A(J,J) in the loop ending with statement number 20 would cause the computer to execute this statement N times instead of 1 time.

The variable K1 is used as a switch to indicate whether the variable, X(J), has reached the desired level of accuracy or not; K1 is set to 2 if the desired level of accuracy has been reached. If K1 equals 1, further calculation must be made on X(J). Notice that K1 is reinitialized at 1 after K has been incremented; if this were not included in the program, all the variables would be assumed to fall within the desired tolerance limits as soon as the first variable was known to fall within the desired tolerance limits.

The method of successive approximations can be used to solve system of simultaneous nonlinear equations as well as linear equations; trigonometric functions, logarithms, and exponential functions may also be included in the system. Consider the following example:

$$e^{-x_1} + 5x_2 = 10 \tag{1}$$
$$x_1 + \log x_2 = 1. \tag{2}$$

Writing the equations in the form

$$x_1 = F_1\,(x_1,\, x_2)$$

and

$$x_2 = F_2\,(x_1,\, x_2)$$

we have

$$x_2 = \frac{10 - e^{-x_1}}{5}$$

where

$$F_2\,(x_1,x_2) = \frac{10 - e^{-x_1}}{5}$$
$$x_1 = -1 + \log x_2 \tag{3}$$

and

$$F_1\,(x_1,x_2) = -1 + \log x_2. \tag{4}$$

The test conditions for convergence are:

$$\left|\frac{\partial F_1}{\partial x_1}\right| = 0 \qquad \left|\frac{\partial F_2}{\partial x_1}\right| = \frac{e^{-x_1}}{5}$$
$$\left|\frac{\partial F_1}{\partial x_2}\right| = \frac{1}{x_2} \qquad \left|\frac{\partial F_2}{\partial x_2}\right| = 0$$

Now it is necessary to specify the initial values of x_1 and x_2. If we let $x_1 = 0$ and $x_2 = 0$, then:

$$\left|\frac{\partial F_1}{\partial x_1}\right| + \left|\frac{\partial F_2}{\partial x_3}\right| = \frac{1}{5} \quad \text{and} \quad \left|\frac{\partial F_1}{\partial x_1}\right| = \frac{1}{0} = \infty \qquad \left|\frac{\partial F_2}{\partial x_2}\right| = 0$$

Therefore, both conditions are not met. One course of action would be to try to express the functions differently; however, a more promising course of action in this case would be to try to find a better starting solution than $x_1 = 0$ and $x_2 = 0$. Plot equations (1) and (2)—

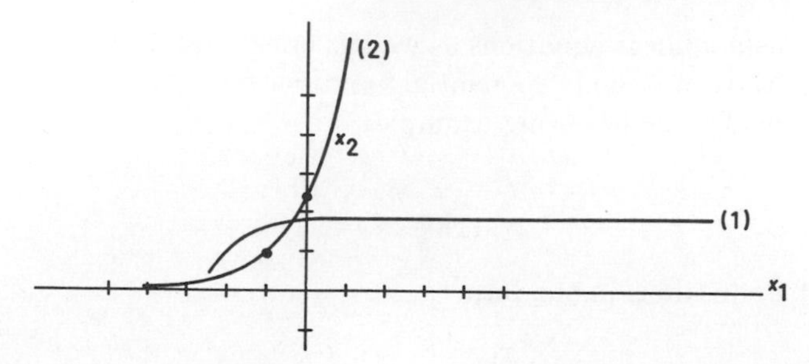

From the graph, try $x_1 = -1$ and $x_2 = 2$, then

$$\left|\frac{\partial F_1}{\partial x_1}\right| = 0 \quad \text{and} \quad \left|\frac{\partial F_2}{\partial x_1}\right| = .54$$

$$\left|\frac{\partial F_1}{\partial x_2}\right| = \frac{1}{2} = .50 \quad \text{and} \quad \left|\frac{\partial F_2}{\partial x_2}\right| = 0$$

Now both conditions are satisfied.

1st approximation

$$\begin{cases} x_1^{(1)} = F_1\,(x_1^{(0)},\, x_2^{(0)}) \\ \qquad = -1 + \log 2 = -1 + .69315 = -.30685 \\ x_2^{(1)} = F_2\,(x_1^{(1)},\, x_2^{(0)}) \\ \qquad = \dfrac{10 - e^{-(-.30685)}}{5} = \dfrac{10 - 1.354}{5} = \dfrac{8.646}{5} = 1.729 \end{cases}$$

2nd approximation

$$\begin{cases} x_1^{(2)} = F_1\,(x_1^{(1)},\, x_2^{(1)}) \\ \qquad = -1 + \log\,(1.729) = -1 + .548 = -.442 \\ x_2^{(2)} = F_2\,(x_1^{(2)},\, x_2^{(1)}) \\ \qquad = \dfrac{10 - e^{-(-.422)}}{5} = \dfrac{10 - e^{.442}}{5} = \dfrac{10 - 1.555}{5} = 1.689 \end{cases}$$

3rd approximation

$$\begin{cases} x_1^{(3)} = F_1\,(x_1^{(2)},\, x_2^{(2)}) \\ \qquad = -1 + \log\,(1.689) = -1 + .524 = -.476 \\ x_2^{(3)} = F_2(x_1^{(3)}, x_2^{(2)}) \\ \qquad = \dfrac{10 - e^{-(-.476)}}{5} = \dfrac{10 - 1.609}{5} = \dfrac{8.391}{5} = 1.678 \end{cases}$$

We can say that x_2 has been calculated to two significant figures, 1.6, and x_1 to one significant figure, .4. With logarithm and exponential function tables of only 3 places, it cannot be expected that more than two significant figures can be obtained; however, if more accurate tables are used, the problem can be solved for x_1 and x_2 to more significant figures. It is left as an exercise for the reader to try to obtain x_1 and x_2 to more significant figures by using more accurate tables and carrying the process of approximation through a greater number of steps.

To see if the program written to solve a system of simultaneous linear equations can be used to solve the system when other than linear equations are contained in the system, compare both cases for a system of two equations. In one case, the system is,

$$a_{11}x_1 + a_{12}x_2 = b_1$$
$$a_{21}x_1 + a_{22}x_2 = b_2$$

while the system for the second case is,

$$a_{11}f_1(x_1) + a_{12}f_1(x_2) = b_1$$
$$a_{21}f_2(x_1) + a_{22}f_2(x_2) = b_2$$

The difference between the two systems is the substitution of $f_i(x_j)$ for x_j, where i represents the number of the equation and j represents the number of the variable. The pertinent question then regarding the generalization of the subroutine, APPSOL, is whether or not functions can be transmitted as arguments to subprograms in the same way that variables can be transmitted as arguments.

The reader may recall from Chapter 5 that the FORTRAN IV compiler permits the use of a dummy function name in the subroutine provided the name of the functional rule being transmitted is mentioned in an EXTERNAL statement in the calling program. For example, define F(X,I) = X(I) ** 2, as an arithmetic statement function in the calling program. Preceding this functional definition the programmer must write the statement,

```
EXTERNAL (F)
```

to indicate to the compiler that F is the name of a function and not a variable. Suppose that the programmer then wishes to call the subroutine, GAS, to do some calculations.

```
CALL SUBROUTINE GAS (A, K,F),
```

where A and K are variables and F is a function. The subroutine would take on the following appearance:

```
      SUBROUTINE GAS (B, N, Z)
      ______
      ______
      ______
   10 B (J) = B (J) - R * Z (X,J)
      ______
      ______
      ______
```

Statement number 10 resembles the statement

```
B(J)=B(J)-A(J,L)*X (L)
```

in APPSOL; the variable X(L) must be changed to F(X,L), where in the most general case, the programmer will want to be able to choose from a set of possible functions for F for each problem. Using the notation F (X,L), the programmer utilizes the index, L, of the variable to index the function as well. However, it should be noted that this notation will provide for the labeling of (or for the reservation of storage) only N functions, where L = 1,2, . . . , N. Referring back to the general system of equations,

$$a_{11}f_1\ (x_1) + a_{12}f_1\ (x_2) = b_1$$
$$a_{21}\, f_2\ (x_1) + a_{22}\, f_2\ (x_2) = b_2$$

Observe that four functions are necessary to make the program entirely general. One way to handle the problem would be to define each of the functions in terms of three arguments; that is, instead of F (X,L), we may write F (X,L,J), where the index J can be used to indicate the equation number. The new notation provides for the use of (J·L) functions.

Before writing the more general version of the subprogram, APPSOL, examine the statement, IF(L·EQ·J) GO TO 20. For the case of simultaneous linear equations, this statement is appropriate because the variable X(J), does not enter into the calculation of $X(J)$ in equation J (B (J) = B(J) − A(J,L) * X(L) for L = 1, . . . , N but not for L = J). However, in the most general case $x_1^{(k)} = F_1\ (x_1^{(k-1)}, x_2^{(k-1)}, \ldots, x_n^{(k-1)}$; in other words, X(J) may appear on the right-hand side of the statement used to determine X(J) from the Jth equation.

All initial values of the variables, x_{jj}, $j = 1, \ldots, n$, must be supplied from the calling program as well as the definition of all functions which are available to the subprogram. These functions may be defined as follows:

F (X, 1, 1) = EXPF (X (1, 1))
F (X,2,1) = X (2,1)
F (X, 1, 2) = −X (1, 2)
F (X, 2, 2) = LOG (X (2,2))

This nomenclature is clumsy; the only reason for using two subscripts on X is because three arguments, including L and J, are needed for the functions, F. X(1,1) and X(1,2) contain the same value; namely, x_1. X(2,1) and X(2,2) also contain the same value; namely, x_2. Therefore, the above nomenclature causes a great deal of waste in the allocation of storage locations.

An alternative nomenclature would be to actually index the functions, F; for example, F_J (X,L), where J would indicate the number of the equation; J has a range of 1 to N. The new nomenclature would certainly not reduce the number of functions which are required to completely generalize the program, but it does eliminate the need for two subscripts on the variables, X, resulting in a savings of storage space.

Although the nomenclature, F_J (X,L) has an advantage in the program,

PROGRAM—Solution of a General System of Simultaneous Equations by Approximation

```
      SUBROUTINE GENSOL (X,A,B,N,E,F)
      DIMENSION X(10,10),A(10,10),B(10),K1(10)
      IF(N.LE.10) GO TO 15
      WRITE (6,127)
  127 FORMAT (19HDIMENSION TOO LARGE)
      RETURN
   15 DO 17 I=1,N
      K1(I)=1
   17 X(I,1)=0
   32 DO 50 J=1,N
      IF(K1(J).EQ.2) GO TO 50
      C=B(J)
      DO 20 L=1,N
      IF(L.EQ.J) GO TO 20
      C=C-A(J,L)*F(X,L,J)
   20 CONTINUE
      C=C/A(J,J)
      IF(ABS(C-X(J,J)).LT.E) K1(J)=2
      X(J,J)=C
   50 CONTINUE
      DO 40 K=1,N
   40 IF(K1(K).EQ.1) GO TO 32
      RETURN
      END
```

it is not possible to program this nomenclature in a direct way; a variable standing for a functional rule cannot be subscripted in an arithmetic statement function. The reader should try different ways of directly applying the nomenclature F_J (X,L) to the problem by using FORTRAN IV statements.

The difficulty arises in the basic design of FORTRAN IV. A variable appearing on the left-hand side of an arithmetic statement must take on a value at run time. For example, when the statement F (J,K) = X(J) ** 2+3./X(J), is executed by the FORTRAN IV Compiler at run time, F(J,K) will take on a value; in other words the arithmetic expression on the right-hand sign of the statement must be evaluated—the programmer does not have the ability to carry F(J,K) along as the expression X(J) ** 2 + 3./X(J); in FORTRAN IV the only way to have F(J,K) represent the expression is via a functional statement. The reader may recall that in Chapter 5, the ability to carry along an arithmetic expression by a variable name is one of the big advantages of FORMAC (there, it was demonstrated that this property simplified the process of differentiation, etc.).

7.4. Interpolation

Many times data from an experiment is taken in following form:

t	$f(t)$
0	31
1	21
2	8
3	17
4	61
5	37
6	41
7	37
.	.
.	.
.	.

that is, the process of taking data starts at a certain point in time, which may be denoted time 0. Then, readings which measure some property of a system are taken at successive time intervals (not necessarily equal intervals). At the end of the experiment, it may be necessary to give the property of the system at some point at which data had not been taken during the experiment.

One solution to the problem is to fit a polynomial of the form $p(x) = a_1x^n + a_2\ x^{n-1} + a_3\ x^{n-1} + \ldots + a_{n-2}\ x^3 + a_{n-1}\ x^2 + a_nx^1 + a_{n+1}$ to the set of $(n+1)$ points $(t_1, f(t_1))$, $(t_2, f\ (t_2))$, . . . , $(t_{n+1}, f\ (t_{n+1}))$. We can state

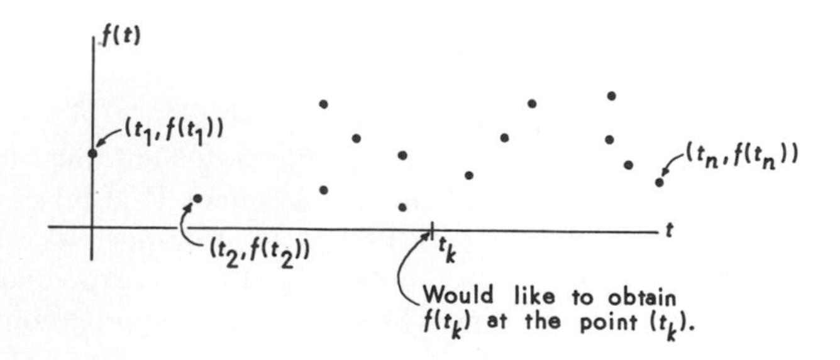

FIG. 7–2

this in the form of a theorem: for $(n+1)$ points (x_j, y_j), there exists one and only one polynomial of the form,

$$y = p(x) = \sum_{k=1}^{n+1} a_k \, x^{n-k+1}$$

such that, the polynomial passes through each point—$p(x)$ is a polynomial in x of degree equal to or less than n (some of the a_k could be zero) and $x_1 < x_2 < \ldots < x_{n+1}$. With this nomenclature, $x_j = t_j$ and $y_j = f(t_j)$ for $j = 1, \ldots, n$.

The above theorem implies that

$$y_j = \sum_{k=1}^{n+1} a_k \, x_j^{n-k+1}$$

for $j = 1, \ldots, n$; or each point j, the polynomial in x represented by the right hand must be equal to the value at that point, y_j. If one can find the coefficients $a_1, a_2, \ldots, a_k$, then to find the value of $f(t_r) \equiv y_r$ at some point r, other than the original $(n+1)$ points, $t_1, t_2, \ldots, t_{n+1}$, but included in the interval t_1 to t_{n+1}, it is simply necessary to evaluate the polynomial

$$y = p(x) = \sum_{k=1}^{n+1} a_k \, x_r^{n-k+1}$$

at the point $t_r \equiv x_r$; or

$$y_r = p(x_r) = \sum_{k=1}^{n+1} a_k x_r^{n-k+1}$$

Actually, we already know a method to calculate the coefficients because the system

$$y_j = \sum_{k=1}^{n+1} a_k \, x_j^{n-k+1}$$

for $j = 1, \ldots, n$, is a system of simultaneous equations; in other words, $y = AX$ in which we treat the a's as the variables. In other words, for $j = 1$, we have $y_1 = a_1 x_1^n + a_2 \, x_1^{n-1} + a_3 x_1^{n-2} + \ldots + a_n x_1^1 + a_{n+1}$, where y_1 and the x's are known. Equation 1 can then be used to express a_1 in terms of $a_2, a_3, \ldots, a_{n+1}$ and this value substituted in equations $2,3, \ldots, n+1$ to eliminate a_1 from these equations; the process is the same as that described earlier in this chapter. The process can be seen as the need for finding the inverse of the matrix X; then, $Y = AX$ becomes $YX^{-1} = AXX^{-1} = A$.

If we have available a subroutine, SIMUL, which can solve a system of simultaneous equations and a subroutine, EVAL, which evaluates polynomials, it is an easy matter to write a program to find $f(t_r)$ at some point x_r in the interval $x_1 < x_r < x_{n+1}$, where x_r is not one of the $(n+1)$ original data points. To see how the matrix X will be found, consider the first equation again—$y_1 = a_1x_1^n + a_2x_1^{n-1} + a_3x_1^{n-2} + \ldots + a_nx_1^1 + a_{n+1}$; if we use the nomenclature, $x_1^n \equiv x_{1,n+1}$; $x_1^{n-1} \equiv x_{1,n}$; $\ldots$ $x_1^1 \equiv x_{1,2}$; and $x_1^0 \equiv x_{1,1} = 1$; or better yet $x_1^n = x_{11}$; $x_1^{n-1} = x_{12}, \ldots, x_1^1 = x_{1,n}$; $x_1^0 = x_{1,n+1} = 1$. If we are given the vector X,

$$\begin{bmatrix} x_1 \\ x_2 \\ \cdot \\ \cdot \\ \cdot \\ x_{n+1} \end{bmatrix}$$

calculate the matrix X′X by the following routine;

```
      DO  20   I = 1, N
      DO  20   J = 1, N
      K=N+1 - J
20    XX(I,J)=X(I) ** (K)
      J = N+1
      DO  30   I = 1, N
30    XX(I,J)=1.
```

FLOW CHART—Interpolation

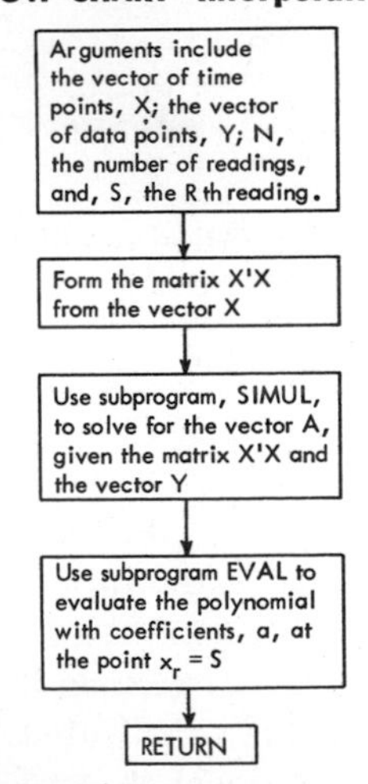
Arguments include the vector of time points, X; the vector of data points, Y; N, the number of readings, and, S, the R th reading.
Form the matrix X'X from the vector X
Use subprogram, SIMUL, to solve for the vector A, given the matrix X'X and the vector Y
Use subprogram EVAL to evaluate the polynomial with coefficients, a, at the point x_r = S
RETURN

The coefficients are calculated in the first CALL statement, and the value for $T \equiv x_r$ is calculated in the second CALL statement.

It may be better to pass a function other than a polynomial through all the points; perhaps a trigonometric function will result in less chance of a large error when interpolating with the function. The interpolating func-

PROGRAM—Polynomial Interpolation

```
      SUBROUTINE INTERP(X,Y,N,S,T)
      DIMENSION X(11),Y(11),XX(11,11)
      DO 2Ø I=1,N
      DO 2Ø J=1,N
      K=N+1-J
   2Ø XX(I,J)=X(I)**(K)
      J=N+1
      DO 3Ø I=1,N
   3Ø XX(I,J)=1.
      CALL SIMUL(A,X,Y,N)
      CALL EVAL(T,A,X,N)
      RETURN
      END
```

tion may be integrated to give the area under the curve if this is desirable; or, other operations may be performed using the interpolating function.

In the next chapter, a different approach will be taken to the problem. There, we shall not try to pass a function through all the given points, but given some prior information as to the type of function, we shall try to fit a function to the points which will minimize the square of the distance between all the points and the function; the function which minimizes the sum of squares probably will not go through any single point. A function set up in this way contains a good deal of statistical information which can then be analyzed to see how good the function is in the estimation of some point other than the original data points.

Problems

7.1. In some problems utilizing matrices, it is never necessary to use more than one-half of the matrix; i.e., a triangular matrix.

Lower Triangular Matrix or *Upper Triangular Matrix*

$$\begin{bmatrix} a_{11} & 0 & 0 & 0 \\ a_{21} & a_{22} & 0 & 0 \\ a_{31} & a_{32} & a_{33} & 0 \\ a_{41} & a_{42} & a_{43} & a_{44} \end{bmatrix} \quad \text{or} \quad \begin{bmatrix} a_{11} & a_{12} & a_{13} & a_{14} \\ 0 & a_{22} & a_{23} & a_{24} \\ 0 & 0 & a_{33} & a_{34} \\ 0 & 0 & 0 & a_{44} \end{bmatrix}$$

If the programmer reserves a two-dimensional array for either of the above two matrices, a total of $\frac{n^2 - n}{2}$ storage locations are wasted. To avoid this waste of storage space for the above types of matrices using FORTRAN, devise a method of addressing any element in the special two-dimensional arrays (triangular) above through the use of only one subscript; i.e., if the subscripts I(row subscript) and J(column subscript) are used to specify the element in the two-dimensional array, find the index L which specifies the same element in the one-dimensional array. In other words, given A(I,J), find A(L).

Hint: For the lower triangular matrix, arrange the elements in the following way:

L =	(a_{11}	a_{21}	a_{22}	a_{31}	a_{32}	a_{33}	a_{41}	a_{42}	a_{43}	a_{44}	. . .)
	1	2	3	4	5	6	7	8	9	10	. . .

7.2. Two special types of matrices which are important in many applications are the symmetric matrix and the skew-symmetric matrix. The symmetric matrix is characterized by having $a_{ij} = a_{ji}$; the skew-symmetric matrix is characterized by having $a_{ij} = -a_{ji}$. For example,

Symmetric Matrix *Skew-Symmetric Matrix*

$$\begin{bmatrix} 1 & 2 & -4 \\ 2 & 3 & 2 \\ -4 & 2 & -6 \end{bmatrix} \qquad \begin{bmatrix} 0 & 2 & 4 \\ -2 & 0 & -1 \\ -4 & 1 & 0 \end{bmatrix}$$

Write a FORTRAN program which will multiply two symmetric matrices using one-dimensional arrays for both matrices.

7.3. To invert a very large matrix (large depending on the computer and the desired accuracy) it may be necessary to not only revert to an iterative-type process, such as the approximate method used for solving simultaneous equations, but also to divide the matrix into parts, because the size of the computer memory is too small to hold the entire matrix.

Given a matrix A, find A^{-1}, where

$$A = \left[\begin{array}{cc|ccc} a_{11} & a_{12} & a_{13} & \cdots & a_{1n} \\ a_{21} & a_{22} & a_{23} & \cdots & a_{2n} \\ \cdot & \cdot & \cdot & \cdots & \cdot \\ \hline \cdot & \cdot & \cdot & \cdots & \cdot \\ \cdot & \cdot & \cdot & \cdots & \cdot \\ a_{n1} & a_{n2} & a_{n3} & \cdots & a_{nn} \end{array}\right]$$

if we can divide A into four parts called partitions, such that A is composed of the four submatrices, U,V,X, and Y, of which Y has an inverse,

$$A = \begin{bmatrix} U & V \\ X & Y \end{bmatrix}$$

then A^{-1} can be computed as

$$A^{-1} = \begin{bmatrix} R1 & R2 \\ R3 & R4 \end{bmatrix}$$

where

$$R1 = (U-VY^{-1}X)^{-1}$$
$$R2 = -R1VY^{-1}$$
$$R3 = -Y^{-1}XR1$$
$$R4 = Y^{-1}-Y^{-1}XR2$$

Assuming the matrix A to be on tape unit number 3 in order by columns (assume each column to be a logical record in binary; i.e., use the READ(3) . . . list . . . statement), write a FORTRAN program which allows the analyst to specify his own partitions and computes the new inverse. The inverse should be stored in logical records (one column per record) on tape unit 2. Use one of the subroutines in the chapter to do any necessary inversions of the submatrices; also use subroutines for matrix multiplication and addition.

Note that more than one partition may be necessary before the inversion is completed; where are the intermediate results to be placed if more than one partitioning step is necessary? Pay particular attention to the fact that only parts of columns are needed and only certain columns are needed. Try to obtain the most efficient way of bringing the necessary elements into the memory from tape unit number 3.

7.4. Given that matrix addition and multiplication of partitioned matrices follows the same rules as those for matrix addition and multiplication of unpartitioned matrices, write a FORTRAN program to multiply the partitioned matrix A and the partitioned matrix B to obtain the matrix C, where C = AB (the partitioning of A and B is such that the partitioned matrices conform to the rules for multiplication of matrices). Assume A is on tape unit number 3 and B is on tape unit number 4, both in column order, one column per logical record.

7.5. For the system of simultaneous linear equations, $AX = 0$, in which the vector of constants, b, is zero, a necessary condition for the existence of a solution other than $X = 0$, is $|A| = 0$ (the necessity is proved easily by reference to Cramer's Rule). A very common system of equations in which b equals zero, is the system $AX = \lambda X$, or $AX - \lambda X = 0$, or $X(A - \lambda I) = 0$. If A is of order n, there are at most n values of λ for which there are nonzero roots to the equation, $X(A - \lambda I) = 0$; the λ are called characteristic values of the equation and the associated roots, X, are called characteristic vectors.

It is possible to utilize the approximation procedure given in the chapter for simultaneous equations to obtain the largest characteristic value and its associated characteristic vector. Take $X^{(0)}$ as the initial approximation to the characteristic vector, X. Now for $X^{(1)}$, use the equation $AX^{(0)} = X^{(1)}$; but notice that when we multiply $X^{(0)}$ by A, we obtain $\lambda X^{(1)}$ and not $X^{(1)}$. If one component of X is always kept at the same value, λ will be determined when X has been obtained to the desired accuracy; i.e. $AX^{(0)} = \lambda^{(1)} X^{(1)}$, where $\lambda^{(1)}$ is the first approximation to λ, the largest characteristic value.

If

$$A = \begin{bmatrix} 3 & 1 \\ 1 & 3 \end{bmatrix}$$

and if we start with the vector

$$X^{(0)} = \begin{bmatrix} 0 \\ 1 \end{bmatrix},$$

then

$$AX^{(0)} = \begin{bmatrix} 3 & 1 \\ 1 & 3 \end{bmatrix} \begin{bmatrix} 0 \\ 1 \end{bmatrix} = \begin{bmatrix} 1 \\ 3 \end{bmatrix} = 3 \begin{bmatrix} 1/3 \\ 1 \end{bmatrix}$$

where $\lambda^{(1)} = 3$ and $X^{(1)} = \begin{bmatrix} 1/3 \\ 1 \end{bmatrix}$; here, the last component of X is always kept at 1. The procedure is to keep iterating until there is no change in the last desired decimal place from one iteration to the next.

Write a FORTRAN program to find the largest characteristic value and its associated characteristic vector.

(NOTE: If the two large stcharacteristic values have the same modulus or when the desired characteristic vector is orthogonal to $X^{(0)}$, this method does not yield convergence to the largest characteristic value; the process will either diverge or oscillate.)

7.6. Given n observations (readings) on each of p variables, the coefficient of correlation between any of two these variables, X_i and X_j, is defined as

$$r_{x_i x_j} = \frac{\sum_{k=1}^{n} (x_{ik} x_{jk}) - nMx_i Mx_j}{\sqrt{\left[\sum_{k=1}^{n} (x_{ik}^2) - nMx_i^2\right]\left[\sum_{k=1}^{n} (x_{jk}^2) - nMx_j^2\right]}}$$

where

$$Mx_i = \frac{\sum_{k=1}^{n} x_{ik}}{n}$$

Earlier in the book, programs have been given to calculate the mean, M.

Write a FORTRAN program to calculate the p^2 correlation coefficients; in your program try to take advantage of the fact that the square matrix of dimension p of correlation coefficients is a symmetric matrix with ones down the main diagonal (i.e., $a_{kk} = 1$ for $k = 1, \ldots, p$).

7.7. A quadratic form is defined to be

$$X^T A X$$

where X is a column vector with n rows and A is a square matrix of dimension n. The expected value of $X^T A X$ is equal to $\mu' A \mu + trAC$, where μ is the mean of the vector X, μ' is the mean of the vector X^T, C is the covariance matrix which was calculated in problem 7.6, and the trace of a matrix is defined to be the sum of the elements down the main diagonal. The expected value of a variable x is defined as

$$\sum_{i=1}^{n} \frac{x_i P(x_i)}{n},$$

where $P(x_i)$ is the probability of obtaining the value x_i.

Write a FORTRAN program which will evaluate the quadratic form $X^T A X$.

8. Application of Previously Presented Methods to Two Practical Problems

This chapter will be confined to two fairly long problems which are applicable in the areas of science and business. First, we shall consider the problem of fitting a curve to a set of points such that the results can be analyzed in a statistical framework; second, we shall consider one method of sorting information. Both programs will be concerned with not only the method of analysis and the programming but also with providing the program as a service on a systematic basis. In the first case, we assume that magnetic tape units are available; in the second case, we assume that the only type of available input is the card reader.

8.1. Least Squares and Regression Analysis

8.1.1. Relationship between Two Variables

Given a set of n readings of each of two variables—say, pressure and temperature during a certain chemical reaction or demand of an item and time—can we imply anything about variable 2 if we are given a value of variable 1 other than at one of the n points. In one case, the given value of variable 2 falls between two readings (interpolation) and in the other case, the given value of variable 2 falls outside of the range of the n readings (extrapolation).

The purpose of analyzing the relationship between two variables is two-

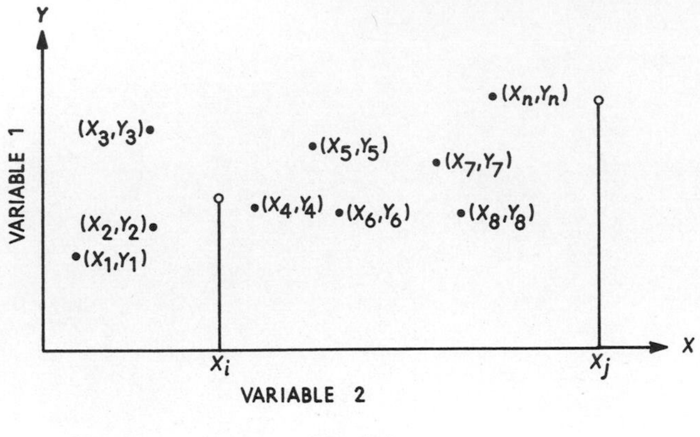

FIG. 8–1

fold. First we would like to predict the value of one variable from a knowledge of the other; or, stated somewhat differently, we would like to establish a mathematical functional relationship between variable 1 and variable 2—variable 1 = f (variable 2)—such that given any value of variable 2 within a certain range, we can obtain a value for variable 1. Second, we would like to know how closely the data obey the proposed mathematical relationship. If the data obey the proposed mathematical relationship very closely, we would have more confidence in a prediction using this relationship.

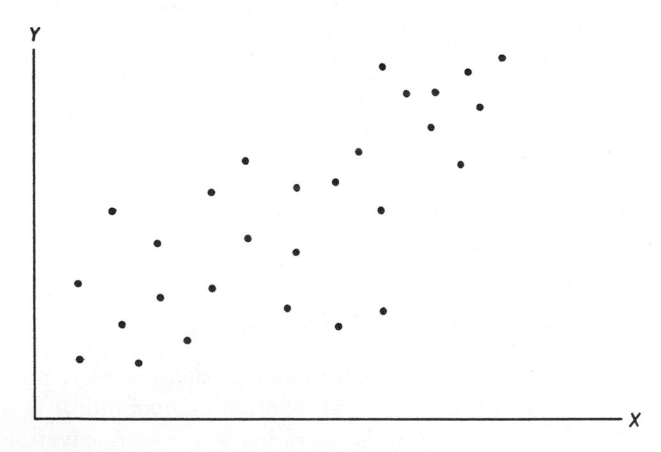

FIG. 8–2

One way of establishing a mathematical relation is to fit a curve to the points of the scatter diagram. We shall not go into the methods of fitting different types of curves beyond saying that the curve is determined by the parameters. For example, the curves

$$Y = b + a(\sinh X) \quad (1)$$
$$Y = be^{aX} \quad (2)$$
$$Y = aX^2 + b \quad (3)$$

may all be fitted to the above scatter diagram; that is, the same set of data may be used to determine the parameters a and b of equation (1), a of equation (2) and a of equation (3). It is readily apparent that the difference in the shapes of the three curves are due solely to the particular form of equation used in computing them and that each curve seems to fit the points equally well. Which equation should we use to express the relationship of the two variables, if there is any relationship? We may answer this important question in the following way: Before taking the data, there should have been sufficient thought and study given to the problem to be able to make a hypothesis on the relationship between the two variables. In the example, let us say that after a preliminary study, the user makes the hypothesis that the relationship between the variables could be given mathematically by equation (3); i.e., $Y = aX^2 + b$. The next step would be to take the data (it may be necessary in some cases to set up the experiment and then take the data), and then fit the curve represented by the equation $Y = aX^2 + b$. If there is a "good" fit, we say that the hypothesis has been verified, and we therefore have established a "law" which states the nature of the relationship. On the other hand, if a preliminary study does not lead to a hypothesis or there is no preliminary study, a curve drawn freehand through the points is as good as any curve representing an equation. As was previously illustrated, many curves could fit the same points equally well.

Let us assume that a mathematical relation is established between the variables (i.e., a hypothesis is verified). We should reconsider the main purpose of establishing the mathematical relation; that is, whether we can estimate values of one variable from given values of another variable for cases in addition to those from which the functional relation was determined. Whether such estimated values, for cases not included in the original study, can be expected to agree with the true values if they could be determined, depends upon two considerations; (1) exactly what the curve means with regard to the particular cases from which it was determined; and (2) the degree of dependability of the curve with regard both to the ability of those observations to represent all possible observations and the ability of the curve to represent the actual relations which exist among all possible observations. The means of fitting a curve by methods referred to in the above paragraph would probably be sufficient for the first criteria. However, since the second criteria involves the statistical method of estimation, we have to estimate the parameter of the true equation (that equation which is fitted to all possible data observations) from the parameters calculated from this one small sample (the data).

8.1.2. The Least Squares Method—Two Variables, Linear Form

A mathematical method exists which meets both criteria and has other advantages as well. The idea is to fit a curve which minimizes the sum of the squares of the deviations from the observations to the curve. Figure 8–3

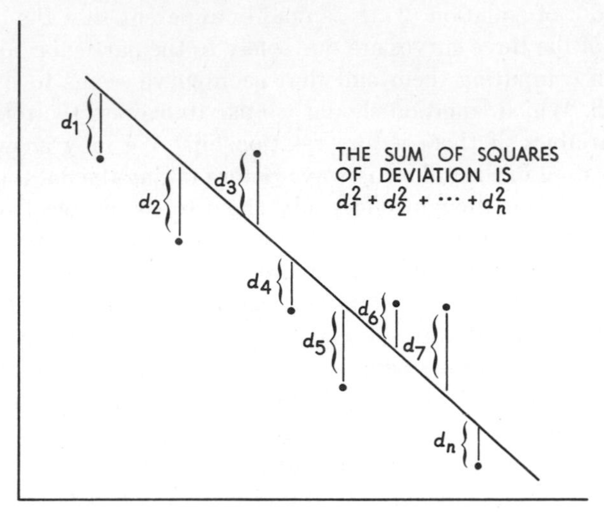

FIG. 8–3

shows a curve (in this case, a straight line $Y = aX + b$), with the deviations shown as vertical lines from the observations (data) to the curve. A great deal is known about the statistical theory needed to find the answers to the following questions:

1. How well does the curve fit this data?
2. With what reliability can I predict one variable from a knowledge of the other?
3. If there are more than two variables involved, how much does each contribute to my knowledge of the variables I am trying to estimate?

Other advantages of the method of least squares are the following:

1. The simplicity of the mathematics.
2. The ability to handle curves other than straight lines under the same type of calculations.
3. The ability to try different curves so we can pick the best (the one giving the lowest sum of squares of deviations from the curve).

For two variables, consider the relation

$$Y = a + bX \tag{a}$$

Given n points (x_1, y_1), (x_2, y_2), . . . , (xn, yn), find a and b such that the graph of (a) results in a minimum of the sum of the squares of the deviations of each point from the graph. Mathematically we have,

$$\begin{aligned} d_1 &= a + bx_1 - y_1 \\ d_2 &= a + bx_2 - y_2 \\ &\cdot \quad \cdot \quad \cdot \quad \cdot \\ &\cdot \quad \cdot \quad \cdot \quad \cdot \\ &\cdot \quad \cdot \quad \cdot \quad \cdot \\ d_n &= a + bx_n - y_n \end{aligned}$$

$\sum d^2 = d_1^2 + d_2^2 + \ldots + d_n^2$, where $\sum d^2$ is to be minimized. The sum of the deviations is a function of a and b; therefore, to minimize this function we must set the partial derivatives of this function with respect to a and b to zero.

$$\frac{\partial f}{\partial a} = 2(a+bx_1 - y_1) + 2(a+bx_2 - y_2) + \ldots + 2(a+bx_n+y_n) = 0$$

$$\frac{\partial f}{\partial b} = 2(a+bx_1-y_1)x_1 + 2(a+bx_2 - y_2)x_2 + \ldots + 2(a+bx_n-y_n)x_n = 0$$

The above equations may be divided by 2; then we get the "normal" equations. Obviously, the number of normal equations must be the same as the number of constants to be determined in the fitted equation, (a). We may also observe that the number of readings (x_i, y_i) must be greater than the number of constants of the fitted equation which we wish to determine; if the number of readings is the same as the number of constants to be determined, there is a unique solution to the normal equations, and the graph of the fitted equation will pass through the readings.

The normal equations are a set of simultaneous linear equations which may be solved for the constants a and b by the methods of Chapter 7.

8.1.3. Least Squares Extended to Several Variables and Utilization of Forms Which Are Nonlinear in the Variables

Earlier we suggested that it might be desirable to consider more variables to explain or predict the variables in question. In the equation,

$$Y = a + bX_1 + CX_2$$

the variable Y depends on the values assigned to X_1 and X_2; therefore, Y is called the dependent variable and X_1 and X_2, the independent variables. In other words, X_1 alone cannot explain how Y varies, but X_2 is also needed to explain this variation. It is conceivable that the relation might be of the following type:

$$Y = a + b \log X_1 + \frac{c}{X_2}$$

We imply that to explain the variation in Y we may have to consider some function of X_1 and X_2 or we might have to raise X_1 and X_2 to a power other than 1. If all the independent variables enter in the equation to the 0 or 1 power, we say that we are employing a linear equation. If the independent variables appear to higher powers or as functions of the variable (such as X^2, $\log X$, $\sin X$, etc.), we are employing a nonlinear equation. Here we have introduced the concept of dependent and independent variables. Another way of expressing the technique of finding the relationship between one variable (the dependent variable) and others (the independent variables) is to say we are regressing one variable on one or several others. That is why we call this a regression program.

When variables appear in a nonlinear form, they may be transformed into an equation in which the variables appear in a linear form; for example,

$$K = be^{aX};$$

taking logarithms of both sides, we obtain

$$\log K = \log b + aX\log e$$

or

$$\log K = \log b + aX\,.$$

In this instance, we have readings on the variables K and X; these will be called the data variables. To obtain the variables which will be used in the normal equations in order to determine the constants of the fitted equation, we employ the logarithmic transformation on the data variable K; one of the constants to be determined will then be $\log b$. To obtain b one may take the antilogarithm of $\log b$. X and $\log K$ are the variables which appear in the normal equations; these variables will be called the regression variables.

When there are two variables involved in the analysis, two constants are to be determined from two normal equations. The method of establishing the normal equations and solving these simultaneous linear equations for more than two variables can be naturally extended to m variables, where $m < n$, the number of readings being n. If there are m independent variables in the analysis, there must be $m+1$ normal equations to be solved for the $m+1$ constants necessary to be specified for the fitted equation.

Not only must the variables which enter the analysis in a nonlinear form be transformed to linear form; the unknown constants must also be in such a form that when a transformation is performed on the variables, the constants which are to be determined must appear in a linear form. For example,

$$Y = bX^{\frac{as}{\log c + s}}$$

with a, b, and c the undetermined constants; (even this type of equation may be handled by the least squares method if one takes a slightly different approach.[1]

8.1.4. General Linear Regression Analysis—Statistical Theory, the Gauss-Markoff Theorem

If X is an mxn ($m \leqslant n$) matrix (the matrix X must be of rank m) of constants, b is a vector of m unknown parameters, and Y is a vector of n random variables,[2] (such that the expected value of Y equals $X^T b$ and the variance of Y is $\sigma^2 I$ (where σ^2 = expected value of $(y_i)^2$ − (expected value of $Y)^2$); then the best estimate of any linear function, $\Lambda = r^T b$, where r is a vector of p elements, is obtained by utilizing the β_i as estimates for the b_i (the elements of the vector b). The β_i are obtained through the minimization of the sum of squares $S = (Y - X^T b)^T (Y - X^T b)$ with respect to each element of b; i.e., b_i. The β_i are obtained by solving the set of m simultaneous equations

$$\beta = \frac{XY}{XX^T}$$

The matrix X is composed of the readings,

$$x_{ij},\ i = \ , \ldots, m, j = \ , \ldots, n$$

The above theorem, attributed to Gauss and Markoff, proves that the least squares estimates of the constants in the regression equation are actually the best estimates in the sense that the variance of the linear function, Λ, is minimized. It can also be shown that

$$S^2 = \frac{(Y - X^T B)^T (Y - X^T \beta)}{n - m}$$

is an unbiased estimate of σ^2 (g is an unbiased estimate of f if the expected value of g equals f), the variance of Y. Other important statistical quantities which may be derived from a least squares analysis will be explained in section 8.1.6 and 8.1.7, the sections involved with the writing of the regression program.

8.1.5. The System Approach

Many practical applications, both business and scientific, not only require an efficient and general program to solve the problem but also must

---

[1] See J. B. Scarborough, *Numerical Mathematical Analysis* (Baltimore: Johns Hopkins Press, 1962).

[2] See Chapter 6 for a definition of a random variable.

be offered to the user in a very simple form and with a short "turnaround" time for a series of related problems.

By a simple form we imply that the input must be of such a nature that the user will have little difficulty filling out forms which go to the key-punching section; the output must be clear and meaningful; the description of the system must be clear and concise. Input-output will be covered in detail in section 8.1.7; the program which calculates the results will be explained in section 8.1.8.

To obtain a fast "turnaround," the system must be able to handle such options as running many problems (i.e., trying different regression equations) with the same set of data. In this case, tape input possesses great advantage over a card input; the data come in on cards and are placed on tape. For each equation, the tape is rewound, so the same data are available for each problem. If only card input were permitted, each problem would either have to be accompanied by a set of data or the operator would be required to intervene in the operation in order to put the data cards in back of the problem control information for each problem.

8.1.6. The System—Explanation

Step 1. Tape units 0 and 3 are rewound. The original data is stored on tape unit 3; the transformed variable which serves as the dependent variable Y for the analysis will be on tape unit 0. If the user specifies a check on the solution, then tape unit 2 is rewound and the matrix of coefficients is then stored on tape unit 2.

Step 2. Two title cards are read. Columns 1 through 70 of the first card and columns 1 through 60 of the second card can be punched with any information the user desires to head the sheet of results. The user must submit two title cards even if less than 70 columns of information are desired. In this case, the second title card would be blank.

Step 3. A control card is read. If column 1 is punched with a 1, the computer assumes that data is on tape unit 3. If column 1 is punched with an 0, it is assumed that data will be given on cards. This provision which allows the analyst to read the data from tape enables an analyst to solve two or more problems, the same set of data being common to all of the problems. Each problem will require its own title card, control cards, and transform card(s). Data are written on tape unit 3 each time the input is from cards. In this way, only the most recent set of data remains on tape 3. A modest change in the program would allow the analyst to save the last 2, 3, etc. sets of data; however, this does not appear to provide great advantages.

Columns 2 and 3 contain the number of independent variables.

Columns 4, 5 and 6 contain number of data sets. A data set is defined to be a set of data values (one value for each data variable in the problem).

Columns 7 and 8 contain the number of data variables.

Column 9 must contain 0 (or blank), 1, 2, or 3. If the column is left blank, then neither the original nor the transformed data will be given in the output. By placing a 1 in column 9, the user specifies that the original data should be given in the output. A 2 in column 9 implies that the transformed data be given in the output. Finally, a 3 in column 9 implies that both types of data be given in the output.

Column 10 must contain either 0 or 1. If it is 0, the differences are not given in the output; if 1, the differences are given in the output.

Column 11 must contain either 0 or 1. If 0, the transformation cards and the transformations are not given in the output; if 1, they are given in the output.

Column 12 must contain either 0 or 1. If 0, the matrix of coefficients, its determinant, the right-hand side of the system of equations, and a check on the solution are not given in the output; if 1, the above items are given in the output.

Step 4. A transformation card is read. If there is a 1 in column 80, the machine assumes that another transformation card follows. The process is repeated until a card without a 1 in column 1 is found.

The following 18 transformations are provided by the program:

(1) $X_i = aX_j + b$
(2) $X_i = aX_j$
(3) $X_i = ae^{bX_j}$
(4) $X_i = a \text{ In}(b\, X_j)$
(5) $X_i = a \log_{10}(bX_j)$
(6) $\hat{X}_i = \hat{X}_i + aX_j^b$
(7) $\hat{X}i = \hat{X}_i \cdot aX_j^b$
(8) $\hat{X}i = \hat{X}_i / aX_j^b$
(9) $X_i = |X_j|$
(10) $X_i = X_j$
(11) $X_i = aX_j^k$
(12) $X_i = X_i + aX_j^k$ ⎫ Where k denotes a
(13) $X_i = X_i \cdot aX_j^k$ ⎬ fixed-point number
(14) $X_i = X_i / aX_j^k$ ⎭
(15) $X_i = \sin(aX_j)$
(16) $X_i = \cos(aX_j)$
(17) $X_i = aX_j$
(18) $X_i = X_j^{a/b}$

X_i (or j) represents any data variable (in this case, i has a range of 1 to 50) or any regression variable (in this case, i has a range of 1 to 30). To specify a data variable, the analyst should prefix the number of the variable i with a plus sign (+). To specify a regression variable, the analyst should prefix the number of the variable i with a negative sign (−). X_i represents any regression variable, but no data variable. The first regression variable, number +01, will be used by the program as the dependent regression variable.

On each transformation card, columns 4 and 5 are provided for specification of the transformation code (01 , . . . , 09). Columns 1 through 3 are provided for specifying the number of the variable which results from the transformation, and columns 6 through 8 are provided for specifying the number of the variable which is to be transformed.

The constants a and b, which are used in some of the transformations, should be specified in columns 9 through 18 and 19 through 28. If these columns are left blank, the program assumes that each constant is equal to 1.

Later in this chapter some entire examples will be presented; at this time consider the following simple example:

The equation to be considered is: $Y = f(X_1, X_2)$ $Y = (5.2+3.6 \log_{10} X_1) +2.51/X_2$.

There are three data variables available; 01, 02, and 03. The first data variable, 01, is to be the dependent regression variable.

The second data variable, 02, is to be the first independent regression variable.

The third data variable, 03, is to be the third data variable, 03.

The following transformation cards are necessary:

Card Columns	*123*	*45*	*6789*	*18*	*19* *28*	*29*
	−01	01	+01			
	−02	05	+02	3.6		
	−02	01	−02		5.2	
	−03	02	+03	2.51	−1.	

One card is needed for construction of the dependent regression variable. It specifies that the dependent regression variable be equal to the first data variable:

$$\text{Dependent regression variable} = 1 * (\text{data variable } \#1)^1.$$

Two cards are needed for construction of the first independent variable (regression variable #2). First, we form $3.6 * \log (\text{data variable } \#2)^1$ and call this regression variable #2; then, we add 5.2 to regression variable #2 to get the desired form for regression variable #2. One card is needed for construction of the second independent regression variable (regression variable #3). This card specifies:

$$\text{Regression variable } \#3 = 2.51 * (\text{data variable } \#3)^{-1}$$

Step 5. Data are read, from tape or from cards, according to the given specifications. The input cards are to be sorted on columns 71 through 79 before being taken to the computer; this allows multiple runs for one customer, and if the computation center keeps track of and assigns the run numbers, multiple runs for many different people can be sorted at one time and run at one time.

Step 6. The required transformations are performed; these are then stored in the matrix XDEP. The first column of this matrix is the dependent variable, column vector Y. The transpose of XDEP is placed in XT; then 1's are placed in the first row of XT. XT is multiplied by the vector Y (equivalent to the first column of XDEP) to obtain the right hand side of the system of equations. 1's are placed in the first column of XDEP (remember Y is still on tape unit 0). The product of the matrices XT and XDEP is now the matrix of coefficients—this is given the name BB, a double-precision matrix.

The product form of BB (the method of calculation and its advantage over other methods of calculating the inverse, are presented along with the program in Appendix I), is calculated, and the subroutine PFORM is used to calculate the vector solution β by using the product form of BB, and the product of X^T and Y.

The difference between the given Y and the calculated Y are given in the output. According to the specifications in the control card, either the original data, the transformed data, or both are given in the output.

If also indicated, the given Y, calculated Y and the difference are given. The estimated variance is calculated by the formula:

$$S^2 = \frac{Y^TY - \beta X^TY}{n - k}$$

where n is the number of data points and k is the number of independent variables 1. The "explained SS" is calculated by the formula

$$\beta^TX^TY - \frac{1}{n}(\Sigma Y)^2$$

and the coefficient of multiple correlation is given by:

$$R^2_{1.2.3\ldots k} = \frac{\beta^TX^TY - \frac{1}{n}(\Sigma Y)^2}{Y^TY - \frac{1}{n}(\Sigma Y)^2}$$

R^2 ranges from 0 to 1; the closer to 1, the better the relation between the dependent variable and the independent variable. A coefficient of .1 implies that the hypothesized relation does not hold.

8.1.7. Input Systems Cards

Title Cards

Any alphameric information in columns 1 to 70;

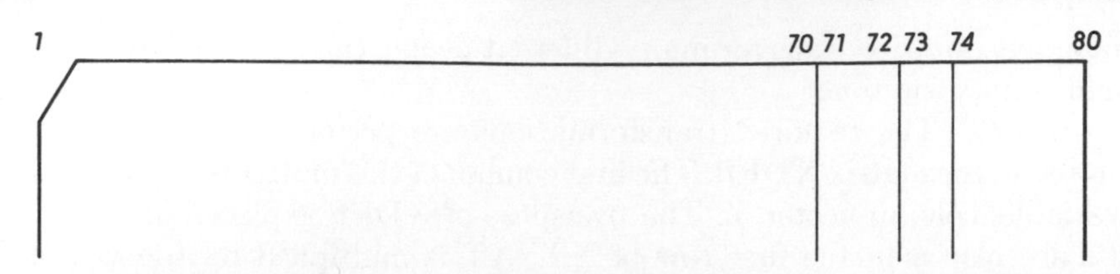

FIG. 8–4. Card 1

Columns

1–70 Alphameric heading information (name of problem, etc.)
71–72 Run number—xx
73 Type of card—1
74–80 Blank

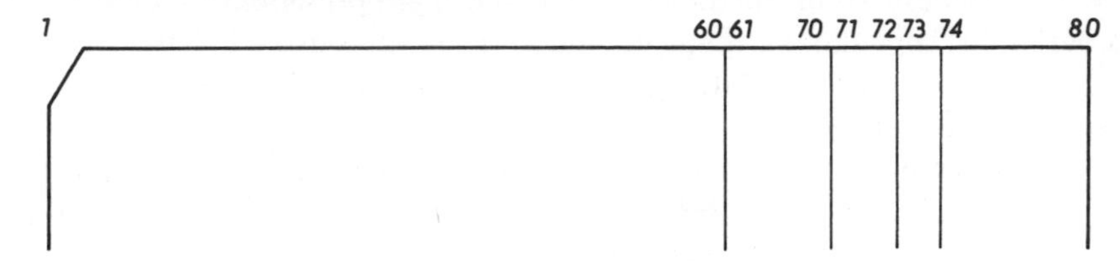

FIG. 8–5. Card 2

Columns

1–60 Alphameric heading information (continued)
61–70 Blank
71–72 Run number—xx (same a number on card 1)
73 Type of card—1
74–80 Blank

Cards 1 and 2 allow 130 consecutive alphameric characters to be used for the problem heading information. There must be two title cards even if less than 70 columns are used; in this case, the second title card will be blank.

Control Card

FIG. 8–6

Columns

1 Code for input; 0 for card; 1 for tape
2–3 Number of independent regression variables—1 to 29.

4–6 Number of data sets
The product of the following two quantities must not exceed 3,000:
(1) Number of independent variables plus 1; and
(2) Number of data sets
7–8 Number of data variables—1 to 60.
9 *Code* for output of data
0 or blank—no output
1—original data
2—transformed data
3—both
10 *Code* for output of differences
0 or blank—no differences are printed
1—actual observations, calculated observations, and the differences are printed
11 *Code* for listing transformation cards and transformations.
0 or blank—no listing
1—output list of the transformations which were used.
12 *Code* for listing the matrix of coefficients, its determinant, the right-hand side of the system of equations, and a check on the solution is printed. This is in addition to the β coefficients which are listed in any case.
0 or blank—no listing
1—output listing of above items
13–70 Blank
71–72 Run number
73 Type of card—2
74–80 Blank

Transform Card (s)

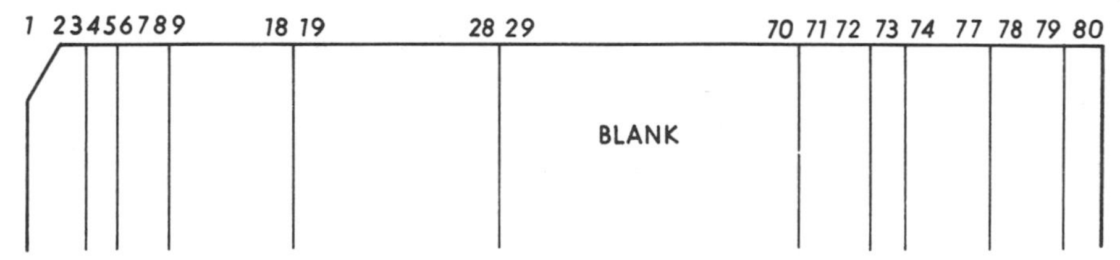

FIG. 8–7

Columns 1–3	Left-hand side
Columns 4–5	Transformation code
Columns 6–8	Right-hand side
Columns 9–18	Constant *a*
Columns 19–28	Constant *b*
Columns 29–70	Blank
Columns 71–72	Run number . . xx

Column 73	Type of card—3
Columns 74–77	Blank
Columns 78–79	Card number—start at 01 and increase by 1 for each line (i.e.; each card).
Column 80;	Signal for end of transform cards; 0 implies no more transformation cards 1 implies that another transformation card follows

A maximum of 200 transformation cards is permitted by the program.

Data Card (s)

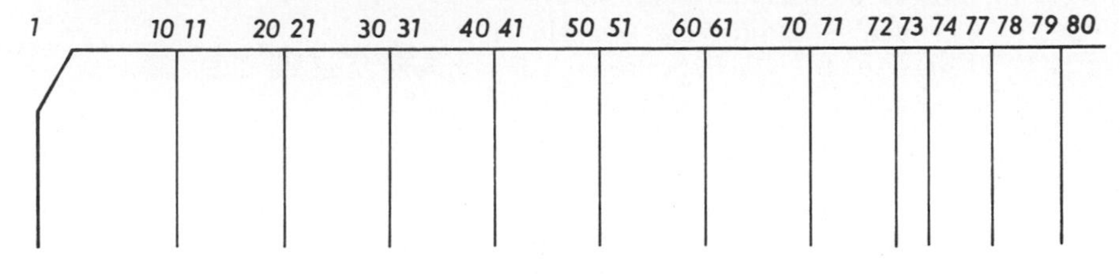

FIG. 8–8

Columns

1–10	Data variable #1
11–20	Data variable #2
21–30	Data variable #3
31–40	Data variable #4
41–50	Data variable #5
51–60	Data variable #6
61–70	Data variable #7
71–72	Run number—xx FORMAT I2
73	Type of card—4
74–77	Number of data set—xxxx; start out at 0001 and increase by 1 for each line (each card)
71–79	Card number—xx; start at 01 and increase by 1 for every card within a data set; that is, if there are 20 data variables, three cards will be needed for each data set—these cards will be numbered 01, 02, and 03. For the next data set, the card numbers should start again at 01.

{Data to be read in under format F10.4} (applies to data variables #3–#5 as bracketed)

8.1.8. Output—Explanation

The output will be in the following order:

Depending on the coding in column 9 of the control card, the user may get the original data, the transformed data, or both. In any case, the output will appear in matrix form.

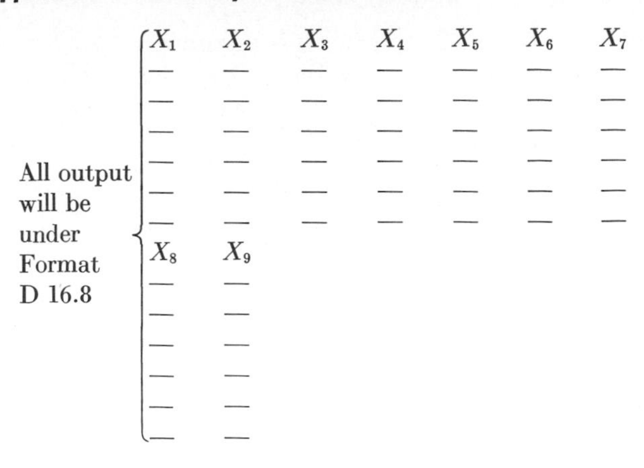

FIG. 8–9

If a second matrix, the transformed data, is requested, it will be printed in the same way immediately following the original data.

The equation to be fitted is of the form $Y = X_\beta + Y$; we have data on X and Y—

$$Y = \begin{bmatrix} y_1 \\ y_2 \\ \cdot \\ \cdot \\ \cdot \\ y_n \end{bmatrix} \quad X = \begin{bmatrix} 1 & x_{21} & x_{31} & \cdots & x_{k1} \\ 1 & x_{22} & x_{32} & \cdots & x_{k2} \\ \cdot & \cdot & \cdot & & \cdot \\ \cdot & \cdot & \cdot & & \cdot \\ \cdot & \cdot & \cdot & & \cdot \\ 1 & x_{2n} & x_{3n} & \cdots & x_{kn} \end{bmatrix} \quad \beta = \begin{bmatrix} \beta_1 \\ \beta_2 \\ \cdot \\ \cdot \\ \cdot \\ \beta_k \end{bmatrix} \quad V = \begin{bmatrix} v_1 \\ v_2 \\ \cdot \\ \cdot \\ \cdot \\ v_n \end{bmatrix}$$

$$\begin{aligned} X_\beta = &(\beta_1 + x_{21}\beta_2 + x_{31}\beta_3 + \ldots + x_{k1}\beta_k) = y_1 \\ &(\beta_1 + x_{22}\beta_2 + x_{32}\beta_3 + \ldots + x_{k2}\beta_k) = y_2 \\ &\quad \cdot \qquad \cdot \qquad \cdot \qquad \cdot \\ &\quad \cdot \qquad \cdot \qquad \cdot \qquad \cdot \\ &\quad \cdot \qquad \cdot \qquad \cdot \qquad \cdot \\ &(\beta_1 + x_{2n}\beta_2 + x_{3n}\beta_3 + \ldots + x_{kn}\beta_k) = y_n \end{aligned}$$

or

$$Y_{\text{calc.}} = \beta'_1 + x_2\beta'_2 + x_3\beta'_3 + \ldots + x_k\beta'_k \tag{1}$$

where

$$\beta_i{}^1 = \begin{bmatrix} \beta_i \\ \beta_i \\ \cdot \\ \cdot \\ \cdot \\ \beta_i \end{bmatrix}$$

Now call the vector β_i^1, β. The vector β is unknown and the vector e represents the random part of the relation. We try to estimate β with the estimate $\tilde{\beta}$, where $\tilde{\beta}$ is calculated by minimizing the sum of the squares of the residuals. The resulting equation is

$$\mathrm{Y} = \mathrm{X}\tilde{\beta} + \mathrm{e}$$

where

$$\tilde{\beta} = (\mathrm{X^T X})^{-1}\mathrm{X^T Y}$$

The vector $\tilde{\beta}$ is printed out in column form,

$$\begin{array}{ll} \beta_1 & \text{———} \\ \beta_2 & \text{———} \\ \cdot & \\ \cdot & \\ \cdot & \\ \beta_k & \text{———} \end{array}$$

These $\tilde{\beta}_i$, $i = 1, \ldots, k$, are then substituted back into equation (1) to obtain the calculated vector $\mathrm{Y_{calc}}$. The residuals e_j, $j = 1, \ldots, n$, are then calculated by subtracting the vector of observations, Y actual, from Y calc. By placing a "1" in column 10 of the control card the user obtains the printout shown in Figure 8–10.

Y Observed	*Y Calculated*	*Residuals*
—	—	—
—	—	—
—	—	—
—	—	—
—	—	—

FIG. 8–10

The variance of β is estimated by

$$\hat{s}^2 = \frac{Y^T Y - \tilde{\beta}^T X^T Y}{n - k}$$

which is the next item to be included in the output, where n is the number of observations and k is the number of independent variables plus one. Sometimes it is advantageous to be able to say which part of the total variation is due to the relation with the independent variables (the explained variation) and which part is due to random variation (the unexplained variation). The total sum of squares is $\Sigma\,(Y - \bar{Y})^2$, where $\bar{Y}$ is the mean of the observations and e_i is the residual in the ith equation. Therefore, the explained sum of squares is $\Sigma\,(Y - \bar{Y})^2 - \Sigma e_i^2$.

The explained sum of squares is calculated by the formula $\tilde{\beta}^T X^T Y - 1/n(\Sigma\, Y)^2$. Finally the multiple correlation coefficient is calculated as

$$R^2 = \frac{\tilde{\beta}^T X^T Y - (1/n)\,(\Sigma Y)^2}{Y^T Y - (1/n)\,(\Sigma Y)^2}$$

An examination of the programs which follows will reveal that only a slight modification is necessary to obtain the partial correlation coefficients and other results, such as the t test and the F test.

Notice that the variance—covariance matrix is $X^T X$; the matrix the reader is asked to calculate in the problem section of Chapter 7.

8.1.9. Operation, Flow Chart, and Listing of Programs

The Regression Analysis System is composed of 10 programs.

1. Main Program
2. Subroutine CNTRL
3. Subroutine OUTPUT
4. Subroutine NUPAGE
5. Subroutine MPY
6. Subroutine MAGNIT
7. Subroutine TRFORM
8. Subroutine TRFOUT
9. Subroutine INV
10. Subroutine PFORM

The main program initializes the subroutine MAGNIT, reads the title cards and the control card. Storage locations are allocated for the necessary arrays, and a check is performed to see if the user is asking for more than the allowable amount of space. The only other purpose of the main program is to CALL the subroutine CNTRL; CNTRL is responsible for logical operations and for calling other subroutines to perform the necessary tasks. CNTRL is separated from the main program to simplify modifications to the system.

SUBROUTINE CNTRL

CNTRL is responsible for reading the transformation cards and the data cards. In conjunction with these cards, including error analysis, all the necessary logical operations are performed in accordance with the options specified by the user. CNTRL utilizes the other eight subroutines for such tasks as output, matrix inversions, matrix multiplication, etc., in order to arrive at the desired results and to list them on the output media.

A discussion of a few features of CNTRL follows:

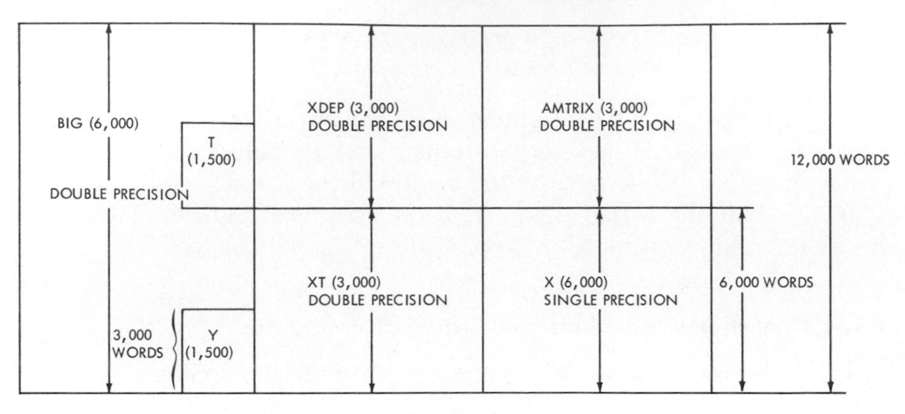

FIG. 8–11

The total core reserved for data is the array BIG—6,000 variables in double precision or 12,000 words (a word corresponds to a single-precision variable). Six thousand words are reserved for the input data; data are read into the single-precision array X.

If the user specifies that the original data should appear in the output, X is changed to double precision and the subroutine OUTPUT is called. Notice that if all the words reserved for X are used, when this array is changed to double precision, it will use all the reserved words for BIG.

XT (1), X (1) and BIG (1) are equivalent, and XDEP (1), AMTRIX (1) and BIG (3001) are equivalent. To avoid destruction of the data stored in X when this array is changed to double precision, a technique is used which is illustrated with the following example:

Suppose we have an array called A, which is dimensioned as A(4) and is a double-precision array. Suppose also that the single-precision array, dimensioned as B(4), is placed into equivalence with A.

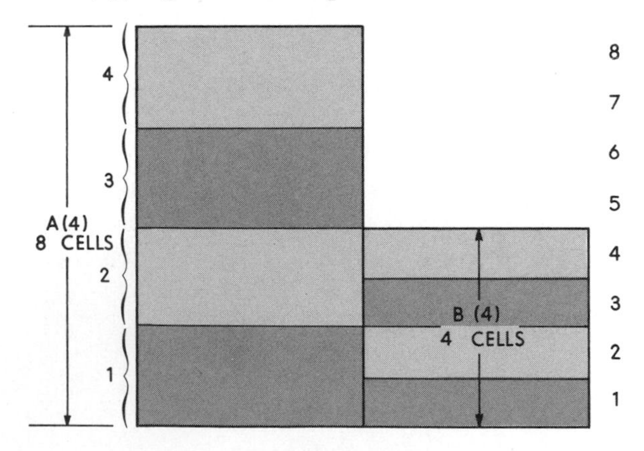

If we start from the highest address of B and change B to double precision, notice that word 4 is transformed to double precision and then occupies cells 8 and 7. After being changed to double precision, word 3 occupies cells 6 and 5, and word 2 occupies cells 4 and 3. At this point, the data in cells 3 and 4 are destroyed, i.e., B(3) and B(4), but these data have already been changed to double precision and moved to cells 5–6 and 7–8. Finally, word 1 will be changed to double precision and occupy cells 1–2.

In general, when the number of words reserved for A is P and number of words reserved for B is N, and if transmission of data starts from the upper part of B to the upper part of A (as in FORTRAN IV), then after transmission of K words the next available address in A is $P-2K$. The next available address in B is $N-K$. Data will be destroyed when $P-2K > N-K$. At the breaking point, $P-2K = N-K$, or $P-N = K$. We are interested in transmitting N words; therefore, setting K equal to N gives $P-N = N$ or $P = 2N$. Thus, in order to transmit N words successfully, it is necessary to reserve twice as many words for the double-precision array as for the single-precision array. This is illustrated in Figure 8–12.

The transformed data are stored in the array XDEP. Because transformations can be performed on previously transformed variables, it is advantageous to keep both the original and transformed data in the computer. After the transformations have been performed, the original data (stored in X) are no longer needed. The transpose of the matrix XDEP is placed back into the matrix XT (in double precision), which destroys the original data because XT was placed in equivalence with X.

The author wishes to point out that it is not necessary to keep a matrix and its transpose in core to obtain their product. For instance consider the following: $B = A^T A$, where

$$A = \begin{bmatrix} a_{11} & a_{12} & a_{13} & a_{14} \\ a_{21} & a_{22} & a_{23} & a_{24} \\ a_{31} & a_{32} & a_{33} & a_{34} \end{bmatrix}$$

B will be a symmetric 4×4 matrix:

$$\begin{bmatrix} b_{11} & b_{12} & b_{13} & b_{14} \\ & b_{22} & b_{23} & b_{24} \\ & & b_{33} & b_{34} \\ & & & b_{44} \end{bmatrix}$$

The sum of the square of the elements in the first column of A will yield b_{11}. The sum of the products of the elements in column 1 of A and column 2 of A will yield b_{12}. The sum of the products of the elements in column 1 and column 3 will yield b_{13} and the sum of the products of column 1 of A column 4 of A will yield b_{14}; b_{22} is obtained by summing the square of the elements in column 2; b_{23} is obtained by summing the product of the elements in columns 2 and 3. The remaining elements are formed in the same way. After the upper triangular part of the product matrix is obtained, it can be copied into the lower triangular part. In order to avoid complications in the subroutine MPY, the above procedure was not followed. When the transposed matrix is obtained and placed in the array X, the subroutine MPY is called to multiply the matrix and its transpose. A parameter in the calling sequence informs the subroutine MPY that the matrix formed by this multiplication will be symmetric; the subroutine MPY will then follow the above procedure resulting in a reduction (of ½) of computation time.

Another feature of these programs is the use of a variable DIMENSION statement to provide for a more general input to the system. The FORTRAN compiler allocates the storage locations for the data via the DIMENSION statement. Analysis of the statement

DIMENSION A (10)

by the compiler, results in allocation of 10 words to the array A; these 10 words will, say, start at address 25 and go through address 34 (if we assume one address number for each word). A reference to A(6) would cause the compiler to generate the address of A(6) as $A + 6 - 1$ where A refers to the location with address 25. Because A was declared to be a one-dimensional array, the compiler will generate the address $A + I - 1$ for any reference to the element A (I).

For a two-dimensional array, say A (100,20), the compiler will reserve 2,000 locations with the first word located at symbolic address A and last word located at symbolic address A + 1,999. A reference to the element A (I,K) will cause the compiler to generate the address.

$$A + 100\,(K-1) + I-1$$

The above procedure causes the two-dimensional array to be stored in core with the first subscript varying faster than the second subscript.

A	$A_{1,1}$
$A+1$	$A_{2,1}$
.	.
.	.
.	.
$A+99$	$A_{100,1}$
	$A_{1,2}$
.	$A_{2,2}$
.	.
.	.
	.
$A+198$	$A_{99,2}$
$A+199$	$A_{100,2}$

$$
\begin{array}{ccc}
 & & \cdot \\
 & & \cdot \\
 & & \cdot \\
\cdot & & A_{1,20} \\
\cdot & & A_{2,20} \\
\cdot & & \cdot \\
 & & \cdot \\
 & & \cdot \\
A + 1999 & \rule{2cm}{0.4pt} & A_{100,20}
\end{array}
$$

Consider the element A(99,2). It is located at A+100 (2−1)+99 or A+198. For this reason the first entry of a DIMENSION statement in the main program must agree with the first entry of a DIMENSION statement of the subroutine; the second entry does not have to agree with its counterpart in the subroutine. The second entry is needed in the main program to reserve the total space necessary for the array.

When a subroutine is called and one of the arguments is an array, a DIMENSION statement is needed in the subroutine only to indicate to the compiler the way in which the elements of the array should be located.

Suppose we have the statements

```
DIMENSION A (10,4)
CALL SSS (A)
```

in the main program and the statements

```
SUBROUTINE SSS (A)
DIMENSION A (10.1)
```

in the subroutine. The DIMENSION statement in the main program reserves 40 locations for the matrix A. If A is given the address 2,000, then positions 2,000 to 2,039 are reserved for the matrix A. When the subroutine SSS is called, the starting address is transmitted to the subroutine; no space is reserved for A at this time. The DIMENSION statement is interpreted by the compiler as a rule through which the location of an element of A is determined. A reference to A (3,4) would generate the address A+10 (4−1)+3−1 or A+32. As location 2,000 had been allocated to A, the address 2,032 is allocated to A (3,4) in the subroutine. If A had been dimensioned as A (8,1), a reference to A(3,4) would have generated the address as 2,000+8 (4−1)+(3−1) or 2,026.

If A had been dimensioned as A(40) in the main program and as A (8,1) in the subroutine (this is allowed in FORTRAN), a reference to A (3,4) would generate the address 2,026 as above even though the DIMENSION statement in the main program is different.

In the regression analysis system demonstrated here, the DIMENSION statement is used to allocate locations for a one-dimensional array. A variable DIMENSION statement is then used in the subroutine CNTRL to instruct the compiler in the generation of storage location addresses for the matrix of input data. This procedure allows the user to have any combination of variables and data points whose product is less than, or equal to, 3,000. Therefore, if the problem involves less variables it can handle more data points per variable; in this way, the memory of the computer is utilized more efficiently.

SUBROUTINE OUTPUT

The purpose of this subroutine is to print in an organized way the matrices involved in a given application. Seven elements per line are printed in FORMAT 7(2XD 16.8). The matrix to be printed must be double precision. The call to this subroutine is

CALL OUTPUT (BIG, M, N, L, J)

where BIG is a double-precision array of DIMENSION BIG (L,J) and the matrix to be printed, which is stored in BIG, is an M by N matrix.

SUBROUTINE NUPAGE

To avoid printing very close to the bottom (or beginning) of a page, or between two pages, NUPAGE acts as a skip control. The call to this subroutine is:

CALL NUPAGE (K),

where K indicates the number of lines just printed. The subroutine keeps track of the number of printed lines by increasing the variable LINE by K, every time the subroutine is called. When LINE reaches 56, a skip to a new page is executed. The variable LINE is in the COMMON block (NUXXXX) and at the beginning of the program is set to 0. After every skip, LINE is set to 0.

SUBROUTINE MPY

This subroutine multiplies a matrix A of size M by N with a matrix B of size N by L and stores the result in a matrix P of size M by L.

The call statement to this subroutine is

CALL MPY (A, B, C, M, N, L, I1, I2, I3, K)

A, B, and C are double-precision arrays. (I1, I2) is the dimension of A in the calling program, (I2, I3) is the dimension of B in the calling program, and C is assumed to be an array of dimension (I1, I3). The size of A is M by N, that of B is N by L, and the product is M by L. K is a variable that is always 1, except when A and B are transpose matrices. In this case K = 2 when calling MPY.

SUBROUTINE MAGNIT

A common mistake in computation occurs when numbers of different order of magnitude are added. In a computer with a precision of four digits, the following operations would yield I instead of 2.3:

$$4364. + 0.1 + 0.9 + 0.3 - 4363$$

MAGNIT guards against this error.

The subroutine is initialized in the main program, where 41 locations are set to 0. Also, in 41 locations the numbers from 10^{20} to 10^{-20} are stored in multiples of 10. If in the previous example MAGNIT had been used to add the five numbers shown, six calls to the subroutine would have been required. The first call, CALL MAGNIT (1,P) where P= 4364, would inspect the order of magnitude of 4364. (10^4 in this case) and would add it to the adjacent cell which originally contained 0.

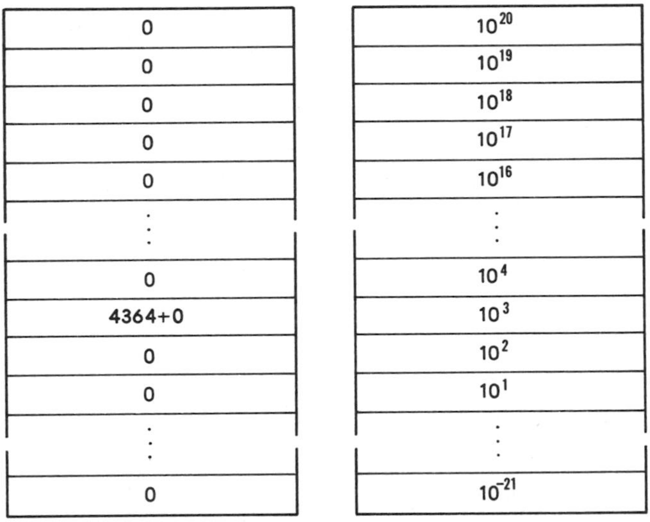

0	10^{20}
0	10^{19}
0	10^{18}
0	10^{17}
0	10^{16}
⋮	⋮
0	10^{4}
4364+0	10^{3}
0	10^{2}
0	10^{1}
⋮	⋮
0	10^{-21}

FIG. 8–13

The second call to MAGNIT:

CALL MAGNIT (1,P) where P= 0.1 checks the magnitude of 0.1 and adds 0.1 to the number in the cell adjacent to 10^{-1}. The magnitude of this result is checked again. In this case 0.1+0 = 0.1 and the magnitude does not change. The next call adds to the cell that contains 0.1 the number 0.9; the resulting number in that cell is now 1. As the magnitude has changed, it is moved to the corresponding cell. The next call places 0.1 in the corresponding cell. The result is as follows:

4634	10^3
0	10^2
0	10^1
1	10^0
0.1	10^{-1}
0	
0	

FIG. 8–14

Now the third call adds the number -4633 to the number in the cell for numbers of order of magnitude 10^3. The result is 1, which is then added to the number in the cell of order of magnitude 10^0. The result is as follows:

0
.
.
.
2
0.1

One more call to MAGNIT is needed, this time with parameter 3:

CALL MAGNIT (3, VALUE)

the numbers are now added from bottom to top, the corresponding cells are reset to 0, and the answer is stored in VALUE. The numbers to be added must be double precision. The answer is a double-precision number.

SUBROUTINE TRFORM

A COMPUTED GO TO is utilized to go to the transformation specified on the transformation card. As a result of this procedure, it is easy to add more transformations as needed.

SUBROUTINE TRFOUT

List the transformations specified and the variables involved in these transformations.

SUBROUTINE INV

The only difference between the subprogram INV as listed in this section and the version written in detail in Appendix I is the change to double precision. This change involves the following statements:

The DOUBLE-PRECISION statement
Statement #3 + 1
Statement #2 + 3

Statement #100
Statement #101
Statement #101 + 1
Statement #103
Statement #103 + 1
Statement #102 + 1

FLOW CHARTS for Programs—Main Program

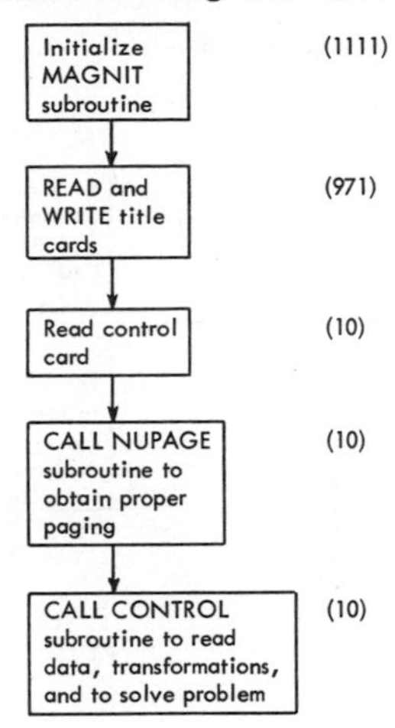
Initialize MAGNIT subroutine
(1111)
READ and WRITE title cards
(971)
Read control card
(10)
CALL NUPAGE subroutine to obtain proper paging
(10)
CALL CONTROL subroutine to read data, transformations, and to solve problem
(10)

SUBROUTINE CNTRL and Remaining Routines Which Perform Operations

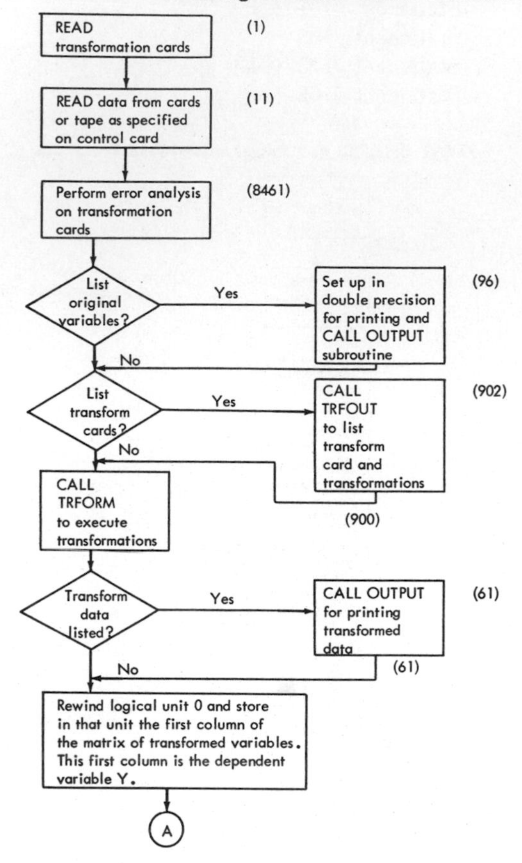

FLOW CHART—*Continued*

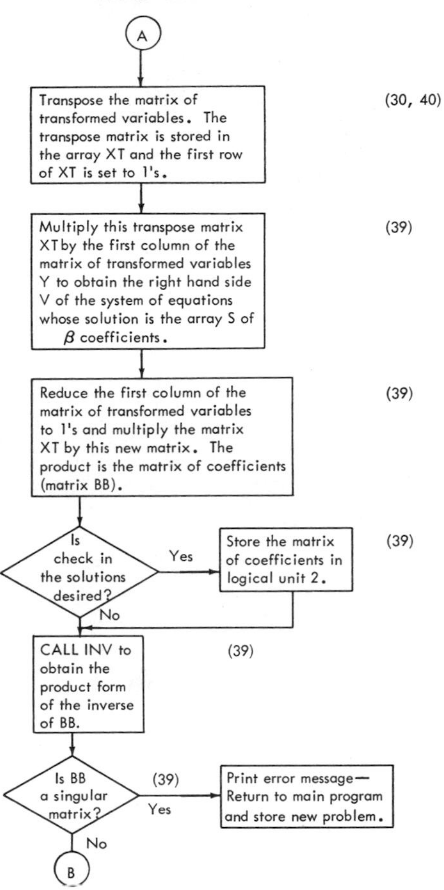
A
Transpose the matrix of transformed variables. The transpose matrix is stored in the array XT and the first row of XT is set to 1's.
(30, 40)
Multiply this transpose matrix XT by the first column of the matrix of transformed variables Y to obtain the right hand side V of the system of equations whose solution is the array S of β coefficients.
(39)
Reduce the first column of the matrix of transformed variables to 1's and multiply the matrix XT by this new matrix. The product is the matrix of coefficients (matrix BB).
(39)
Is check in the solutions desired?
Yes
Store the matrix of coefficients in logical unit 2.
(39)
No
CALL INV to obtain the product form of the inverse of BB.
(39)
Is BB a singular matrix?
(39)
Yes
Print error message— Return to main program and store new problem.
No
B

FLOW CHART—*Continued*

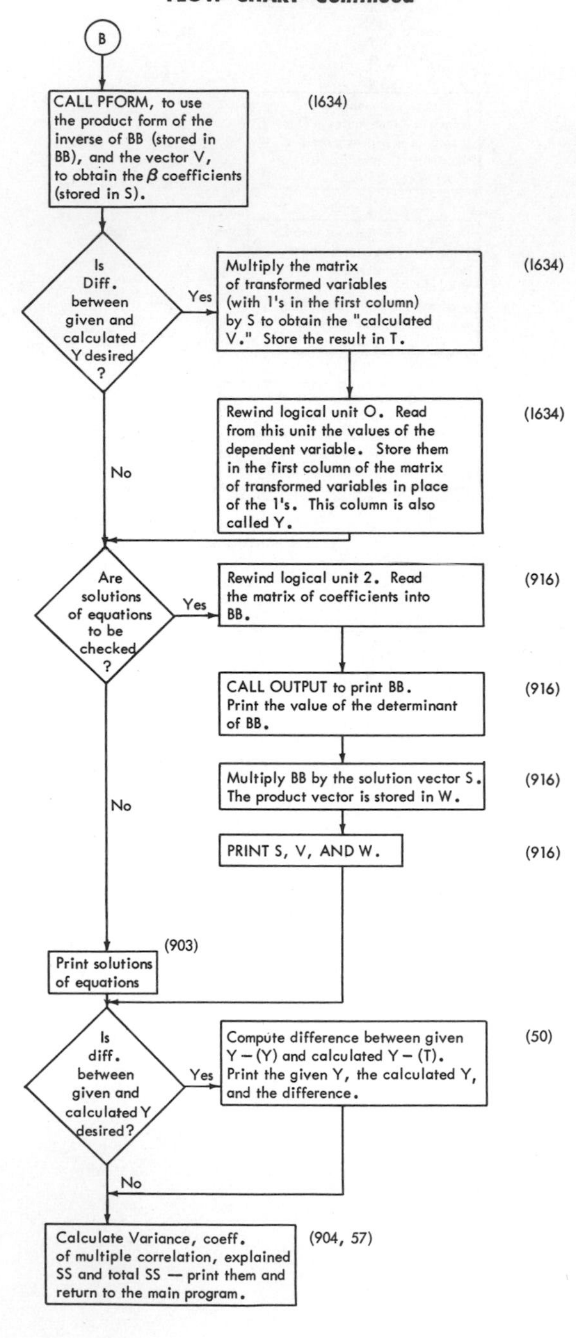
B
CALL PFORM, to use the product form of the inverse of BB (stored in BB), and the vector V, to obtain the β coefficients (stored in S).
(1634)
Is Diff. between given and calculated Y desired ?
Yes
Multiply the matrix of transformed variables (with 1's in the first column) by S to obtain the "calculated V." Store the result in T.
(1634)
Rewind logical unit O. Read from this unit the values of the dependent variable. Store them in the first column of the matrix of transformed variables in place of the 1's. This column is also called Y.
(1634)
No
Are solutions of equations to be checked ?
Yes
Rewind logical unit 2. Read the matrix of coefficients into BB.
(916)
CALL OUTPUT to print BB. Print the value of the determinant of BB.
(916)
Multiply BB by the solution vector S. The product vector is stored in W.
(916)
PRINT S, V, AND W.
(916)
No
Print solutions of equations
(903)
Is diff. between given and calculated Y desired?
Yes
Compute difference between given Y – (Y) and calculated Y – (T). Print the given Y, the calculated Y, and the difference.
(50)
No
Calculate Variance, coeff. of multiple correlation, explained SS and total SS — print them and return to the main program.
(904, 57)

```
C   ---LINEAR ANALYSIS. MAIN PROGRAM
C   ---MAXIMUM NUMBER OF TRANSFORMED VARIABLES IS 30
C   ---MAXIMUM NUMBER OF POINTS PER VARIABLE IS 3000 DIVIDED BY
C   ---THE NUMBER OF TRANSFORMED VARIABLES.
C   ---THE MAXIMUM NUMBER OF GIVEN VARIABLES IS TWICE THAT OF INDEPENDENT
C   ---VARIABLES
C
      DIMENSION X(6000),HEADER(22),PVAR(2)
      DOUBLE PRECISION BIG(6000),XDEP(3000),AMTRIX(3000),XT(3000), Y(1500
     1),T(1500),TEN(41),AAAA(2,41),BB(30,30),DETT
      INTEGER TAPECD,DATAVA,DATAST,CODE,OPTION,TOP,TFM,CHECK
      EQUIVALENCE (X(1),XT(1),BIG(1),T(1)),(AMTRIX(1),XDEP(1),BIG(3001),
     1Y(1))
      COMMON BB,N,LEST,DETT,LEXP,LS,LP(30)
      COMMON /MXXXXX/TEN, AAAA
      COMMON /NUXXXX/LINE
      COMMON /CNXXXX/TAPECD,OPTION,TOP,TFM,CHECK,KARRAY(30)
      DATA PVAR/5HCARDS,4HTAPE/
C
C   ---INITIALIZE SUBROUTINE MAGNIT
C
      DO 1111 J=1,41
      TEN(J)=10.**(21-J)
      AAAA(1,J)=0.
 1111 AAAA(2,J)=0.
C
      LS=1
  971 READ(5,99)HEADER
      REWIND 3
      LINE=0
      DO 17 J=1,30
   17 KARRAY(J)=0
      WRITE(6,107)HEADER
      CALL NUPAGE(5)
C
C   ---TWO HEADER CARDS
```

```
C   ---FIRST HEADER CARD, CC 1-70, SECOND HEADER CARD, CC1-60.
C   ---OUTPUT APPEARS IN ONE LINE.
C   ---TAPECD = 0, DATA ON CARDS. TAPECD = 1, DATA ON TAPE
C   ---N, NUMBER OF TRANSFORMED VARIABLES.
C   ---DATAVA, NUMBER OF POINTS PER VARIABLE
C   ---DATAST, NUMBER OF GIVEN VARIABLES
C   ---OPTION = 0, NEITHER ORIGINAL DATA, NOR TRANSFORMED DATA
C   ---APPEAR IN THE OUTPUT
C   ---OPTION = 1, ORIGINAL DATA APPEARS IN THE OUTPUT.
C   ---OPTION = 2, TRANSFORMED DATA APPEARS IN THE OUTPUT
C   ---OPTION = 3, ORIGINAL AND TRANSFORMED DATA APPEAR IN THE OUTPUT
C   ---TOP EQUAL 1 TO PRINT GIVEN Y, CALCULATED AND ERROR
C   ---TFM = 1, TO PRINT TRANSFORMATIONS
C   ---CHECK = 1, TO CHECK SOLUTION OF EQUATIONS
C
      READ(5,100)TAPECD,N,DATAVA,DATAST,OPTION,TOP,TFM,CHECK
      IF(N*DATAVA.LE.3000.AND.DATAST*DATAVA.LE.6000)GO TO 10
      PRINT 620
      CALL EXIT
   10 IF(CHECK.EQ.1)REWIND 2
      IIXX1=N-1
      LAX=TAPECD+1
      PRINT 973,DATAST,DATAVA,IIXX1,PVAR(LAX)
      CALL NUPAGE(9)
      CALL CNTRL(X,BIG,XDEP,XT,AMTRIX,Y,T,DATAVA,DATAST,N)
      GO TO 971
  620 FORMAT(/98H REQUESTED STORAGE LOCATIONS IN EXCESS OF RESERVED CORE
     1POSITIONS FOR DATA. EXECUTION TERMINATED./38H CONTROL TRANSFERRED
     2TO SYSTEMS MONITOR//)
   99 FORMAT(11A6,A4/10A6)
  100 FORMAT(I1,I2,I3,I2,4I1)
  107 FORMAT(1H1//1X11A6,A4,10A6//)
  973 FORMAT(//27X27HNUMBER OF GIVEN VARIABLES= 14/23X31HNUMBER OF POINT
     1S PER VARIABLE= I4/21X33HNUMBER OF INDEPENDENT VARIABLES=14//58X8
     2HDATA ON A6//)
      END
```

```
      SUBROUTINE  CNTRL(X,BIG,XDEP,XT,AMTRIX,Y,T,DATAVA,DATAST,N)
      INTEGER  DATAVA,DATAST,TAPECD,OPTION,TOP,TFM,CHECK,CODE,T1(200),T2(
     1200),T3(200),Z
      DIMENSION  X(DATAVA,DATAST)
      DOUBLE  PRECISION  BIG(DATAVA,DATAST),XDEP(DATAVA,N),AMTRIX(DATAVA,N
     1),XT(N,DATAVA),Y(DATAVA),T(DATAVA),BB(30,30),V(30),S(30),W(30),VAL
     2UE,RRR1,RRR2,RRR3,XP,XX,TT,EE,TOTAL,ERROR,DETT
      LOGICAL  SSS111,TTT111,ER1,ER2,ER3,ER4,SWITCH
      COMMON  BB,Z,LEST,DETT,LEXP,LS,LP(30)
      COMMON  /NUXXXX/LINE
      COMMON  /CNXXXX/TAPECD,OPTION,TOP,TFM,CHECK,KARRAY(30)
      COMMON  /BXXXXX/A(200),B(200),T1,T2,T3,I
C
      SSS111=OPTION.NE.3
      TTT111=TOP.EQ.1
C
C  ---READ  TRANSFORMATION  CARDS,  MAXIMUM  NUMBER  IS  200
C
      DO  1  J=1,200
      READ  102,T1(J),T2(J)T3(J),A(J),B(J),CODE
    1 IF(CODE.NE.1)GO  TO  2
    2 I=J
C
C  ---DETERMINE  WHETHER  DATA  IS  ON  CARDS  OR  ON  TAPE
C
      IF(TAPECD-1)11,12,11
   11 DO  723  L=1,DATAVA
  723 READ  101,(X(L,J),J=1,DATAST)
      WRITE(3)((X(J,L),L=1,DATAST),J=1,DATAVA)
      GO  TO  8461
   12 READ(3)( (X(J,L),L=1,DATAST),J=1,DATAVA)
C
C  ---CHECK  FOR  ERRORS  IN  TRANSFORMATION  CARDS
C
```

```
8461  SWITCH =.FALSE.
      DO 200 J=1,I
      ASSIGN 2010 TO IISW
      ER1=T1(J).GE.0.OR.(-T1(J) ).GT.N
      ER2=T2(J).LE.0.OR.T2(J).GT.18
      ER3=T3(J).EQ.0.OR.T3(J).GT.DATAST.OR.(-T3(J) ).GT.N
      ER4=ER1.OR.ER2.OR.ER3
      IF(.NOT.ER4)GO TO 2040
      PRINT 205,T1(J),T2(J),T3(J)
      CALL NUPAGE(4)
      SWITCH=.TRUE.
      GO TO 200
2040  IF(T3(J).GE.0)GO TO 2002
      LSUB=-T3(J)
      IF(KARRAY(LSUB) )2002,2003,2002
2003  PRINT 207,T1(J),T2(J),T3(J),T3(J)
      CALL NUPAGE(4)
      SWITCH=.TRUE.
      ASSIGN 200 TO IISW
2002  DO 3000 K=1,6
      IF(T2(J)-K-5-K/4*3)3000,3001,3000
3000  CONTINUE
      GO TO 2001
3001  LSUB=-T1(J)
      IF(KARRAY(LSUB) )2001,2006,2001
2006  PRINT 208,T1(J),T2(J),T3(J),T1(J),T2(J)
      CALL NUPAGE(3)
      SWITCH=.TRUE
      GO TO 200
2001  GO TO IISW,(2010,200)
2010  LSUB=-T1(J)
      KARRAY(LSUB)=LSUB
 200  CONTINUE
      DO 201 J=1,N
      IF(KARRAY(J) )201,202,201
 202  PRINT 206,J
      CALL NUPAGE(2)
      SWITCH =.TRUE.
```

```
  201 CONTINUE
      IF(SWITCH)PRINT 210
      IF(SWITCH)RETURN
C
      IF(OPTION.NE.1.AND.SSS111)GO TO 84
C
C  ---TRANSFORM ORIGINAL DATA TO DOUBLE PRECISION FOR OUTPUT.
C  ---STORE X BACK IN SINGLE PRECISION.
C
      IX1=DATAVA+1
      IX2=DATAST+1
      DO 96 K=1,DATAST
      IYY=IX2-K
      DO 96 J=1,DATAVA
      IXX=IX1-J
   96 BIG(IXX,IYY)=X(IXX,IYY)
      CALL OUTPUT(BIG,DATAVA,DATAST,DATAVA,DATAST,19H ORIGINAL VARIABLES
     1)
      DO 97 K=1,DATAST
      DO 97 J=1,DATAVA
   97 X(J,K)=BIG(J,K)
C
   84 IF(TFM.NE.1)GO TO 900
C
C  ---PRINT TRANSFORMATION CARDS AND OUTPUT TRANSFORMATIONS
C
      IF(LINE+4.GE.56)CALL NUPAGE(-LINE)
      PRINT 8321
      CALL NUPAGE(5)
      DO 902 J=1,I
      PRINT 8322,T1(J),T2(J),T3(J),A(J),B(J)
  902 CALL NUPAGE(1)
      PRINT 8324
      CALL NUPAGE(2)
      CALL TRFOUT(DATAVA)
C
C  ---EXECUTE TRANSFORMATIONS
```

```
  900 CALL TRFORM(X,XDEP,DATAVA,DATAST,N)
C
      IF(OPTION.NE.2.AND.SSS111)GO TO 61
      CALL OUTPUT(XDEP,DATAVA,N,DATAVA,N,22H TRANSFORMED VARIABLES)
C
   61 REWIND 0
      WRITE(0) (Y(J),J=1,DATAVA)
      DO 40 J=1,DATAVA
      DO 40 L=1,N
   40 XT(L,J)=AMTRIX(J,L)
      DO 30 J=1,DATAVA
   30 XT(1,J)=1.0D+00
C  ---OBTAIN RIGHT HAND SIDE OF SYSTEM OF EQUATIONS
      CALL MPY(XT,Y,V,N,DATAVA,1,N,DATAVA,DATAVA,1,30,1,1)
      DO 39 J=1,DATAVA
   39 XDEP(J,1)=1.0D+00
      CALL MPY(XT,AMTRIX,BB,N,DATAVA,N,N,DATAVA,DATAVA,N,30,30,2)
C
C  ---STORE MATRIX OF COEFFICIENTS ON TAPE TO CHECK SOLUTIONS
      IF(CHECK.EQ.1)WRITE(2) ( (BB(J,K),J=1,N),K=1,N)
C
C  ---THE PRODUCT FORM OF THE INVERSE OF BB IS CALCULATED
C
      CALL INV
      IF(LEST.NE.2)GO TO 1634
      PRINT 1000
      PRINT 8686,DETT,LEXP
      RETURN
C
C  ---BETA COEFFICIENTS ARE IN S
C
 1634 CALL PFORM(BB,V,S,N,LP)
      IF(TTT111)CALL MPY(AMTRIX,S,T,DATAVA,N,1,DATAVA,N,30,1,DATAVA,1,1)
      REWIND 0
      READ(0)(Y(J),J=1,DATAVA)
      IF(CHECK.NE.1)GO TO 910
C
C  ---CHECK SOLUTIONS OF EQUATIONS AND PRINT SOLUTIONS, RIGHT HAND SIDE
C  ---AND CHECK
```

```
C
      REWIND 2
      READ(2)((BB(J,K),J=1,N),K=1,N)
      CALL OUTPUT(BB,N,N,30,30,23H MATRIX OF COEFFICIENTS)
      PRINT 8686,DETT,LEXP
      CALL NUPAGE(1)
      CALL MPY(BB,S,W,N,N,1,30,30,30,1,30,1,1)
      IF(LINE+4.GE.56)CALL NUPAGE(-LINE)
      PRINT 970
      CALL NUPAGE(3)
      DO 916 J=1,N
      PRINT 965,S(J),V(J),W(J)
  916 CALL NUPAGE(1)
      GO TO 912
C
C   ...PRINT SOLUTIONS OF EQUATIONS
C
  910 IF(LINE+4.GE.56)CALL NUPAGE(-LINE)
      PRINT 962
      CALL NUPAGE(3)
      DO 903 J=1,N
      PRINT 963,S(J)
  903 CALL NUPAGE(1)
  912 IF(.NOT.TTT111)GO TO 904
      IF(LINE+4.GE.56)CALL NUPAGE(-LINE)
C
C   ...CALCULATE AND OUTPUT DIFFERENCE BETWEEN GIVEN Y AND CALCULATED Y
C
      PRINT 964
      CALL NUPAGE(3)
      DO 50 J=1,DATAVA
      ERROR=Y(J)-T(J)
      PRINT 965,Y(J),T(J),ERROR
   50 CALL NUPAGE(1)
C
  904 CALL MPY(V,S,RRR1,1,N,1,1,30,30,1,1,1,1)
      CALL MPY(Y,Y,RRR2,1,DATAVA,1,1,DATAVA,DATAVA,1,1,1,1)
      XP=DATAVA-N
```

```
      EE=(RRR2-RRR1)/XP
      DO 57 J=1,DATAVA
      VALUE=Y(J)
   57 CALL MAGNIT(1,VALUE)
      CALL MAGNIT(3,RRR3)
      XP=DATAVA
      VALUE=RRR3**2/XP
      XX=RRR1-VALUE
      TT=XX/(RRR2-VALUE)
      TOTAL=EE+XX
      IF(LINE+5.GE.56)CALL NUPAGE(-LINE)
      PRINT 783,EE,XX,TOTAL,TT
      CALL NUPAGE(5)
      RETURN
C
  101 FORMAT(7F10.4)
  102 FORMAT(13,12,13,2F10.4,51X,I1)
  963 FORMAT(D16.8)
  965 FORMAT(3(D16.8,4X) )
  962 FORMAT(//7X4HBETA)
 1000 FORMAT(19H MATRIX IS SINGULAR)
  964 FORMAT(//5X8HOBSERVED11X10HCALCULATED10X10HDIFFERENCE)
 8322 FORMAT(43X1H*314,2E16.8,2H *)
  970 FORMAT(/ /7X4HBET(14X6HVECTOR14X5HCHECK)
 8321 FORMAT(///43X12H************22HTRANSFORMATION   CARDS13H**********
     1***/43X1H*45X1H*)
 8324 FORMAT(43X1H*45X1H*/43X47H****************************************
     1*******)
  783 FORMAT(//17X20H ESTIMATED VARIANCE=D16.8/23X14H EXPLAINED SS=D16.8
     1/16X21HTOTAL SUM OF SQUARES=D16.8/37H COEFFICIENT OF MULTIPLE CORR
     2ELATION=D16.8)
 8686 FORMAT(42H THE DETERMINANT OF THE PREVIOUS MATRIX IS D16. 8,22H TIM
     1ES 10 TO THE POWER15)
  205 FORMAT(/  34H ERROR IN THIS TRANSFORMATION CARD//34X314)
  206 FORMAT(/  21H REGRESSION VARIABLE 13,12H NOT DEFINED)
  207 FORMAT(/4X3I4/16X83HATTEMPT TO EXECUTE A TRANSFORMATION ON A REGRE
     1SSION VARIABLE NOT PREVIOUSLY DEFINED/16XI4,15H IS NOT DEFINED)
  208 FORMAT(/4X314/9H VARIABLEI4,90H HAS NOT BEEN DEFINED. THIS VARIAB
     1LE APPEARS ON THE RIGHT HAND SIDE OF THE TRANSFORMATION 14)
  210 FORMAT(23X11HJOB SKIPPED)
```

```
      SUBROUTINE  TRFORM(XX,XDEP,DATAVA,DATAST,N)
      INTEGER  T1(200),T2(200),T3(200),DATAVA,DATAST,ST1,ST2,ST3
      DIMENSION  XX(DATAVA,DATAST)
      DOUBLE  PRECISION  XDEP(DATAVA,N),X,P,Q
      COMMON  /BXXXXX/A(200),B(200),T1,T2,T3,I
C
      DO  160  J=1,I
      ST1=-T1(J)
      ST2=T2(J)
      ST3=T3(J)
      P=A(J)
      Q=B(J)
      IF(ST3.LT.0)ST3=-ST3
      IF(ST2.EQ.11.OR.ST2.EQ.12.OR.ST2.EQ.13.OR.ST2.EQ.14)K=B(J)
      DO  160  L=1,DATAVA
      IF(T3(J))111,111,113
  111 X=XDEP(L,ST3)
      GO  TO  115
  113 X=XX(L,ST3)
C
  115 GO  TO  (1,2,3,4,5,6,7,8,9,10,11,12,13,14,15,16,17,18),ST2
    1 XDEP(L,ST1)=P*X+Q
      GO  TO  160
    2 XDEP(L,ST1)=P*X**Q
      GO  TO  160
    3 XDEP(L,ST1)=P*DEXP(Q*X)
      GO  TO  160
    4 XDEP(L,ST1)=P*DLOG(Q*X)
      GO  TO  160
    5 XDEP(L,ST1)=P*DLOG10(Q*X)
      GO  TO  160
    6 XDEP(L,ST1)=XDEP(L,ST1)+P*X**Q
      GO  TO  160
    7 XDEP(L,ST1)=XDEP(L,ST1)*P*X**Q
      GO  TO  160
    8 XDEP(L,ST1)=XDEP(L,ST1)/(P*X**Q)
      GO  TO  160
```

```
    9 XDEP(L,ST1)=DABS(X)
      GO TO 160
   10 XDEP(L,ST1)=X
      GO TO 160
   11 XDEP(L,ST1)=P*X**K
      GO TO 160
   12 XDEP(L,ST1)=XDEP(L,ST1)+P*X**K
      GO TO 160
   13 XDEP(L,ST1)=XDEP(L,ST1)*P*X**K
      GO TO 160
   14 XDEP(L,ST1)=XDEP(L,ST1)/(P*X**K)
      GO TO 160
   15 XDEP(L,ST1)=DSIN(P*X)
      GO TO 160
   16 XDEP(L,ST1)=DCOS(P*X)
      GO TO 160
   17 XDEP(L,ST1)=DSQRT(P*X)
      GO TO 160
   18 XDEP(L,ST1)=X**(P/Q)
  160 CONTINUE
      RETURN
      END
      SUBROUTINE TRFOUT(DATAVA)
      INTEGER T1(200),T2(200),T3(200),VAR(2),DATAVA
      COMMON /NUXXXX/LINE
      COMMON /BXXXXX/A(200),B(200),T1,T2,T3,I
      DATA VAR /6HXTRFRM,6HXGIVEN/
C
      IF(LINE+4.GE.56)CALL NUPAGE(-LINE)
      PRINT 99
      CALL NUPAGE(3)
      DO 1111 J=1,I
      LL1=T2(J)
      LL2=T3(J)/IABS(T3(J))+3)/2
      LL3=T1(J)
      LL4=T3(J)
      IF(LL4.LT.0)LL4=-LL4
      IF(LL1.EQ.11.OR.LL1.EQ.12.OR.LL1.EQ.13.OR.LL1.EQ.14)KK=B(J)
      GO TO(1,2,3,4,5,6,7,8,9,10,11,12,13,14,15,16,17,18),LL1
```

```
   1 PRINT  101,LL3,VAR(LL2),LL4,A(J),B(J)
     GO  TO  1111
   2 PRINT  102,LL3,VAR(LL2),LL4,A(J),B(J)
     GO  TO  1111
   3 PRINT  103,LL3,VAR(LL2),LL4,A(J),B(J)
     GO  TO  1111
   4 PRINT  104,LL3,VAR(LL2),LL4,A(J),B(J)
     GO  TO  1111
   5 PRINT  105,LL3,VAR(LL2),LL4,A(J),B(J)
     GO  TO  1111
   6 PRINT  106,LL3,LL3,VAR(LL2),LL4,A(J),B(J)
     GO  TO  1111
   7 PRINT  107,LL3,LL3,VAR(LL2),LL4,A(J),B(J)
     GO  TO  1111
   8 PRINT  108,LL3,LL3,VAR(LL2),LL4,A(J),B(J)
     GO  TO  1111
   9 PRINT  109,LL3,VAR(LL2),LL4
     GO  TO  1111
  10 PRINT  110,LL3,VAR(LL2),LL4
     GO  TO  1111
  11 PRINT  111,LL3,VAR(LL2),LL4,A(J),KK
     GO  TO  1111
  12 PRINT  112,LL3,LL3,VAR(LL2),LL4,A(J),KK
     GO  TO  1111
  13 PRINT  113,LL3,LL3,VAR(LL2),LL4,A(J),KK
     GO  TO  1111
  14 PRINT  114,LL3,LL3,VAR(LL2),LL4,A(J),KK
     GO  TO  1111
  15 PRINT  115,LL3,VAR(LL2),LL4,A(J)
     GO  TO  1111
  16 PRINT  116,LL3,VAR(LL2),LL4,A(J)
     GO  TO  1111
  17 PRINT  117,LL3,VAR(LL2),LL4,A(J)
     GO  TO  1111
  18 PRINT  118,LL3,VAR(LL2),LL4,A(J),B(J)
1111 CALL  NUPAGE(1)
```

```
      PRINT 1117
      CALL NUPAGE(4)
      RETURN
C
   99 FORMAT(//16H TRANSFORMATIONS)
  101 FORMAT(16X9H*  (XTRFRMI3,7H) = A*(A6,I3,3H)+B23X3HA= E16.8, 5X3HB= E
     116.8)
  102 FORMAT(16X9H*  (XTRFRMI3,7H) = A*(A6,I3,4H)**B22X3HA= E16.8, 5X3HB=
     1E16.8)
  103 FORMAT(16X9H*  (XTRFRMI3,13H) = A*EXP(B*(A6,I3,2H))18X3HA= E16.8,5X
     13HB= E16.8)
  104 FORMAT(16X9H*  (XTRFRMI3,12H) = A*LN(B*(A6,I3,2H))19X3HA= E16.8,5X3
     1HB= E16.8)
  105 FORMAT(16X9H*  (XTRFRMI3,15H) = A*LOG10(B*(A6,I3,2H))16X3HA= E16.8,
     15X3HB= E16.8)
  106 FORMAT(16X9H*  (XTRFRMI3,11H) = (XTRFRMI3,5H)+A*(A6,I3,4H)**B10X3HA
     1= E16.8,5X3HB= E16.8)
  107 FORMAT(16X9H*  (XTRFRMI3,11H) = (XTRFRMI3,5H)*A*(A6,I3,4H)**B10X3HA
     1=E16.8,5X3HB= E16.8)
  108 FORMAT(16X9H*  (XTRFRMI3,11H) = (XTRFRMI3,6H)/(A*(A6,I3,5H)**B)8X3H
     1A= E16.8,5X3HB= E16.8)
  109 FORMAT(16X9H*  (XTRFRMI3,9H) = ABS( (A6,13,2H)))
  110 FORMAT(16X9H*  (XTRFRMI3,5H) = (A6,I3,1H))
  111 FORMAT(16X9H*  (XTRFRMI3,7H) = A*(A6,I3,4H)**K22X3HA= E16.8,5X3HK=
     1I8)
  112 FORMAT(16X9H*  (XTRFRMI3,11H) = (XTRFRMI3,5H)+A*(A6,I3,4H)**K10X3HA
     1= E16.8,5X3HK= I8)
  113 FORMAT(16X9H*  (XTRFRMI3,11H) = (XTRFRMI3,5H)*A*(A6,I3,4H)**K10X3HA
     1= E16.8,5X3HK= I8)
  114 FORMAT(16X9H*  (XTRFRMI3,11H) = (XTRFRMI3,6H)/(A*(A6,I3,5H)**K)8X3H
     1A= E16.8,5X3HK= I8)
  115 FORMAT(16X9H*  (XTRFRMI3,11H) = SIN(A*(A6,I3,2H))20X3HA= E16.8)
  116 FORMAT(16X9H*  (XTRFRMI3,11H) = COS(A*(A6,I3,2H))20X3HA= E16.8)
  117 FORMAT(16X9H*  (XTRFRMI3,12H) = SQRT(A*(A6,I3,2H))19X3HA= E16.8)
  118 FORMAT(16X9H*  (XTRFRMI3,5H) = (A6,I3,6H)**A/B22X3HA= E16.8,5X3HB=
     1E16.8)
 1117 FORMAT(16X1H*/16X97H************************************************
     1*************************************************//)
      END
```

```
      SUBROUTINE OUTPUT(ARRAY,N,L,D1,D2,ALPHA)
      DIMENSION ALPHA(4)
      INTEGER D1,D2
      DOUBLE PRECISION ARRAY(D1,D2)
      COMMON /NUXXXX/LINE
C
      IF(LINE+7.GE.56)CALL NUPAGE(-LINE)
      WRITE(6,99)ALPHA
      CALL NUPAGE(6)
      DO 1 LLL=1,L,7
      MMM=LLL+6
      IF(MMM-L)4,4,5
    5 MMM=L
    4 DO 6 J=1,N
      PRINT 100, (ARRAY(J,K),K=LLL,MMM)
    6 CALL  NUPAGE(1)
      PRINT 101
    1 CALL  NUPAGE(1)
      RETURN
C
   99 FORMAT(////4A6/)
  100 FORMAT(7(2XD16.8))
  101 FORMAT(1H )
      END

      SUBROUTINE NUPAGE(K)
      COMMON /NUXXXX/LINE
      LINE=LINE+K
      IF(LINE.GE.56.OR.LINE.EQ.0)GO TO 1
      RETURN
    1 WRITE(6,100)
      LINE=0
      RETURN
  100 FORMAT(1H1)
      END
```

```
      SUBROUTINE  PFORM(A,V,S,N,LP)
      DIMENSION  LP(30)
      DOUBLE  PRECISION  A(30,30),V(30),S(30)P
      DO  10  I=1,N
      LTEMP=LP(I)
   10 S(I)=V(LTEMP)
      DO  11  I=1,N
      L=N-I+1
      P=S(I)
      DO  11  K=1,N
   11 S(K)=S(K)+A(K,L)*P
      RETURN
      END

      SUBROUTINE  MPY(A,B,P,R1,C,C2,D1,D2,D3,D4,D5,D6,LL)
C
C   ---LL=1, TO MULTIPLY TWO MATRICES. LL=2, TO MULTIPLY A MATRIX
C   ---BY ITS TRANSPOSE. ONLY THE UPPER TRIANGULAR PART OF THE PRODUCT
C   ---MATRIX IS CALCULATED
C
      INTEGER  R1,C,C2,D1,D2,D3,D4,D5,D6,Q
      DOUBLE  PRECISION  A(D1,D2),B(D3,D4),P(D5,D6),TP
      Q=1
      DO  6  I=1,R1
      GO  TO(80,90),LL
   90 Q=I
   80 DO  6  J=Q,C2
      DO  5  K=1,C
      TP=A(I,K)*B(K,J)
    5 CALL  MAGNIT(1,TP)
      CALL  MAGNIT(3,TP)
    6 P(I,J)=TP
      GO  TO(100,200),LL
  100 RETURN
  200 DO  7  J=1,C2
      DO  7  K=J,C2
    7 P(K,J)=P(J,K)
      RETURN
      END
```

```
      SUBROUTINE INV
C     IF MATRIX IS SINGULAR, THEN LEST=2.
C     LS=1 TO OBTAIN PRODUCT FORM OF THE INVERSE.
C     DETT HAS THE VALUE OF THE DETERMINANT.
      DOUBLE PRECISION A(30,30),DETT,BIG,BETT,C(30)
      DIMENSION LP(30)
      COMMON A,N,LEST,DETT,LEXP,LS,LP
      NN=N
      DETT=1.
      LEST=1
      M2=1
      LEXP=0
      LP(1)=0
      DO 1 M1=1,N
      BIG=0.
      DO 2 I=1,N
      DO 3 J=1,M2
      IF(I-LP(J))3,2,3
    3 CONTINUE
      IF(DABS(BIG)-DABS(A(I,1)))4,2,2
    4 BIG=A(I,1)
      L1=I
    2 CONTINUE
      DETT=DETT*BIG
      BETT=DABS(DETT)
      IF(BETT-1.0D+2 )100,100,101
  100 IF(BETT-1.0D-20)103,102,102
  101 DETT=DETT/1.0D+20
      LEXP=LEXP+20
      GO TO 102
  103 DETT=DETT/1.0D-20
      LEXP=LEXP-20
  102 M2=M1
      IF(DABS(BIG)-1.0D-06)5,5,6
    5 LEST=2
      RETURN
    6 LP(M1)=L1
      IF(NN-1)50,51,50
```

```
 50   DO 8 I=2,NN
  8   A(L1,I-1)=A(L1,I)/BIG
      IF(L1-1)9,10,9
 10   LN=2
 13   LM=N
      GO TO 15
  9   LM=L1-1
      LN=1
 15   DO 11 I=LN,LM
      C(I)=-A(I,1)
      IF(C(I))12,111,12
111   DO 112 J=2,NN
112   A(I,J-1)=A(I,J)
      GO TO 11
 12   DO 11 J=2,NN
      A(I,J-1)=C(I)*A(L1,J-1)+A(I,J)
 11   CONTINUE
      IF(LN-1)19,18,19
 18   LN=LN+L1
      IF(LN-N)13,13,19
 19   C(L1)=1.
      DO 77 I=1,N
 77   A(I,NN)=C(I)/BIG
  1   NN=NN-LS
 55   DO 34 K=1,N
      DO 16 J=1,N
 16   C(J)=A(J,K)
      DO 34 J=1,N
      L=LP(J)
      IF(K-J)56,34,34
 56   IF(LP(K)-L)34,34,57
 57   DETT=-DETT
 34   A(J,K)=C(L)
      IF(LS)70,71,70
 71   DO 20 J=1,N
      DO 21 K=1,N
 21   C(K)=A(J,K)
      DO 20 K=1,N
      L=LP(K)
 20   A(J,L)=C(K)
      RETURN
```

```
51    A(L1,1)=-1.
      DO 52 I=1,N
52    A(I,1)=-A(I,1)/BIG
      GO TO 55
70    DO 83 I=1,N
      J=N+1-I
83    A(I,J)=A(I,J)-1.
      RETURN
      END

      SUBROUTINE MAGNIT(K,VALUE)
      DOUBLE PRECISION TEN(41),A(2,41),VALUE
      COMMON /MXXXXX/TEN,A
      GO TO(1,1,2,2),K
 2    VALUE=0.
      DO 30 J=1,41
      I=42-J
      VALUE=VALUE+A(K-2,I)
30    A(K-2,I)=0.
      RETURN
 1    DO 3 J=1,41
      IF(DABS(VALUE)-TEN(J))3,4,4
 4    A(K,J)=A(K,J)+VALUE
      I=J
      GO TO 5
 3    CONTINUE
      A(K,41)=A(K,41)+VALUE
 7    IF(DABS(A(K,41))-1.0D-30)15,15,16
15    A(K,41)=0.
16    RETURN
 5    IF(I-1)10,7,10
10    IF(DABS(A(K,I))-TEN(I-1))7,8,8
 8    VALUE=A(K,I)
      A(K,I)=0.
      GO TO 1
      END
```

TRANSFORMED VARIABLES

```
0.19900000D 03    0.21200000D 03
0.20400000D 03    0.21400000D 03
0.21600000D 03    0.23100000D 03
0.21800000D 03    0.23700000D 03
0.22400000D 03    0.24400000D 03
0.23500000D 03    0.25500000D 03
0.23800000D 03    0.25700000D 03
0.25600000D 03    0.27300000D 03
0.26400000D 03    0.28400000D 03
0.27000000D 03    0.29000000D 03
```

MATRIX OF COEFFICIENTS

```
0.10000000D 02    0.24970000D 04
0.24970000D 04    0.63016500D 06
```

THE DETERMINANT OF THE PREVIOUS MATRIX IS 0.66641000D 05 TIMES 10 TO THE POWER 0

BETA	VECTOR	CHECK
0.70513798D 01	0.23240000D 04	0.23240000D 04
0.90247745D 00	0.58631700D 06	0.58631700D 06

OBSERVED	CALCULATED	DIFFERENCE
0.19900000D 03	0.19837660D 03	0.62340001D 00
0.20400000D 03	0.20018155D 03	0.38184451D 01
0.21600000D 03	0.21552367D 03	0.47632839D 00
0.21800000D 03	0.22093854D 03	—0.29385363D 01
0.22400000D 03	0.22725588D 03	—0.32558785D 01
0.23500000D 03	0.23718313D 03	—0.21831305D 01
0.23800000D 03	0.23898809D 03	—0.98808541D 00
0.25600000D 03	0.25342772D 03	0.25722753D 01
0.26400000D 03	0.26335498D 03	0.64502333D 00
0.27000000D 03	0.26876984D 03	0.12301586D 01

8.1.10. Examples

```
INCOME AND CONSUMPTION IN THE UNITED STATES, 1978–1957. EXAMPLE
NUMBER 1. DATA ON CARDS

                    NUMBER OF GIVEN VARIABLES=  2
                NUMBER OF POINTS PER VARIABLE= 10
              NUMBER OF INDEPENDENT VARIABLES=  1
                                                       DATA ON CARDS


ORIGINAL VARIABLES

  0.19900000D 03    0.21200000D 03
  0.20400000D 03    0.21400000D 03
  0.21600000D 03    0.23100000D 03
  0.21800000D 03    0.23700000D 03
  0.22400000D 03    0.24400000D 03
  0.23500000D 03    0.25500000D 03
  0.23800000D 03    0.25700000D 03
  0.25600000D 03    0.27300000D 03
  0.26400000D 03    0.28400000D 03
  0.27000000D 03    0.29000000D 03

        ************TRANSFORMATION CARDS************
        *                                          *
        *        -1  10  1 -0.        -0.          *
        *        -2  10  2 -0.        -0.          *
        ********************************************

TRANSFORMATIONS

              * (XTRFRM   1) = (XGIVEN   1)
              * (XTRFRM   2) = (XGIVEN   2)
              *
              *********************************************
```

```
                 ESTIMATED VARIANCE=   0.60900122D 01
                       EXPLAINED SS=   0.54276799D 04
               TOTAL SUM OF SQUARES=   0.54337699D 04
COEFFICIENT OF MULTIPLE CORRELATION=   0.99110363D 00

EXAMPLE NUMBER 2.  REVERSE PREVIOUS VARIABLES.

                     NUMBER OF GIVEN VARIABLES=  2
                 NUMBER OF POINTS PER VARIABLE= 10
               NUMBER OF INDEPENDENT VARIABLES=  1
                                                   DATA ON TAPE

TRANSFORMED VARIABLES
  0.21200000D 03     0.19900000D 03
  0.21400000D 03     0.20400000D 03
  0.23100000D 03     0.21600000D 03
  0.23700000D 03     0.21800000D 03
  0.24400000D 03     0.22400000D 03
  0.25500000D 03     0.23500000D 03
  0.25700000D 03     0.23800000D 03
  0.27300000D 03     0.25600000D 03
  0.28400000D 03     0.26400000D 03
  0.29000000D 03     0.27000000D 03

BETA
-0.55224235D 01
 0.10982032D 01

                 ESTIMATED VARIANCE=   0.74107899D 01
                       EXPLAINED SS=   0.66048137D 04
               TOTAL SUM OF SQUARES=   0.66122245D 04
COEFFICIENT OF MULTIPLE CORRELATION=   0.99110363D 00
```

```
EXAMPLE NUMBER 3.   BITUMINOUS COAL OUTPUT IN THE UNITED STATES 1841–1910.

                    NUMBER OF GIVEN VARIABLES= 2
                 NUMBER OF POINTS PER VARIABLE= 7
              NUMBER OF INDEPENDENT VARIABLES= 1

                                           DATA ON CARDS


ORIGINAL VARIABLES
    0.18370000D 04   —0.30000000D 01
    0.48680000D 04   —0.20000000D 01
    0.12411000D 05   —0.10000000D 01
    0.32617000D 05   —0.
    0.82770000D 05    0.10000000D 01
    0.14845700D 06    0.20000000D 01
    0.32295800D 06    0.30000000D 01

        ************* TRANSFORMATION CARDS *************
        *                                                *
        *  —1    5    1    0.10000000E 01    0.10000000E 01  *
        *  —2   10    2   —0.               —0.              *
        *                                                *
        **************************************************

TRANSFORMATIONS
              *  (XTRFRM   1) = A*LOG10(B*(XGIVEN   1))        A=    0.10000000E 01      B=    0.10000000E 01
              *  (XTRFRM   2) = (XGIVEN   2)
              *
              ************************************************************************************

TRANSFORMED VARIABLES
    0.32641092D 01     —0.30000000D 01
    0.36873506D 01     —0.20000000D 01
    0.40938068D 01     —0.10000000D 01
    0.45134440D 01     —0.
    0.49178730D 01      0.10000000D 01
    0.51716007D 01      0.20000000D 01
    0.55091460D 01      0.30000000D 01
```

```
MATRIX OF COEFFICIENTS

     0.70000000D 01      0.
     0.                  0.28000000D 02

THE DETERMINANT OF THE PREVIOUS MATRIX IS  0.19600000D 03 TIMES 10  TO THE POWER    0

       BETA               VECTOR               CHECK
   0.44510472D 01     0.31157330D 02      0.31157330D 02
   0.37598847D 00     0.10527677D 02      0.10527677D 02

     OBSERVED           CALCULATED          DIFFERENCE
   0.32641092D 01     0.33230818D 01     -0.58972614D-01
   0.36873506D 01     0.36990702D 01     -0.11719668D-01
   0.40938068D 01     0.40750587D 01      0.18748071D-01
   0.45134440D 01     0.44510472D 01      0.62396843D-01
   0.49178730D 01     0.48270356D 01      0.90837317D-01
   0.51716007D 01     0.52030241D 01     -0.31423425D-01
   0.55091460D 01     0.55790126D 01     -0.69866525D-01

                   ESTIMATED VARIANCE=   0.43960314D-02
                         EXPLAINED SS=   0.39582852D  01
                 TOTAL SUM OF SQUARES=   0.39626812D  01
COEFFICIENT OF MULTIPLE CORRELATION=   0.99447772D  00

LINEAR ANALYSIS. DATA ON CARDS. EXAMPLE NUMBER 1
                                 NUMBER OF GIVEN VARIABLES= 40
                              NUMBER OF POINTS PER VARIABLE= 42
                           NUMBER OF INDEPENDENT VARIABLES= 30

    -4    12   40
VARIABLE  -4 HAS NOT BEEN DEFINED. THIS VARIABLE APPEARS ON THE RIGHT HAND SIDE OF THE TRANSFORMATION  12

    -5    12   -1
              ATTEMPT TO EXECUTE A TRANSFORMATION ON A REGRESSION VARIABLE NOT PREVIOUSLY DEFINED
                -1 IS NOT DEFINED

    -5    12   -1
VARIABLE  -5 HAS NOT BEEN DEFINED. THIS VARIABLE APPEARS ON THE RIGHT HAND SIDE OF THE TRANSFORMATION  12
```

```
    -6    12  -2
                ATTEMPT TO EXECUTE A TRANSFORMATION ON A REGRESSION VARIABLE NOT PREVIOUSLY DEFINED
                  -2 IS NOT DEFINED

    -6    12  -2
VARIABLE   -6 HAS NOT BEEN DEFINED. THIS VARIABLE APPEARS ON THE RIGHT HAND SIDE OF THE TRANSFORMATION  12
    -7    12  -3
                ATTEMPT TO EXECUTE A TRANSFORMATION ON A REGRESSION VARIABLE NOT PREVIOUSLY DEFINED
                  -3 IS NOT DEFINED

    -7    12  -3
VARIABLE   -7 HAS NOT BEEN DEFINED. THIS VARIABLE APPEARS ON THE RIGHT HAND SIDE OF THE TRANSFORMATION  12
    -8    12  -4
                ATTEMPT TO EXECUTE A TRANSFORMATION ON A REGRESSION VARIABLE NOT PREVIOUSLY DEFINED
                  -4 IS NOT DEFINED

    -8    12  -4
VARIABLE   -8 HAS NOT BEEN DEFINED. THIS VARIABLE APPEARS ON THE RIGHT HAND SIDE OF THE TRANSFORMATION  12

   -10    12  12
VARIABLE  -10 HAS NOT BEEN DEFINED. THIS VARIABLE APPEARS ON THE RIGHT HAND SIDE OF THE TRANSFORMATION  12
   -13    12  13
VARIABLE  -13 HAS NOT BEEN DEFINED. THIS VARIABLE APPEARS ON THE RIGHT HAND SIDE OF THE TRANSFORMATION  12
   -14    12  14
VARIABLE  -14 HAS NOT BEEN DEFINED. THIS VARIABLE APPEARS ON THE RIGHT HAND SIDE OF THE TRANSFORMATION  12
   -15    12  15
VARIABLE  -15 HAS NOT BEEN DEFINED. THIS VARIABLE APPEARS ON THE RIGHT HAND SIDE OF THE TRANSFORMATION  12
   -16    12  16
VARIABLE  -16 HAS NOT BEEN DEFINED. THIS VARIABLE APPEARS ON THE RIGHT HAND SIDE OF THE TRANSFORMATION  12
   -17    12  17
VARIABLE  -17 HAS NOT BEEN DEFINED. THIS VARIABLE APPEARS ON THE RIGHT HAND SIDE OF THE TRANSFORMATION  12
   -18    12  18
VARIABLE  -18 HAS NOT BEEN DEFINED. THIS VARIABLE APPEARS ON THE RIGHT HAND SIDE OF THE TRANSFORMATION  12
```

```
    -20     12   20
VARIABLE -20 HAS NOT BEEN DEFINED. THIS VARIABLE APPEARS ON THE RIGHT HAND SIDE OF THE TRANSFORMATION   12
    -21     12   21
VARIABLE -21 HAS NOT BEEN DEFINED. THIS VARIABLE APPEARS ON THE RIGHT HAND SIDE OF THE TRANSFORMATION   12
    -22     12   22
VARIABLE -22 HAS NOT BEEN DEFINED. THIS VARIABLE APPEARS ON THE RIGHT HAND SIDE OF THE TRANSFORMATION   12
    -23     12   23
VARIABLE -23 HAS NOT BEEN DEFINED. THIS VARIABLE APPEARS ON THE RIGHT HAND SIDE OF THE TRANSFORMATION   12
    -24     12   24
VARIABLE -24 HAS NOT BEEN DEFINED. THIS VARIABLE APPEARS ON THE RIGHT HAND SIDE OF THE TRANSFORMATION   12
    -26     12   26
VARIABLE -26 HAS NOT BEEN DEFINED. THIS VARIABLE APPEARS ON THE RIGHT HAND SIDE OF THE TRANSFORMATION   12
    -27     12   27
VARIABLE -27 HAS NOT BEEN DEFINED. THIS VARIABLE APPEARS ON THE RIGHT HAND SIDE OF THE TRANSFORMATION   12
    -28     12   28
VARIABLE -28 HAS NOT BEEN DEFINED. THIS VARIABLE APPEARS ON THE RIGHT HAND SIDE OF THE TRANSFORMATION   12
    -29     12   29
VARIABLE -29 HAS NOT BEEN DEFINED. THIS VARIABLE APPEARS ON THE RIGHT HAND SIDE OF THE TRANSFORMATION   12
    -30     12   30
VARIABLE -30 HAS NOT BEEN DEFINED. THIS VARIABLE APPEARS ON THE RIGHT HAND SIDE OF THE TRANSFORMATION   12
    -11     12   11
VARIABLE -11 HAS NOT BEEN DEFINED. THIS VARIABLE APPEARS ON THE RIGHT HAND SIDE OF THE TRANSFORMATION   12
    -12     12   12
VARIABLE -12 HAS NOT BEEN DEFINED. THIS VARIABLE APPEARS ON THE RIGHT HAND SIDE OF THE TRANSFORMATION   12
    -19     12   19
VARIABLE -19 HAS NOT BEEN DEFINED. THIS VARIABLE APPEARS ON THE RIGHT HAND SIDE OF THE TRANSFORMATION   12
                        JOB SKIPPED
```

NUMBER OF GIVEN VARIABLES= 12
NUMBER OF POINTS PER VARIABLE= 20
NUMBER OF INDEPENDENT VARIABLES= 8

ORIGINAL VARIABLES

```
 0.10000000D 01   0.70000000D 01   0.60000000D 01   0.41000000D 00   0.35200000D 02   0.67100000D 03   0.80000000D 01
 0.60000000D 01   0.30000000D 01   0.20000000D 01   0.10000000D 02   0.31400000D 01   0.27100000D 01   0.70000000D 01
 0.71000000D 01   0.72000000D 01   0.73000000D 01   0.60000000D 01   0.90000000D 01   0.11200000D 03  -0.11000000D 01
 0.61000000D 02   0.81000000D 01   0.11000000D 01   0.21000000D 02   0.61000000D 02   0.31000000D 02   0.41000000D 02
 0.73000000D 02  -0.11500000D 01   0.21000000D 01   0.63000000D 02   0.41000000D 02   0.13610000D 02   0.14110000D 02
 0.60000000D 01  -0.12100000D 01   0.71000000D 01   0.21000000D 02   0.63000000D 02   0.14100000D 02   0.31400000D 01
 0.70000000D 01   0.16110000D 02   0.67100000D 02   0.63000000D 02   0.41000000D 02   0.21000000D 02   0.11000000D 02
 0.80000000D 01   0.72150000D 02   0.53100000D 02   0.41000000D 02   0.30000000D-01   0.70000000D-01   0.60000000D-01
 0.90000000D 01   0.74110000D 02   0.26200000D 02   0.31000000D 02   0.71000000D 02  -0.13000000D 02   0.15000000D 02
 0.10000000D 02   0.13110000D 02   0.11400000D 02  -0.11000000D 02   0.61000000D 02   0.71000000D 02   0.16000000D 02
 0.15000000D 02   0.21600000D 02  -0.11200000D 02   0.12000000D 02   0.13000000D 02   0.16000000D 02   0.61000000D 02
 0.17000000D 02   0.71200000D 02  -0.11600000D 02   0.14000000D 02   0.14000000D 02   0.12000000D 02   0.21000000D 02
 0.23000000D 02   0.14500000D 02  -0.11700000D 02   0.15000000D 02   0.19000000D 02   0.13000000D 02   0.22000000D 02
 0.31400000D 01   0.31100000D 01  -0.11800000D 02   0.19000000D 02   0.21000000D 02   0.21000000D 02   0.15000000D 02
 0.81210000D 02   0.26120000D 02  -0.11900000D 02   0.41000000D 02   0.26000000D 03   0.12000000D 02   0.10000000D 03
 0.16110000D 02   0.71800000D 01  -0.25600000D 02   0.62000000D 02   0.31400000D 01   0.11000000D 02   0.10100000D 03
 0.17210000D 02   0.21140000D 02   0.31400000D 02   0.31000000D 02   0.21500000D 03   0.14000000D 02  -0.10500000D 03
 0.15420000D 02   0.15160000D 02   0.16420000D 03   0.22000000D 02   0.21600000D 03   0.31000000D 02  -0.10600000D 03
 0.16110000D 02   0.11110000D 02   0.73500000D 02   0.63000000D 02   0.21000000D 02   0.42000000D 02  -0.10700000D 03
 0.31120000D 02  -0.15120000D 02   0.41200000D 02   0.81000000D 02   0.21400000D 03   0.16000000D 02  -0.10800000D 03

 0.19000000D 02   0.21000000D 02   0.54000000D 02   0.12000000D 02   0.63000000D 02
 0.53000000D 01   0.61100000D 01   0.72100000D 01   0.14200000D 02   0.61400000D 01
-0.11200000D 01  -0.11300000D 01  -0.11400000D 01   0.71000000D 02   0.15000000D 02
 0.12000000D 02   0.13000000D 02   0.16000000D 02   0.15000000D 02   0.11110000D 02
 0.12210000D 02   0.16200000D 02   0.13100000D 02   0.14000000D 02   0.15220000D 02
 0.27180000D 01   0.31600000D 01   0.22200000D 01   0.15100000D 02  -0.11110000D 02
 0.10000000D 01   0.20000000D 01   0.30000000D 01   0.40000000D 01   0.50000000D 01
 0.11000000D 00   0.15000000D 00   0.13000000D 00   0.17000000D 00   0.16000000D 00
 0.12000000D 02   0.61000000D 02   0.13000000D 02   0.15000000D 02   0.17000000D 02
 0.13000000D 02   0.21000000D 02   0.14000000D 02   0.15000000D 02   0.32000000D 02
 0.14000000D 02   0.11000000D 02  -0.12000000D 02  -0.13000000D 02  -0.14000000D 02
 0.               0.               0.               0.10000000D 00   0.13000000D 00
 0.73000000D 02   0.70000000D 00   0.90000000D 00   0.14000000D 00   0.16000000D 00
 0.14000000D 02   0.71000000D 02  -0.10000000D 00   0.61000000D 00   0.16000000D 02
```

```
 0.13000000D 02   0.11000000D 02  -0.30000000D 00  -0.63000000D 00  -0.63000000D  00
 0.21000000D 02  -0.16000000D 02   0.60000000D 00   0.64000000D 00   0.11000000D  02
 0.16000000D 02   0.13000000D 02  -0.11000000D 00   0.11000000D 02   0.12000000D  02
 0.11000000D 02   0.14000000D 02  -0.12000000D 00   0.12000000D 02   0.10000000D 01
 0.12000000D 02   0.15000000D 02  -0.60000000D 00   0.13000000D 02   0.70000000D 01
-0.50000000D 00   0.12000000D 02  -0.51000000D 00   0.21000000D 02   0.40000000D 01

              ************** TRANSFORMATION  CARDS **************
              *                                                         *
              *  -1    1    1    0.30000000E 01    0.                   *
              *  -1   12    2    0.10000000E 01    0.10000000E 01       *
              *  -1   12    3    0.10000000E 01    0.10000000E 01       *
              *  -2    9   -1    0.10000000E 01    0.10000000E 01       *
              *  -2   12    1    0.10000000E 01    0.10000000E 01       *
              *  -2    9   -2   -0.               -0.                   *
              *  -3    9    4   -0.               -0.                   *
              *  -3   12    5    0.10000000E 01    0.10000000E 01       *
              *  -3   12    6    0.10000000E 01    0.10000000E 01       *
              *  -4    9   -3   -0.               -0.                   *
              *  -4   12    7    0.10000000E 01    0.10000000E 01       *
              *  -5   10    8    0.10000000E 01    0.10000000E 01       *
              *  -6   10    9    0.10000000E 01    0.10000000E 01       *
              *  -7    1   10    0.10000000E 01    0.10000000E 01       *
              *  -7   12   12    0.10000000E 01    0.10000000E 01       *
              *  -8    9   12   -0.               -0.                   *
              *                                                         *
              ***********************************************************

TRANSFORMATIONS
          * (XTRFRM 1) = A*(XGIVEN 1)+B                 A= 0.30000000E 01  B= 0.
          * (XTRFRM 1) = (XTRFRM 1)+A*(XGIVEN 2)**K     A= 0.10000000E 01  K=     1
          * (XTRFRM 1) = (XTRFRM 1)+A*(XGIVEN 3)**K     A= 0.10000000E 01  K=     1
          * (XTRFRM 2) = ABS((XTRFRM 1))
          * (XTRFRM 2) = (XTRFRM 2)+A*(XGIVEN 4)**K     A= 0.10000000E 01  K=     1
          * (XTRFRM 2) = ABS((XTRFRM 2))
          * (XTRFRM 3) = ABS((XGIVEN 4))
          * (XTRFRM 3) = (XTRFRM 3)+A*(XGIVEN 5)**K     A= 0.10000000E 01  K=     1
          * (XTRFRM 3) = (XTRFRM 3)+A*(XGIVEN 6)**K     A= 0.10000000E 01  K=     1
          * (XTRFRM 4) = ABS((XTRFRM 3))
          * (XTRFRM 4) = (XTRFRM 4)+A*(XGIVEN 7)**K     A= 0.10000000E 01  K=     1
          * (XTRFRM 5) = (XGIVEN 8)
```

```
*  (XTRFRM 7) = A*(XGIVEN 10)+B                A= 0.10000000E 01  B= 0.10000000E 01
*  (XTRFRM 7) = (XTRFRM 7)+A*(XGIVEN 12)**K    A= 0.10000000E 01  K=          1
*  (XTRFRM 8) = ABS((XGIVEN 12))
*
**************************************************************************
```

TRANSFORMED VARIABLES

```
0.16000000D 02 0.16410000D 02 0.70661000D 03 0.71461000D 03  0.19000000D 02  0.21000000D 02  0.11800000D 03
0.23000000D 02 0.33000000D 02 0.15850000D 02 0.22850000D 02  0.53000000D 01  0.61100000D 01  0.14350000D 02
0.35800000D 02 0.41800000D 02 0.12700000D 03 0.12590000D 03 -0.11200000D 01 -0.11300000D 01  0.14860000D 02
0.19220000D 03 0.21320000D 03 0.11300000D 03 0.15400000D 03  0.12000000D 02  0.13000000D 02  0.28110000D 02
0.21995000D 03 0.28295000D 03 0.11761000D 03 0.13172000D 03  0.12210000D 02  0.16200000D 02  0.29320000D 02
0.23890000D 02 0.44890000D 02 0.98100000D 02 0.10124000D 03  0.27180000D 01  0.31600000D 01 -0.78900000D 01
0.10421000D 03 0.16721000D 03 0.12500000D 03 0.13600000D 03  0.10000000D 01  0.20000000D 01  0.90000000D 01
0.14925000D 03 0.19025000D 03 0.41100000D 02 0.41160000D 02  0.11000000D 00  0.15000000D 00  0.12900000D 01
0.12731000D 03 0.15831000D 03 0.89000000D 02 0.10400000D 03  0.12000000D 02  0.61000000D 02  0.31000000D 02
0.54510000D 02 0.43510000D 02 0.14300000D 03 0.15900000D 03  0.13000000D 02  0.21000000D 02  0.47000000D 02
0.55400000D 02 0.67400000D 02 0.41000000D 02 0.10200000D 03  0.14000000D 02  0.11000000D 02 -0.25000000D 02
0.11060000D 03 0.12460000D 03 0.40000000D 02 0.61000000D 02  0.              0.              0.11300000D 01
0.71800000D 02 0.86800000D 02 0.47000000D 02 0.69000000D 02  0.73000000D 02  0.70000000D 00  0.20600000D 01
0.73000002D 00 0.19730000D 02 0.61000000D 02 0.76000000D 02  0.14000000D 02  0.71000000D 02  0.16900000D 02
0.25785000D 03 0.29885000D 03 0.31300000D 03 0.41300000D 03  0.13000000D 02  0.11000000D 02  0.69999997D-01
0.29910000D 02 0.91910000D 02 0.76140000D 02 0.17714000D 03  0.21000000D 02 -0.16000000D 02  0.12600000D 02
0.10417000D 03 0.13517000D 03 0.26000000D 03 0.15500000D 03  0.16000000D 02  0.13000000D 02  0.12890000D 02
0.22562000D 03 0.24762000D 03 0.26900000D 03 0.16300000D 03  0.11000000D 02  0.14000000D 02  0.18800000D 01
0.13294000D 03 0.19594000D 03 0.12600000D 03 0.19000000D 02  0.12000000D 02  0.15000000D 02  0.74000000D 01
0.11944000D 03 0.20044000D 03 0.31100000D 03 0.20300000D 03 -0.50000000D 00  0.12000000D 02  0.44900000D 01

0.63000000D 02
0.61400000D 01
0.15000000D 02
0.11110000D 02
0.15220000D 02
0.11110000D 02
```

```
0.50000000D  01
0.16000000D  00
0.17000000D  02
0.32000000D  02
0.14000000D  02
0.13000000D  00
0.16000000D  00
0.16000000D  02
0.63000000D  00
0.11000000D  02
0.12000000D  02
0.10000000D  01
0.70000000D  01
0.40000000D  01
```

MATRIX OF COEFFICIENTS

```
0.20000000D 02  0.26599900D 04  0.31204100D 04  0.31286200D 04  0.24971800D 03  0.27419000D 03  0.31946000D 03
0.26599900D 04  0.50565048D 06  0.43058009D 06  0.41374030D 06  0.29737572D 05  0.33517876D 05  0.30373761D 05
0.31204100D 04  0.43058009D 06  0.96312215D 06  0.92174339D 06  0.38484970D 05  0.46972247D 05  0.10931852D 06
0.31286200D 04  0.41374030D 06  0.92174339D 06  0.95341681D 06  0.41762126D 05  0.44714173D 05  0.11045184D 06
0.24971800D 03  0.29737572D 05  0.38484970D 05  0.41762126D 05  0.78570781D 04  0.33441560D 04  0.45833909D 04
0.27419000D 03  0.33517876D 05  0.46972247D 05  0.44714173D 05  0.33441560D 04  0.11360547D 05  0.73448438D 04
0.31946000D 03  0.30373761D 05  0.10931852D 06  0.11045184D 06  0.45833909D 04  0.73448438D 04  0.20634995D 05
0.24166000D 03  0.20519060D 05  0.65487120D 05  0.67272009D 05  0.31429828D 04  0.49327330D 04  0.10777951D 05

0.24166000D 03
0.20519060D 05
0.65487120D 05
0.67272009D 05
0.31429828D 04
0.49327330D 04
0.10777951D 05
0.68316772D 04
```

```
THE DETERMINANT OF THE PREVIOUS MATRIX IS 0.77552669D 11 TIMES 10 TO THE POWER   20

      BETA                VECTOR               CHECK
-0.15894918D 02     0.20545800D 04     0.20545800D 04
 0.84912579D 00     0.39865462D 06     0.39865462D 06
-0.44923060D-01     0.33920457D 06     0.33920457D 06
 0.47155169D-01     0.32857076D 06     0.32857076D 06
 0.12836756D 00     0.23491184D 05     0.23491184D 05
 0.11132976D 00     0.26724336D 05     0.26724336D 05
 0.40781112D-01     0.24634321D 05     0.24634321D 05
 0.12766235D 00     0.16076740D 05     0.16076740D 05

    OBSERVED            CALCULATED          DIFFERENCE
 0.16000000D 02     0.17625516D 02    -0.16255162D 01
 0.23000000D 02     0.15221327D 02     0.77786734D 01
 0.35800000D 02     0.22081515D 02     0.13718485D 02
 0.19220000D 03     0.17287667D 03     0.19323326D 02
 0.21995000D 03     0.23180273D 03    -0.11852735D 02
 0.23890000D 02     0.24386646D 02    -0.49664644D 00
 0.10421000D 03     0.12824149D 03    -0.24031494D 02
 0.14925000D 03     0.14584969D 03     0.34003142D 01
 0.12731000D 03     0.13120217D 03    -0.38921715D 01
 0.54510000D 02     0.32132830D 02     0.22377170D 02
 0.55400000D 02     0.48093660D 02     0.73063398D 01
 0.11060000D 03     0.91048377D 02     0.19551623D 02
 0.71800000D 02     0.68504721D 02     0.32952792D 01
 0.73000002D 00     0.14135177D 02    -0.13405177D 02
 0.25785000D 03     0.24625718D 03     0.11592821D 02
 0.29910000D 02     0.69913428D 02    -0.40003428D 02
 0.10417000D 03     0.10006926D 03     0.41007451D 01
 0.22562000D 03     0.19314259D 03     0.32477410D 02
 0.13294000D 03     0.15012421D 03    -0.17184205D 02
 0.11944000D 03     0.15187081D 03    -0.32430813D 02

                      ESTIMATED VARIANCE=   0.55416335D 03
                            EXPLAINED SS=   0.10408902D 06
                   TOTAL SUM OF SQUARES=   0.10464319D 06
     COEFFICIENT OF MULTIPLE CORRELATION=   0.93994924D 00
```

8.2. Sorting by Stimulating Four Tape Drives

The second case study program involves the very important concept of sorting under the restraint of being unable to use magnetic tape. We include the restriction on tape not only because the user may not have magnetic tape units on his installation but also to illustrate the very practical process of simulation.

Records are sorted on their key numbers by a two-way merge utilizing four simulated tape drives. A two-way merge operates in the following way:

Block 1

15 48 62 78 80 81

Block 2

10 13 51 64 84 85

The first number in each group is compared, and the lesser of the two numbers is recorded: namely, 10. Then the second number in block 2 is compared with the first number in block 1; again, the number from block 2 is smaller, so it is recorded; i.e., the sequence is now 10,13. The number 15, the first number in block 1, is compared to the first of the remaining numbers in block 2, i.e. 51. Because $15<51$, 15 is the next number to be recorded, the sequence is now 10, 13, 15. The next two numbers to be compared are 48 and 51; this procedure is continued and leads to a final sequence of

10,13,15,48,51,62,64,78,80,81,84,85

If all the records to be sorted can be stored on one tape reel, the first step in the process calls for all records to be read into the computer and broken down into small blocks, say of six records per block. For each block the records may be sorted by some procedure such as that given in the last section of Chapter 6. Then each block is placed on alternate tape units.

At this point the merge routine is called to merge two blocks of six records each; one block resides on tape unit number 1 and the other block residing on tape unit number 2. At the conclusion of one pass of both tape units number 1 and number 2, there will be half as many blocks, each containing 12 records except, perhaps, for the last block. These blocks again will be placed on the two remaining tape units in the same alternate way. The first two tape units are then rewound, and the process continues until the records are in ascending order by key number.

8.2.1. Sorting Program

The entire program was written in three parts—the main program—SORT—primarily involving input and output, and two subprograms:

1. MERGE—a subprogram that merges two lists of numbers into two other lists, importing the maximum order possible while looking only at the top number of each list at any one time.
2. TAPE—a subprogram for simulating a system of four tapes and eliminating the need for four fully dimensioned arrays.

All programs were written in FORTRAN II using variable word length. A machine of this type is the IBM 1620 computer; here an alphameric character is coded as two numeric digits. The word length could be varied from 2 to 28 decimal digits.

Information being sorted consists of two parts: a key word or number and the information that goes along with it. In the merging program, the key consists of a 4-digit number; the information consists of 12 alphameric characters stored as 24 numeric digits in positions 5–28 of the 28-digit word; thus as the words are sorted by the key number, the information is carried along—if two items have the same key number, they will be arranged in alphabetical order. If items are to be sorted in alphabetical order, all the key numbers should be the same. For format of input data see Comments to the SORT program.

The capacity of the program is 950, 28-digit words.

8.2.2. Subroutine Tape (Simulation)

This subroutine is designed to simulate a system of 4 tapes with a total maximum of 30 (can be∼40) records. Each record contains 25 30-digit words. The records may be divided between the tapes or all records may be devoted to one tape. Extension to a system of more tapes—say, 11 for radix sorting—can be accomplished by changing a digit in the dimension statement. The system can do the following operations:

1. Read a record
2. Read a record and clear that position
3. Write a record
4. Back space
5. Rewind
6. Rewind & clear entire tape
7. Rewind & clear all tapes (initialize)

As a record is cleared, it is free to be written on as part of the same or another tape.

The CALL statement is of the following form:

CALL TAPE (B, I, J)

where

A—25 digit record
I—TAPE NUMBER (1→4)
J—OPERATION (1→7)

TAPE uses the following arrays and variables

A (25,30)—30 records of 25 words each

B (25)—transfer array

INDEX (4,30)

INDEX (i,j) is the location in A of the jth record on tape i

if 0, then the record is not written

IOPEN (30)

IOPEN (i) contains:

i = NEXT – next unused record

i > NEXT – other available records

i < NEXT – No meaningful information

8.2.2.–A. Tape Flow Chart

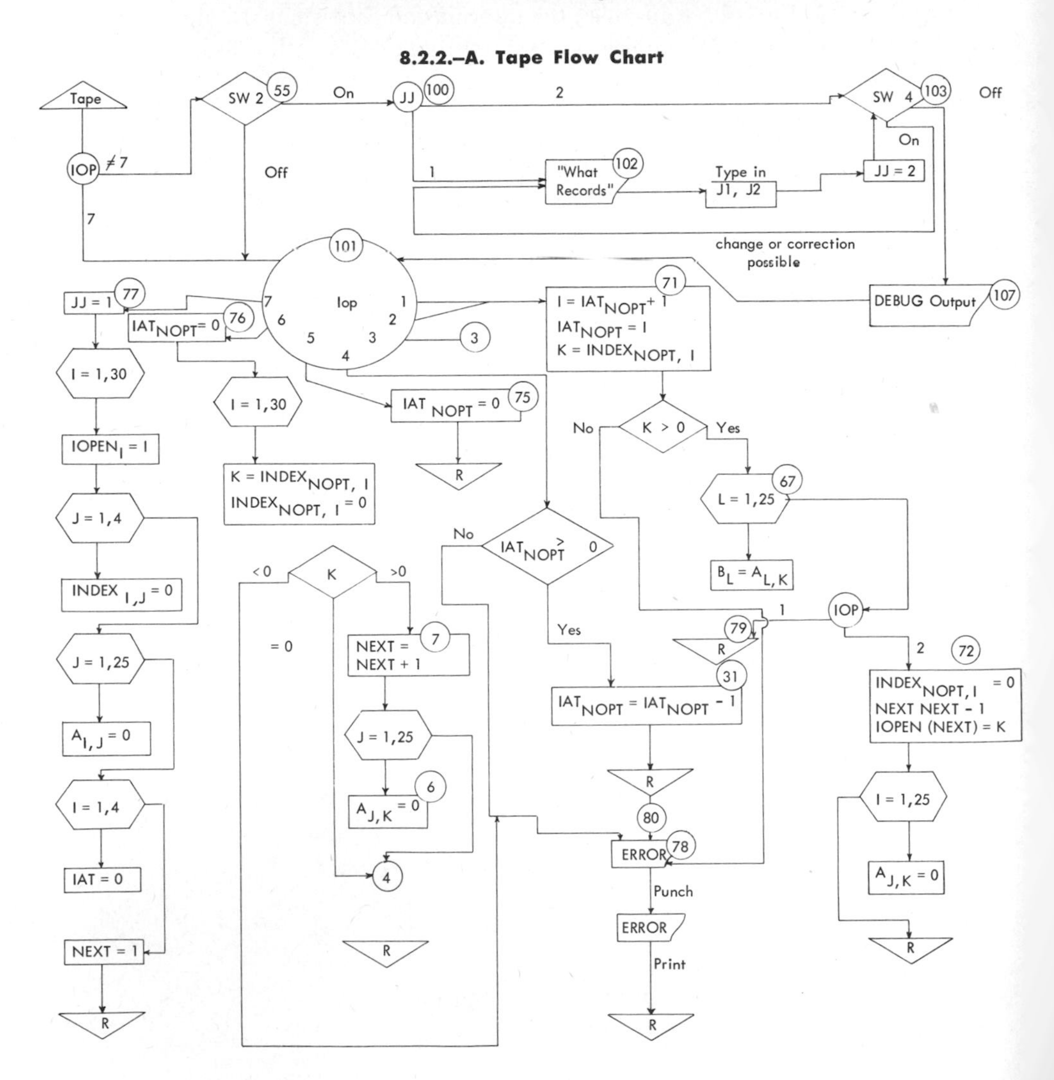

NEXT—See IOPEN above

NEXT is changed as a tape is written or cleared

IAT (4) tape i is at IAT (i)

IAT (i) = 0 if tape i is clear:

Note: Using SW2 and SW4, the tape routine can punch out all or some of its records; thus it can be used as a debugging tool.

8.22—A Tape Flow Chart—*Continued*

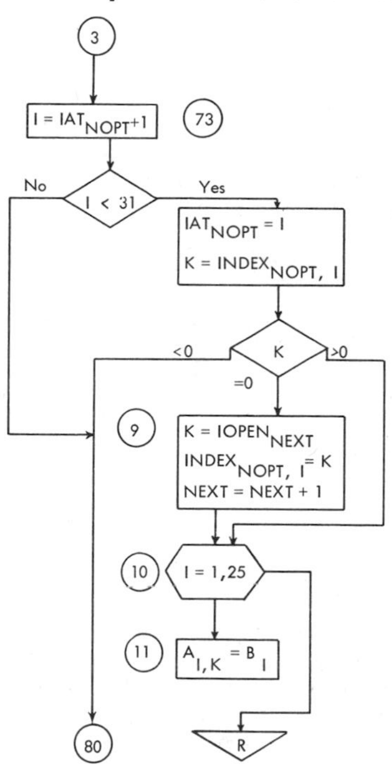

8.2.2.–B. Subroutine Tape—Program

```
*2805
      SUBROUTINE TAPE(B,NOPT,IOP)
      DIMENSION A(25,30),B(25),INDEX(4,30),IOPEN(30),IAT(4)
  108 FORMAT(5H TAPE,I2,5H   OP,I2,7H   NEXT,I3,5H   AT,4I3/25I3/1HI,26X
     1,5I3//4(25I3/1HI,26X,5I3/)/(7H RECORD,I3,25X,25X,E12.5/1HI,23X,4E1      DEBUG output format
     22.5/6E12.5/1HI,23X,4E12.5/6E12.5/1HI,23X,4E12.5))
      GO TO(55,55,55,55,55,55,101),IOP     if IOP = 7 NO DEBUG output allowed (due to undefined
   55 IF(SENSE SWITCH 2)100,101             variables)
  100 GO TO(102,103),JJ                     DEBUG?
  102 PRINT 105                             Have debug parameters been entered JJ = 1 NO
                                                                               JJ = 2 YES
  105 FORMAT(18HWHAT RECORDS (2I2))         Print, Request for debug parameters—"WHAT RECORDS 2(I2)"
      ACCEPT 104,J1,J2     DEBUG punches records J1 to J2
  104 FORMAT(2I2)
      JJ=2                              DEBUG parameters defined
  103 IF(SENSE SWITCH 4)102,107         Change debug parameters? SW4 on—YES
                                                                 SW4 off—NO
  107 PUNCH 108,NOPT,IOP,NEXT,IAT,IOPEN,((INDEX(I,J),J=1,30),I=1,4),B,
     1(J,(A(I,J),I=1,25),J=J1,J2)                                          DEBUG output
  101 GO TO (71,71,73,74,75,76,77),IOP
   77 DO 1 I=1,30
      IOPEN(I)=I                        What operation?
      DO 2 J=1,4                        —CLEAR ALL TAPES—
    2 INDEX(J,I)=0                      DEBUG parameters have to be reentered with each clearing of all records
      DO 1 J=1,25                       All records open
    1 A(J,I)=0.                         Do 4 tapes
      JJ=1                              All tapes clear
                                        Clear all words
      DO 3 I=1,4  }    All tapes at 0th record
    3 IAT(I)=0    }    Next open record is the 1st record in IOPEN
      NEXT=1
```

```
      RETURN                    REWIND & CLEAR one tape
76    IAT(NOPT)=0               Put tape at 0th record
      DO 4 I=1,30
      K=INDEX(NOPT,I)           All records
      INDEX(NOPT,I)=0           Location of Ith record
      IF(K)78,4,5               Ith record removed
                                If K=0 - record does not exist in the 1st place
5     NEXT=NEXT-1               K > 0 - return this record to the stack of open records (to IOPEN)
      IOPEN(NEXT)=K
      DO 6 J=1,25             }
6     A(J,K)=0.               }   Clear the record
4     CONTINUE
      RETURN
75    IAT(NOPT)=0          REWIND—Don't clear
      RETURN               Put tape at 0th record
74    IF(IAT(NOPT))78,78,31     BACK SPACE
31    IAT(NOPT)=IAT(NOPT)-1     Is tape at the 0th record? if YES—ERROR
      RETURN                    BACK SPACE
71    I=IAT(NOPT)+1                          READ OR READ & CLEAR
      IAT(NOPT)=I          I = NEXT RECORD
      K=INDEX(NOPT,I)      Advance tape 1 record
      IF(K)78,78,67        K = location in A of the record
67    DO 7 L=1,25     }    K = 0 the record does not exist
7     B(L)=A(L,K)     }          Put the record into B
      GO TO (79,72),IOP     READ ONLY—RETURN
72    INDEX(NOPT,I)=0      READ & CLEAR
                           Set nonexistant record indicator
      NEXT=NEXT-1     }    Returns its position to IOPEN
      IOPEN(NEXT)=K   }
      DO 8 I=1,25     }
8     A(I,K)=0.       }    Clear to zero
```

```
/9 RETURN                 WRITE
73 I=IAT(NOPT)+1          Next location on tape
   IF(I-31)33,78,78       At end of tape yet?
33 IAT(NOPT)=I            Advance tape
   K=INDEX(NOPT,I)        K = location in storage of the record if K ≠ 0  { old record will be
                                                                           cleared out by
   IF(K)78,9,10           K = 0, record does not exist                      new record
 9 K=IOPEN(NEXT)          Next available record
   INDEX(NOPT,I)=K        Record the location in the index
   NEXT=NEXT+1            Advance next
10 DO 11 I=1,25    }
11 A(I,K)=B(I)     }      WRITE the information
   RETURN
78 PUNCH 69               ERROR ROUTINE
   RPINT 69
69 FORMAT(14H ERROR IN TAPE)
   RETURN
   END
```

8.2.3. Program to Test Subroutine

```
*2805
    DIMENSION B(25)
  1 READ2,ITP,IOP,(B(I),I=1,25)
    PUNCH 3,ITP,IOP,(B(I),I=1,25)
    CALL TAPE(B,ITP,IOP)
    PUNCH 4,ITP,IOP,(B(I),I=1,25)
    GO TO 1
  2 FORMAT(2I2/16F5.2/9F5.2)
  3 FORMAT(1H),2I5/(5F10.2))
  4 FORMAT(////2I5/(5F10.2))
    END
```

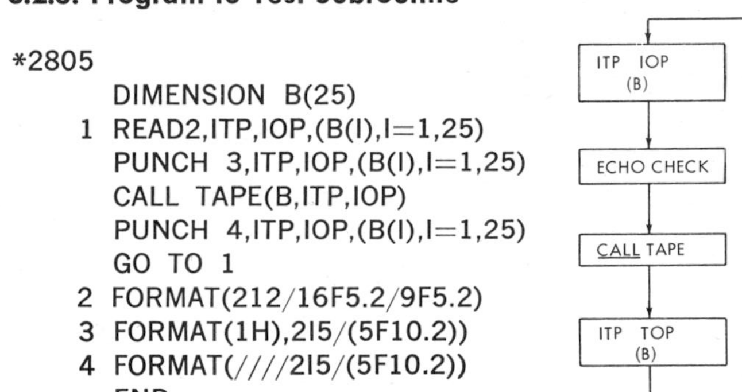

Output of Tape in Debug Made—Records 1–20 Requested

```
TAPE 1    OP 1    NEXT 17    AT  2  0 15  1
 1  2  3  4  5  6  7  8  9 10 11 12 13 11  1 12  2 18 19 20 21 22 23 24 25 26 27 28 29 30 — IOPEN

 8 15  9  5 11  6 17 10 14 16 13  7  3  4  1 12  0  0  0  0  0  0  0  0  0  0  0  0  0  0 — INDEX (1, - )
 0  0  0  0  0  0  0  0  0  0  0  0  0  0  0  0  0  0  0  0  0  0  0  0  0  0  0  0  0  0
 0  0  0  0  0  0  0  0  0  0  0  0  0  0  0  0  0  0  0  0  0  0  0  0  0  0  0  0  0  0   CLEANED BY READING
 0  0  0  0  0  0  0  0  0  0  0  0  0  0  0  0  0  0  0  0  0  0  0  0  0  0  0  0  0  0   BUT NOT REWOUND

RECORD  0                                                            3.44962E-01 3.47176E-01 4.16244E-01 4.50044E-01 4.75152E-01
-9.99858E+03-9.99858E+03-9.99858E+03-9.99858E+03-9.99857E+03-9.99856E+03-9.99855E+03-9.99855E+03-9.99854E+03-9.99854E+03
-9.99854E+03-9.99854E+03-9.99854E+03-9.99854E+03-9.99854E+03-9.99854E+03-9.99853E+03-9.99853E+03-9.99853E+03-9.99852E+03
RECORD  1                                                            6.32594E+02 6.33624E+02 6.34444E+02 6.35634E+02 6.36455E+02
6.37634E+02 6.38494E+02 6.39634E+02 6.40484E+02 6.41664E+02 6.42645E+02 6.43634E+02 6.45470E+02 6.46435E+02 6.47555E+02
6.48435E+02 6.49664E+02 6.50624E+02 6.51456E+02 6.52416E+02 6.53576E+02 6.56624E+02 6.57556E+02 6.58564E+02 6.59564E+02
RECORD  2                                                            0.00000E-99 0.00000E-99 0.00000E-99 0.00000E-99 0.00000E-99
0.00000E-99 0.00000E-99 0.00000E-99 0.00000E-99 0.00000E-99 0.00000E-99 0.00000E-99 0.00000E-99 0.00000E-99 0.00000E-99
0.00000E-99 0.00000E-99 0.00000E-99 0.00000E-99 0.00000E-99 0.00000E-99 0.00000E-99 0.00000E-99 0.00000E-99 0.00000E-99
RECORD  3                                                           -5.52000E+02-5.44000E+02-5.36000E+02-5.28000E+02-5.20000E+02
-5.12000E+02-5.04000E+02-4.96000E+02-4.88000E+02-4.80000E+02-4.72000E+02-4.64000E+02-4.56000E+02-4.48000E+02-4.40000E+02
-4.32000E+02-4.24000E+02-4.16000E+02-4.08000E+02-4.00000E+02 6.02646E+02 6.03634E+02 6.04494E+02 6.05466E+02 6.06564E+02
RECORD  4                                                            6.07575E+02 6.08634E+02 6.09576E+02 6.10555E+02 6.11630E+02
6.12646E+02 6.13416E+02 6.14494E+02 6.15455E+02 6.16484E+02 6.17415E+02 6.18424E+02 6.19465E+02 6.20004E+02 6.21634E+02
6.22416E+02 6.23664E+02 6.24634E+02 6.25634E+02 6.26494E+02 6.27414E+02 6.28645E+02 6.29554E+02 6.30664E+02 6.31454E+02
RECORD  5                                                           -9.99844E+03-9.99844E+03-9.99843E+03-9.99843E+03-9.99843E+03
-9.99843E+03-9.99843E+03-9.99843E+03-9.99843E+03-9.99843E+03-9.99843E+03-9.99843E+03-9.99842E+03-9.99842E+03-9.99842E+03
-9.99842E+03-9.99840E+03-9.99840E+03-9.99840E+03-9.99840E+03-9.99840E+03-9.99840E+03-9.99840E+03-9.99840E+03-9.99840E+03
RECORD  6                                                           -9.99454E+03-9.99396E+03-9.99258E+03-9.99136E+03-9.99065E+03
-9.98936E+03-9.98844E+03-9.98735E+03-9.98446E+03-9.98340E+03-9.98165E+03-9.98042E+03-9.97936E+03-9.97840E+03-9.97753E+03
-9.97665E+03-9.97540E+03-9.97443E+03-9.97351E+03-9.97244E+03-9.97142E+03-9.97065E+03-9.96952E+03-9.96843E+03-9.96736E+03
RECORD  7                                                           -7.60000E+02-7.52000E+02-7.44000E+02-7.36000E+02-7.28000E+02
-7.20000E+02-7.12000E+02-7.04000E+02-6.96000E+02-6.88000E+02-6.80000E+02-6.72000E+02-6.64000E+02-6.48000E+02-6.40000E+02
-6.32000E+02-6.24000E+02-6.16000E+02-6.08000E+02-6.00000E+02-5.92000E+02-5.84000E+02-5.76000E+02-5.68000E+02-5.60000E+02
RECORD  8                                                           -9.99896E+03-9.99865E+03-9.99865E+03-9.99865E+03-9.99865E+03
-9.99865E+03-9.99865E+03-9.99865E+03-9.99865E+03-9.99865E+03-9.99865E+03-9.99865E+03-9.99865E+03-9.99865E+03-9.99865E+03
-9.99865E+03-9.99865E+03-9.99865E+03-9.99865E+03-9.99865E+03-9.99865E+03-9.99858E+03-9.99858E+03-9.99858E+03-9.99858E+03
RECORD  9                                                           -9.99852E+03-9.99851E+03-9.99851E+03-9.99851E+03-9.99851E+03
-9.99851E+03-9.99851E+03-9.99850E+03-9.99850E+03-9.99850E+03-9.99848E+03-9.99846E+03-9.99846E+03-9.99846E+03-9.99845E+03
-9.99845E+03-9.99845E+03-9.99844E+03-9.99844E+03-9.99844E+03-9.99844E+03-9.99844E+03-9.99844E+03-9.99844E+03-9.99844E+03
RECORD 10                                                           -9.94037E+03-9.93965E+03-9.93865E+03-9.93758E+03-9.93635E+03
-9.93532E+03-9.93444E+03-9.93365E+03-9.93254E+03-9.93144E+03-9.93065E+03-9.92936E+03-9.92843E+03-9.92743E+03-9.92633E+03
-9.92526E+03-9.92465E+03-9.92365E+03-9.92243E+03-9.92158E+03-9.92043E+03-9.91944E+03-9.91865E+03-9.91758E+03-9.91640E+03
RECORD 11                                                           -9.99837E+03-9.99837E+03-9.99837E+03-9.99837E+03-9.99836E+03
-9.99836E+03-9.99836E+03-9.99836E+03-9.99836E+03-9.99836E+03-9.99836E+03-9.99836E+03-9.99836E+03-9.99836E+03-9.99835E+03
-9.99835E+03-9.99835E+03-9.99835E+03-9.99835E+03-9.99834E+03-9.99833E+03-9.99832E+03-9.99826E+03-9.99826E+03-9.99565E+03
RECORD 12                                                            6.60575E+02 6.61634E+02 6.62554E+02 6.63595E+02 6.64004E+02
6.66495E+02 6.38494E+02 6.39634E+02 6.40484E+02 6.41664E+02 6.42645E+02 6.43634E+02 6.45470E+02 6.46435E+02 6.47555E+02
6.48435E+02 6.49664E+02 6.50624E+02 6.51456E+02 6.52416E+02 6.53576E+02 6.56624E+02 6.57556E+02 6.58564E+02 6.59564E+02
RECORD 13                                                           -9.60000E+02-9.52000E+02-9.44000E+02-9.36000E+02-9.28000E+02
-9.20000E+02-9.12000E+02-9.04000E+02-8.96000E+02-8.88000E+02-8.80000E+02-8.72000E+02-8.64000E+02-8.56000E+02-8.48000E+02
-8.40000E+02-8.32000E+02-8.24000E+02-8.16000E+02-8.08000E+02-8.00000E+02-7.92000E+02-7.84000E+02-7.76000E+02-7.68000E+02
RECORD 14                                                           -9.91565E+03-9.91458E+03-9.91358E+03-9.91243E+03-9.91144E+03
-9.91042E+03-9.90958E+03-9.90843E+03-9.90737E+03-9.90636E+03-9.90565E+03-9.90453E+03-9.90365E+03-9.90251E+03-9.90151E+03
-9.90040E+03-9.89965E+03-9.89856E+03-9.89537E+03-9.89465E+03-9.89343E+03-9.89254E+03-9.89154E+03-9.89036E+03-9.88936E+03
RECORD 15                                                           -9.99858E+03-9.99858E+03-9.99858E+03-9.99858E+03-9.99858E+03
-9.99858E+03-9.99858E+03-9.99858E+03-9.99858E+03-9.99857E+03-9.99856E+03-9.99855E+03-9.99855E+03-9.99854E+03-9.99854E+03
-9.99854E+03-9.99854E+03-9.99854E+03-9.99854E+03-9.99854E+03-9.99854E+03-9.99853E+03-9.99853E+03-9.99853E+03-9.99852E+03
RECORD 16                                                           -9.88837E+03-9.38744E+03-9.88654E+03-9.88535E+03-9.88445E+03
-9.88344E+03-9.88258E+03-9.88165E+03-9.88040E+03-9.87965E+03-9.87865E+03-9.87752E+03-9.87653E+03-9.87344E+03-9.87248E+03
-9.87158E+03-9.87055E+03-9.86952E+03-9.86858E+03-9.86740E+03-9.86631E+03-9.92000E+02-9.84000E+02-9.76000E+02-9.68000E+02
RECORD 17                                                           -9.96655E+03-9.96550E+03-9.96457E+03-9.96340E+03-9.96254E+03
-9.96158E+03-9.96050E+03-9.95936E+03-9.95734E+03-9.95643E+03-9.95546E+03-9.95465E+03-9.95365E+03-9.95235E+03-9.95136E+03
-9.95035E+03-9.94937E+03-9.94854E+03-9.94758E+03-9.94643E+03-9.94540E+03-9.94442E+03-9.94326E+03-9.94245E+03-9.94154E+03
RECORD 18                                                            0.00000E-99 0.00000E-99 0.00000E-99 0.00000E-99 0.00000E-99
0.00000E-99 0.00000E-99 0.00000E-99 0.00000E-99 0.00000E-99 0.00000E-99 0.00000E-99 0.00000E-99 0.00000E-99 0.00000E-99
0.00000E-99 0.00000E-99 0.00000E-99 0.00000E-99 0.00000E-99 0.00000E-99 0.00000E-99 0.00000E-99 0.00000E-99 0.00000E-99
RECORD 19                                                            0.00000E-99 0.00000E-99 0.00000E-99 0.00000E-99 0.00000E-99
0.00000E-99 0.00000E-99 0.00000E-99 0.00000E-99 0.00000E-99 0.00000E-99 0.00000E-99 0.00000E-99 0.00000E-99 0.00000E-99
0.00000E-99 0.00000E-99 0.00000E-99 0.00000E-99 0.00000E-99 0.00000E-99 0.00000E-99 0.00000E-99 0.00000E-99 0.00000E-99
RECORD 20                                                            0.00000E-99 0.00000E-99 0.00000E-99 0.00000E-99 0.00000E-99
0.00000E-99 0.00000E-99 0.00000E-99 0.00000E-99 0.00000E-99 0.00000E-99 0.00000E-99 0.00000E-99 0.00000E-99 0.00000E-99
0.00000E-99 0.00000E-99 0.00000E-99 0.00000E-99 0.00000E-99 0.00000E-99 0.00000E-99 0.00000E-99 0.00000E-99 0.00000E-99
```

8.2.4. MERGE Subroutine—Comments

The MERGE subroutine is written to take two lists of numbers, one on tape 1 and the second on tape 2, or one on tape 3 and one on tape 4, and merge these lists by the 2-to-2 merge procedure to the remaining two tapes.

Input to the subroutine consists of 3 numbers:

NTAP—Starting tape (1 or 3)
N1—Number of words in the 1st list
N2—No Words in the 2nd list

Output—consists of 4 numbers:

NTAP—Tape with 1st new list (3 or 1)
N1—Number of words in the 1st new list

N2—No words in 2nd new list
LINE—Number of lines drawn (i.e., number of ordered sublists in the result − 1). When line = 0, there is only one list.

The words being ordered are stored in the tape subroutine. To use MERGE, a program is required which will read the words, count them, write them on tapes 1 and 2 (or 3 and 4); call MERGE, test for zero line, if not zero, go to call MERGE—if zero, route out words.

The MERGE subprogram consists of:

26	statements	Initializing indexes, etc.
19	"	Debugging printouts
17	"	Make merge selection
13	"	Record
50	"	Transmit data, check For end, etc.
125	"	Total

8.2.5.—MERGE Subroutine—Flow Chart

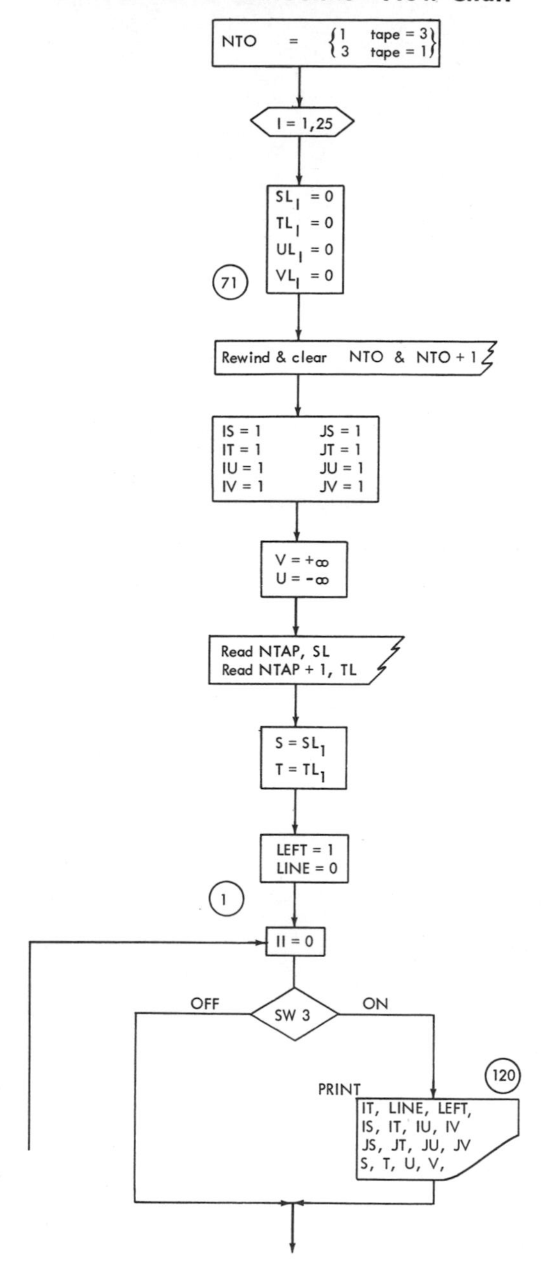

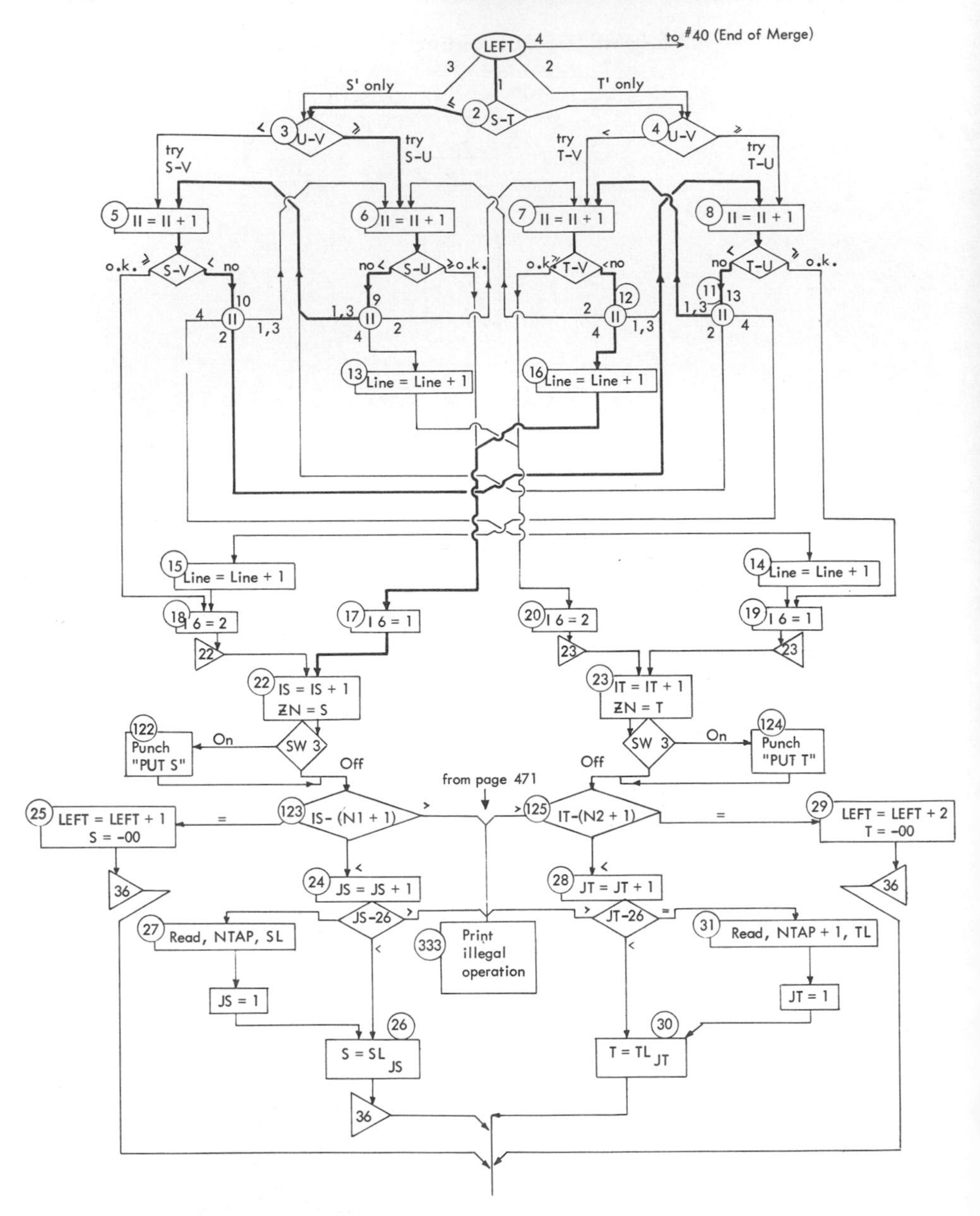

LEFT
to #40 (End of Merge)
S' only
T' only
S-T
U-V
try S-V
try S-U
try T-V
try T-U
II = II + 1
S-V
S-U
T-V
T-U
o.k.
no
II
1,3
Line = Line + 1
I 6 = 2
I 6 = 1
IS = IS + 1
ZN = S
IT = IT + 1
ZN = T
SW 3
On
Off
Punch "PUT S"
Punch "PUT T"
from page 471
LEFT = LEFT + 1
S = -00
IS- (N1 + 1)
IT-(N2 + 1)
LEFT = LEFT + 2
T = -00
JS = JS + 1
JT = JT + 1
JS-26
JT-26
Read, NTAP, SL
Read, NTAP + 1, TL
Print illegal operation
JS = 1
JT = 1
S = SL JS
T = TL JT

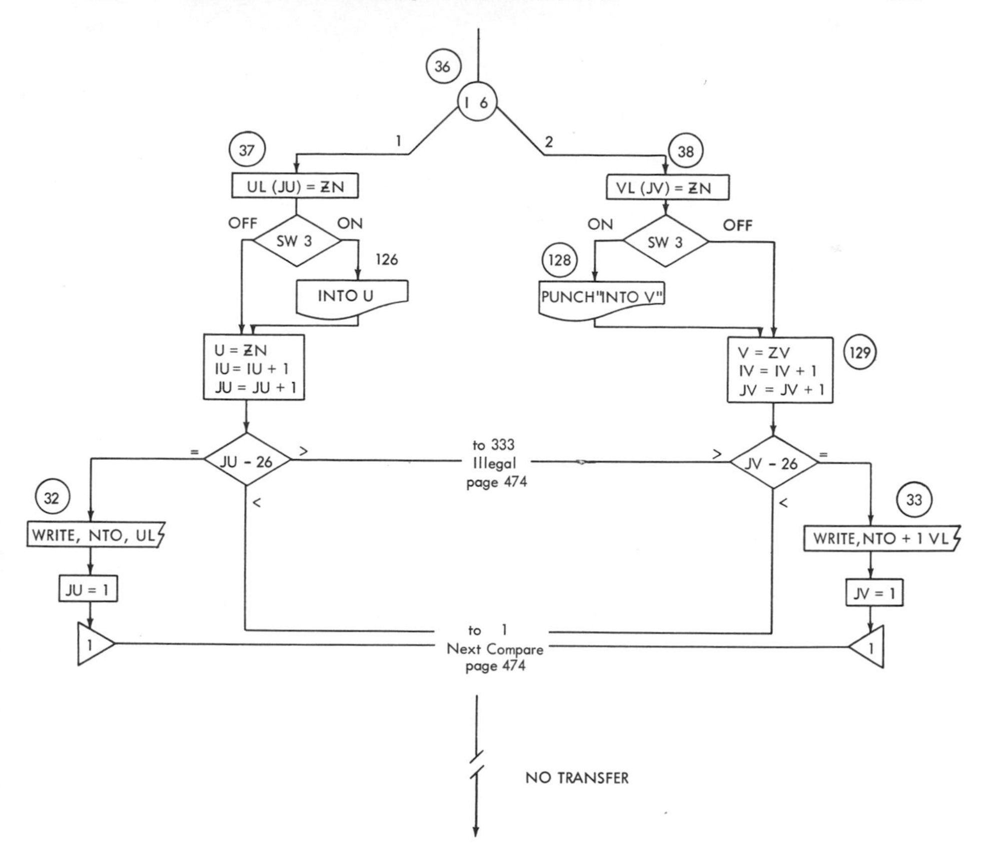
36
1 6
1
2
37
38
UL (JU) = ƵN
VL (JV) = ƵN
OFF
ON
SW 3
126
INTO U
128
PUNCH "INTO V"
U = ƵN
IU = IU + 1
JU = JU + 1
V = ZV
IV = IV + 1
JV = JV + 1
129
JU - 26
JV - 26
to 333
Illegal
page 474
32
33
WRITE, NTO, UL
WRITE, NTO + 1 VL
JU = 1
JV = 1
to 1
Next Compare
page 474
NO TRANSFER

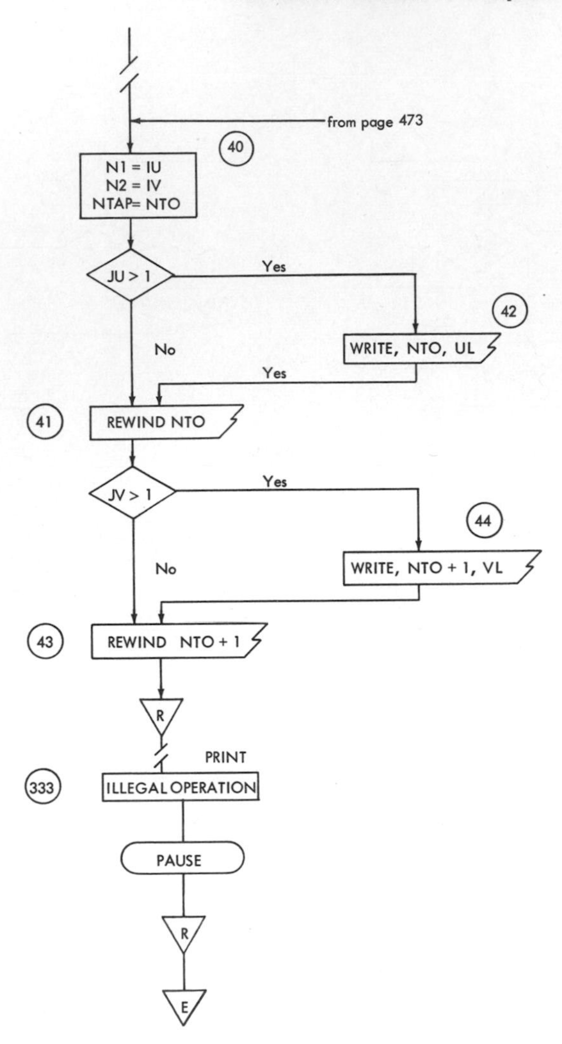

from page 473
40
N1 = IU
N2 = IV
NTAP= NTO
JU > 1
Yes
42
No
WRITE, NTO, UL
Yes
41
REWIND NTO
JV > 1
Yes
44
No
WRITE, NTO + 1, VL
43
REWIND NTO + 1
R
PRINT
333
ILLEGAL OPERATION
PAUSE
R
E

8.2.6. MERGE Subroutine—Program

```
        *2805
           SUBROUTINE MERGE(NTAP,N1,N2,LINE)
           DIMENSION SL(25),TL(25),UL(25),VL(25)     Records being used
           NTO=((NTAP—2)*(—1)+2)=→4—NTAP             Gives 1 for 3 & 3 for 1
           DO 71 I=1,25  ⎫
           SL(I)=0.      ⎪
           TL(I)=0.      ⎬  To avoid trouble in call tape where these may be
           UL(I)=0.      ⎪  used as dummy variables (see 71+1, 71+2)
        /1 VL(I)=0.      ⎭
           CALL TAPE(SL,NTO,6)    ⎫
           CALL TAPE(SL,NTO+1,6)  ⎭   Rewind receiving tape
           IS=1          Current S word is 1st word on S List
           IT=1             "    T  "   "   "   "   "  T List
           IU=0             "    U  "   " 0th  "   "  U List
           IV=0             "    V  "   "   "   "   "  V List
           JS=1          Location of Current word in S Record is 1
           JT=1             "     "     "      "  " T    "    is 1
           JU=1          Space for next        "  " U    "    is 1
           JV=1             "    "    "        "  " V    "    is 1
           V=10.**10.    +∞ 0th V word i.e. must close list before using
           U=—V          —∞ 0th U  "   i.e. open list
           CALL TAPE(SL,NTAP,2)       Read 1st S Record
           CALL TAPE(TL,NTAP+1,2)     Read 1st T Record
           S=SL(1)     Current S
           T=TL(1)     Current T                        1 both S & T Available
           LEFT=1      Left is a 4 way switch setting:  2 S empty T   "
           LINE=0      Number of closed sublists        3 T   "   S   "
         1 II=0        Number of unsuccessful tapes     4 S & T EMPTY
```

This may seem inconsistent however it simplifies programming further on. (marginal note beside IV=0 … JU=1)

```
    IF( SENSE SWITCH 3)120,121        Debug?
120 PUNCH 101,II,LINE,LEFT,IS,IT,IU,IV,JS,JT,JU,JV,S,T,U,V   } Debug
101 FORMAT(I2,I3,I2,2X,4I3,2X,4I3,4X,4F7.2)                  }
121 GO TO (2,4,3,40),LEFT
  2 IF(S−T)3,3,4
  3 IF(U−V)5,6,6
  4 IF(U−V)7,8,8
  5 II=II+1              II=1      IS   MIN(S,T) ≥ MAX(U,V)      IF YES make the transfer
    IF(S−V)10,18,18         IF NO:
  6 II=II+1              II=2      "    MIN(S,T) ≥ MIN(U,V)          "    SEE
    IF(S−U)9,17,17          "
  7 II=II+1              II=3      "    MAX(S,T) ≥ MAX(U,V)          "    FLOW
    IF(T−V)12,20,20         "
  8 II=II+1              II=4      "    MAX(S,T) ≥ MIN(U,V)          "    CHART
    IF(T−U)11,19,19         "      PUT  MIN(S,T) in MAX(U,V) & Draw Line
  9 GO TO (5,7,5,13),II
 10 GO TO (6,8,6,14),II
 11 GO TO (7,5,7,15),II
 12 GO TO (8,6,8,16),II
 13 LINE=LINE+1          }
 20 I6=2 → Into V        }    T into V
    GO TO 23.            }    Go to take T
 14 LINE=LINE+1          }
 19 I6=1      Into U     }    T into U
    GO TO 23             }    Go to take T
 15 LINE=LINE+1          }
 18 I6=2      Into V     }    S into V
    GO TO 22             }    Go to take S
```

```
 16 LINE=LINE+1  }
 17 I6=1      Into U }          S into U
 22 IS=IS+1      NEXT CURRENT S word
    ZN=S         THE "NUMBER BEING PLACED IN S                                  }
    IF (SENSE SWITCH 3) 122,123     Debug?                                      }
122 PUNCH 102              }                                                    }
102 FORMAT(6H PUT S)       }  Debug                                             }
123 IF(IS-N1-1)24,25,333   IF (next current word -(N1+1))                       }
 25 LEFT=LEFT+1         NO NEXT word—forces selection of routine to take        }
    S=-(10.**10.)                    the T X case even though in reality        }
                                     S<T ∴ S cannot be chosen                   } Take S
    GO TO 36               To U or V                                            }
 24 JS=JS+1                Increment record location                            }
    IF(JS-26)26,27,333     If JS=26 get out another record                      }
 27 CALL TAPE(SL,NTAP,2)          "   "    "    "                               }
    JS=1                   Start with 1st word                                  }
 26 S=SL(JS)               New S word                                           }
    GO TO 36               GO TO U or V                                         }
 23 IT=IT+1                                                          }
    ZN=T                                                             }
    IF (SENSE SWITCH 3) 124,125                                      }
124 PUNCH 103                                                        } Take T
103 FORMAT(6H PUT T)             Same as set above with T for S      }
125 IF(IT-N2-1)28,29,333                                             }
 29 LEFT=LEFT+2                                                      }
    T=-(10.**10.)                                                    }
    GO TO 36                                                         }
 28 JT=JT+1                          Same as S set                   }
    IF(JT-26)30,31,333                                               } Take T
 31 CALL TAPE(TL,NTAP+1,2)                                           }
    JT=1                                                             }
 30 T=TL(JT)                                                         }
```

```
 36 GO TO (37,38),I6                       Either U or V
 37 UL(JU)=ZN                              ZN into next space for U      )
    IF (SENSE SWITCH 3) 126,127            Debug?                        |
126 PUNCH 104                  }           Debug                         |
104 FORMAT(7H INTO U)          }                                         |
127 U=ZN                                   U value for comparing         |
    IU=IU+1                                total number of U words       }  Put ZN into U
    JU=JU+1                                Next current u space          |
    IF(JU-26) 1,32,333                     Is record full?               |
 32 CALL TAPE(UL,NTO,3)                    If full, write the record     |
    JU=1                                   Start next record             |
    GO TO 1                                Next comparison               )
 38 VL(JV)=ZN                                                            )
    IF (SENSE SWITCH 3) 128,129                                          |
128 PUNCH 105                                                            |
105 FORMAT(7H INTO V)                                                    |
129 V=ZN                                                                 }  Put ZN into V
    JV=JV+1                                Same as above                 |
    IV=IV+1                                                              |
    IF(JV-25) 1,33,333                                                   |
 33 CALL TAPE(VL,NTO+1,3)                                                |
    JV=1                                                                 )
    GO TO 1                      All words have been moved
 40 N1=IV                        No Words in new List #1
    N2=IV                        "  "     "  "    "   #2
    NTAP=NTO                     New "from" tape is old "to" tape
    IF(JU-1)41,41,42             Does the last U write record contain anything?
 42 CALL TAPE(UL,NTO,3)          If so, record it;
 41 CALL TAPE(UL,NTO,5)          Rewind the tape of first new list
    IF(JV-1)43,43,44            )
 44 CALL TAPE(VL,NTO+1,3)       }  Repeat for V
 43 CALL TAPE(VL,NTO+1,5)       )
```

```
      RETURN
  333 PRINT 334                    ERROR MESSAGE
  334 FORMAT(20HILLEGAL  OPERATION    )
      PAUSE
      RETURN
      END
```

8.2.7. Program to Test MERGE Subroutine—Flow Chart

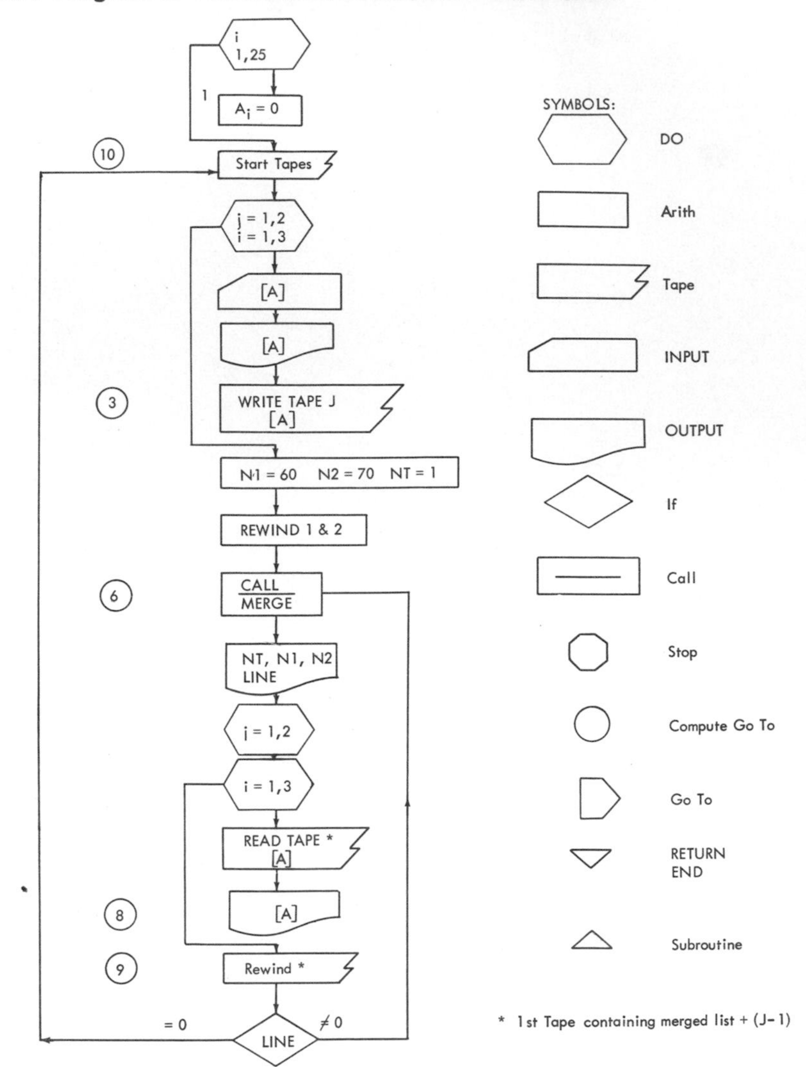

* 1st Tape containing merged list + (J– 1)

8.2.8. Program to Test MERGE Subroutine—Program

```
*2805
      DIMENSION A(25)
      DO 1 I=1,25
    1 A(I)=0.
   10 CALL TAPE(A,5,7)
      DO 3 J=1,2
      DO 3 I=1,3
      READ 4,A
    4 FORMAT(25F3.1)
    5 FORMAT(10F8.2)
      PUNCH 5,A
    3 CALL TAPE(A,J,3)
      N1=60
      N2=70
      CALL TAPE(A,1,5)
      CALL TAPE(A,2,5)
      NT=1
    6 CALL MERGE(NT,N1,N2,LINE)
      PUNCH7,NT,N1,N2,LINE
    7 FORMAT(1H),4I5//)
      DO 9 J=1,2
     DO 8 I=1,3
      CALL TAPE(A,NT+J-1,1)
    8 PUNCH5,A
    9 CALL TAPE(A,NT+J-1,5)
      IF(LINE)6,10,6
      END
```

8.2.9. Partial Test MERGE Input and Output

Input

23.60	98.40	79.60	42.60	14.50	15.70	16.40	67.50	47.10	64.70
14.60	55.40	13.40	31.20	47.10	45.90	17.80	94.10	57.60	12.40
37.10	46.80	14.50	31.20	43.10					
28.90	12.90	82.90	81.20	81.60	21.80	19.80	67.30	24.00	70.20
13.80	99.80	73.80	18.20	65.70	35.60	18.90	18.70	23.40	78.90
84.90	58.10	67.90	89.40	56.20					
97.80	86.50	35.40	1.20	54.50	79.80	85.60	53.20	3.40	54.80
79.80	65.30	50.20	15.80	48.50	34.20	54.60	25.30	12.40	65.60
47.00	75.30	56.10	26.80	98.20					
43.40	76.50	62.40	10.30	46.70	10.20	35.40	66.60	44.20	10.10
23.50	65.90	84.70	65.60	13.10	46.50	30.10	47.30	14.50	83.00
28.10	43.50	47.80	31.00	47.80					
54.70	36.50	73.60	15.10	38.20	61.20	57.30	97.60	95.70	43.60
67.20	1.40	32.60	94.60	53.80	2.10	55.40	67.30	50.20	15.40
87.60	57.00	10.30	61.80	73.10					
2.30	46.50	85.50	61.30	24.50	89.70	57.10	81.80	52.50	8.20
72.10	45.80	38.30	28.40	85.70	30.20	98.50	42.70	65.40	54.30
21.40	85.10	32.40	4.00	68.00					

Output

1st TAPE N1 N2 LINES
3 66 64 25

23.60	43.40	76.50	98.40	10.30	42.60	46.70	66.60	67.50	10.10
14.60	23.50	55.40	65.60	30.10	45.90	83.00	94.10	12.40	31.00
37.10	46.80	47.80	54.70	73.60					
15.10	28.90	38.20	57.30	95.70	1.40	32.60	81.20	81.60	2.10
19.80	24.00	50.20	87.60	99.80	10.30	~~18.20~~	~~61.80~~	~~65.70~~	~~73.10~~
85.50	18.90	24.50	57.10	81.80					
84.90	8.20	58.10	67.90	72.10	97.80	35.40	38.30	54.50	79.80
85.60	85.70	3.40	30.20	42.70	65.40	18.20	61.80	65.70	73.10
~~85.50~~	~~18.90~~	~~24.50~~	~~57.10~~	~~81.80~~					
62.40	79.60	10.20	14.50	15.70	16.40	35.40	44.20	47.10	64.70
65.90	84.70	13.10	13.40	31.20	46.50	47.10	47.30	14.50	17.80
28.10	43.50	47.80	57.60	14.50					
31.20	36.50	43.10	61.20	97.60	12.90	43.60	67.20	82.90	94.60
21.80	53.80	55.40	67.30	67.30	70.20	13.80	15.40	57.00	73.80
2.30	35.60	46.50	61.30	89.70					
18.70	23.40	52.50	78.90	89.40	45.80	56.20	86.50	1.20	28.40
53.20	54.80	98.50	54.30	~~67.30~~	~~70.20~~	~~13.80~~	~~15.40~~	~~57.00~~	~~73.80~~
~~2.30~~	~~35.60~~	~~46.50~~	~~61.30~~	~~89.70~~					
18.70	23.40	52.50	78.90	89.40	45.80	56.20	86.50	1.20	28.40
53.20	54.80	98.50	54.30	67.30					

1st PASS
Unused portion of record

	1st TAPE 1	N1 60	N2 70	LINES 12					
23.60	43.40	62.40	76.50	79.60	98.40	10.10	13.10	13.40	14.60
23.50	31.20	46.50	47.10	47.30	55.40	65.60	83.00	94.10	12.40
14.50	31.00	31.20	36.50	37.10					
43.10	46.80	47.80	54.70	57.30	67.20	82.90	94.60	95.70	1.40
21.80	32.60	50.20	57.00	73.80	87.60	99.80	2.30	10.30	18.20
18.90	24.50	57.10	81.80	84.90					
89.40	97.80	35.40	38.30	45.80	54.50	56.20	65.40	98.50	54.30
~~21.80~~	~~32.60~~	~~50.20~~	~~57.00~~	~~73.80~~	~~87.60~~	~~99.80~~	~~2.30~~	~~10.30~~	~~18.20~~
~~18.90~~	~~24.50~~	~~57.10~~	~~81.80~~	~~84.90~~					
10.20	10.30	14.50	15.70	16.40	35.40	42.60	44.20	46.70	47.10
64.70	65.90	66.60	67.50	84.70	14.50	17.80	28.10	30.10	43.50
45.90	47.80	57.60	61.20	73.60					
97.60	12.90	15.10	28.90	38.20	43.60	53.80	55.40	67.30	67.30
70.20	81.20	81.60	2.10	13.80	15.40	19.80	24.00	35.60	46.50
61.30	61.80	65.70	73.10	85.50					
89.70	8.20	18.70	23.40	52.50	58.10	67.90	72.10	78.90	79.80
85.60	85.70	86.50	1.20	3.40	28.40	30.20	42.70	53.20	54.80
~~61.30~~	~~61.80~~	~~65.70~~	~~73.10~~	~~85.50~~					

	1st TAPE	N1	N2	LINES					
	3	72	58	6					
10.20	10.30	14.50	15.70	16.40	23.60	35.40	42.60	43.40	44.20
46.70	47.10	62.40	64.70	65.90	66.60	67.50	76.50	79.60	84.70
98.40	12.40	12.90	14.50	15.10					
28.90	31.00	31.20	36.50	37.10	38.20	43.10	43.60	46.80	47.80
53.80	54.70	55.40	57.30	67.20	67.30	67.30	70.20	81.20	81.60
82.90	94.60	95.70	99.80	2.30					
8.20	10.30	18.20	18.70	18.90	23.40	24.50	52.50	57.10	58.10
67.90	72.10	78.90	79.80	81.80	84.90	85.60	85.70	86.50	89.40
98.50	54.30	~~95.70~~	~~99.80~~	~~2.30~~					
10.10	13.10	13.40	14.50	14.60	17.80	23.50	28.10	30.10	31.20
43.50	45.90	46.50	47.10	47.30	47.80	55.40	57.60	61.20	65.60
73.60	83.00	94.10	97.60	1.40					
2.10	13.80	15.40	19.80	21.80	24.00	32.60	35.60	46.50	50.20
57.00	61.30	61.80	65.70	73.10	73.80	85.50	87.60	89.70	97.80
1.20	3.40	28.40	30.20	35.40					
38.30	42.70	45.80	53.20	54.50	54.80	56.20	65.40	~~46.50~~	~~50.20~~
~~57.00~~	~~61.30~~	~~61.80~~	~~65.70~~	~~73.10~~	~~73.80~~	~~85.50~~	~~87.60~~	~~89.70~~	~~97.80~~
~~1.20~~	~~3.40~~	~~28.40~~	~~30.20~~	~~35.40~~					

8.2.10. SORT—Control Program for Sorting—Comments

This program is written to execute the following procedure:

1. Read in the data, transform it into one word form and record A on (simulated tape; Rewind tapes).
2. Call merge
3. Test if sort is complete; if not, go to step 2; if yes, continue
4. Punch out data.

Input data:

Title card Columns 1–70 (alphameric) up to 750 cards with the following format:

Columns 1–2—K—Blank or zero on all cards except last card and *some* card *about* in the middle.

Columns 6–10—NSORT—Sorting key number; any 4-digit number and sign.

Columns 21–32—BB—Any alphameric characters to be carried along with the key.

Output:—

NSORT and BB in ascending numeric order of NSORT and alphabetic on BB for equal NSORT's with SW1 on TYPED: No lines drawn at end of each merge pass.

Output Format (Expected):

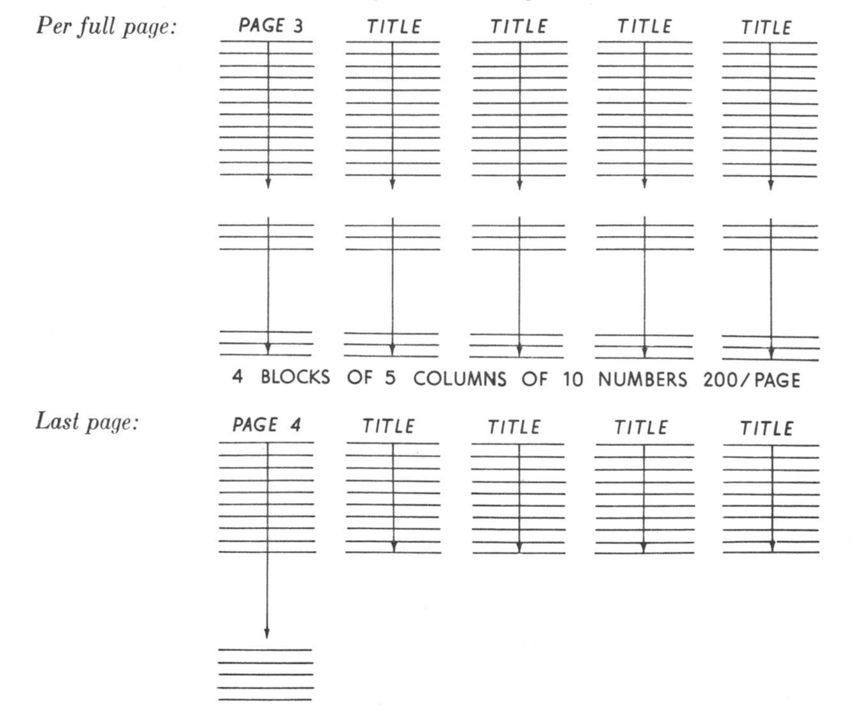

8.2.11. SORT Program

```
*2805
      DIMENSION TITLE(5),A(25),B(50),MN(5)
    1 READ 2,TITLE                                  Read Title
    2 FORMAT(5A14)
      DO 3 I=1,25
    3 A(I)=0.                                      } Initialize
      CALL TAPE(A,5,7)
                                 Rewind & Clear All tapes – initialize tape system –
      L=1                        1st half of data
   10 N2=0                       Clear Accumulator
      DO 4 I=1,50
      DO 5 J=1,25                               25 words/record
      READ 6,K,NSORT,BB                         Data
    6 FORMAT(I2,3X,I5,10X,A12)
   31 FORMAT(2X,I5,1X,A12,2(7X,I5,1X,A12)/1HI,21X,2(7X,I5,1X,A12)) Input format
      ZN=NSORT                                                      Output format
                             Float (>0)    Key             Information
      A(J)=ZN+BB             A(J) is of form 1234 – 11 22 33 44 55 66 77 88 99 10 11 12
      N2=N2+1                Increment for each number read in
      IF(K) 7,5,7            Test end 1/2 indicator
    5 CONTINUE
    4 CALL TAPE(A,L,3)              WRITE RECORD
    7 CALL TAPE(A,L,3)              WRITE LAST RECORD
      GO TO (8,9),L                 1st or 2nd 1/2 ?
    8 N1=N2                         1st Half – put total number of words in N1
      L=2                           2nd 1/2 next
      GO TO 10                      go to read next 1/2
    9 N=N1+N2                       Total number
      CALL TAPE(A,1,5)              Rewind
      CALL TAPE(A,2,5)              Rewind
      L=1                           1st list is on tape 1
   12 CALL MERGE(L,N1,N2,LINE)      Merge Lists
      IF(SENSE SWITCH 1)14,15       Test location—to give some idea of the progress of the program
   14 PRINT 16,LINE          TEST Output
   16 FORMAT(I3)
   15 IF(LINE)1,18,12               Complete?
   18 NP=0                          Yes – Number of Words Punched out
      DO 20 I=1,9                   I = output page number
      PUNCH 21,I, TITLE
   21 FORMAT(12H)OUTPUT PAGE,I2,1X,5A13)     Page heading
      DO 20 J=1,4                   J = Block number      4 Blocks/page
      IR=N-NP                       Number of words remaining
      IF(IR)1,1,34                  If there are no numbers left-end
   34 CALL TAPE(A,L,1)              Read 25 words
      DO 23 K=1,25                  Put 25 words into B1-25
```

```
 23 B(K)=A(K)
    IF(IR-25)24,24,25                      Any more left?
 25 CALL TAPE(A,L,1)                       Read next 25 words
    DO 26 K=1,25         }
 26 B(K+25)=A(K)         }                 Put into B26-50
 24 DO27 K=1,10                            10 lines/block
    IF(K-IR)33,33,1                        If K>number left-end
 33 NN=0 IF(IR-50)121,121,122              Start Block, if IR>50 Set IR=50
122 IR=50                                            {1,11,21,31,41
121 DO 28 M=K,IR,10            Column number         {2,22,32,42,50
    NN=NN+1                                          {3,33
    MN(NN)=B(M)
    IF(B(M))130,131,131
130 MN(NN)=MN(NN)-1            Key number
131 Z=MN(NN)                   Float key
 28 A(NN)=B(M)-Z               Restore alphameric portion
    NP=NP+NN                   Number punched here
    IF(K-6)27,29,27            Going to the 6th line?
 29 PUNCH 30             }
 30 FORMAT(1X)           }      If yes—Skip a line
 27 PUNCH 31,(MN(M),A(M),M=1,NN)      Punch out data—
 20 PUNCH 32             }
 32 FORMAT(///)          }      Skip 3 lines between blocks
    END                  }
```

8.2.12. SORT—Flow Chart

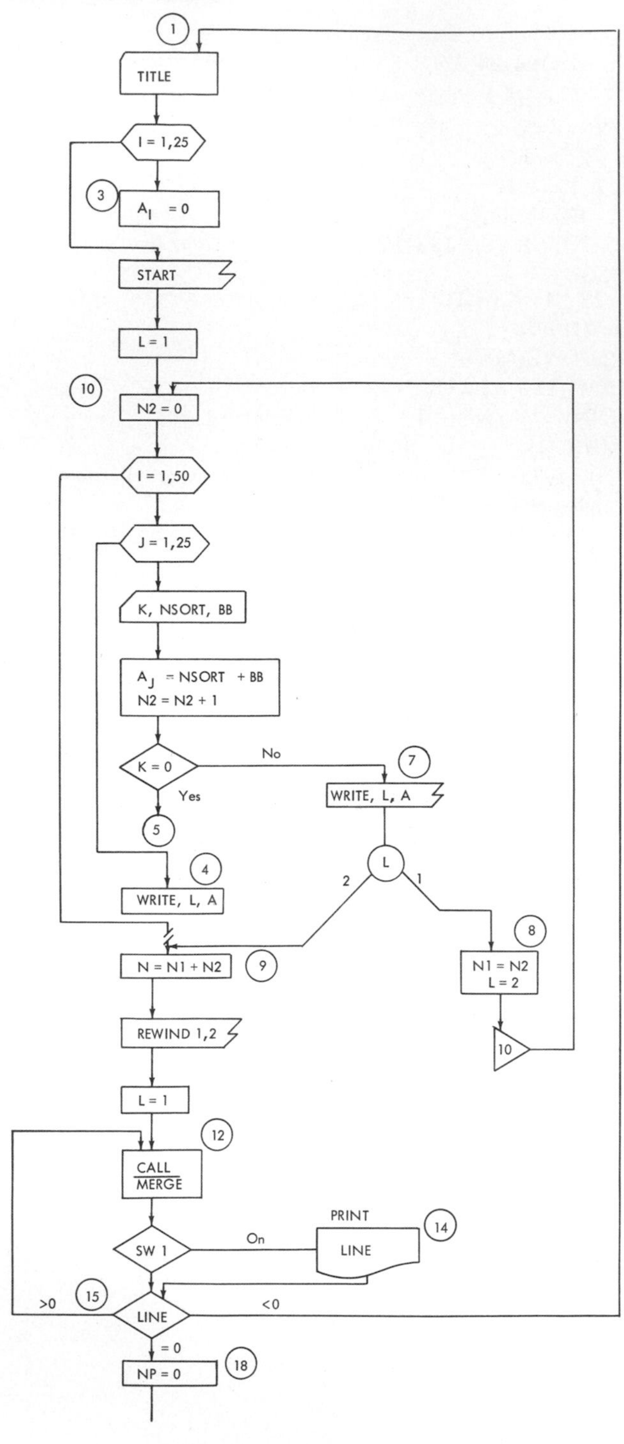

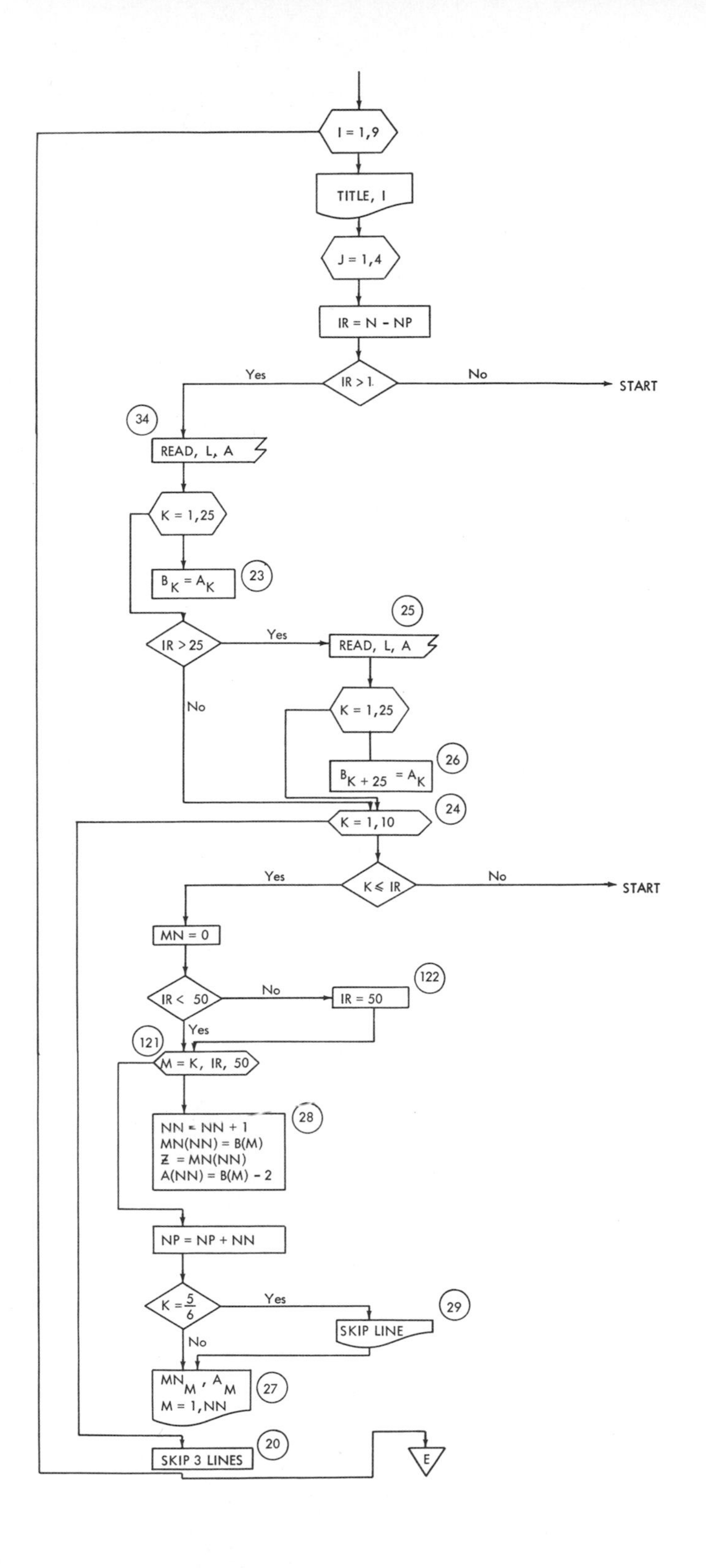

I = 1,9
TITLE, I
J = 1,4
IR = N - NP
IR > 1
Yes
No
START
34
READ, L, A
K = 1,25
B K = A K
23
IR > 25
Yes
25
READ, L, A
No
K = 1,25
B K + 25 = A K
26
24
K = 1, 10
K ≤ IR
Yes
No
START
MN = 0
IR < 50
No
IR = 50
122
Yes
121
M = K, IR, 50
NN = NN + 1
MN(NN) = B(M)
Z = MN(NN)
A(NN) = B(M) - 2
28
NP = NP + NN
K = 5/6
Yes
SKIP LINE
29
No
MN M , A M
M = 1, NN
27
SKIP 3 LINES
20
E

8.2.13. SORT—Data

```
FULL DECK OF DATA
   658          OF THAT ALL
   612          US SERT OF D
   646          CODES WEW E
 -9920          N 3'WRITE A40
 -9939          '25'WORDS E60
 -9965          BRAM -'SUBP50
 -9999          IRST SUBPRO50
 -9938          ACH'AND A G10
 -9873          JHJJHJHJHJH30
 -9919          'TECORD 4 B40
 -9918          ACKSFA E 5 50
 -9917          REWIND'TAPE50
 -9999          BRAM -'SUBP50
 -9958          VCESS)(PARD30
   619          FORE WERE NE
   641          WAS MESSED U
   636          ERROR THUS T
   613          ATA    I BEL
 -9999          MBERING,THE30
 -9963          E DOES'THE 60
 -9999          TEN'FOR THE40
   622          AS THE KEY W
 -9931          'IN'FORGO) 40
 -9999          ROGRAM'IS T60
 -9999          OGRAM CAN D50
 -9916          '6 REWIND T60
 -9913          ORDS 7'REWI10
 -9999          O READ'IN T60
 -9999          O THE FOLLO60
   652          AWAS INTERRU
 -9999          HE DATA, CO10
   659          OF WHICH ARE
 -9999          RTRAN II)) 20
 -9999          NTHE DECK W40
 -9999          IT CONSISTS20
 -9999          F A'4 DIGIT50
 -9999          ACTUAL'SORT10
 -9950          SES'THE OTH10
   647          NON EXISTANT
   620           GATIVE AND
 -9999          'THE BASIS 40
 -9999          OF THE'PREC50
 -9936          X. WORDS CO20
 -9935          NSIST OF 2820
 -9884          NTHE DECK W40
 -9883          AS SHUFFLED40
 -9999          EEDING'NUMB50
 -9901          RT IS BASED10
 -9934          'DIGITS( TH30
 -9953          ULTT) NOTE 50
 -9999          ROGRAM'MERG60
 -9999          CHARACTER A20
 -9927          WING FUNCTI60
 -9999          LPHAMERIC N30
 -9985          LANGUAGE(FO10
 -9885          MBERING,THE30
```

First position
Blank
Will be left justified in output

```
  -504          RAMS).'THE 40
 -9979          THE TAPE PR50
 -9930          RAM'IS'A TA30
 -9999          ATE'ALL REC30
 -9910          ORDS. DATA 30
 -9909          PE SIMMULAT30
 -9999          ER SUBPROGR10
 -9949          PUTOR WOULD
   609          'BY'THE PRO60
 -9999          GRAM BNFHYG10
 -9999          3ING PROGRA40
 -9999          M WNICH IN 40
 -9999          ER.'THIS DA60
 -9999          TA BEING OU60
 -9999          ESSENSE CON50
 -9999          UTE'OF'TECH60
  -576
 -9882          'BY'AN'EXPE50
 -9999          NOLOGY'IN T60
 -9874          NHJJNMNHHHH30
 -9978          FUNCTION OF50
 -9999          THE TAPE PR50
   653          PTED THE PRE
 -9999          ATE'THE REC30
 -9999          ORD'LOCATIO30
 -9999          HE FORTRAM 10
 -9967          DATA. THE F40
 -9941          SISTS OF 4050
   638          IC REPERESEN
   632          RECTION OPPO
 -9999          EER'WITH SQ20
 -9999          UBPROGRAM U60
 -9999          UENTIOAL NU30
 -9999          HJJHHHHJJHJ20
 -9999          HMNMHNMNJHM20
 -9999          LANGUAGE(FO10
 -9999          NHJJNMNHHHH30
 -9999          N 3'WRITE A40
   649          WITH THE PRE
 -9999          SES'THE OTH10
 -9999          'CONSISTS O50
 -9872          ASDFGHJKLAS40
 -9940          'RECORDS OF60
 -9973          NTROL THE O10
 -9999          'THE MAIN P50
 -9908          SUPLIED TO 40
 -9957          ON THE'SPEL30
 -9956          LING BUT IT40
 -9915          APE'AND VAC60
 -9982          'OF'A MAIN 30
 -9999          ACH'AND A G10
 -9999          UIDING'INDE10
 -9896          S SORTED ON40
   639          TATION OF TH
 -9914          ATE'ALL REC10
   635          THE ORIGINAL
```

```
          -688
          -680
  02       625          THE ALPHAMER
          -568
          -808
         -9877          FTGDHYUHHJJ10
         -9999          'TYPISTS FA50
         -9969          O PUNCH OUT30
          -944
         -9968          THE'SORTED 40
         -9961          ING'BY'THE 10
           616          HE FOLLOWING
         -9902          HICH THE SO10
         -9999          TWO'TO'TWO 20
          -456
          -632
         -9989          NOIS INSTIT50
         -9999          ULTT) NOTE 50
         -9988          UTE'OF'TECH60
         -9999          THE'MERGE S60
         -9929          OGRAM CAN D50
         -9888          NTED IN ORN20
          -560
          -552
          -544
          -536
         -9999          ING'BY'THE 10
         -9999          FUNCTION OF50
         -9925          'A RECORD 210
         -9999          SUPLIED TO 40
         -9999          X. WORDS CO20
         -9999          THE'PROGRAM40
         -9999          'IS'ALL THE40
           617          ALL KEY NUME
           618          BERS USED BE
           633          SITE TO THE
           629          ND OF ERROR
           611          T THE PREVIO
           666          IN THE SAME
          -512
          -752
          -744
          -736
         -9999          VCESS)(PARD30
         -9999          ON THE'SPEL30
         -9999          LINC BUT IT40
           605          FTHE SORT PR
          -520
           650          SENT DATAS
          -984
           606          OGRAM   THE
           607          PROBLEM WAS
           608          THAT THE COM
          -872
         -9999          'PROGRAM AR20
         -9999          E AS FOLLOW20
         -9933          EREFORE CAN30
```

```
         -9999          'READ A REC20
         -9999          ORD'AND VAC20
         -9999          'AND SORTED60
           645          G ALPHAMERIC
         -9999          '1620 COMPU40
           660          POSITIVE SO
         -9999          'OF'A MAIN 30
         -9999          TER'AT'ILLI50
           640          HE NUMEBER W
         -9999          'NUMBER WIT60
         -9894          OF THE'PREC50
         -9999          AS SHUFFLED40
         -9999          NOIS INSTIT50
           631          ED IN THE DI
         -9999          H SIGN'ON W60
           624          TED FROM HTH
           626          IC REPRESENT
         -9893          EEDING'NUMB50
           662          ND DING ERRO
           663          ROR SHOULD A
           664           ALWAYS BE I
         -9999          WING FUNCTI60
           627          AGION OF THE
           610          NOT PUNCH OU
           661          THAT THE ROU
         -9980          THW'SUBPROG40
         -9999          3NS. 1'RAED10
         -9892          ER.'THIS DA60
         -9891          TA BEING OU60
         -9999          'A RECORD 210
         -9999          HICH THE SO10
           628         NUMNER A ROU
         -9999          'BY'AN'EXPE50
         -9999          DETAILS OF 10
         -9999          THE'SORTING10
         -9999          RT IS BASED10
         -9999          'AND AN 11 20
         -9999          ASDFGHJKQWE50
         -9999          GRAMS AND T30
         -9999          O PUNCH OUT30
         -9999          SISTS OF 4050
         -9999          'RECORDS OF60
         -9999          '25'WORDS E60
         -9898          LPHAMERIC N30
         -9897          AME'WHICH I30
         -9999          THE'SORTED 40
         -9959          MERGING PRO20
         -9983          IT CONSISTS20
         -9999          DATA. THE F40
  02     -9999          RTYUIOPWERT60
```

```
-9871     DFGHKL'ASDF40
-9937     UIDING'INDE10
-9907     THE'PROGRAM40
-9906     'CONSISTS O50
  637     THE ALPHAMER
  656     SENT DATA CO
-9977     'THE MAIN P50
-9944     3ING PROGRA40
-9999     AME'WHICH I30
-9999     S FIRST PRI10
-9870     GJK'ASDFGHJ50
-9869     ASDFGHJKQWE50
-9999     NTED IN ORN20
-9999     E DOES'THE 60
-9999     S SORTED ON40
-9999     ASDFGHJKLAS40
 -864
 -672
 -664
 -856
 -408
 -952
 -904
-9999     ACKSPA E 5 50
 -840
 -704
 -528
 -624
 -616
 -608
 -928
-9999     REWIND'TAPE50
 -800
 -600
 -728
 -696
 -920
-9999     DFGHKL'ASDF40
-9955     'IS'ALL THE40
-9954     'TYPISTS FA50
-9895     'THE BASIS 40
-9981     PROGRAM AND30
 -592
-9952     THE'MERGE S60
 -584
-9951     UBPROGRAM U60
-9887     EER'WITH SQ20
-9999     MERGING PRO20
-9886     UENTIOAL NU30
-9999     NSIST OF 2820
 -720
-9911     PES'AND VAC20
-9999     ER SUBPROGR10
-9999     AM.'THE SEC20
-9999     OND'SUBPROG20
-9928     O THE FOLLO60
-9923     ORD'AND VAC20
```

```
-9999     'TECORD 4 B40
-9999     JHJJHJHJHJH30
  648     CODES ETC
  614     IEVE THAT TE
  615     EREASON IS T
  604     IC PORTION O
  634     DIRFCTION OF
-9999     'DIGITS( TH30
-9999     EREFORE CAN30
  643     THE RESULTIN
-9922     ATE'THE REC30
-9932     NOT'BE'DONE40
-9881     RT SHUFFLER50
  651     EXCUSE ME I
 -976
-9904     'NUMBER WIT60
-9924     'READ A REC20
 -712
-9890     TPUT NOW WA10
  602     USED TO TEST
 -496
 -488
 -960
 -816
 -880
 -936
 -832
 -432
 -784
 -640
 -480
  603     THE ALPHAMER
 -968
 -776
 -472
 -424
-9879     'BY'THE PRO60
 -448
-9878     GRAM BNFHYG10
-9972     PERATION OF20
-9971     'THE SUBPRO20
-9994     . THE PROGR30
-9993     AM WAS'WRIT30
-9889     S FIRST PRI10
 -896
-9992     TEN'FOR THE40
-9912     ND ALL'4 TA20
 -888
 -824
-9970     GRAMS AND T30
-9945     PE SIMMULAT30
-9991     '1620 COMPU40
-9990     TER'AT'ILLI50
-9962     ACTUAL'SORT10
 -768
 -760
 -440
```

```
  621     THERE FORE S
  642     UP SO THAT T
  630     WAS COMMITTE
-9926     3NS. 1'RAED10
-9903     H SIGN'ON W60
-9966     IRST SUBPRO50
-9921     ORD'LOCATIO30
-9984     RTRAN II)) 20
-9960     TWO'TO'TWO 20
-9899     CHARACTER A20
-9999     TPUT NOW WA10
-9999     NTROL THE O10
-9999     PERATION OF20
-9999     'THE SUBPRO20
-9976     ROGRAM'IS T60
-9999     PROGRAM AND30
-9999     NOT'BE'DONE40
-9868     RTYUIOPWERT60
-9999     '6 FEWIND T60
-9999     APE'AND VAC60
-9999     ATE'ALL REC10
-9999     THW'SUBPROG40
-9943     M WNICH IN 40
-9999     . THE PROGR30
-9999     GJK'ASDFGHJ50
-9999     AM WAS'WRIT30
-9942     ESSENSE CON50
-9999     ORDS. DATA 30
-9996     'PROGRAM AR20
-9995     E AS FOLLOW20
-9948     AM.'THE SEC20
-9947     OND'SUBPROG20
-9880     'AND SORTED60
-9946     RAM'IS'A TA30
-9999     FTGDH' HJJ10
 -792
 -912
 -648
 -848
-9999     ORDS 7'REWI10
-9999     ND ALL'4 TA20
-9964     ROGRAM'MERG60
-9999     'IN'FORGO) 40
-9867     YUIASDFGHJK60
-9905     F A'4 DIGIT50
-9975     O READ'IN T60
-9999     RAMS).'THE 40
 -464
 -400
 -992
-9974     HE DATA, CO10
-9900     'AND AN 11 20
-9999     PES'AND VAC20
-9999     ATE'ALL REC30
  657     NTAINS KEYS
  623     WAS SUBTARAC
-9999     RT SHUFFLER50
```

8.2.14. SORT—Output

```
OUTPUT PAGE 1        FULL DEK OF DATA
 -9999 'A RECORD 21      -9999 'OF'A MAIN 3     -9999 ACH'AND A G1     -9999 ATE'ALL REC1     -9999 EER'WITH SQ2
 -9999 'AND AN 11 2      -9999 'PROGRAM AR2     -9999 ACKSPA E 5 5     -9999 ATE'ALL REC3     -9999 ER SUBPROGR1
 -9999 'AND SORTED6      -9999 'READ A REC2     -9999 ACTUAL'SORT1     -9999 ATE'THE REC3     -9999 ER.'THIS DA6
 -9999 'BY'AN'EXPE5      -9999 'TECORD 4 B4     -9999 AM WAS'WRIT3     -9999 BRAM -'SUBP5     -9999 EREFORE CAN3

 -9999 'BY'THE PRO6      -9999 'THE BASIS 4     -9999 AM.'THE SEC2     -9999 CHARACTER A2     -9999 ESSENSE CON5
 -9999 'CONSISTS O5      -9999 'THE MAIN P5     -9999 AME'WHICH I3     -9999 DETAILS OF 1     -9999 F A'4 DIGIT5
 -9999 'DIGITS( TH3      -9999 'THE SUBPRO2     -9999 APE'AND VAC6     -9999 DFGHKL'ASDF4     -9999 FTGDHYUHHJJ1
 -9999 'IN'FORGO) 4      -9999 'TYPISTS FA5     -9999 AS SHUFFLED4     -9999 E AS FOLLOW2     -9999 FUNCTION OF5
 -9999 'IS'ALL THE4      -9999 '1620 COMPU4     -9999 ASDFGHJKLAS4     -9999 E DOES'THE 6     -9999 GJK'ASDFGHJ5


 -9999 GRAM BNFHYG1      -9999 JHJJHJHJHJH3     -9999 NOIS INSTIT5     -9999 OGRAM CAN D5     -9999 PROGRAM AND3
 -9999 H SIGN'ON W6      -9999 LANGUAGE(FO1     -9999 NOLOGY'IN T6     -9999 ON THE'SPEL3     -9999 RAM'IS'A TA3
 -9999 HE DATA, CO1      -9999 LING BUT IT4     -9999 NOT'BE'DONE4     -9999 OND'SUBPROG2     -9999 RAMS).'THE 4
 -9999 HE FORTRAM 1      -9999 LPHAMERIC N3     -9999 NSIST OF 282     -9999 ORD'AND VAC2     -9999 REWIND'TAPE5
 -9999 HICH THE SO1      -9999 M WNICH IN 4     -9999 NTED IN ORN2     -9999 ORD'LOCATIO3     -9999 ROGRAM'IS T6

 -9999 HJJHHHHJJHJ2      -9999 MBERING,THE3     -9999 NTHE DECK W4     -9999 ORDS 7'REWI1     -9999 ROGRAM'MERG6
 -9999 HMNMMNMNJHM2      -9999 MERGING PRO2     -9999 NTROL THE O1     -9999 ORDS. DATA 3     -9999 RT IS BASED1
 -9999 ING'BY'THE 1      -9999 N 3'WRITE A4     -9999 O READ'IN T6     -9999 PE SIMMULAT3     -9999 RT SHUFFLER5
 -9999 IRST SUBPRO5      -9999 ND ALL'4 TA2     -9999 O THE FOLLO6     -9999 PERATION OF2     -9999 RTRAN II)) 2
 -9999 IT CONSISTS2      -9999 NHJJNMNHHHH3     -9999 OF THE'PREC5     -9999 PES'AND VAC2     -9999 RTYUIOPWERT6


 -9999 S FIRST PRI1      -9999 THE'SORTING1     -9999 WING FUNCTI6     -9990 TER'AT'ILLI5     -9977 'THE MAIN P5
 -9999 S SORTED ON4      -9999 THW'SUBPROG4     -9999 X. WORDS CO2     -9989 NOIS INSTIT5     -9976 ROGRAM'IS T6
 -9999 SES'THE OTH1      -9999 TPUT NOW WA1     -9999 3ING PROGRA4     -9988 UTE'OF'TECH6     -9975 O READ'IN T6
 -9999 SUPLIED TO 4      -9999 TWO'TO'TWO 2     -9999 3NS. 1'RAED1     -9985 LANGUAGE(FO1     -9974 HE DATA, CO1
 -9999 TA BEING OU6      -9999 UBPROGRAM U6     -9996 'PROGRAM AR2     -9984 RTRAN II)) 2     -9973 NTROL THE O1

 -9999 TEN'FOR THE4      -9999 UENTIOAL NU3     -9995 E AS FOLLOW2     -9982 'OF'A MAIN 3     -9972 PERATION OF2
                                                                       -9981 PROGRAM AND3     -9971 'THE SUBPRO2
 -9999 THE TAPE PR5      -9999 ULTT) NOTE 5     -9993 AM WAS'WRIT3     -9980 THW'SUBPROG4     -9970 GRAMS AND T3
 -9999 THE'MERGE S6      -9999 UTE'OF'TECH6     -9992 TEN'FOR THE4     -9979 RAMS).'THE 4     -9969 O PUNCH OUT3
 -9999 THE'PROGRAM4      -9999 VCESS)(PARD3     -9991 '1620 COMPU4     -9978 FUNCTION OF5     -9968 THE'SORTED 4


 -9967 DATA. THE F4      -9956 LING BUT IT4     -9946 RAM'IS'A TA3     -9936 X. WORDS CO2     -9926 3NS. 1'RAED1
 -9966 IRST SUBPRO5      -9955 'IS'ALL THE4     -9945 PE SIMMULAT3     -9935 NSIST OF 282     -9925 'A RECORD 21
 -9965 BRAM -'SUBP5      -9954 'TYPISTS FA5     -9944 3ING PROGRA4     -9934 'DIGITS( TH3     -9924 'READ A REC2
 -9964 ROGRAM'MERG6      -9953 ULTT) NOTE 5     -9943 M WNICH IN 4     -9933 EREFORE CAN3     -9923 ORD'AND VAC2
 -9963 E DOES'THE 6      -9952 THE'MERGE S6     -9942 ESSENSE CON5     -9932 NOT'BE'DONE4     -9922 ATE'THE REC3

 -9962 ACTUAL'SORT1      -9951 UBPROGRAM U6     -9941 SISTS OF 405     -9931 'IN'FORGO) 4     -9921 ORD'LOCATIO3
 -9961 ING'BY'THE 1      -9950 SES'THE OTH1     -9940 'RECORDS OF6     -9930 THE TAPE PR5     -9920 N 3'WRITE A4
 -9960 TWO'TO'TWO 2      -9949 ER SUBPROGR1     -9939 '25'WORDS E6     -9929 OGRAM CAN D5     -9919 'TECORD 4 B4
 -9958 VCESS)(PARD3      -9948 AM.'THE SEC2     -9938 ACH'AND A G1     -9928 O THE FOLLO6     -9918 ACKSPA E 5 5
 -9957 ON THE'SPEL3      -9947 OND'SUBPROG2     -9937 UIDING'INDE1     -9927 WING FUNCTI6     -9917 REWIND'TAPE5
```

```
OUTPUT PAGE 2        FULL DEK OF DATA
 -9916 '6 REWIND T6        -9906 'CONSISTS O5        -9894 OF THE'PREC5        -9884 NTHE DECK W4        -9872 ASDFGHJKLAS4
 -9915 APE'AND VAC6        -9905 F A'4 DIGIT5        -9893 EEDING'NUMB5        -9883 AS SHUFFLED4        -9871 DFGHKL'ASDF4
 -9914 ATE'ALL REC1        -9904 'NUMBER WIT6        -9892 ER.'THIS DA6        -9882 'BY'AN'EXPE5        -9870 GJK'ASDFGHJ5
 -9913 ORDS 7'REWI1        -9903 H SIGN'ON W6        -9891 TA BEING OU6        -9881 RT SHUFFLER5        -9869 ASDFGHJKQWE5
 -9912 ND ALL'4 TA2        -9902 HICH THE SO1        -9890 TPUT NOW WA1        -9880 'AND SORTED6        -9868 RTYUIOPWERT6

 -9911 PES'AND VAC2        -9901 RT IS BASED1        -9889 S FIRST PRI1        -9879 'BY'THE PRO6        -9867 YUIASDFGHJK6
 -9910 ATE'ALL REC3        -9900 'AND AN 11 2        -9888 NTED IN ORN2        -9878 GRAM BNFHYG1         -993 +
 -9909 ORDS. DATA 3        -9899 CHARACTER A2        -9887 EER'WITH SQ2        -9877 FTGDHYUHHJJ1         -985 +
 -9908 SUPLIED TO 4        -9896 S SORTED ON4        -9886 UENTIOAL NU3        -9874 NHJJNMNHHHH3         -977 +
 -9907 THE'PROGRAM4        -9895 'THE BASIS 4        -9885 MBERING,THE3        -9873 JHJJHJHJHJH3         -969 +


  -961 +                    -881 +                    -801 +                    -721 +                    -633 +
  -953 +                    -873 +                    -793 +                    -713 +                    -625 +
  -945 +                    -865 +                    -785 +                    -705 +                    -617 +
  -937 +                    -857 +                    -777 +                    -697 +                    -609 +
  -929 +                    -849 +                    -769 +                    -689 +                    -601 +

  -921 +                    -841 +                    -761 +                    -681 +                    -593 +
  -913 +                    -833 +                    -753 +                    -673 +                    -585 +
  -905 +                    -825 +                    -745 +                    -665 +                    -577 +
  -897 +                    -817 +                    -737 +                    -649 +                    -569 +
  -889 +                    -809 +                    -729 +                    -641 +                    -561 +


  -553 +                    -473 +                     602 USED TO TEST          612 US SERT OF D          622 AS THE KEY W
  -545 +                    -465 +                     603 THE ALPHAMER          613 ATA    I BEL          623 WAS SUBTARAC
  -537 +                    -457 +                     604 IC PORTION O          614 IEVE THAT TE          624 TED FROM HTH
  -529 +                    -449 +                     605 FTHE SORT PR          615 EREASON IS T          625 THE ALPHAMER
  -521 +                    -441 +                     606 OGRAM   THE           616 HE FOLLOWING          626 IC REPRESENT

  -513 +                    -433 +                     607 PROBLEM WAS           617 ALL KEY NUME          627 AGION OF THE
  -505 +                    -425 +                     608 THAT THE COM          618 BERS USED BE          628 UMNER A ROU
  -497 +                    -417 +                     609 PUTOR WOULD           619 FORE WERE NE          629 ND OF ERROR
  -489 +                    -409 +                     610 NOT PUNCH OU          620 GATIVE AND            630 WAS COMMITTE
  -481 +                    -401 +                     611 T THE PREVIO          621 THERE FORE S          631 ED IN THE DI


   632 RECTION OPPO          642 UP SO THAT T          653 PTED THE PRE          666 IN THE SAME
   633 SITE TO THE           643 THE RESULTIN          656 SENT DATA CO
   634 DIRECTION OF          645 G ALPHAMERIC          657 NTAINS KEYS
   635 THE ORIGINAL          646 CODES WEW E           658 OF THAT ALL
   636 ERROR THUS T          647 NON EXISTANT          659 OF WHICH ARE

   637 THE ALPHAMER          648 CODES ETC             660 POSITIVE SO
   638 IC REPERESEN          649 WITH THE PRE          661 THAT THE ROU
   639 TATION OF TH          650 SENT DATAS            662 ND DING ERRO
   640 HE NUMEBER W          651 EXCUSE ME I           663 ROR SHOULD A
   641 WAS MESSED U          652 AWAS INTERRU          664 ALWAYS BE I
```

8.2.15. Programs—Final Version

```
*2805
      DIMENSION TITLE(5),A(25),B(50),MN(5)
    1 READ 2,TITLE
    2 FO?MAT(5A14)
      DO 3 I=1,25
    3 A(I)=0.
      CALL TA?E(A,5,7)
      L=1
   10 N2=0
      DO 4 I=1,50
      DO 5 J=1,25
      READ 6,K,NSORT,BB
    6 FORMAT(I2,3X,I5,10X,A12)
   31 FORMAT(2X,I5,1X,A12,2(7X,I5,1X,A12)/1HI,21X,2(7X,I5,1X,A12))
      ZN=NSORT
      A(J)=ZN+BB
      N2=N2+1
      IF(K) 7,5,7
    5 CONTINUE
    4 CALL TAPE(A,L,3)
    7 CALL TAPE(A,L,3)
      GO TO (8,9),L
    8 N1=N2
      L=2
      GO TO 10
    9 N=N1+N2
      CALL TAPE(A,1,5)
      CALL TAPE(A,2,5)
      L=1
   12 CALL MERGE(L,N1,N2,LINE)
      IF(SENSE SWITCH 1)14,15
   14 PRINT 16,LINE
   16 FORMAT(I3)
   15 IF(LINE)1,18,12
   18 NP=0
      DO 20 I=1,9
      PUNCH 21,I, TITLE
   21 FORMAT(12H)OUTPUT PAGE,I2,1X,5A13)
      DO 20 J=1,4
      IR=N-NP
      IF(IR)1,1,34
   34 CALL TAPE(A,L,1)
      DO 23 K=1,25
   23 B(K)=A(K)
      IF(IR-25)24,24,25
   25 CALL TA?E(A,L,1)
      DO 26 K=1,25
   26 B(K+25)=A(K)
   24 DO27 K=1,10
      IF(K-IR)33,33,1
   33 NN=0
      IF(IR-50)121,121,122
  122 IR=50
  121 DO 28 M=K,IR,10
      NN=NN+1
      MN(NN)=B(M)
```

```
      IF(B(M))130,130,131
  130 MN(NN)=MN(NN)-1
  131 Z=MN(NN)
   28 A(NN)=B(M)-Z
      NP=NP+NN
      IF(K-6)27,29,27
   29 PUNCH 30
   30 FORMAT(1X)
   27 PUNCH 31,(MN(M),A(M),M=1,NN)
   20 PUNCH 32
   32 FORMAT(///)
      END
*1605
```

```
*2805
      SUBROUTINE MERGE(NTAP,N1,N2,LINE)
      DIMENSION  SL(25),TL(25),UL(25),VL(25)
      NTO=(NTAP-2)*(-1)+2
      DO 71 I=1,25
      SL(I)=0.
      TL(I)=0.
      UL(I)=0.
   71 VL(I)=0.
      CALL TAPE(SL,NTO,6)
      CALL TAPE(SL,NTO+1,6)
      IS=1
      IT=1
      IU=0
      IV=0
      JS=1
      JT=1
      JU=1
      JV=1
      V=10.**10.
      U=-V
      CALL TAPE(SL,NTAP,2)
      CALL TAPE(TL,NTAP+1,2)
      S=SL(1)
      T=TL(1)
      LEFT=1
      LINE=0
    1 II=0
      IF( SENSE SWITCH 3)120,121
  120 PUNCH 101,II,LINE,LEFT,IS,IT,IU,IV,JS,JT, J,JV,S,T,U,V
  101 FORMAT(I2,I3,I2,2X,4I3,2X,4I3,4X,4F7.2)
  121 GO TO (2,4,3,40),LEFT
    2 IF(S-T)3,3,4
    3 IF(U-V)5,6,6
    4 IF(U-V)7,8,8
    5 II=II+1
      IF(S-V)10,18,18
    6 II=II+1
      IF(S-U)9,17,17
    7 II=II+1
      IF(T-V)12,20,20
    8 II=II+1
      IF(T-U)11,19,19
    9 GO TO (5,7,5,13),II
   10 GO TO (6,8,6,14),II
   11 GO TO (7,5,7,15),II
   12 GO TO (8,6,8,16),II
   13 LINE=LINE+1
   20 ZN=T
      I5=2
      I6=2
      GO TO 21
   14 LINE=LINE+1
   19 ZN=T
      I5=2
      I6=1
      GO TO 21
   15 LINE=LINE+1
   18 ZN=S
      I5=1
      I6=2
      GO TO 21
   16 LINE=LINE+1
   17 ZN=S
      I5=1
      I6=1
   21 GO TO (22,23),I5
   22 IS=IS+1
      IF (SENSE SWITCH ?) 122,123
  122 PUNCH 102
  102 FORMAT(6H PUT S)
  123 IF(IS-N1-1)24,25,333
   25 LEFT=LEFT+1
      S=-(10.**10.)
      GO TO 36
   24 JS=JS+1
      IF(JS-25)26,26,27
   27 CALL TAPE(SL,NTAP,2)
      JS=1
   26 S=SL(JS)
      GO TO 36
   23 IT=IT+1
      IF (SENSE SWITCH 3) 124,125
  124 PUNCH 103
  103 FORMAT(6H PUT T)
  125 IF(IT-N2-1)28,29,333
   29 LEFT=LEFT+2
      T=-(10.**10.)
      GO TO 36
   28 JT=JT+1
      IF(JT-25)30,30,31
   31 CALL TAPE(TL,NTAP+1,2)
      JT=1
   30 T=TL(JT)
   36 GO TO (37,38),I6
   37 UL(JU)=ZN
      IF (SENSE SWITCH 3) 126,127
  126 PUNCH 104
  104 FORMAT(7H INTO U)
  127 U=ZN
      IU=IU+1
      JU=JU+1
      IF(JU-25)  1,1,32
   32 CALL TAPE(UL,NTO,3)
      JU=1
      GO TO 1
   38 VL(JV)=ZN
      IF (SENSE SWITCH ?) 128,129
  128 PUNCH 105
  105 FORMAT(7H INTO V)
  129 V=ZN
      JV=JV+1
      IV=IV+1
      IF(JV-25)1,1,33
   33 CALL TAPE(VL,NTO+1,3)
      JV=1
      GO TO 1
   40 N1=IU
      N2=IV
      NTAP=NTO
      IF(JU-1)41,41,42
   42 CALL TAPE(UL,NTO,3)
   41 CALL TAPE(UL,NTO,5)
      IF(JV-1)43,43,44
   44 CALL TAPE(VL,NTO+1,3)
   43 CALL TAPE(VL,NTO+1,5)
      RETURN
  333 PRINT 334
  334 FORMAT(20HILLEGAL OPERATION    )
      PAUSE
      RETURN
      END
```

```
*2805
      SUBROUTINE TAPE(B,NOPT,IOP)
      DIMENSION A(25,30),B(25),INDEX(4,30),IOPEN(30),IAT(4)
  108 FORMAT(5H)TAPE,I2,5H   OP,I2,7H   NEXT,I3,5H   AT,4I3/25I3/1HI,26X
     1,5I3//4(25I3/1HI,26X,5I3/)/(7H RECORD,I3,25X,25X,E12.5/1HI,23X,4E1
     22.5/6E12.5/1HI,23X,4E12.5/6E12.5/1HI,23X,4E12.5))
      GO TO(55,55,55,55,55,55,101),IOP
   55 IF(SENSE SWITCH 2)100,101
  100 GO TO(102,103),JJ
  102 PRINT 105
  105 FORMAT(18HWHAT RECORDS (2I2))
      ACCEPT 104,J1,J2
  104 FORMAT(2I2)
      JJ=2
  103 IF(SENSE SWITCH 4)102,107
  107 I00=0
      PUNCH 108,NOPT,IOP, NEXT,IAT,IOPEN,((INDEX(I,J),J=1,30),I=1,4),I00
     1,B,(J,(A(I,J),I=1,25),J=J1,J2)
  101 GO TO (71,71,73,74,75,76,77),IOP
   77 DO 1 I=1,30
      JJ=1
      IOPEN(I)=I
      DO 2 J=1,4
    2 INDEX(J,I)=0
      DO 1 J=1,25
    1 A(J,I)=0.
      DO 3 I=1,4
    3 IAT(I)=0
      NEXT=1
      RETURN
   76 IAT(NOPT)=0
      DO 4 I=1,30
      K=INDEX(NOPT,I)
         INDEX(NOPT,I)=0
      IF(K)78,4,5
    5 NEXT=NEXT-1
      IOPEN(NEXT)=K
      DO 6 J=1,25
    6 A(J,K)=0.
    4 CONTINUE
      RETURN
   75 IAT(NOPT)=0
      RETURN
   74 IF(IAT(NOPT))78,78,31
   31 IAT(NOPT)=IAT(NOPT)-1
      RETURN
   71 I=IAT(NOPT)+1
      IAT(NOPT)=I
      K=INDEX(NOPT,I)
      IF(K)78,78,67
   67 DO 7 L=1,25
    7 B(L)=A(L,K)
      GO TO (79,72),IOP
   72 INDEX(NOPT,I)=0
      NEXT=NEXT-1
      IOPEN(NEXT)=K
      DO 8 I=1,25
    8 A(I,K)=0.
   79 RETURN
   73 I=IAT(NOPT)+1
      IF(I-31)33,78,78
   33 IAT(NOPT)=I
      K=INDEX(NOPT,I)
      IF(K)78,9,10
    9 K=IOPEN(NEXT)
      INDEX(NOPT,I)=K
      NEXT=NEXT+1
   10 DO 11 I=1,25
   11 A(I,K)=B(I)
      RETURN
   78 PUNCH 69
      PRINT 69
   69 FORMAT(14H ERROR IN TAPE)
      RETURN
      END
```

Appendix A

Matrix Inversion Program

Using the Gauss-Jordan Method with the

Product Form of the Inverse

The program is written in FORTRAN II for a word length of 15 characters; it can easily be transformed into FORTRAN IV. For the regression system of Chapter 8, the program was transformed to FORTRAN IV using double precision on the IBM 7040 computer.

INDEX

Programs

Main Program

```
*1504
      DIMENSION A(30,30),B(30,30),V(30),S(30),C(30),V1(30,1),S1(30,1),C
     11(30,1)
      COMMON C,A,N,L,D,LX,KKKM
      EQUIVALENCE(V1(1),V(1)),(S1(1),S(1)),(C1(1),C(1))
      D=ABSF(1.)
    1 READ 99,N,IP
   12 IF(N)60,61,60
   61 STOP
   60 IF(IP-6200)90,91,90
   91 KKKP=0
      KKKM=1
      GO TO 92
   90 KKKP=1
      KKKM=0
   92 READ 100,((A(J,K),J=1,N),K=1,N)
      DO 2 J=1,N
      DO 2 K=1,N
    2 B(J,K)=A(J,K)
      IF(SENSE SWITCH 3)80,81
   80 PUNCH 110
      GO TO 82
   81 PRINT 110
   82 IF(SENSE SWITCH 1)3,4
    3 IF(SENSE SWITCH 3)5,6
    5 PUNCH 101,N
      CALL OUTPUT(1)
      GO TO 4
    6 PRINT 101,N
      CALL OUTPUT(2)
    4 CALL INV
      IF(SENSE SWITCH 3)40,41
   40 PUNCH 103,D,LX
      GO TO(7,8),L
   41 PRINT 103,D,LX
      GO TO(7,8),L
    8 IF(SENSE SWITCH 3)9,10
    9 PUNCH 102
      GO TO 11
   10 PRINT 102
   11 READ 99,N,IP
      IF(N)60,70,60
   70 IF(IP-4500)11,61,11
    7 IF(IP-6200)88,14,88
   88 IF(SENSE SWITCH 3)15,16
   15 PUNCH 104
      CALL OUTPUT(1)
      GO TO 14
   16 PRINT 104
      CALL OUTPUT(2)
   14 READ 99,J,IPP,(V(K),K=1,4)
      IF(J)17,18,17
   18 IF(IPP-4500)50,17,50
   50 IF(N-4)19,19,20
   20 READ 107,(V(K),K=5,N)
   19 CALL MPY(A,N,V1,KKKP,S)
      IF(SENSE SWITCH 4)21,22
   21 CALL MPY(B,N,S1,1,C)
      IF(SENSE SWITCH 3)23,24
   23 PUNCH 108,L,L,(J,S(J),J,V(J),C(J),J=1,N)
   68 L=L+1
      GO TO 14
   24 PRINT 108,L,L,(J,S(J),J,V(J),C(J),J=1,N)
      GO TO 68
   22 IF(SENSE SWITCH 3)25,26
   25 PUNCH 106,L,L,(J,S(J),J,V(J),J=1,N)
      GO TO 68
   26 PRINT 106,L,L,(J,S(J),J,V(J),J=1,N)
      GO TO 68
   17 IF(IP-6200)13,27,13
   13 IF(SENSE SWITCH 2)28,27
   27 N=J
      IP=IPP
      GO TO 12
   28 CALL MPY(A,N,B,N,S)
      IF(SENSE SWITCH 3)29,30
   29 PUNCH 109
      CALL OUTPUT(1)
      GO TO 27
   30 PRINT 109
      CALL OUTPUT(2)
      GO TO 27
   99 FORMAT(I2,A1,4E19.11)
  100 FORMAT(8F10.4)
  101 FORMAT(1X15HORIGINAL MATRIX/1X5HORDERI3/)
  102 FORMAT(1X18HMATRIX IS SINGULAR/)
  103 FORMAT(1X13HDETERMINANT= E14.7,22H TIMES 10 TO THE POWER I4)
  104 FORMAT(/ 1X17HRECIPROCAL MATRIX/)
  106 FORMAT(//6H GROUPI4,16X13HCOLUMN VECTORI4//(2H XI3,2H= E14.7,5X1HV
     1I3,2H= E14.7))
  107 FORMAT(3X4E19.11)
  108 FORMAT(//6H GROUPI4,16X13HCOLUMN VECTORI4,8X5HCHECK//(2H XI3,2H= E
     114.7,5X1HVI3,2H= E14.7,4XE14.7))
  109 FORMAT(/1X7HPRODUCT/)
  110 FORMAT(1H ///)
      END
```

Subroutine OUTPUT

```
*1504
      SUBROUTINE OUTPUT(NA)
      DIMENSION ARRAY(30,30),C(30)
      COMMON C,ARRAY,NUMBER
  100 FORMAT(5(2XE14.7))
  101 FORMAT(2H  )
      DO 1 LLL=1,NUMBER,5
      MMM=LLL+4
      IF(MMM-NUMBER)4,4,5
    5 MMM=NUMBER
    4 DO 6 J=1,NUMBER
      GO TO(7,8),NA
    7 PUNCH 100,(ARRAY(J,K),K=LLL,MMM)
      GO TO 6
    8 PRINT 100,(ARRAY(J,K),K=LLL,MMM)
    6 CONTINUE
      GO TO(9,10),NA
    9 PUNCH 101
      GO TO 1
   10 PRINT 101
    1 CONTINUE
      RETURN
      END
```

Subroutine MPY

```
*1504
      SUBROUTINE MPY(A1,N1,A2,N2,TEMP)
      DIMENSION A1(30,30),A2(30,30),TEMP(30),A(30,30),C(30),LP(30)
      COMMON C,A,N,L1,D1,L2,L3,LP
      IF(N2)18,19,18
   18 DO 5 I=1,N1
      DO 1 J=1,N2
      SUM=0
      DO 2 K=1,N1
    2 SUM=SUM+A1(I,K)*A2(K,J)
      IF(N2-1)1,9,1
    9 TEMP(I)=SUM
      GO TO 5
    1 TEMP(J)=SUM
      DO 5 M=1,N2
      A1(I,M)=TEMP(M)
    5 CONTINUE
    7 RETURN
   19 DO 10 I=1,N1
      LTEMP=LP(I)
   10 TEMP(I)=A2(LTEMP,1)
      DO 11 I=1,N1
      L=N1-I+1
      P=TEMP(I)
      DO 11 K=1,N1
   11 TEMP(K)=TEMP(K)+A1(K,L)*P
      RETURN
      END
```

Subroutine INV

```
*1504
      SUBROUTINE INV
      DIMENSION A(30,30),LP(30),C(30)
      COMMON C,A,N,LEST,DETT,LEXP,LS,LP
      NN=N
      DETT=1.
      LEST=1
      M2=1
      LEXP=0
      LP(1)=0
      DO 1 M1=1,N
      BIG=0.
      DO 2 I=1,N
      DO 3 J=1,M2
      IF(I-LP(J))3,2,3
    3 CONTINUE
      IF(ABSF(BIG)-ABSF(A(I,1)))4,2,2
    4 BIG=A(I,1)
      L1=I
    2 CONTINUE
      DETT=DETT*BIG
      BETT=ABSF(DETT)
      IF(BETT-1.0E+85)100,100,101
  100 IF(BETT-1.0E-85)103,102,102
  101 DETT=DETT/1.0E+85
      LEXP=LEXP+85
      GO TO 102
  103 DETT=DETT/1.0E-85
      LEXP=LEXP-85
  102 M2=M1
      IF(ABSF(BIG)-1.0E-06)5,5,6
    5 LEST=2
      RETURN
    6 LP(M1)=L1
      IF(NN-1)50,51,50
   50 DO 8 I=2,NN
    8 A(L1,I-1)=A(L1,I)/BIG
      IF(L1-1)9,10,9
   10 LN=2
   13 LM=N
      GO TO 15
    9 LM=L1-1
      LN=1
   15 DO 11 I=LN,LM
      C(I)=-A(I,1)
      IF(C(I))12,111,12
  111 DO 112 J=2,NN
  112 A(I,J-1)=A(I,J)
      GO TO 11
   12 DO 11 J=2,NN
      A(I,J-1)=C(I)*A(L1,J-1)+A(I,J)
   11 CONTINUE
      IF(LN-1)19,18,19
   18 LN=LN+L1
      IF(LN-N)13,13,19
   19 C(L1)=1.
      DO 77 I=1,N
   77 A(I,NN)=C(I)/BIG
    1 NN=NN-LS
   55 DO 34 K=1,N
      DO 16 J=1,N
   16 C(J)=A(J,K)
      DO 34 J=1,N
      L=LP(J)
      IF(K-J)56,34,34
   56 IF(LP(K)-L)34,34,57
   57 DETT=-DETT
   34 A(J,K)=C(L)
      IF(LS)70,71,70
   71 DO 20 J=1,N
      DO 21 K=1,N
   21 C(K)=A(J,K)
      DO 20 K=1,N
      L=LP(K)
   20 A(J,L)=C(K)
      RETURN
   51 A(L1,1)=-1.
      DO 52 I=1,N
   52 A(I,1)=-A(I,1)/BIG
      GO TO 55
   70 DO 83 I=1,N
      J=N+1-I
   83 A(I,J)=A(I,J)-1.
      RETURN
      END
```

Flow Charts

Main Program

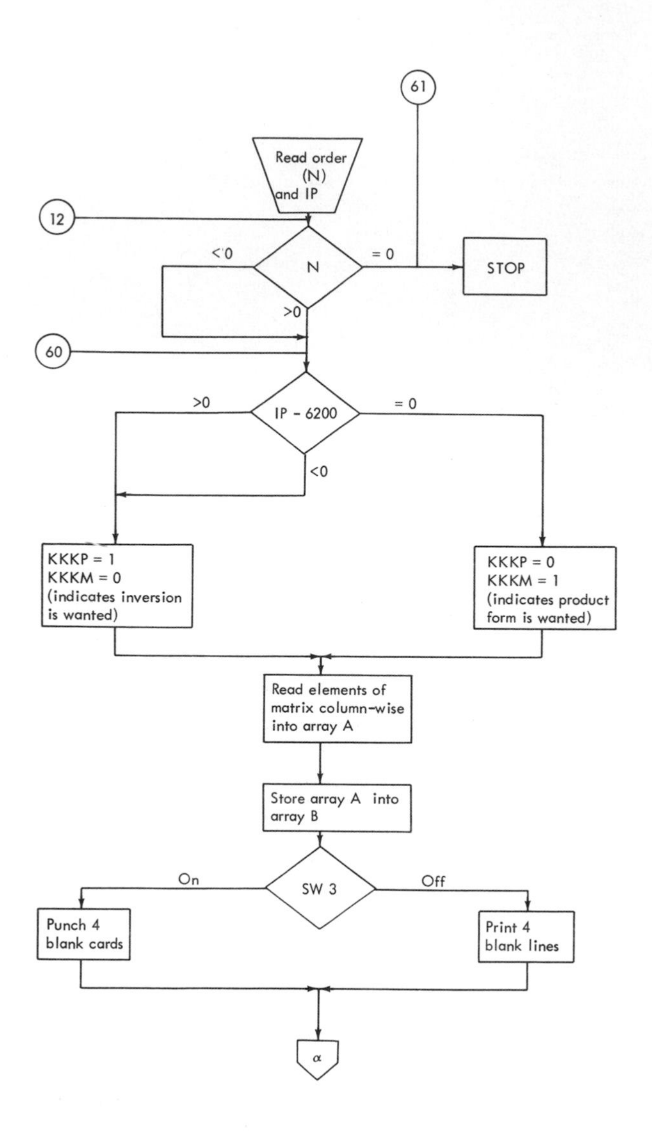

Main Program—Continued

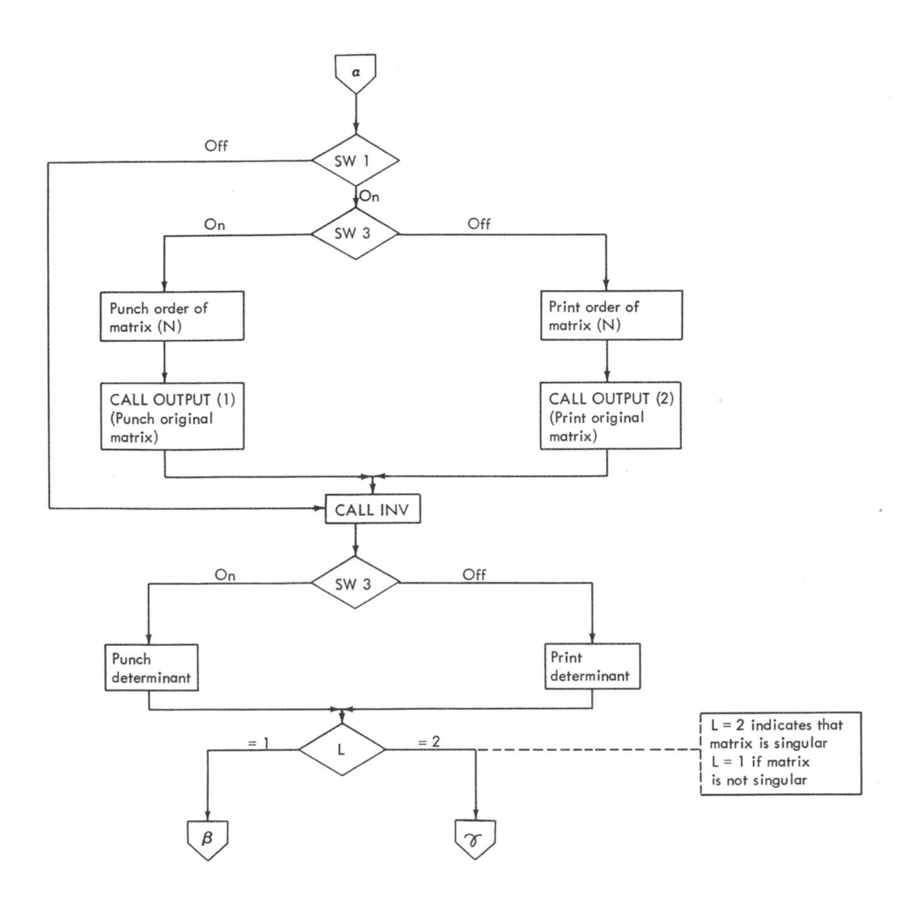

Main Program—Continued

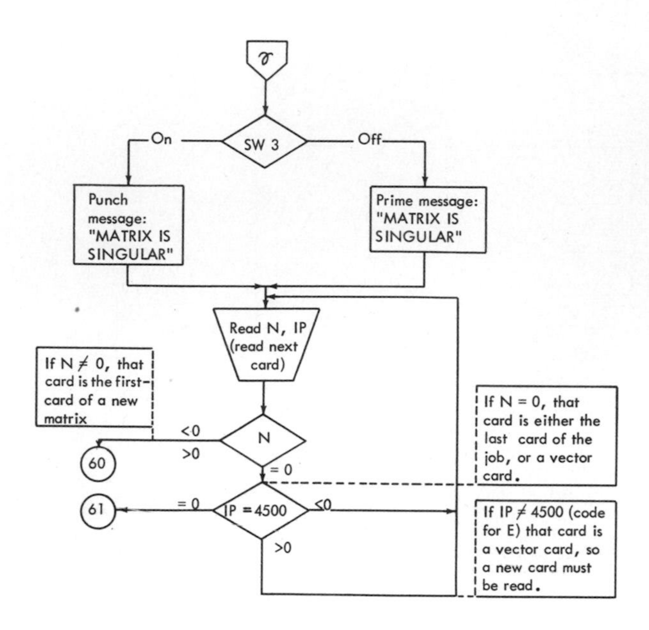

Main Program—Continued

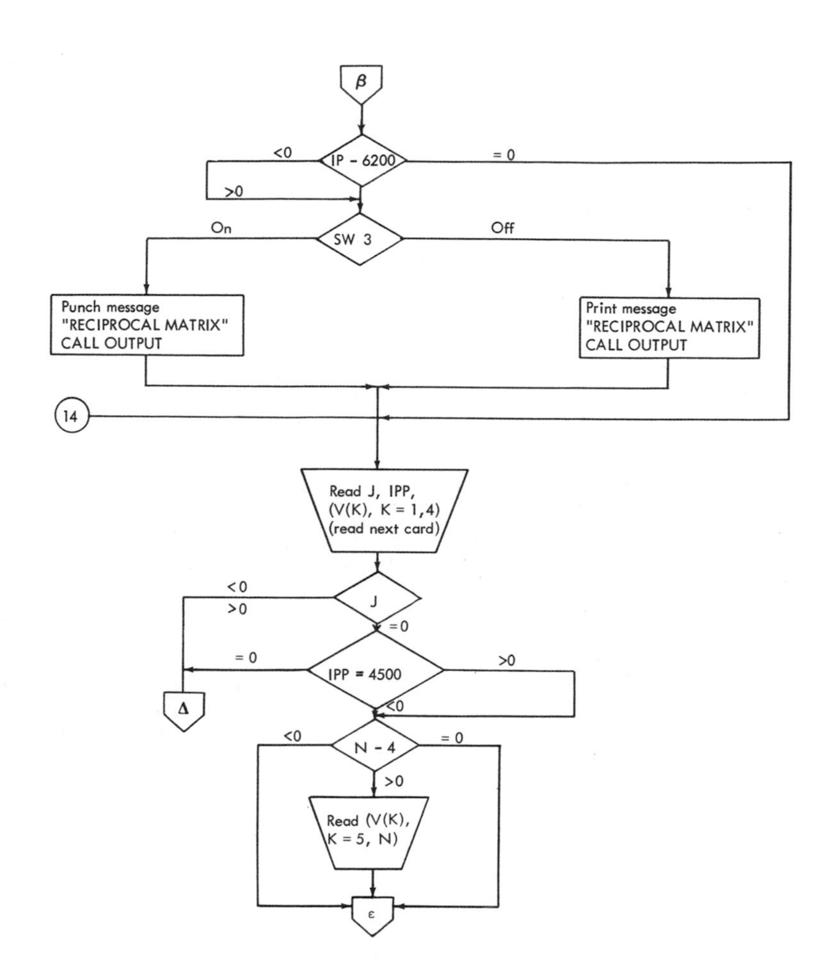

Main Program—Continued

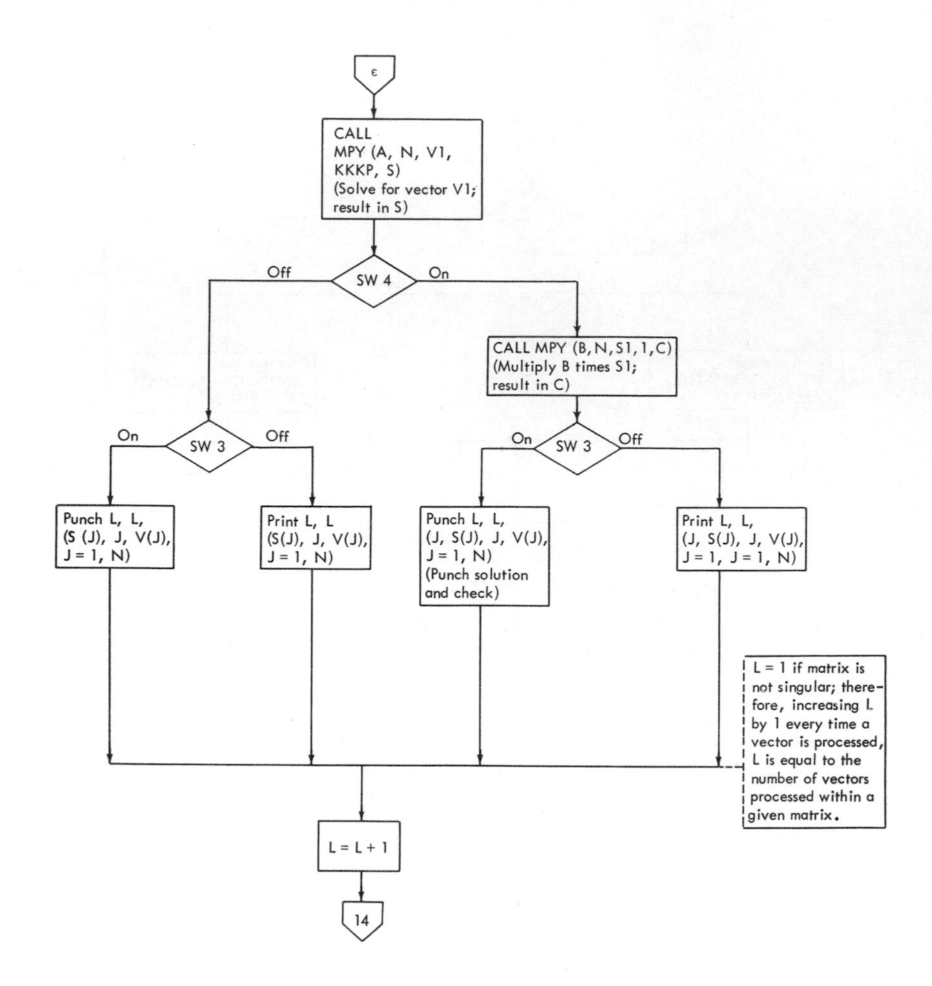

Main Program—*Continued*

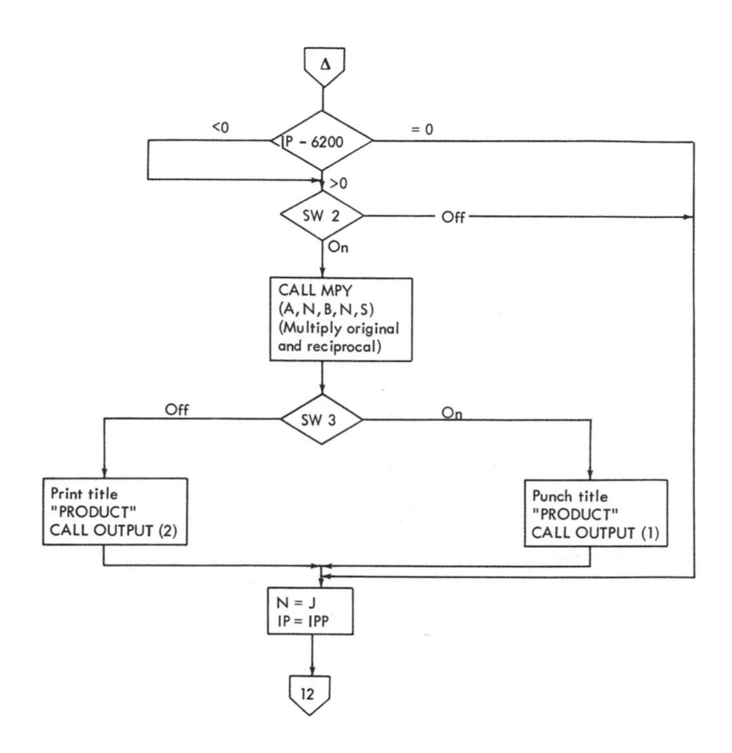

Subroutine OUTPUT

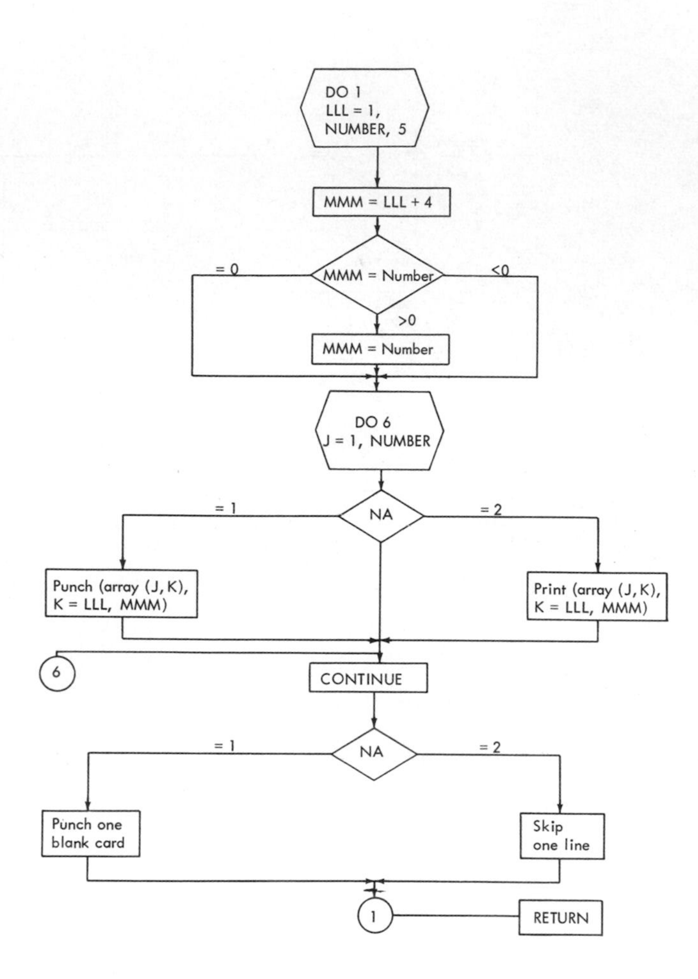

Subroutine MPY

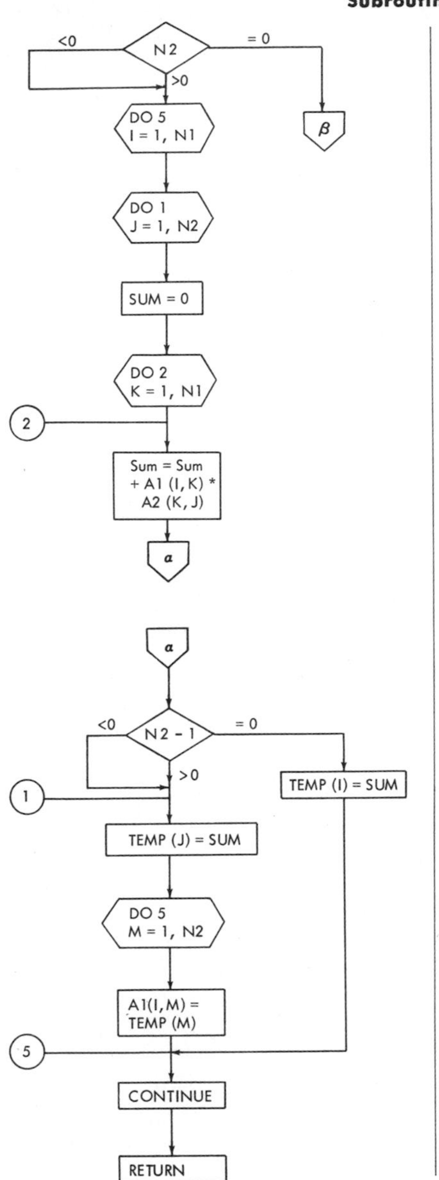

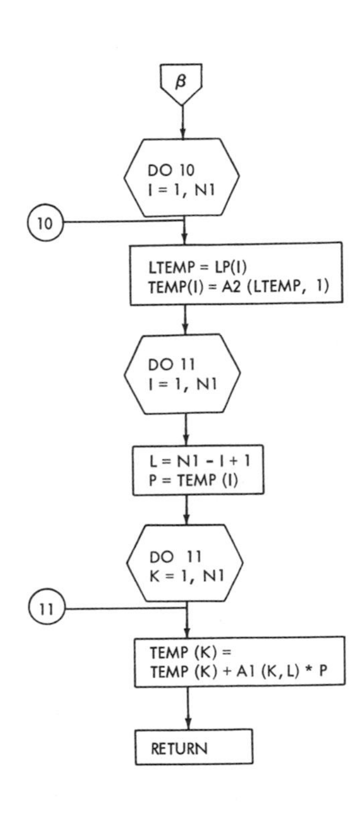

Subroutine INV

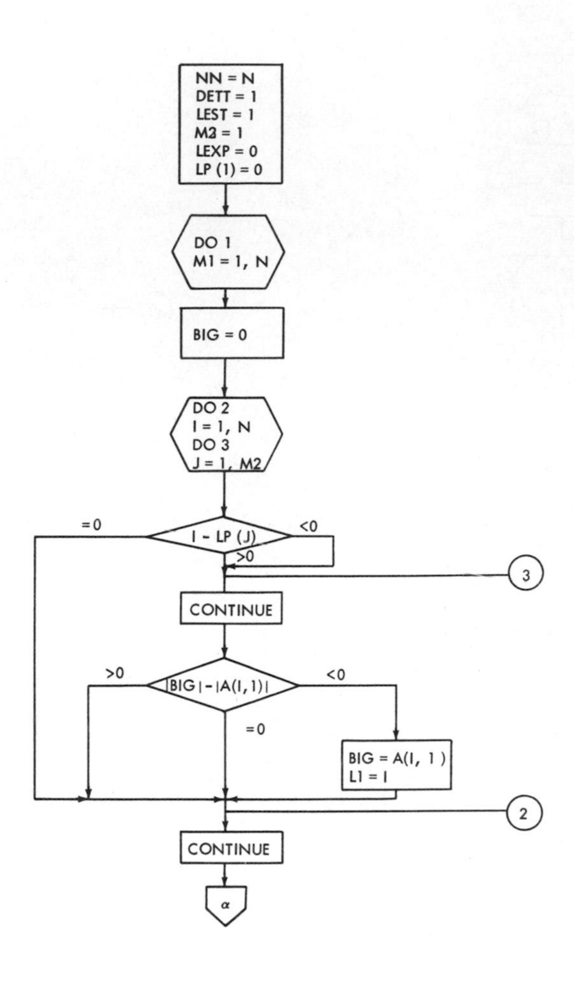

Subroutine INV—*Continued*

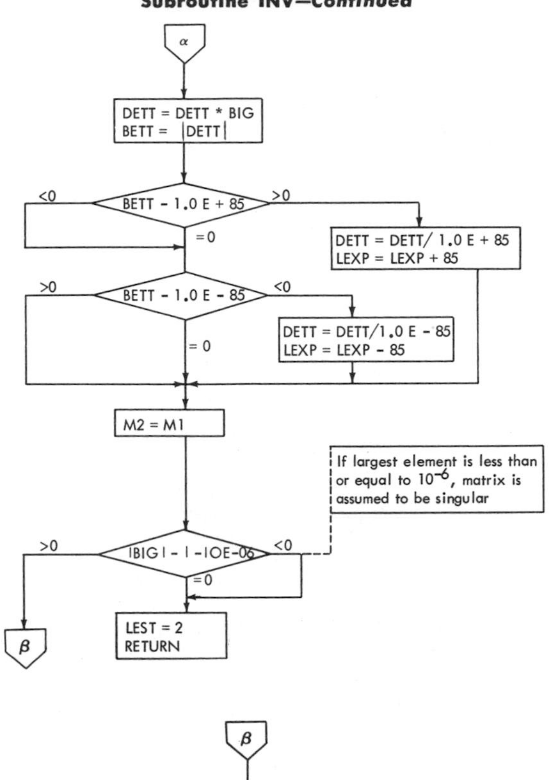

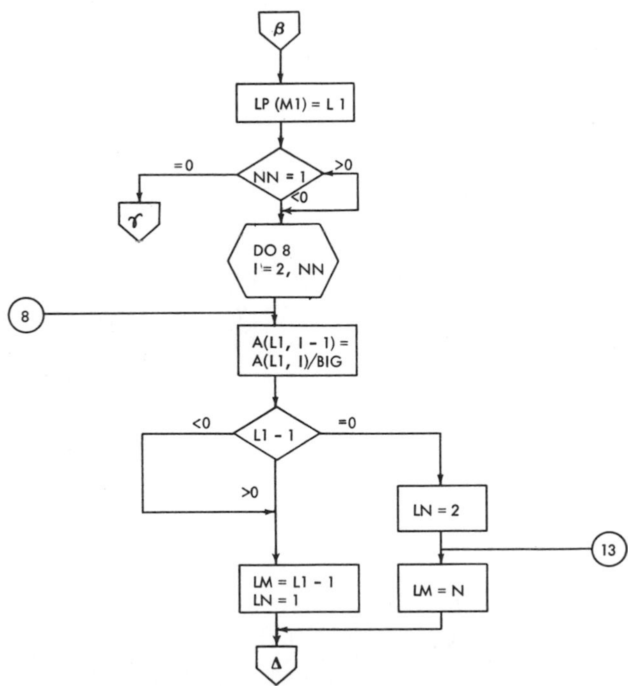

Subroutine INV—Continued

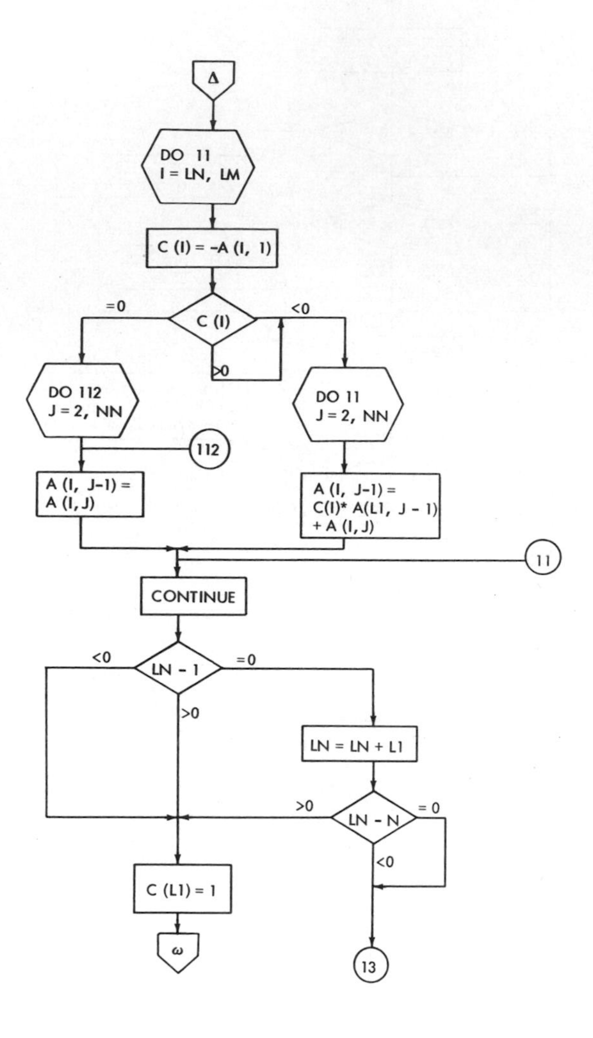

Subroutine INV—Continued

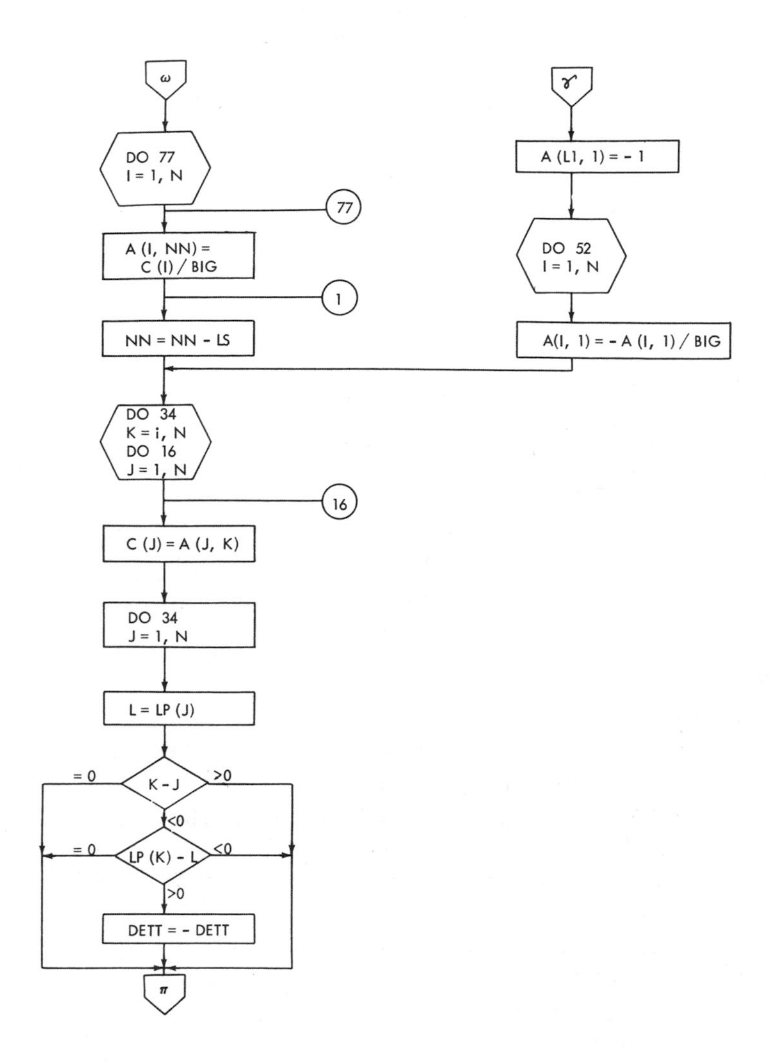

Subroutine INV—Continued

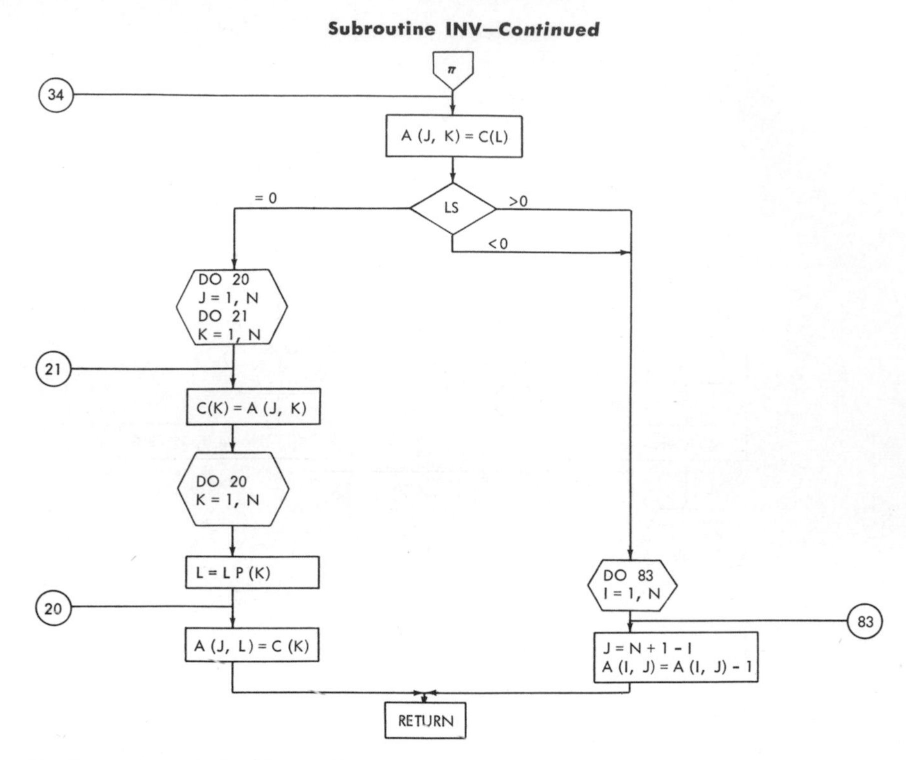

Explanation of the Flow Charts

a) Main Program:

Page 500 The order of the matrix N, is read from columns 1 and 2 of the first card. The third column is read in A format and its value is stored in IP.

If IP = 6,200, an S is punched in column 3. This letter indicates that the product form of the inverse is to be calculated. KKKP and KKKM are set, respectively, to 0 and 1. The first variable is used in the subroutine MPY, the second in the subroutine INV.

If IP $\neq$ 6,200, the inverse is sought. Consequently KKKP and KKKM are respectively set to 1 and 0.

The elements of the matrix are read, columnwise, into array A, then stored in array B.

Output space is provided by punching 4 blank cards or by skipping 4 lines, according to whether switch 3 is on or off.

Page 501 The position of switch 1 is checked. If the switch is on, the original matrix is either printed or punched, according to the status of switch 3. The output of the original matrix is obtained by calling the subroutine OUTPUT—OUTPUT(1) for punching, OUTPUT(2) for printing. Next, the subroutine INV is called. If switch 1 is off, the original matrix is not obtained, and INV is called.

After control returns to the main program, the determinant of the matrix is either printed or punched, according to the position of switch 3.

When an ill-conditioned matrix has a "small" determinant (anything below 10^{-6}), the program could assume that matrix to be singular. Such extreme cases must be judged individually.

The value of L is tested. If L = 2, the matrix is singular.

Page 502 If the matrix is singular, a message regarding this is punched or printed, according to the setting of switch 3. The next card is read; if columns 1 and 2 are blank, that card is either a vector card or the last card of the job. The information read from column 3 into IP is tested to see if it is equal to 4,500. This would indicate that the card read had an E in column 3, thus being the "last card of job." If IP $\neq$ 4,500, that card is a vector card which is ignored, because the matrix is singular. The next card is read in, and the analysis is repeated until the first card of a new matrix or the "last card of job" is reached. If the latter occurs, the program branches to statement 61. If the former occurs, the program branches to statement 60. Statement 61 is a STOP statement, and statement 60 begins the analysis of the new matrix, repeating the process described in the second paragraph of the former page.

Page 503 Unless a matrix is singular, a check is made to determine if the inverse or just the product form was obtained.

If IP is 6,200, the leading card of the last matrix processed had "S" punched in column 3, indicating that the product form of the inverse was calculated. Hence, control transfers to read the next card of the job. If IP $\neq$ 6,200, the inverse was obtained and will be printed or punched according to the setting of switch 3.

The next card is read in (statement 14). Columns 1 and 2 are read into location J; column 3 is read alphamerically into location IPP; columns 4 through 79 are read in the array V(K), from K = 1 to 4; 19 columns are devoted to each element of V.

If J $\neq$ 0, the last card read is the first card of a new matrix and control passes to part "Δ."

If J = 0, that card is either the last card of the job or a vector card. When IPP = 4,500, that card is the last card of the job and control passes to "Δ." When IPP $\neq$ 4,500, that card is a vector card.

V(1) through V(4) contain the information in columns 4 to 79 of that card; a check is made to determine that all the elements of the vector to be processed have been read in.

If the order of the previously processed matrix is greater than 4, the remaining elements are read into the array V and the vector is processed. If the order of the matrix is less than or equal to 4, V(I), I = 1, 2, . . . N, where N is the order of the matrix, contain all the elements of said vector.

Page 504 The subroutine MPY is called. When KKKP = 1, A is multiplied by V1 and the result is stored in S. If KKKP is 0, the subroutine MPY is instructed to calculate the answer, using the product form, and store the result in S.

Neither A nor V1 is destroyed in the process.

If switch 4 is on, MPY is again called. The original matrix, previously saved in array B is multiplied by the solution vector S1. The result is stored in C.

The solution vector; the vector read in and the check are printed or punched according to the position of switch 3.

If switch 4 is off, then no check on the calculations is made and just the solution vector and the vector read in are obtained.

As L = 1 if the matrix is not singular, L can be used as a count to indicate the number of vectors processed with a given matrix. This is accomplished by increasing L by 1 every time a vector is processed.

Control is then transferred to statement 14 to read a new card and carry the same analysis as explained above.

Page 505 A card other than a vector card was found. The information read from column 3 of the first card of the matrix just processed is checked, to see if the inverse or the product form was calculated. In the first case, the product of the original matrix and the reciprocal matrix will be obtained if switch 2 is on. MPY will be called in that case, and A will be multiplied by B. The product is stored in A, and is either printed or punched according to the position of switch 3.

The values in J and IPP are stored respectively in N and IP.

Control transfers to statement 12; this statement determines whether the last card read is the beginning of a new matrix, or the last card of the job.

b) *Subroutine OUTPUT:*

Page 506 This subroutine produces order in the output of matrices. When printed, each matrix is easily discernible, rather than appearing as part of one large mass of numbers.

c) *Subroutine MPY:*

Page 507 The variable N2 is checked. If $N2 \neq 0$, the first matrix in the calling sequence is multiplied by the second matrix in the calling sequence. If N2 = 1, the second matrix is assumed to be a column vector. The first matrix is not destroyed in the process. If N2 is greater than 1, the second matrix is assumed to be a square matrix of order N2. The first matrix is destroyed in the process.

If N2 is equal to 0, control passes to part "β."

The given column vector is scrambled according to the permutation used to unscramble the rows of the product form, in the subroutine INV.

The solution vector is obtained by performing the corresponding operations required when using the product form.

d) Subroutine INV:

Page 508 NN is made equal to N, the order of the matrix being processed. DETT, which will finally contain the value of the determinant is made equal to 1. LEST, which indicates whether the matrix is singular or not, is originally set to 1.

M2 is set to 1. LEXP will contain the exponent of the determinant if bigger than 85 or less than -85; it is set initially to 0. Vector LP contains the position of the largest element per column, picked at every stage in the process. LP(1) is initially set to 0.

The first loop governs the N steps necessary in calculating the inverse or the product form.

The second loop chooses the largest element per column. The third loop ensures that the element chosen as largest in a given column is in a position different from any of those previously chosen.

Page 509 The determinant is the product of the pivotal elements. DETT, originally set to 1, is multiplied by the pivot; the result is stored back in DETT.

A check is made to see if the determinant is, in absolute value, within the interval $(10^{-85}, 10^{85})$. The largest possible element of any given matrix is, due to the input format, $999\,999\,999 \approx 10^9$. If f is used to represent the floating-point precision, the largest exponent a number can have without causing overflow is $(1-10^{-f})\times 10^{99}$, or approximately 10^{99}. The maximum value of the determinant at stage k, to insure against an overflow at stage $k + 1$, is approximately 10^{89}. Hence by decreasing the exponent of DETT when near 10^{89}, overflow is avoided. By a similar procedure we can also check for underflow. Arbitrarily we have chosen 10^{85} and 10^{-85} as the limit points.

When the largest element per column is 0, the matrix is singular; this is a necessary and sufficient condition. We have assumed that any pivot less than 10^{-6} corresponds to a singular matrix. An excessive round-off error is often introduced in dividing by small elements likely to be in error. When a matrix is found to be singular, the message "MATRIX IS SINGULAR" appears in the output. Previous to this message, a value appears for the determinant of that matrix. That value is the product of the pivots up to the point where the inversion process was interrupted.

The order of the row where the pivot lies is stored in the array LP. The variable NN is decreased by LS at every stage. If the inverse is sought, $LS = 0$ and NN maintains its original value. NN determines the number of columns transformed per stage. In calculating the inverse, all columns are transformed. When calculating the product form the number of columns transformed decreases, one per stage.

When NN = 1, control transfers to part "γ." When NN $\neq$ 1, the elements in columns 2 to NN of the row containing the pivot are divided by this pivot.

Page 510 The array C contains all elements in the column of the pivot, except the pivot itself. If the position of the pivot is I, then C(I) = 1. When element C(L) $\neq$ 0, the elements in the row of the pivot are multiplied by C(L) and the product is added to the elements in row L. When each element is calculated, it is moved one position to the left. When C(L) = 0, computation is bypassed, and all elements in row L are moved to the left.

Page 511 The last column of the matrix is obtained at every stage through dividing C(I) by the pivot BIG. The element in the row of the pivot will be the inverse of that pivot. NN is decreased by LS and the process is repeated.

The rows of the matrix are unscrambled according to the permutation

$$\begin{pmatrix} 1, & 2, & 3, \ldots\ldots\ldots N \\ f_1, & f_2, & f_3, \ldots\ldots\ldots f_n \end{pmatrix}$$

The number of inversions presented by $f_1, f_2, f_3, \ldots f_n$ with respect to 1, 2, 3,....N is checked. With each inversion, the sign of the determinant changes.

Page 512 If LS = 0, the inverse was calculated; therefore, the columns are unscrambled. If LS $\neq$ 0, the columns remain scrambled, and the elements forming the diagonal from the "upper right hand corner" of the matrix to the "lower left hand corner" are each decreased by 1. Calculations by MPY, for the solution corresponding to a given vector, is thus simplified.

For programming ease, the columns of the product form of the inverse have been allocated in reverse order. MPY, in using this product form to calculate the solutions, is unhindered by the reverse order.

Label Table

a) Main Program

A	Array of dimension 30 $\times$ 30 used to process the matrix read in.
B	Array of dimension 30 $\times$ 30 where the matrix read in is saved.
V	Vector of dimension 30, where the vector to be processed is read n.
S	Vector of dimension 30, where the solution of a system of equations is stored.
C	Vector of dimension 30, where the product of the original matrix and the solution vector is stored. C is placed in COMMON, and is used in the subroutine INV to unscramble the matrices pocessed.
V1	Array of dimension 30 $\times$ 1, in equivalence with V.
S1	Array of dimension 30 $\times$ 1, in equivalence with S.
C1	Array of dimension 30 $\times$ 1, in equivalence with C.
N	Order of the matrix being processed.
L	Index which is equal to 2 if a matrix is found to be singular, and

	equal to 1 if a matrix is not singular. L is also used as a count to indicate the number of vectors processed with a given matrix.
D	Contains the value of the determinant.
LX	Contains part of the exponent of the determinant.
KKKM	Index used when calling INV. When KKKM = 0, the inverse of the matrix A is calculated. When KKKM = 1, the product form of the inverse of A is obtained.
IP	The third column of the first card of every matrix to be processed is read into IP. If an S was punched in that column, IP = 6,200; then KKKM is set to 1, and the product form is obtained. When no S was punched, IP = 0; KKKM is set to 0, and the inverse is obtained.
KKKP	When calling MPY, KKKP is 0 if the product form was calculated. KKKP is equal to 1 is the inverse was calculated.
J	Used as an index when reading or given output. Also used as an index in DO loops, and used to read the first two columns of any card following the last card of a matrix read in. An analysis is made on J to determine if that card is the beginning of a new matrix.
IPP	The information from column 3 of any card following the last card of a matrix read in is stored in IPP.
K	Used when reading, as a parameter. It is also used as the index of a DO loop.

b) *Subroutine OUTPUT*

NA	Argument of the subroutine which gives cards output when being equal to 1. If NA is equal to 2, all output is via the typewriter.
C	Used in INV and in the mainline program. It appears dimensioned in OUTPUT because of its presence in COMMON. It is transmitted implicitly to the main program.
ARRAY	In common with A in the mainline program.
NUMBER	In common with N, the order of the matrix.
LLL	Index of a DO loop.
MMM	Index used in giving the output.
J	Index of a DO loop.
K	Index used when given output.

c) *Subroutine MPY*

A1	Dummy array name of dimension 30 × 30. A1 is the first parameter of MPY.
N1	Second parameter of the subroutine; represents the order of the matrix A1 when calling this subroutine.
A2	Dummy array name of dimension 30 × 30. Third parameter.
N2	Fourth parameter. Represents the number of columns of the matrix A2 if its value is greater than 0. If N2 is equal to 0, then this variable is used as a switch to transfer control to that part of MPY which uses the product form to obtain solutions of equations.

TEMP	Dummy array of dimension 30. It is the fifth parameter of the subroutine. The solution of equations or their check are stored in TEMP. It is also used as partial storage in matrix multiplication.
I	Index of a DO loop.
J	Index of a DO loop.
M	Index of a DO loop.
K	Index of a DO loop.
SUM	Temporary storage used when multiplying matrices.
LTEMP	Partial storage used to permute a given column vector when using the product form to solve equations.
C	Placed in COMMON; used in INV and in the mainline program as one of the calling arguments for MPY. When checking equations, the fifth parameter of the subroutine MPY in the calling sequence is C; hence, in this case, it is made equivalent to TEMP.
L	Used to calculate a subscript of an array.
P	Used as temporary storage.
L1	Dummy to assign the proper place in COMMON for LP.
D1	Dummy to assign the proper place in COMMON for LP.
L2	Dummy to assign the proper place in COMMON for LP.
L3	Dummy to assign the proper place in COMMON for LP.
LP	Contains the row where the pivotal element lies; used when solving equations by the product form.

d) Subroutine INV

A	Where the matrix read in will be processed. After control transfers to the main program, A contains either the inverse or the product form. A is an array of 30 × 30 dim.
LP	Vector of dimension 30; it is used to store the order of the row where the pivot lies at every stage in the transformation.
C	Used as temporary storage when permuting the rows or the columns of a given matrix.
N	Contains the order of the matrix.
LEST	If equal to 2, the matrix is singular. If equal to 1, the matrix is nonsingular.
DETT	The value of the determinant is stored in DETT.
LEXP	Contains part of the exponent of the determinant to guard against overflow or underflow.
LS	If when calling INV, LS = 0, the inverse of the given matrix is obtained; if LS = 1, the product form is obtained. LS is in COMMON with KKKM of the main program.
NN	Number of columns to be transformed at every stage.
M2	Index of a DO loop.
M1	Keep track of the number of stages through which the process has gone. It is used as an index of a DO loop to perform this function.

BIG	Contain the value of the pivotal element at every stage.
I	Index of a loop.
J	Index of a loop.
L1	The order of the row where the pivot lies at a given stage is stored in L1.
BETT	Contains the absolute value of the product of the pivotal elements.
LN	Index of a loop.
LM	Index of a loop.
K	Index of a loop.
L	Used for counting the number of inversions in the permutations which is applied to the rows of the matrix. For every inversion, the sign of the determinant changes.

Mathematical Method

The mathematical method used is basically the Gauss-Jordan.

Throughout this discourse, capital letters denote matrices; corresponding lower case letters denote their elements.

Let A be a square matrix of order n; let I be the unit matrix of the same order.

It is known from linear algebra that if a sequence of elementary row operations reduces the matrix A to the unit matrix, then the same sequence of elementary row operations when applied to I yields A^{-1}.

In the Gauss-Jordan reduction, a transformation is applied to A which reduces it to a new matrix having its first column equal to the first column of the identity matrix. When the same transformation is applied to this new matrix, the resulting matrix has its first and second columns equal respectively to the first and second columns of I.

When the process is repeated n times, the resulting matrix is equal to I.

Let the notation A_k denote the matrix resulting from applying the transformation k times. Let $(a_{ij})_k$ denote the element in row i and column j of this matrix A_k.

With this notation the original matrix is represented as A_0.

The transformation to obtain the elements of the matrix A_k in terms of the elements of the matrix A_{k-1} is given by:

$$\begin{aligned} (a_{ij})_k &= (a_{ij})_{k-1} - (a_{kj})_{k-1} \cdot \frac{(a_{ik})_{k-1}}{(a_{kk})_{k-1}} \quad \text{for all } i \neq k \\ & \qquad\qquad\qquad\qquad\qquad\qquad\qquad \text{for all} \\ (a_{kj})_k &= \frac{(a_{kj})_{k-1}}{(a_{kk})_{k-1}} \quad \text{for all } j \end{aligned} \tag{1}$$

It is assumed $a_{kk} \neq 0$. Let:

$$(d_i)_k = \frac{(a_{ik})_{k-1}}{(a_{kk})_{k-1}}$$

Then (1) can be written as:

$$(a_{ij})_k = (a_{ij})_{k-1} - (a_{kj})_{k-1} \cdot (d_i)_k \quad \text{for all } i \neq k \text{ and for all } j \tag{2}$$

$$(a_{kj})_k = (a_{kj})_{k-1} \cdot \frac{1}{(a_{kk})_{k-1}} \quad \text{for all } j$$

(2) can be written as the matrix product

$$A_k = C_k \cdot -1 \tag{3}$$

where C_k is a square matrix of order n that differs from the unit matrix of the same order in its kth column given by:

$$\begin{bmatrix} (c_{ik})_k \\ (c_{2k})_k \\ \cdot \\ \cdot \\ \cdot \\ \cdot \\ (c_{nk})_k \end{bmatrix} = \begin{bmatrix} -(d_i)_k \\ \cdot \\ \cdot \\ \dfrac{1}{(a_{kk})_{k-1}} \\ \cdot \\ \cdot \\ -(d_n)_k \end{bmatrix}$$

So

$$C_k = \begin{bmatrix} 1 & 0 & \cdots\cdots & -(d_1)_k & \cdots\cdots & 0 \\ 0 & 1 & \cdots\cdots & -(d_2)_k & \cdots\cdots & 0 \\ \cdot & \cdot & \cdots\cdots & \cdot & \cdots\cdots & \cdot \\ \cdot & \cdot & \cdots\cdots & \cdot & \cdots\cdots & \cdot \\ 0 & 0 & \cdots\cdots & 1/(a_{kk})_{k-1} & \cdots\cdots & 0 \\ \cdot & \cdot & \cdots\cdots & \cdot & \cdots\cdots & \cdot \\ 0 & 0 & \cdots\cdots & 0 & \cdots\cdots & 1 \end{bmatrix} \tag{4}$$

It can easily be shown by induction that (3) applied n times to A reduces it to the unit matrix of the same order. Hence, when this transformation is applied n times to the unit matrix of order n, this matrix is reduced to the inverse of A.

It is easy to note that when $k = 1$ and the transformation (1) is applied to the unit matrix, only the first column is transformed and the remaining columns do not change. When $k = I$, I columns are transformed and $n-I$ columns are still unit vectors.

The kth time the transformation is applied, the unit vector

$$\begin{bmatrix} i_{ik} \\ i_{2k} \\ i_{3k} \\ \cdot \\ i_{kk} \\ \cdot \\ i_{nk} \end{bmatrix} = \begin{bmatrix} 0 \\ 0 \\ 0 \\ \cdot \\ 1 \\ \cdot \\ 0 \end{bmatrix}$$

in column k of the matrix A_{k-1}, changes to:

$$\begin{bmatrix} (c_{1k})_k \\ \cdot \\ \cdot \\ \cdot \\ \cdot \\ \cdot \\ \cdot \\ (c_{nk})_k \end{bmatrix} \qquad (5)$$

Where (5) is the kth column of the matrix C_k, as given in (4).

From the programming point of view, it is unnecessary to keep the unit matrix in core. As the first column of the matrix A will be transformed to a unit vector, no calculations are performed on this column. Every time an element is calculated, it is "moved" one position to the left. When the elements in column n of A_{k-1} are transformed, they are placed in column $n-1$ of A_k. (5) is then calculated and stored in column n of A_k.

This process is repeated every time the transformation (1) is applied. In this way the total core needed for the inversion process is nxn, n being the order of the matrix.

In this program, an extra column is used for the permutation process, as shown later.

Product Form of the Inverse

From (3), at stage k, we have:

$$A_k = C_k \cdot A_{k-1}$$

When $k = 1, 2, 3, \ldots\ldots. n$, we obtain:

$$\begin{aligned} A_1 &= C_1 \cdot A_0 = C_1 \cdot A \\ A_2 &= C_2 \cdot A_1 = C_2 \cdot (C_1 \cdot A) = C_2 \cdot C_1 \cdot A \\ &\cdot \\ &\cdot \\ A_n &= C_n \cdot A_{n-1} = C_n \cdot C_{n-1} \ldots\ldots\ldots\ldots C_1 \cdot A \end{aligned} \qquad (6)$$

But the matrix A_n is equal to I, because A_n is the matrix obtained after applying the transformation (1) n times.

Hence (6) can be written as:

$$I = C_n \cdot C_{n-1} \ldots\ldots\ldots\ldots C_1 \cdot A$$

and premultiplying by A^{-1}, we obtain:

$$A^{-1} = C_n \cdot C_{n-1} \cdot \ldots\ldots\ldots\ldots \cdot C_1 \qquad (7)$$

If at every stage throughout the process, column

$$\begin{bmatrix} (c_{1k})_k \\ \cdot \\ \cdot \\ \cdot \\ \cdot \\ \cdot \\ (c_{nk})_k \end{bmatrix}$$

of each of the matrices C_k is stored, and only the remaining columns are transformed, we obtain the matrix:

$$P = \begin{bmatrix} p_{11} & p_{12} & \cdots\cdots\cdots & p_{1n} \\ p_{21} & p_{22} & \cdots\cdots\cdots & p_{2n} \\ \cdot & & & \\ \cdot & & & \\ p_{n1} & p_{n2} & \cdots\cdots\cdots & p_{nn} \end{bmatrix} \tag{8}$$

The matrix P is called the product form of the inverse of A.

Each column of P is the kth column of each of the matrices C_k; that is:

$$\begin{bmatrix} p_{1j} \\ \cdot \\ \cdot \\ \cdot \\ p_{jj} \\ \cdot \\ \cdot \\ \cdot \\ p_{nj} \end{bmatrix} = \begin{bmatrix} -(d_1)_j \\ \cdot \\ \cdot \\ \cdot \\ 1/(a_{jj})_{j-1} \\ \cdot \\ \cdot \\ \cdot \\ -(d_n)_j \end{bmatrix}$$

At every stage throughout the process of obtaining the inverse, n columns are transformed. Under the assumption that it takes the same time to process each column, let t be the time taken in processing one column. Every stage takes nt. It follows that the total time should be n^2t.

When obtaining the product form, n columns are transformed at stage 1, $n - 1$ columns at stage 2, and so on.

Hence the time it takes for the whole process is:

$$T = nt + (n-1)t + (n-2)t + \ldots\ldots + t$$

or

$$T = t(n+1)n/2$$
$$T = \tfrac{1}{2}n_2t + \tfrac{1}{2}nt,$$

which is approximately half the time needed to calculate the inverse.

These results are only approximate, because the assumption that it takes the same time to process each column is not completely valid. Also, there are other processes involved, such as finding the largest element per column and performing the permutations of the rows and/or columns, etc.

In solving a system:

$$\begin{aligned} A\,X &= K \\ X &= A^{-1}\,K = C_n \cdot C_{n-1} \,\ldots\ldots\ldots\, C_1 \cdot K \end{aligned}$$

Let $X_0 = K$; then the final answer is given by:

$$X_k = C_k \cdot X_{k-1} \tag{9}$$

where k varies from 1 to n.

Because of the form of the matrices C_k, each of the matrix-by-vector products in (9) requires only n multiplications. The total time is proportional to n^2.

Consider:

$$\begin{bmatrix} (x_1)_k \\ \cdot \\ \cdot \\ \cdot \\ (x_k)_k \\ \cdot \\ \cdot \\ \cdot \\ (x_n)_k \end{bmatrix} = \begin{bmatrix} 1 & \ldots\ldots\ldots\ldots & (c_{1k})_k & \ldots\ldots\ldots & 0 \\ \cdot & & & & \\ \cdot & & & & \\ \cdot & & & & \\ 0 & \ldots\ldots\ldots\ldots & (c_{kk})_k & \ldots\ldots\ldots & 0 \\ \cdot & & & & \\ \cdot & & & & \\ \cdot & & & & \\ 0 & \ldots\ldots\ldots\ldots & (c_{nk})_k & \ldots\ldots\ldots & 1 \end{bmatrix} \begin{bmatrix} (x_1)_{k-1} \\ \cdot \\ \cdot \\ \cdot \\ (x_k)_{k-1} \\ \cdot \\ \cdot \\ \cdot \\ (x_n)_{k-1} \end{bmatrix} \tag{10}$$

Then, from (10), we have:

$$\begin{aligned} (x_1)_k &= (x_1)_{k-1} + (c_{1k})_k \cdot (x_k)_{k-1} \\ &\cdot \\ &\cdot \\ &\cdot \\ (x_k)_k &= (x_k)_{k-1} \cdot (c_{kk})_k \\ &\cdot \\ &\cdot \\ &\cdot \\ (x_n)_k &= (x_n)_{k-1} + (c_{nk}) \cdot (x_k)_{k-1} \end{aligned} \tag{11}$$

From (8), equations (11) can be written as:

$$\begin{aligned} (x_j)_k &= (x_j)_{k-1} + p_{jk} \cdot (x_k)_{k-1} \qquad \text{for all } j \neq k \\ (x_k) &= (x_k)_{k-1} + p_{kk} \end{aligned} \tag{12}$$

Let

$$z_{jk} = p_{jk} - \delta_{jk}$$

where δ_{jk} is the Kronecker's delta, i.e.,

$$\delta_{jk} = 0,\ j \neq k$$
$$\delta_{jk} = 1,\ j = k$$

Then (12) can be written as:

$$(x_j)_k = (x_j)_{k-1} + (z_{jk}\,\delta_{jk}) \cdot (x_k)_{k-1} \qquad \text{for all } j \neq k$$
$$(x_k)_k = (x_k)_{k-1} + (z_{kk}\,\delta_{kk}) \qquad (13)$$

$\delta_{kk} = 1$

and in the first of equations (13), as $j \neq k$, $\delta_{jk} = 0$.

Hence equations (13) are equivalent to:

$$(x_j)_k = (x_j)_{k-1} + z_{jk} \cdot (x_k)_{k-1} \qquad j = 1, 2, \ldots\ldots n \qquad (14)$$

We are actually using the matrix:

$$Z = P - I = \begin{bmatrix} p_{11}-1 & p_{12} & \cdots\cdots & p_{1n} \\ p_{21} & p_{22}-1. & \cdots\cdots & p_{2n} \\ \cdot & & & \\ \cdot & & & \\ \cdot & & & \\ p_{1n} & p_{2n} & \cdots\cdots & p_{nn}-1 \end{bmatrix}$$

instead of the product form. I is the unit matrix of order n.

The time taken by this algorithm is equal to the time needed to multiply a square matrix of order n by a column vector of n elements.

The Determinant

Let the symbol $D(X)$ be used to represent the determinant of the matrix X.

From (3):

$$A_k = C_k \cdot A_{k-1}$$

Then:

$$D(A_k) = D(C_k) \cdot D(A_{k-1})$$

From the form of the matrices C_k,

$$D(C_k) = 1/(a_{kk})_{k-1}$$

Hence:

$$D(A_{k-1}) = (a_{kk})_{k-1} \cdot A_k)$$

Then, by induction:

$$D(A_0) = (a_{11})_0 \cdot (a_{22})_1 \cdots\cdots (a_{kk})_{k-1} \cdots\cdots (a_{nn})_{n-1}$$

Or, as $A_0 = A$:

$$D(A) = \prod_{k=1}^{n} (a_{kk})_{k-1}$$

which shows that the determinant is the product of the pivotal elements.

Permutation Scheme

$(a_{kk})_{k-1}$ could equal 0; then the process has to be modified to guard against this. Moreover, if the largest—in absolute value—of $(a_{1k})_{k-1}$, $1 = 1, 2, \ldots\ldots n$ is chosen as a pivot term, then error propagation can be minimized. Large percentage errors are likely to be found in small terms; when used as pivot terms, they tend to propagate their error levels into all terms of the matrix.

Let $(a_{rk})_{k-1}$ be, at stage k, the largest in absolute value of the terms in the kth column of the matrix A_{k-1}.

Then rows r and k can be interchanged to place element a_{rk} in the position occupied by a_{kk}, or the r values can be recorded and the overall permutation can be applied to the rows of the matrix.

The transformations from A_{k-1} to A_k are then:

$$(d_i)_k = \frac{(a_{ik})_{k-1}}{(a_{rk})_{k-1}} \quad \text{for all } i \neq r$$

$$(a_{ij})_k = (a_{ij})_{k-1} - (a_{rj})_{k-1} \cdot (d_i)_k$$

$$(a_{rj})_k = -\frac{(a_{rj})_{k-1}}{(a_{rk})_{k-1}}$$

It is needless to say that if the pivots at stages k and k' are t_{rk} and $t_{r'k'}$, then $r \neq r'$.

The overall permutation to be applied to the rows of the matrix at the end of the transformation is

$$\begin{matrix} 1, 2, \ldots\ldots\ldots, k, \ldots\ldots\ldots, n \\ p_1, p_2, \ldots\ldots\ldots, p_k, \ldots\ldots\ldots, p_n \end{matrix}$$

where p_1 is the row where the pivot is at stage 1, p_k is the row where the pivot is at stage k, etc.

This permutation indicates that row 1 of the desired inverse is row p_1 of the obtained matrix; row k of the desired inverse is row p_k of the obtained matrix, etc.

Due to the way the calculations are arranged, after the rows are permuted, the columns must be permuted by the inverse of the permutation

$$\begin{matrix} 1, 2, \ldots\ldots\ldots, k, \ldots\ldots\ldots, n \\ p_1, p_2, \ldots\ldots\ldots, p_k, \ldots\ldots\ldots, p_n \end{matrix} \tag{14}$$

In the process of inverting a matrix A, let A' stand for the matrix with its rows already permuted; then the inverse of the permutation (14) indicates that column p_1 of A^{-1} is column 1 of A'; column p_k of A^{-1} is column k of A, etc.

If when solving a system

$$A\,X = K_i \qquad i = 1, 2, \ldots\ldots$$

he product form of the inverse of A is obtained, only row permutation is needed; however, each column vector K_i must be permuted by

$$\begin{pmatrix} 1, 2, \ldots\ldots k, \ldots\ldots, n \\ p_1, p_2, \ldots\ldots p_k, \ldots\ldots, p_n \end{pmatrix}$$

before (14) is used.

Note: When inverting a matrix, or obtaining the product form of the inverse, the program assumes that matrix to be singular if a pivot is found being, in absolute value, less than 10^{-6}. In that case, the value obtained for the determinant in the output is the product of the pivots up to that point.

REFERENCES

1. Dodes, Irving Allen. *IBM 1620 Programming.* New York: John Wiley & Sons, Inc., 1961.
2. Faddeev, D. K., and Faddeeva, V. N. *Computational Methods of Linear Algebra.* San Francisco: W. H. Freeman & Co., 1963.
3. Herstein, I. N. *Topics in Algebra.* New York: Blaisdell Publishing Co., 1964.
4. Hoffman, Kenneth, and Kunze, Ray. *Linear Algebra.* New York: Prentice-Hall, Inc., 1961.
5. McCracken, Daniel D. *A Guide to Fortran Programming.* New York: John Wiley & Sons, Inc., 1961.
6. Miquel y Merino, Pablo. *Elementos de Algebra Superior.* Habana: Cultural S. A., 1950.
7. Organick, Elliot I. *A Fortran Primer.* Reading, Mass.: Addison-Wesley Publishing Co., Inc., 1963.
8. Ralston, Anthony, and Wilf, Herbert S. (eds.). *Mathematical Methods for Digital Computers.* New York: John Wiley & Sons, Inc., 1960.
9. Scarborough, J. B. *Numerical Mathematical Analysis.* Baltimore: Johns Hopkins Press, 1962.
10. IBM Reference Manuals:
    a) C26–5619–4—IBM 1620 FORTRAN (with Format)
    b) C26–5602–3—IBM 1620 FORTRAN II Specifications
    c) C26–5662–2—1620 FORTRAN II Operator's Guide
    d) F28–8074–3—FORTRAN II. General Information Manual
    e) A26–5835–0—IBM 1622 Card Read-Punch
    f) A26–5706–2—IBM 1620 Central Processing Unit, Model 1

Appendix B

Answers to Problems

Answer to ***Problem 2.2***

```
C     PROBLEM ON THE CALCULATION OF THE AVERAGE OF A SET OF
     1NUMBERS
C     VERNOY JOHNSON—1 DECEMBER 1965
C
      DIMENSION X(100)
      I = 1
      SUM = 0
   20 READ (5, 101)X(I)
  101 FORMAT(F10.2)
      IF(X(I) - 999.) 10, 5, 10
   10 SUM = SUM + X(I)
      I = I + 1
      GO TO 20
    5 XN = I - 1
      N = XN
      AVG = SUM/XN
      WRITE (6, 102) XN, AVG
  102 FORMAT(1H1, 15X, 16HAVERAGE OF BELOW, F5.0, 10HNUMBERS IS,
     1F10.2)
      WRITE (6, 103) (X(I), I = 1, N)
  103 FORMAT (1HO, 25X, F10.2)
      STOP
      END
```

Answer to ***Problem 2.3***

```
      PROBLEM NUMBER 2.3
C     PROBLEM ON THE CALCULATION OF THE MEDIAN OF A SET OF
     1NUMBERS
```

```
    VERNOY JOHNSON—1 DECEMBER 1965

    DIMENSION X(100)
    READ (5, 101) N
101 FORMAT (I5)
  5 READ (5, 102) (X(I), I = 1, N)
102 FORMAT(8F10.2)
    L = N - 1
    DO 10 I = 1, L
    M = I + 1
    DO 10 K = M, N
    IF(X(K) - X(I)) 10, 10, 20
 20 TEMP = X(I)
    X(I) = X(K)
    X(K) = TEMP
 10 CONTINUE
    J = N/2 + 1
    XMED = X(J)
    WRITE (6, 103) XMED
103 FORMAT(1H1,34HTHE MEDIAN OF THE BELOW NUMBERS IS, F10.2)
    WRITE (6, 104) (X(I), I = 1, N)
104 FORMAT (1H, 10X, F10.2)
    STOP
    END
```

Answer to **Problem 2.5.** *Arithmetic Progression—Flow Chart*

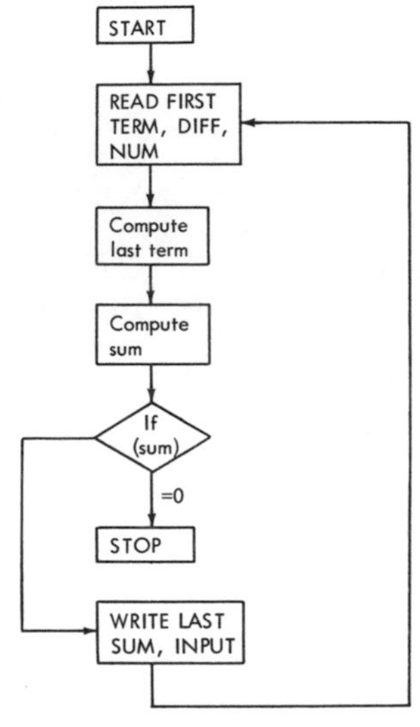

Arithmetic Progression

```
    WRITE (6,4)
  4 FORMAT (11X, 1HA, 9X, 1HN,15X,9H LAST TERM,14X, 3HSUM)
  1 READ(5,2)A,D,N
```

```
 2  FORMAT(2F 10.4,I4)
    XN=N
    X LAST− A+(XN−1.)*D
    SUM= .5*XN*(A+XLAST)
    IF(SUM)10,20,10
10  WRITE(6,3)A,D,N,XLAST,SUM
 3  FORMAT (6X,2F 10.4,I4,2F 18.2)
    GO TO 1
20  STOP
    END
```

TO TEST THE PROGRAM THE DATA CARDS SHOULD BE PLACED AT THE END OF THE DECK OF FORTRAN INSTRUCTIONS AND SHOULD BE PUNCHED AS FOLLOWS:

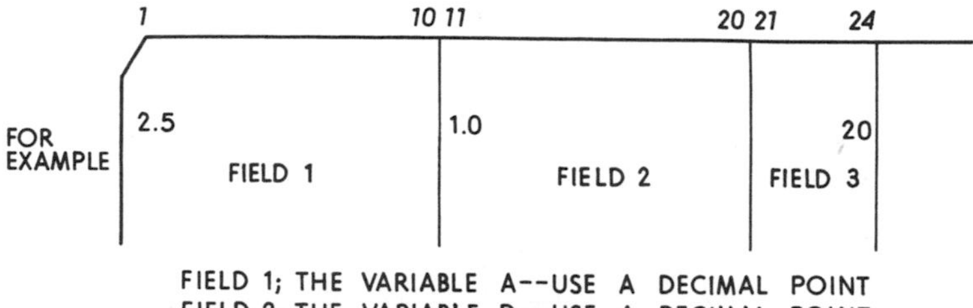

One input card will result in one calculation of the sum of the terms and the last term of any arithmetic progression.

Answer to ***Problem 2.6.*** *Geometric Progression—Flow Chart*

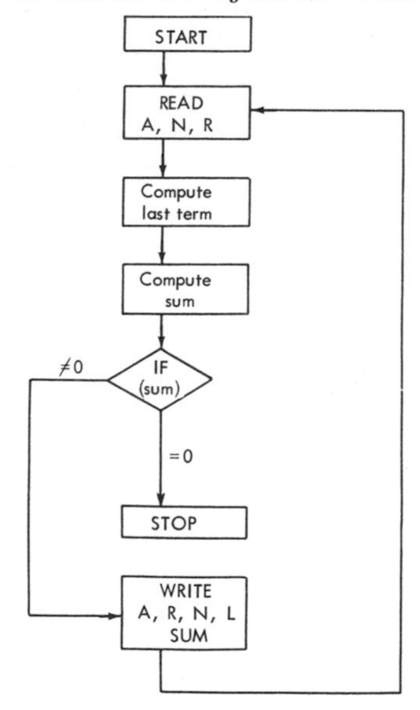

Geometric Progression

```
      WRITE (6,4)
    4 FORMAT (11X, 1HA, 9X, 1HR, 9X, 1HN, 15X, 9HLAST TERM,
     114X, 3HSUM)
  100 READ (5,2) A, R, N
    2 FORMAT (2F10.4, I4)
      XN1 = N-1
      XL = A* (R**XN1)
      S = (A-R*XL)/(1.-R)
      IF (S) 10,20,10
    3 FORMAT (6X,2F10.4, 6XI4, 2F18.2)
   10 WRITE (6,3) A, R, N, XL, S
      GO TO 100
   20 STOP
      END
```

To run this program use same input as Problem **2.1**

Answer to ***Problem 2.7.*** *Simultaneous Equations—Flow Chart*

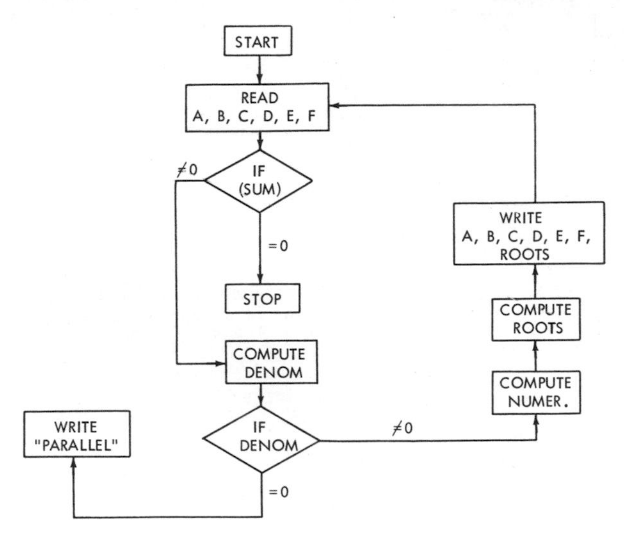

Simultaneous Equations

```
      WRITE (6,6)
    6 FORMAT (11X,1HA,7X,1HB,7X,1HC,7X,1HD,7X,1HE,7X,
     111HX,7X,1HY)
    1 READ(5,2)A,B,C,D,E,F
    2 FORMAT (6F8.3)
      IF(A+B+C+D+E+F)100,200,100
  100 DEN=A*E-B*D
      IF(DEN)300,400,300
      400 WRITE(6,3)A,B,C,D,E,F
```

```
  3   FORMAT (6X,6F8.3,4X,8HPARALLEL)
      GO TO 1
300   XNUM = C*E-B*F
      YNUM = A*F-C*D
      X = XNUM/DEN
      Y = YNUM/DEN
      Write(6,4)A,B,C,D,E,F,X,Y
  4   FORMAT (6X,8F8.3)
      GO TO 1
200   STOP
      END
```

To run this program one input card is needed per problem.

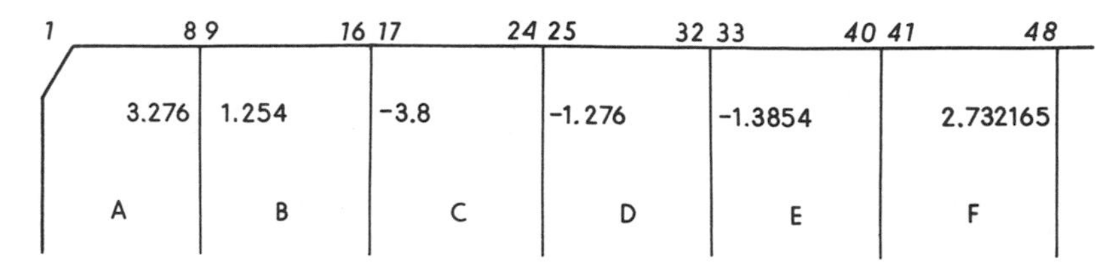

A decimal point must be punched in each field.

Answer to ***Problem 2.8.*** *Flow Chart—Four-Digit Numbers*

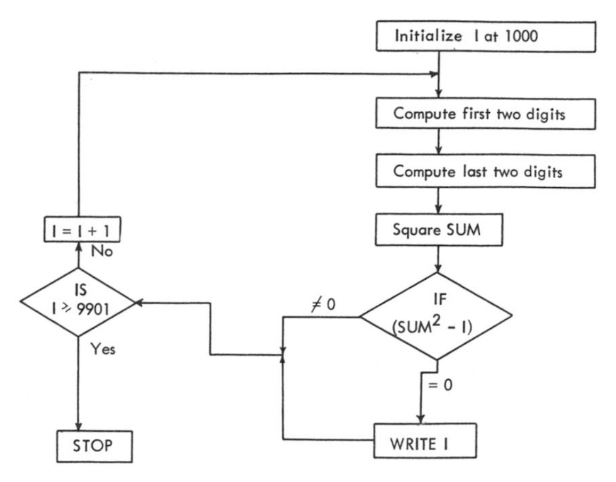

Four-Digit Numbers

```
      DO  10  I=1000, 9901
      K = I/100
      L = I-K*100
      M = (K+L)*(K+L)
      IF(I - M)  10, 20, 10
 20   WRITE (6, 3) I
  3   FORMAT (6X, I4)
```

```
   10 CONTINUE
      STOP
      END
```

Example Analysis—if I = 3025:

$$K = I/100 = 3025/100 - 30 \text{ (because of fixed-point division)}$$
$$L = I - K * 100 = 3025 - 30 * 100 = 3025 - 3000 = 25$$

The first two numbers are 30 and the last two numbers are 25.

Answer to ***Problem 2.9.*** *Monkey Problem—Flow Chart*

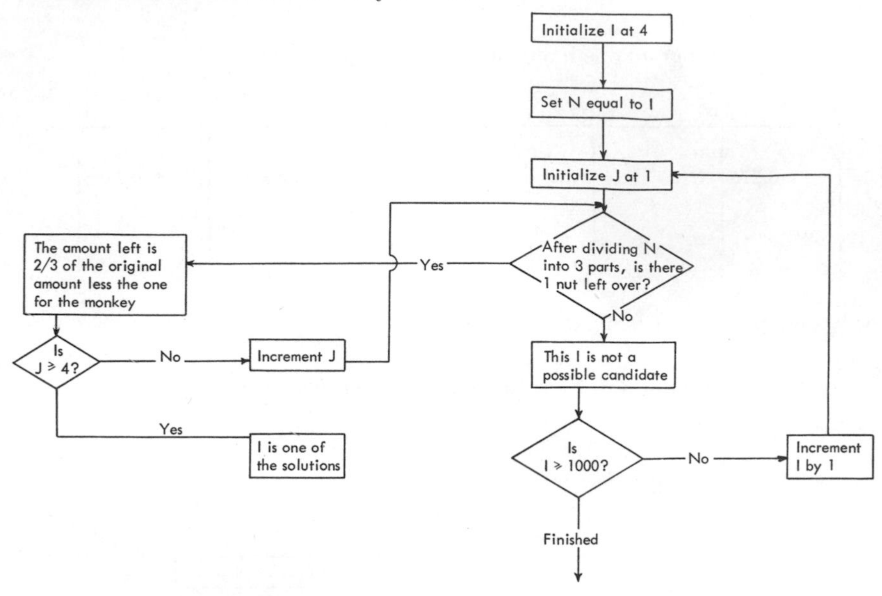

Monkey Problem

```
      DO 1 I=4,1000,3
      N = I
      DO 2 J=1,4
      IF(N - 1)/3*3-(N-1))1,2,1
    2 N = 2*(N-1)/3
      WRITE (6, 10) I
    1 CONTINUE
   10 FORMAT (I4)
      STOP
      END
```

The statement IF ((N−1) /3 * 3−(N−1)) 1,2,1 transfers control to statement number 2 if N can be divided into three parts, with a remainder of 1. Statement number two reduces the amount X which is left for the next sailer by one third. A natural exit from the loop ending at statement number 2 indicates that the original sum may be divided four times into equal thirds; each time the total is reduced by one third and one: the nut for the monkey.

Answer to ***Problem 2.10.*** *The added statements are the following:*

```
      SUM = 0
      SD = 0.
      DO  20  I = 1, N
      SUM = SUM+X (I)
20    SD = SD+X(I) ** 2
      R = N
      SD = SQRT (SD/R - (SUM/R) ** 2)
```

Answer to ***Problem 2.11.*** Intermediate statements to be added:

```
      S = N
      L = LOG (5) / LOG (2.)
      L = L+1
      M = 2. ** L
50    IF (Z - X(M))20, 10, 30
20    M = M- (2. ** (L-1))
      GO TO 50
30    M = M+(2. ** (L-1))
      GO TO 50
      PUNCH 17, Y (M)
17    FORMAT (18H FUNCTION VALUE IS, F 10.4)
      GO TO 99
      END
```

Where 99 is the number of the statement which reads the next argument.

Answer to ***Problem 2.12.*** *Flow Chart*

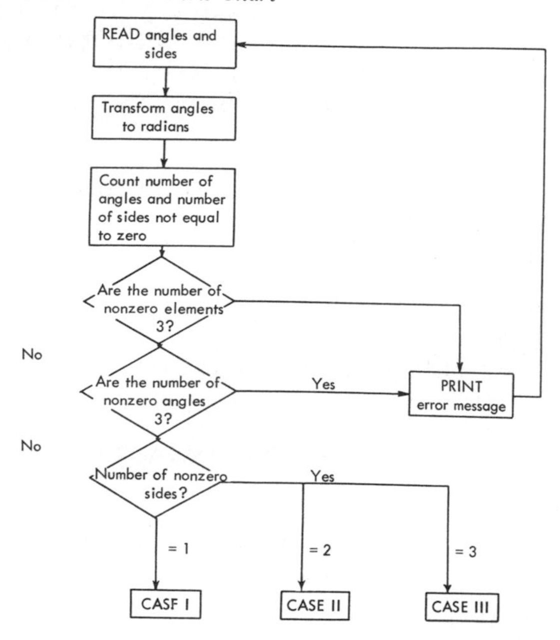

FORTRAN Program

```
      DIMENSION ARRAY (3,3), ANGLE (3), SIDE (3), LA (3), LS(3)
      PI = 3.1415927
      RAD = PI / 180.
      DEG = 180. / PI
 1000 READ 100, ARRAY, SIDE
      DO  1  J = 1, 3
    1 ANGLE(J) = (ARRAY (3,J) / 3600. + ARRAY(2,J) / 60. + ARRAY
     1(1, J)) * PAD
      INDEX  =  0
      K = 0
      M = 0
      DO  5  J = 1, 3
      IF(ANGLE (J)) 2,4,2
    2 K = K + 1
      LA (K) = J
    4 IF (SIDE (J)) 3,5,3
    3 M = M + 1
      LS(M) = J
    5 CONTINUE
      IF (M + K - 3) 231, 6, 231
    6 IF (M) 7, 231, 231
    7 GO TO (21, 22, 23), M
   22 INDEX = 6 - LS(1) - LS(2)
      IF(ANGLE (INDEX)) 30, 243, 30
   30 M = LS (1)
      K  = LS (2)
      SIDE (INDEX) = SQRTF (SIDE (M) ** 2 + SIDE (K) ** 2
      1 - 2. * SIDE (M) * SIDE (K) * COSF (ANGLE (INDEX))
   23 S = 0.5 * (SIDE (1)+SIDE (2)+SIDE (3))
      R = SQRTF ((S-SIDE (1)) * (S-SIDE (2)) * (S - SIDE (3)) / S)
      DO  16  J = 1, 3
      IF (J - INDEX) 19, 16, 19
   19 ANGLE (J) = 2.* ATANF (R / (S-SIDE (J))) * DEG
      IF (ANGLE (J)) 121, 16, 16
  121 ANGLE (J) = ANGLE (J) + 180.
   16 CONTINUE
      GO  TO  170
  243 PRINT 2000
      FORMAT(//14HAMBIGUOUS  CASE //)
      GO  TO  1000
  231 PRINT 2001
 2001 FORMAT (/// 13H ERROR  IN  DATA //)
      GO  TO  1000
   21 INDEX = 6 - LA(1) - LA (2)
      ANGLE (INDEX) = (PI - ANGLE (1) - ANGLE (2) - ANGLE
      (3) * 0.5)
```

```
      M = LS(1)
      DO  717  J=1, 3
      IF  (J - LS (1)) 431, 717, 431
431   SIDE (J) = SIDE (M) * SINF (ANGLE (J)/SINF (ANGLE
      (INDEX))
170   DO  981  I = 1, 3
      ARRAY(1, I) = ANGLE (I)
      DO  981  J = 1, 2
      K = ARRAY (J, I)
      ARRAY (J + 1, I) = K
981   ARRAY (J + 1, I) = (ARRAY (J, I) - ARRAY (J+1, I)) * 60.
      PRINT 101, ((J, (ARRAY (K,J), K=1, 3) P, SIDE (J), J = 1, 3)
100   FORMAT (3 (I4, 2I3), 3F 8.4)
101   FORMAT ((6H ANGLE, I2,I4,2I3, 4X5H SIDE, I2,E14.7))
      END
```

Answer to ***Problem 2.13.*** *Flow Chart—Prime Factor Problem*

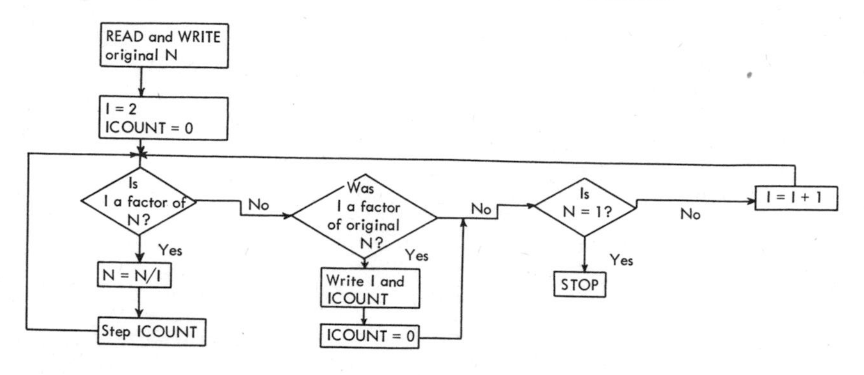

FORTRAN Program

```
 99   FORMAT (I10)
 98   FORMAT (5X,10THE NUMBER,I10,25HHAS THE FOLLOWING
     1 FACTORS)
 97   FORMAT (5X,I10,14H TO THE POWER, I10)
      READ 99, N
      WRITE 98, N
      ICOUNT = 0
      DO 100 I =2,N
103   N1 = N/I
      IF (N-N1 * I) 101,102,101
102   ICOUNT = ICOUNT + 1
      N = N1
      GO TO 103
101   IF (ICOUNT) 105,104,105
105   WRITE 97, I, ICOUNT
      ICOUNT = 0
104   IF(N - 1) 100,200,200
```

```
100 CONTINUE
200 STOP
    END
```

NOTE: The solution given is far from the most efficient, since it tests all positive integers.

There are other possibilities:

1. If one tests only prime numbers, the generation of the primes results in many more FORTRAN statements. It may require appreciably more time also.
2. One could test only 2, and all odd integers for an appreciable saving in time, but at the expense of more FORTRAN statements.
3. This program could be shortened by omitting statement #104. However, this statement saves much time if the number is not prime.

Answer to **Problem 3.2.** The sign is placed immediately to the left of the first nonzero digit in output. The following program will punch I in columns 9 and 10 with the sign in column 8.

```
    IF (I) 2,3,3
2   I = -I
    PUNCH 1,I
1   FORMAT (7X,1H -,I2)
    GO TO 5
3   PUNCH 6, I
6   FORMAT (8X, I2)
5   ______
    ______
    ______
```

If it is desired to punch a sign in column 8 when I is positive, change statement 6 to:

```
6   FORMAT (7X, 1H+,I2)
```

Answer to **Problem 3.3.** *Flow Chart*

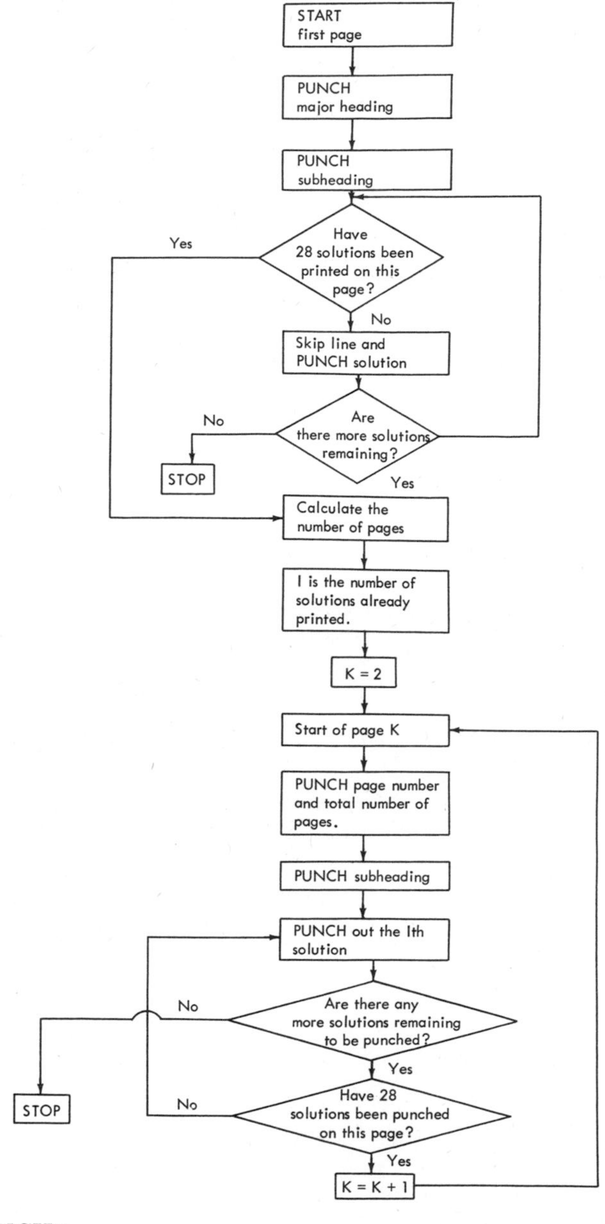


```
      PUNCH 7
 7    FORMAT (7X33HPROBLEM 1 – SOLUTION OF EQUATIONS/)
      PUNCH 17
17    FORMAT (15X8HEQUATION,5X8HSOLUTION)
      DO 28 I = 1,M
      IF (I – 28) 28,28,50
```

```
28  PUNCH 27, I, X(I)
27  FORMAT (//17X,I4,8X,F6.2)
50  IF (M – 28) 40,40,37
37  K = (M–28)/M+2
    I = I – 1
    DO4 8 J = 2,K
    I = I + J – 1
    PUNCH 77, J, K
77  FORMAT (65X,5H PAGE,I3,4H OF, I3)
    PUNCH 17
    DO 48L = 1,28
    PUNCH 27,I,X(I)
    IF (I + L–M) 48,40,40
48  CONTINUE
40  STOP
    END
```

Answer to **Problem 3.6.** Reduce possible list to those numbers between 47 and 99 since only these numbers produce a square of four digits and a cube of six digits.

Eliminate all figures ending in 0,1,5 and 6 because the same last figure occurs in both the square and the cube.

Program

Actually the list can be reduced further if we notice that $x^3 + x^2 = x^2(x+1)$, one of which must be a multiple of nine (law of nines).

Answer to **Problem 3.7.** *Flow Chart*

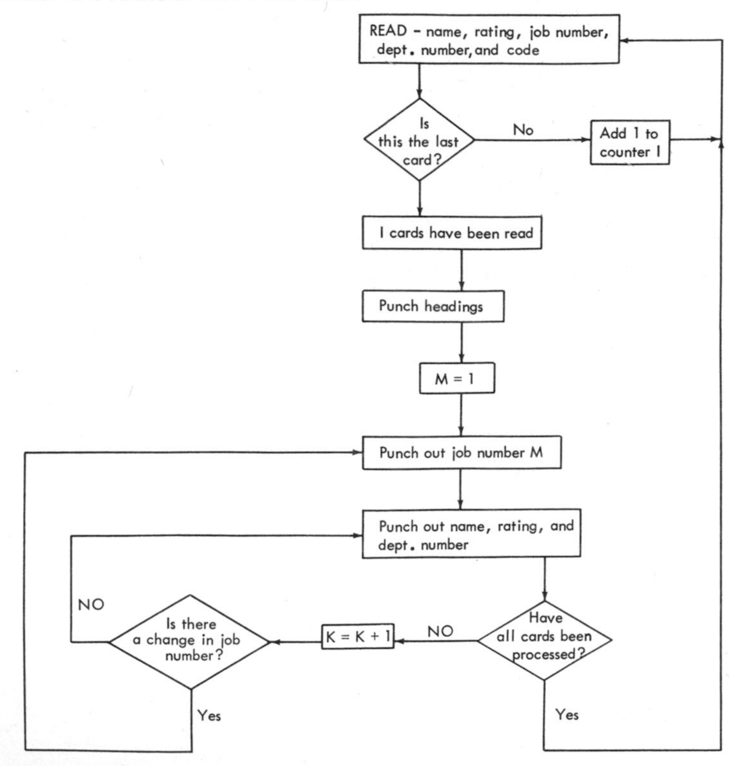

The first report requires a check for a change on JOB NUMBER and printing of a new subtitle for each JOB NUMBER. For the second part of the problem, the records (PERSON, RATING, JOB NUMBER, DEPT. NUMBER) must be ordered on department number.

The second part of the problem will be left for Chapter 8, at which point we introduce a good sorting routine.

For the first part the following is a possible program.

```
      DIMENSION K1(500),R(500),J(500),LD(500)
   99 DO 20 I = 1,1000
      READ 5, K1(I),R(I),J(I),LD(I),L
    5 FORMAT(A10,F5.2,10X,I5,I4,44X,I2)
      IF(L-0) 10,20,10
   20 CONTINUE
   10 PUNCH 61
   61 FORMAT(30X,15HREPORT NUMBER 1/)
      J(I + 1) = 99999
      PUNCH 63
   63 FORMAT(2X,3HJOB)
      PUNCH 64
   64 FORMAT(20X7HPERSONS,4X6HRATING,4X12HPRESENT DEPT)
      DO 30 M = 1,I
      PUNCH 62, J(M)
   62 FORMAT(2X,I5)
      DO 40 N = M,1000
      PUNCH 66, K1(N),R(N),LD(N)
   66 FORMAT(18XA10,3XF6.2,4XI4)
      IF (J(M)-J(N+1)) 40.40,30
   40 CONTINUE
   30 CONTINUE
      GO TO 99
      END
```

Why is it necessary to include the statement, J(I + 1) = 99999?

Answer to ***Problem 3.8.***

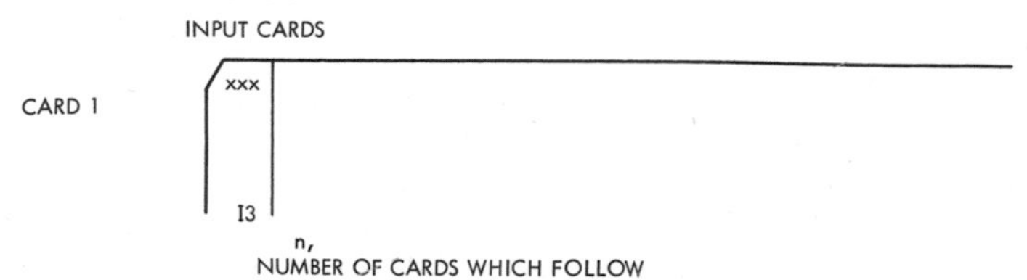

Program

```
99  READ 7, N
 7  FORMAT (I3)
    DO 20 I = 1,N
    READ 8, J, K,L,M,M1,M2
 8  FORMAT (I5, 5I3)
    M2 = M2 + 3
    J = J + M1
    IF (K - M) 30,20,20
30  M = K
20  IF (L-M1) 40,50,50
40  L = M1
50  R = J
    S = M2
    AVG = R/S
    PUNCH 9,AVG,J,M2,K,L
 9  FORMAT (F8.3, 4(4X,I3))
    GO TO 99
    END
```

Analyze the above program to see if it can be modified so that only a small change is necessary to change the output cards for one week so that they can be used as input cards for the next week; in other words, systematize the program.

MODIFIED COMPLETE PROBLEM

The problem is to calculate weekly the season's high game, season's high series, and average and to update records for a league of bowlers and then to find the three bowlers with the highest season's high games and the three bowlers with the highest season's high series. The updated records should be outputed on cards and the output should be designed for maximum ease of input the next week.

Given Assumptions:

Maximum of 100 players in the league
Maximum of 120 games in season
A player may hold one position in the set of three high game players or only one position in the set of three high series players

Additional Assumptions:

Each week a bowler plays three games or none at all
If a three-game series score of 0 is inputed, it is considered that the bowler didn't bowl.
Each week the cards of all players in the league must be inputed (that is, so that they will be included in the calculation of three high-game and series players)

(NOTE: The following method, flow chart, and final program actually describe a form of this program for a two-week test which outputs on the printer. Methods to change this to the above program are given following "final program.")

METHOD

In order to facilitate a two-week test, the whole program (except the stop and end) was placed in a DO loop going from 1 to 2, and two sets of data were inputed.

A WRITE statement was inserted to list the number of the week. Next, the numbe of players, N, was read in. A test was then inserted to test for more than 100 or less than 3 players. In either case, the program was then sent to the END. (Actually, to a WRITE statement that informed the user why the program didn't run and then to STOP and END.)

I decided to use an array A(I,K) where K indicates the player and I indicates some bit of information about the player to store the player's name and his high-game and series scores. This was because the player's name is stored under several variable names, and the high-game and series have to be stored for the final sort of three highest. I also decided to perform the calculations about each player, to read in his past record (also write out his past record), and to print out his revised record in a single DO loop which allowed the player numbers to run from 1 to N. The form of the output was in columns that were headed by titles of the information in them. Besides just the elementary operations, several tests were inserted in the calculations for each player: comparison of this week's high game and series with the season high game and series to allow for update of season's records; if the player bowled (i.e. did

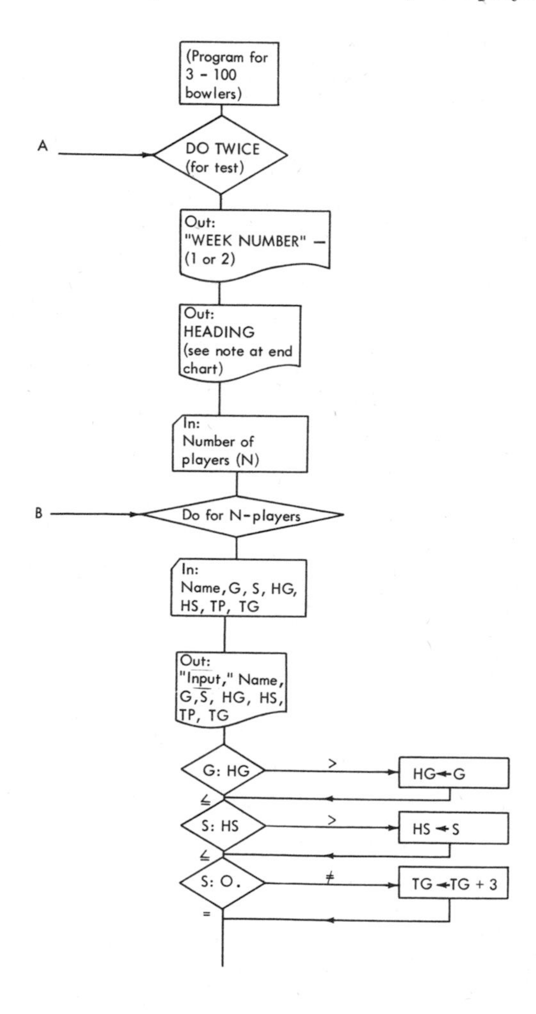

ɔt have a series score of 0.) his total game count was increased by 3; the average ɤas set to zero and then, if the number of total games was not zero, it was set to the number of total points divided by the number of total games (the zero possibility was allowed so that a player's name could be entered in the records although he never played).

After the revisions of the records were performed in the loop, the program next came to the problem of finding the highest three players for each the single-game and three-game series. Since the high game and series were stored under A(4,I) and A(5,I) the sort was performed in a DO loop with K=4,5 (i.e. A(K,I)). The sort itself consisted of finding the index of the player with the highest score. Then this player's name and score were printed out and the score was set to −1. Then an internal loop proceeded to find the index of the highest player again, but with the first highest's score now set to −1, it picked the second highest (or, if a tie existed, it picked another one who tied the first) and proceeded as in the first case, and so forth, for the third highest. These players and their scores were printed under headings indicating

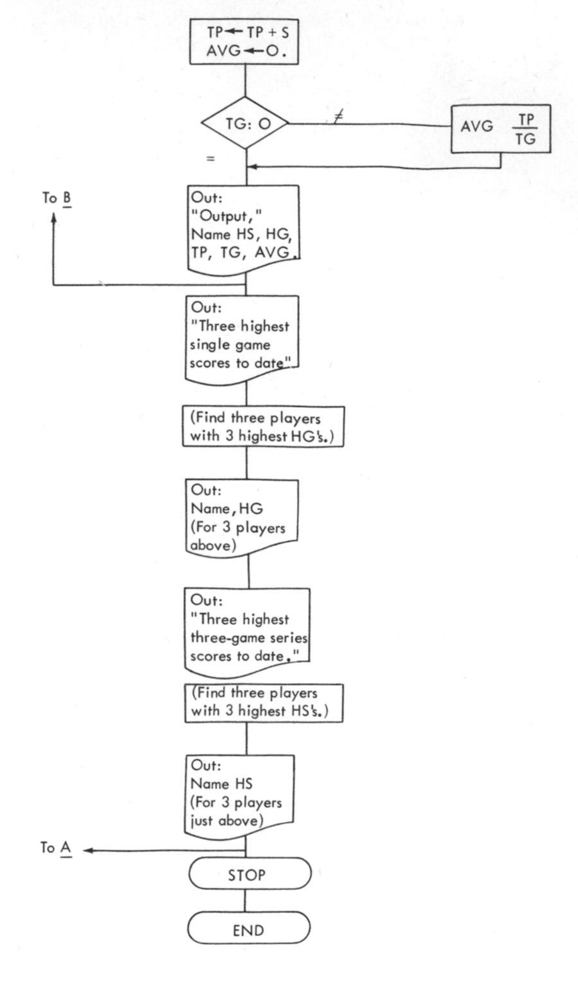

either high single game or high series, which were chosen by an IF statement testing K.

REVISIONS TO GO TO ACTUAL SITUATION

(Numbers refer to ref. nos. of final program which precedes this.)

First in any case numbers 2, 3, and 4 must be removed

For Paper and Card Output

The program may be left alone except for insertion of:

```
      WRITE(7,150)(A(I,J),I=1,5),TP,TG,AVG
150   FORMAT(3A5,12X,2F6.0,F8.0,F6.0,F9.3)
```

between 21 and 22. On the following week the players high game and his series scores may be typed in following his name on the card and the card used for input. (NOTE: read format number 6 for more details on input.) This program provides for the card output, ease of new input, and a printed record of the league players and the three highest players.

For Pure Card Output

Remove:5,6,7,14,15

Substitute write and format given above for 22 and 23

Change 26,28,35,40 so that they use output device "7" instead of output device "6" (i.e. WRITE(7,125))

(NOTE: the titles for highest single game and highest series will start with an 0 and provide 1 blank card following them. If wished they may be changed or simply removed)

Program: Bowling Problem — Programmer: Dennis Weis — Date: 11/11/65 — Page 1 of 2

Ref. Nos.	Statement Number	Cont.	FORTRAN Statement
1			DIMENSION A(5,1ØØ)
2			DO 98 JPP=1,2
3			WRITE(6,1Ø1)JPP
4	1Ø1		FORMAT(1H1,15X,12HWEEK NUMBER ,I3//)
5			WRITE(6,1Ø3)
6	1Ø3		FORMAT(15X4HNAME,6X47HLST.HI LAST HIGH HIGH TOTAL TOTAL AVER
7		1	AGE/26X,37HGAME SERIES GAME SERIES PINS GAMES/)
8			READ(5,1Ø2)N
9	1Ø2		FORMAT(6X,I4)
10			IF(N·LT·3·OR·N·GT·1ØØ)GO TO 154
11			DO 75 J=1,N
12			READ(5,1Ø4)A(1,J),A(2,J),A(3,J),G,S,A(4,J),A(5,J),TP,TG
13	1Ø4		FORMAT(3A5,4F6.Ø,F8.Ø,F6.Ø)
14			WRITE(6,113)A(1,J),A(2,J),A(3,J),G,S,A(4,J),A(5,J),TP,TG
15	113		FORMAT(3X7HINPUT ,3A5,4F6.Ø,F8.Ø,F6.Ø)
16			IF(G·GT·A(4,J)) A(4,J)=G
17			IF(S·GT·A(5,J)) A(5,J)=S
18			IF(S·NE·Ø·) TG=TG+3.
19			TP=TP+S
20			AVG=Ø.
21			IF(TG.NE.Ø.) AVG=TP/TG

* A standard card form, IBM electro 888157, is available for punching source statements from this form.

Program Bowling Problem | Punching Instructions | Graphic | Punch | Card Form # | Page 2 of 2 | Identification 73 80
Programmer Dennis Weis | Date 11/11/65

C FOR COMMENT

REF NOS.	STATEMENT NUMBER	FORTRAN STATEMENT
22	75	WRITE(6,1Ø5)(A(I,J),I=1,5),TP,TG,AVG
23	1Ø5	FORMAT(2X8HOUTPUT ,3A5,12X,2F6.Ø,F8.0,F6.Ø,F9.3)
24		DO 98 K=4,5
25		IF(K-4)13,13,14
26	13	WRITE(6,1Ø6)
27		GO TO 15
28	14	WRITE(6,1Ø7)
29	1Ø6	FORMAT(1HØ,9X,41HTHREE HIGHEST SINGLE GAME SCORES TO DATE /)
30	1Ø7	FORMAT(1HØ,9X,39HTHREE HIGHEST THREE GAME SERIES TO DATE /)
31	15	DO 1Ø IV=1,3
32		IP=1
33		DO 37 J=1,N
34	37	IF(A(K,IP).LT.A(K,J)) IP=J
35		WRITE(6,1Ø8)(A(I,IP),I=1,3),A(K,IP)
36	1Ø	A(K,IP)=-1.
37	1Ø8	FORMAT(1ØX,3A5,F6.Ø)
38	98	CONTINUE
39		GO TO 65
40	154	WRITE(6,155)
41	155	FORMAT(1ØX,42HTHIS PROGRAM ONLY HANDLES 3 TO 1ØØ PLAYERS)
42	65	STOP
43		END

*A standard card form, IBM electro 888157, is available for punching source statements from this form.

WEEK NUMBER 1

	NAME	LST.HI GAME	LAST SERIES	HIGH GAME	HIGH SERIES	TOTAL PINS	TOTAL GAMES	AVEI
INPUT	MURPHY,G.	200.	600.	−0.	−0.	−0.	−0.	
OUTPUT	MURPHY,G.			200.	600.	600.	3.	200.000
INPUT	FULLARD,P.	298.	892.	−0.	−0.	−0.	−0.	
OUTPUT	FULLARD,P.			298.	892.	892.	3.	297.333
INPUT	GARY,M.	149.	410.	−0.	−0.	−0.	−0.	
OUTPUT	GARY,M.			149.	410.	410.	3.	136.667
INPUT	VERNE,J.	130.	302.	−0.	−0.	−0.	−0.	
OUTPUT	VERNE,J.			130.	302.	302.	3.	100.667
INPUT	HAROLD,M.	155.	432.	−0.	−0.	−0.	−0.	
OUTPUT	HAROLD,M.			155.	432.	432.	3.	144.000
INPUT	WEIS,D.	300.	900.	−0.	−0.	−0.	−0.	
OUTPUT	WEIS,D.			300.	900.	900.	3.	300.000

THREE HIGHEST SINGLE GAME SCORES TO DATE

WEIS,D.	300.
FULLARD,P.	298.
MURPHY,G.	200.

THREE HIGHEST THREE GAME SERIES TO DATE

WEIS,D.	900.
FULLARD,P.	892.
MURPHY,G.	600.

WEEK NUMBER 2

	NAME	LST.HI GAME	LAST SERIES	HIGH GAME	HIGH SERIES	TOTAL PINS	TOTAL GAMES	AVERAGE
INPUT	MURPHY,G.	176.	529.	200.	600.	600.	3.	
OUTPUT	MURPHY,G.			200.	600.	1129.	6.	188.167
INPUT	FULLARD,P.	100.	365.	298.	892.	892.	3.	
OUTPUT	FULLARD,P.			298.	892.	1257.	6.	209.500
INPUT	GARY,M.	110.	300.	149.	410.	410.	3.	
OUTPUT	GARY,M.			149.	410.	710.	6.	118.333
INPUT	VERNE,J.	0.	0.	130.	302.	302.	3.	
OUTPUT	VERNE,J.			130.	302.	302.	3.	100.667
INPUT	HAROLD,M.	177.	530.	155.	432.	432.	3.	
OUTPUT	HAROLD,M.			177.	530.	962.	6.	160.333
INPUT	WEIS,D.	300.	900.	300.	900.	900.	3.	
OUTPUT	WEIS,D.			300.	900.	1800.	6.	300.000

THREE HIGHEST SINGLE GAME SCORES TO DATE

WEIS,D.	300.
FULLARD,P.	298.
MURPHY,G.	200.

THREE HIGHEST THREE GAME SERIES TO DATE

WEIS,D.	900.
FULLARD,P.	892.
MURPHY,G.	600.

Answer to Problem 3.9 (*Designed for IBM 1620*)
(Floating-point field length is 6 and fixed-point field length is 4)

```
*0604
      DIMENSION IARRAY (702), NGRADE (662), CRIT(8),LL (3)
      EQUIVALENCE (IARRAY (41), NGRADE (1)
1000  DO 1 J = 1, 3
   1  LL (J) = 0
      DO 12 I = 80, 720, 80
      L = I - 79 - LL (1)
      M = I - LL (1)
      READ 100, (IARRAY (J), J = L,M)
      IF (IARRAY (1) - 1400)3,2,3
   3  IF (IARRAY (M)) 12, 14, 12
  12  LL (1) = LL (1)+2
   2  IF (IRRAY (2) - 1300) 42, 5, 42
   5  READ 101: CRIT
      GO TO 42
  14  M = M - 42
      DO 6 J = 2, M, 2
      LL (2) = LL (2)+NGRADE (J)
   6  LL (3) = LL (3)+(45-NGRADE(J-1)/100)* NGRADE(J)
      P = LL(3)
      Q = LL(2)
      L = (P/Q+ 0.005)* 100.
      P = L
      P = P/100.
      DO   30   J = 1, 8
      IF (P-CRIT (J) 30, 41,41
  30  CONTINUE
      LETER = 4500
      GO TO 42
  41  LETER = 4000+(J+1)/2* 1000+20-(J-J/2 * 2)*10
  42  IF (LL (3)) 21, 22, 21
  22  PRINT 102, (IRRAY (J), J = 3,80)
      GO   TO   1000
  21  PRINT   103,(IRRAY (J) J = 1,40),LL(3),LL(2),P,LETER
      GO   TO   1000
 100  FORMAT(80A1)
 101  FORMAT(8F6.2)
 102  FORMAT  (///  78A1/18X4HNAME,21X6HPOINTS,3X5HHOURS,3X5
     1HAVER.,3X5HGRADE)
 103  FORMAT (40A1,I9,I8,F7.2,A2)
      END

             ______   A3 B4 C2 D4
          *$ ______
```

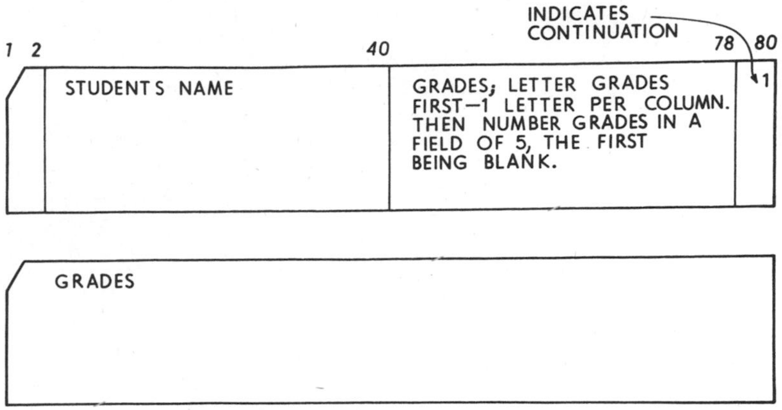

INDICATES CONTINUATION

1 2 40 78 80

STUDENTS NAME

GRADES; LETTER GRADES FIRST—1 LETTER PER COLUMN. THEN NUMBER GRADES IN A FIELD OF 5, THE FIRST BEING BLANK.

1

GRADES

This program is written for the IBM 1620. A useful exercise for the student would be to modify the program for his particular computer.

Answer to **Problem 4.7.**

MAIN PROGRAM	F1	F2	T	I		
Go to BAT) X(1)=1.	1.			1		
RETURN) (1)			1.			
Go to BAT) X(2)=2.				2		Value for X(3) is 4.
RETURN) (2)	2.	3.	2.			
Go to BAT) X(3)=4.				3		
RETURN) (3)						
	4.					

SUBROUTINE BAT	Z		Y	L	M1	
From MAIN)	1.		L/11=1/11=0	1		
(1))					1.	
)	1.		1.			
From MAIN (2))						
Go to TAB)				2		
)			2/11=0			
)					2.	
)	2.		2.		3	
From MAIN (3))	2.		3/11=0.	3		
Go to TAB)					3	
	4.				4	

SUBROUTINE TAB	X				I	T
From BAT (2))	1.				2	1.
)	2.					
)					3	
From BAT (3))	2.				3	2.
)	4.				4	

SUBROUTINE CAB	E	F				X
From TAB (2))	2.					1.
)		3.				
From TAB (3))	4.	3.				2.
)		6.				

BAT

```
M=1
(M−L+1) = 1 − 1+1 = 1>0      }
Y = Y+Z ; 0.+1. = 1.         } (1)
    RETURN TO MAIN           }

M = 1                        }
(M−L+1) = 1 −2+1 = 0         }
CALL TAB                     }
M = M1 − 1 = 3 − 1 = 2       } (2)
(M−L+1) = 2 −2+1 = 1>0       }
Y = Y+Z = 0+2. = 2.          }
RETURN TO MAIN               }
------------------------------
M = 1
(M−L+1) = 1 − 3+1 = −1

CALL TAB
M = 4 − 1 = 3
(M − L+1) = 3 − 3+1 = 1
Y = Y+Z = 0.+4. = 4.
RETURN TO MAIN
```

TAB	*CAB*
T = I − 1 = 2−1 = 1 X=X+T = 1.+1. = 2. CALL CAB I = I+1 = 2+1 = 3 RETURN TO BAT (2)	F = E+X = 2.+1. = 3. RETURN TO TAB (2)
T = 3 − 1 = 2 X = X+T = 2.+2. = 4. CALL CAB I = I+1 = 3+1 = 4 RETURN TO BAT	F = E+X = 4+2. = 6. RETURN TO TAB

Answer to ***Problem 4.10.*** The result depends on the particular FORTRAN compiler being used by the installation. When the above sequence was run on the IBM 1620 computer, the result in location A was 5.; however, when the above sequence was run on the IBM 7040 computer, the result was 2. This is a good point to repeat an earlier statement—"Not all FORTRAN compilers operate in the same way; therefore, it is not possible to make a general statement covering all FORTRAN compilers for all cases.

The above example depends on the way in which the FORTRAN compiler sets up the linkage instructions.

Answer to **Problem 5.2.**

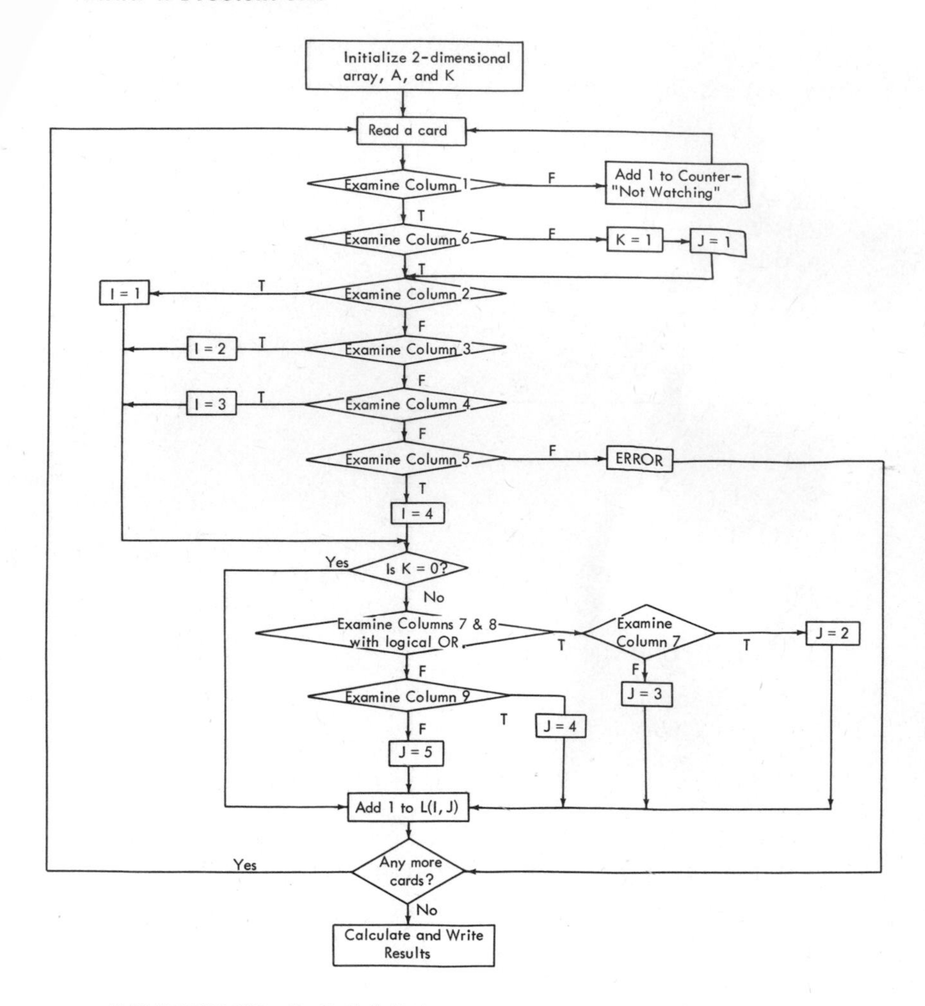


```
      DIMENSION  L1(4,5),L(10)
      L6 = 1
      K = 0
      KE = 0
      NW = 0
      DO  20 I = 1,4
      DO  20 J = 1,5
   20 L1 (I,J) = 0
      READ (5, 101) N1
  101 FORMAT(I3)
  111 READ (5,100) (L (I), I = 1,10)
  100 FORMAT(10L1)
      IF(L(1)) GO TO 25
```

```
      NW = NW+1
      GO TO 111
  25  IF (L(6)) GO TO 35
      K = 1
      J = 1
  35  IF (.NOT. L(2))GO TO 45
      I = 1
      GO TO 725
  45  IF (.NOT. L(3)) GO TO 55
      I = 2
      GO TO 725
  55  IF (.NOT. L(4)) GO TO 65
      I = 3
      GO TO 725
  65  IF (L(5)) GO TO 730
      WRITE (6,109)
 109  FORMAT (5HERROR)
      KE = KE+1
      GO TO 908
 730  I=4
 725  IF (K.EQ.0) GO TO 308
      IF (L(7).OR.L(8)) GO TO 658
      IF (L(9)) GO TO 501
      J=5
      GO TO 308
 501  J = 4
      GO TO 308
 658  IF(L(T)) GO TO 98
      J = 3
      GO TO 308
  98  J = 4
 308  L1(I,J) = L1(I,J)+1
 908  IF (N1-L6) 270,270,111
 270  IW = N1 -KE - NW
      J2 = L1(1,2)+L1(2,3)+L1 (2,4)+L1 (2,5)
      J5 = L1(2,2)+L1(2,3)+L1 (2,4)+L1 (2,5)
      J7 = L1(3,2)+ L1(3,3)+L1 (3,4)+L1 (3,5)
      J9 = L1 (4,2)+L1(4,3)+L1 (4,4)+L1 (4,5)
      J2I = J2+L1(1,1)
      J5I = J5+L1(2,2)
      J7I = J7+L1(3,1)
      J9I = J9+L1(4,1)
      WRITE (6,1000)
1000  FORMAT (22H QUESTIONNAIRE SUMMARY/)
      WRITE (6,1001) N1
1001  FORMAT (32H TOTAL NUMBER OF QUESTIONNAIRES , 45X,I4/)
      WRITE (6,1002) J2I
1002  FORMAT (28APEOPLE WHO WATCHED CHANNEL 2,35X,I4/)
```

```
        WRITE (6,1003) J2
 003    FORMAT (18HWATCHED COMMERCIAL, 25X, I4/)
        WRITE (6,1004)
1004    FORMAT (10X17HCOMMERCIAL RATING)
        WRITE (6,1005), L1(2,2)
        WRITE (6,1006), L1(2,3)
        WRITE (6,1007), L1(2,4)
        WRITE (6,1008), L1(2,5)
1005    FORMAT (17X,1HA, 8X, I4)
1006    FORMAT (17X,1HB, 8X, I4)
1007    FORMAT (17X,1HC, 8X, I4)
1008    FORMAT (17X,IHD, 8X, I4)
```

Continue in this way for channels 5, 7, and 9 to end program. Last card should be END statement.

Try to write the above program more efficiently; it may be necessary to rework the questionnaire format.

Can we use Boolean Algebra to help the efficiency of writing the program?

Answer to ***Problem 5.4.***

FORTRAN II	*FORTRAN IV*
1. A	1. A
2. B and S(1)	2. B and S(1)
3. S(2)	3. C and S(2)
4. S(3)	4. S(3)
5. C	

FORTRAN IV

1. A and C (1) and the most significant part of D.
2. B and C (2) and the least significant part of D.

FORTRAN IV

1. A
2. B and R(1) and the real part of Z1.
3. C and R(2) and the imaginary part of Z1.

Answer to **Problem 5.5**

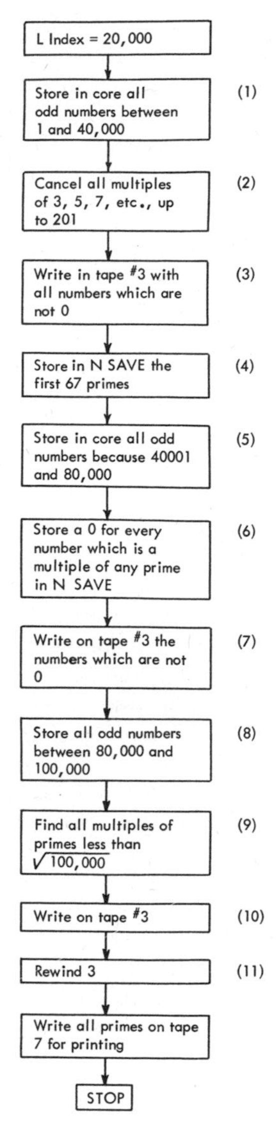

L Index = 20,000
Store in core all odd numbers between 1 and 40,000
(1)
Cancel all multiples of 3, 5, 7, etc., up to 201
(2)
Write in tape #3 with all numbers which are not 0
(3)
Store in N SAVE the first 67 primes
(4)
Store in core all odd numbers because 40001 and 80,000
(5)
Store a 0 for every number which is a multiple of any prime in N SAVE
(6)
Write on tape #3 the numbers which are not 0
(7)
Store all odd numbers between 80,000 and 100,000
(8)
Find all multiples of primes less than √100,000
(9)
Write on tape #3
(10)
Rewind 3
(11)
Write all primes on tape 7 for printing
STOP

DETAILED ANALYSIS

1. Place all odd integers from 3 to 39,999 in the array, NARRAY.
2. Zero out all multiples of the odd integers J from 3 to 201, but not including J. For example, when J = 3, L = 5;

   NARRAY LOCATIONS 1 2 3 4 5 6 7 8 9 1⁄20 11⁄22
   CONTAINS 1 3 5 7 ~~9~~ 11 13 ~~15~~ 17 19 ~~21~~

   K, the index indicating the position of the NARRAY to be zeroed out;

Answer to ***Problem 5.6.*** *Flow Chart—Problem*

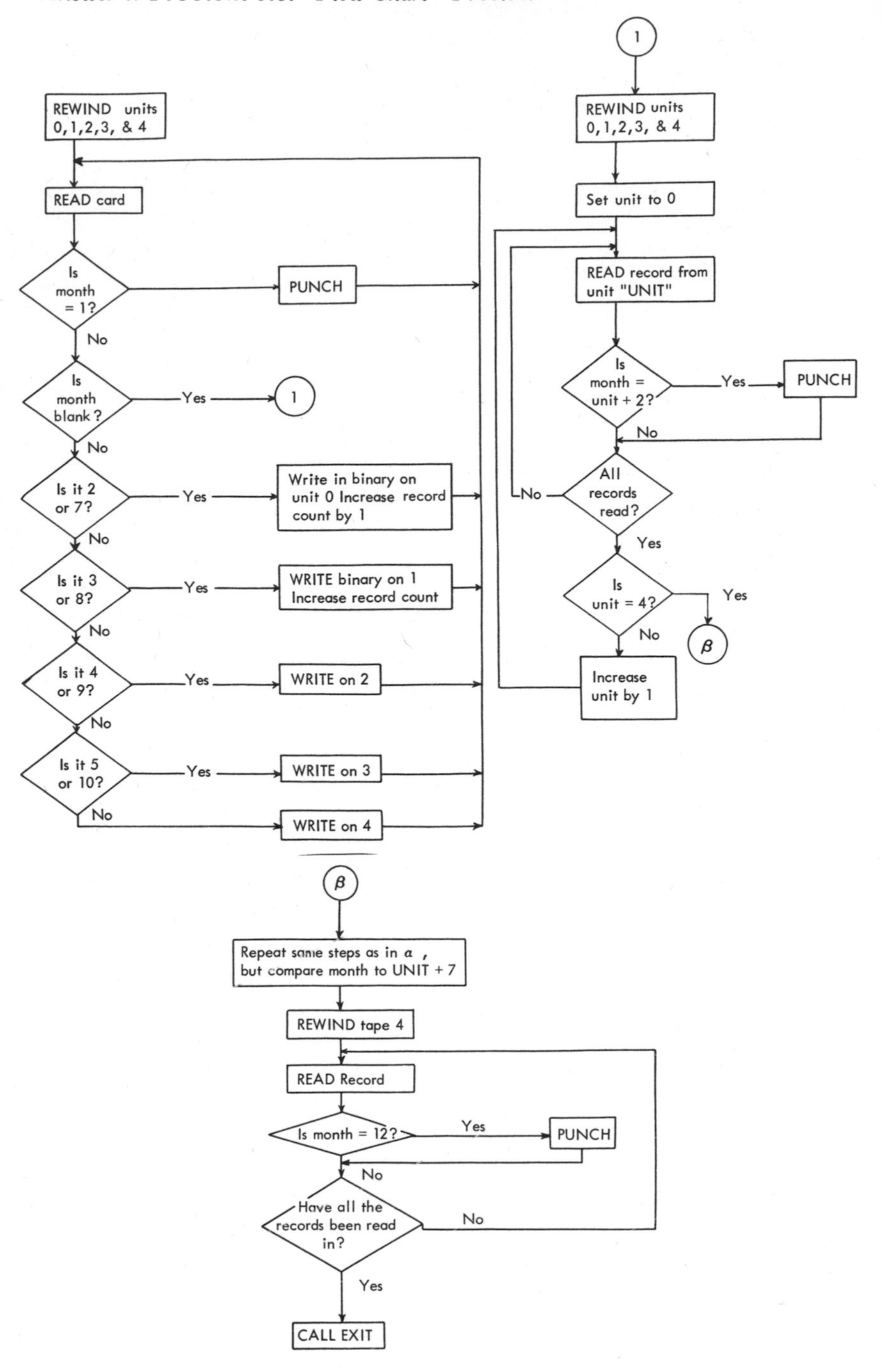

FORTRAN PROGRAM

```
      DIMENSION KOUNT (5), DATA (13)
      INTEGER UNIT
 100  FORMAT(A2,12A6,I2,I4)
      DO 1 J=1, 5
      UNIT = J - 1
      KOUNT (J) = 0
   1  REWIND UNIT
1000  READ  (5,100)  DATA,MONTH,DAYYR
      IF (MONTH.NE.1) IF (MONTH) 3,2,3
      WRITE (7,100) DATA, MONTH
      GO TO 1000
   3  DO 4 J=2, 5
   4  IF (MONTH·EQ.J.OR. MONTH · EQ. J+ 5) GO TO 6
      I = 4
      GO TO 17
   6  I = J - 2
  17  WRITE (I) DATA, MONTH, DAYYR
      KOUNT(I+1) - KOUNT(I+1)+1
      GO TO 1000
   2  DO  9  I = 2,7,5
      DO  7  J = 1,3
      II = J - 1
   7  REWIND II
      II = I + 4
      DO  9  J=I, II
      UNIT = J-2
      M = KOUNT (J-1)
      DO  9  LT = 1, M
   9  READ (UNIT) DATA, MONTH, DAYYR
      IF  (MONTH · EQ. I) WRITE (7,100) DATA, MONTH, DAYYR
      REWIND 4
      M = KOUNT (5)
      DO  13  J = 1, M
      READ (4) DATA, MONTH, DAYYR
  13  IF (MONTH · EQ. 12) WRITE (7,100) DATA, MONTH, DAYYR
      CALL EXIT
      END
```

DESCRIPTION

Seventy-four columns of information are punched per card. Columns 75–80 are devoted to the data, in the form MONTH—DAY—YEAR. It is desired to have the cards sorted on the months in ascending sequence. MONTH is a two-digit field, in fixed point.

The program rewinds units 0,1,2,3 and 4.

Months 2, 3, 4, 5, 6 and 7, 8, 9, 10, 11, 12 are respectively written on units 0,1,2,3, and 4.

At the end, unit 3, for instance, has months 5 and 10; tape 2 has months 4 a etc. Month 1 is punched as soon as it is detected. All the units are rewound.

The first tape through, units 0,1,2,3, and 4 are searched and months 2,3,4,5, and are punched. They are rewound once more, and they are searched now for month 7,8,9,10 and 11. At the end, unit 4 is rewound and search for month 12.

The tapes are written in binary.

KOUNT is an array which keeps track of the number of records written on each unit.

Answer to ***Problem 6.2.***

```
1000  READ  100, N, K
      IF (N·EQ·0) STOP
      SIGMA = N
      IF (K·EQ·0) GO TO 64
      BASE = N + 1
      L = K + 1
      DO  1  J = 1, K
   1  SIGMA = 1./BINOM (L, L−J) * (BASE ** (J+1) − SIGMA)
  64  PRINT 101, SIGMA, N, K
      GO  TO  1000
 100  FORMAT(2I2)
 101  FORMAT(5H SUM = E15.7, 7H FOR N = I2, 3H K = I2)
      END
```

Answer to ***Problem 6.4.*** *Flow Chart*

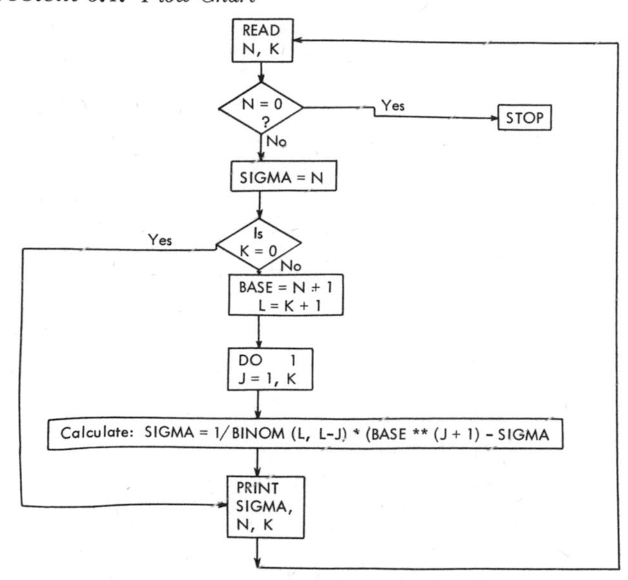


```
C        MACHINE PROGRAM NUMBER TWO
         READ(5,100)A,B,C,X,ERROR
         WRITE(6,100)A,B,C,X,ERROR
```

```
      K=1
      F(X)=2.*ATAN(X)-1./X+1.570796328
      IF(C)12,12,3
    3 IF(F(A)*F(B))4,4,12
    4 IF(ERROR*10.**7-ABS(B))12,12,1
    1 K=K+1
      G(X)=X-F(X)*(B—A)/(F(B)-F(A))
      X=G(X)
      IF(X-A)9,5,5
    5 IF(X-B)6,6,9
    6 IF(F(X)*F(B))7,8,8
    7 A=X
      GO TO 9
    8 B=X
    9 CONTINUE
      IF((B-A)-ERROR)19,19,11
   11 IF(ABS(F(X))-C*ERROR)19,19,1
   12 WRITE(6,103)
      GO TO 18
   19 WRITE(6,104)X
      WRITE(6,102)K
  100 FORMAT(6X4F8.4,E11.4)
  102 FORMAT(6X18)
  103 FORMAT(6X20HIMPROPER INPUT DATA.)
  104 FORMAT(6XF11.8)
   18 STOP
      END
```

Answer to ***Problem 6.5.***

```
      DIMENSION X(20),AB(20)
      READ (5,100)N
      CALL ITER(AB,N,K,X)
      L=2
      CALL FXDERV(A,B,C,N,X,AB,L,FX,DFX,KOR,QQ)
      CALL QUAD(A,B,C)
  100 FORMAT (16)
      END

      SUBROUTINE ITER(AB,N,K,X)
      DIMENSION AB(20),X(20)
      WRITE (6,101)
      NI=N+1
      READ(5,103)(AB(I),I=1,NI)
      J=0
      L=1
      M=N-2
      JI=1
   10 J=J+1
      READ(5,102)C,ERROR,AE,BE,X(J)
      XA=X(J)
```

```
      WRITE(6,104) C,ERROR,AE,BE,XA
      K=1
633   CALL FXDERV(A,B,C,N,Q,AB,L,FAE,DFX,JI,AE)
      GO TO (632,8),K
632   CALL FXDERV(A,B,C,N,Q,AB,L,FBE,DFX,JI,BE)
      IF (SIGN(1.,FAE).EQ.SIGN(1.,FBE)) GO TO 1
      IF (C) 1,2,2
    2 IF (ERROR.LT.(0.1E-06)*(ABS(AE)).OR.ERROR.LT.(0.1E-06)*(ABS(BE)))
      GO TO 1
      GO TO 3
    1 WRITE (6,105)
      GO TO 4
    3 I=0
  803 CALL FXDERV(A,B,C,N,Q,AB,L,Y,Z,J,XA)
      IF (Y) 5,6,5
    5 IF(SIGN(1.,Y).EQ.SIGN(1.,FAE)) GO TO 7
      BE=XA
      GO TO 8
    7 AE=XA
      K=2
      GO TO 633
    8 IF (ABS(BE-AE).LE.ERROR.OR.ABS(Y).LE.C*ERROR) GO TO 6
      W=XA
      XA=XA-Y/Z
      I=I+1
      IF (I-30) 629,629,6
  629 IF (XA.LE.AE.OR.XA.GE.BE) GO TO 9
      GO TO 803
    9 XA=W
      XA=(AE+BE)/2.
      GO TO 803
    6 WRITE (6,106) I,XA
      X(J)=XA
    4 IF (J-M) 10,90,90
   90 RETURN
  105 FORMAT(1H 6X20HIMPROPER INPUT DATA.)
  102 FORMAT (F10.6,E10.2,3F14.8)
  104 FORMAT(1H03HC= F10.6,8H,ERROR= E10.2,4H,A= F14.8,4H,B= F14.8,
     14H,X= F14.8,1H.)
  106 FORMAT(1H 6X23HNUMBER OF ITERATIONS = 14,14H, THE ROOT IS F16.8)
  103 FORMAT(7F10.6)
  101 FORMAT(121H1SOLUTION OF THE POLYNOMIAL P(X)=X**6+5*X**5+2*
     1X**4-13*X**3-11*X**2-8*X+6 USING NEWTONS ITERATION AND
     2SYNTHETIC DIVISION.)
      END

      SUBROUTINE FXDERV (A,B,C,N,Q,AB.LZ,FX,DFX,K,QQ)
      DIMENSION Y(20),Q(20), AB(20)
      M=LZ
```

```
      ) TO (1,2),M
      X=0
      DFX=0
      J=N-1
      P=QQ
      Y(1)=AB(1)
      DO 10 I=1,N
   10 Y(I+1)=Y(I)*P+AB(I+1)
      FX=Y(N+1)
      DO 20 I=1,J
   20 Y(I+1)=Y(I)*P+Y(I+1)
      DFX=Y(N)
      RETURN
    2 IF (N.EQ.3) Q(2)=0
      J=0
      IF (N.EQ.3) GO TO 9
      K=N-2
      GO TO 300
    9 K=2
  300 DO 40 L=2,K
  900 P=Q(L)
      J=J+1
      IF (J-2) 4,5,5
    4 Y(1)=AB(1)
      P=Q(1)
      M=N-J
      DO 50 I=1,M
   50 Y(I+1)=Y(I)*P+AB(I+1)
      IF(N.EQ.3) GO TO 152
      GO TO 900
    5 M=N-J
      DO 60 I=1,M
   60 Y(I+1)=Y(I)*P+Y(I+1)
   40 CONTINUE
  152 A=Y(1)
      B=Y(2)
      C=Y(3)
      RETURN
      END

      SUBROUTINE QUAD (A,B,C)
      IF (A) 10,20,10
   10 B=-B/(2.*A)
      C=C/A
      D=B**2-C
      IF (D) 11,12,13
   11 D=-D
      D=SQRT (D)
      WRITE (6,111) B,D
```

```
      GO TO 90
   12 WRITE (6,110) B
      GO TO 90
   13 D=SQRT (D)
      X1=B+D
      X2=B-D
      WRITE (6,112) X1,X2
      GO TO 90
   20 IF (B) 21,22,21
   21 X=-C/B
      WRITE (6,109) X
      GO TO 90
   22 IF (C) 30,31,30
   30 WRITE (6,108)
      GO TO 90
   31 WRITE (6,107)
   90 RETURN
  107 FORMAT(1H06X17HALL NUMBERS WORK.)
  108 FORMAT (1H06X12HNO SOLUTION.)
  109 FORMAT (1H06X19HONE SINGLE ROOT, X=F16.8,1H.)
  110 FORMAT(1H06X19HONE DOUBLE ROOT, X=F16.8,1H.)
  111 FORMAT(1H06X27HCONJUGATE COMPLEX ROOTS, X=F16.8,6H+OR-I*F16.
     18,1H.)
  112 FORMAT(1H06X27HTWO DISTINCT REAL ROOTS, X=F16.8,2H, F16.8,1H.)
      END
```

```
SOLUTION OF THE POLYNOMIAL P(X)=X**6+5*X**5+2*X**4-13*X**3-11*
X**2-8*X+6 USING NEWTONS ITERATION AND SYNTHETIC DIVISION.

C=   1.000000,ERROR=    0.37E-05,A=    -4.00000000,B=    -3.50000000,X=    -3.69999999.
        NUMBER OF ITERATIONS=   6,  THE ROOT IS   -3.64575130
C=   1.000000,ERROR=    0.25E-05,A=    -3.00000000,B=    -2.00000000,X=    -2.50000000.
        NUMBER OF ITERATIONS=   3,  THE ROOT IS   -2.41421357
C=   1.000000,ERROR=    0.40E-06,A=    -1.00000000,B=     1.00000000,X=    -0.40000000.
        NUMBER OF ITERATIONS=   5,  THE ROOT IS    0.41421356
C=   1.000000,ERROR=    0.18E-05,A=     1.50000000,B=     2.00000000,X=     1.80000000.
        NUMBER OF ITERATIONS=   4,  THE ROOT IS    1.64575131
        CONJUGATE COMPLEX ROOTS, X=    -0.50000001+OR-I*    0.86602538.
```

Answer to **Problem** 7.1 Notice that in the following suggested arrangement,

$$\underbrace{a_{11}}_{1}\ \underbrace{a_{21}\ a_{22}}_{2}\ \underbrace{a_{31}\ a_{32}\ a_{33}}_{3}\ \underbrace{a_{41}\ a_{42}\ a_{43}\ a_{44}}_{4} \ldots$$

the number of elements in group 1 is 1, the number of elements in group 2 is 2, and the number of elements in group i is i. If it would be possible to sum up all the numbers up to the group number I, then L would be this sum plus the number J, which indexes the element within each group.

For the arithmetic progression $1 + 2 + \ldots + m$, the sum is

$$\frac{m(m+1)}{2}$$

In this case, we have the sum of

$$1 + 2 + \ldots + m-1 = \frac{(m-1)m}{2}$$

Therefore,

$$\mathrm{L} = \frac{I(I-1)}{2} + J\,.$$

For example, the element A(3,4) is the element A(9) in the new one-dimensional array; I = 4, J = 3, so

$$\mathrm{L} = \frac{4(4-1)}{2} + 3 = \frac{12}{2} + 3 = 6 + 3 = 9\,.$$

Answer to ***Problem 7.2.*** *Flow Chart*

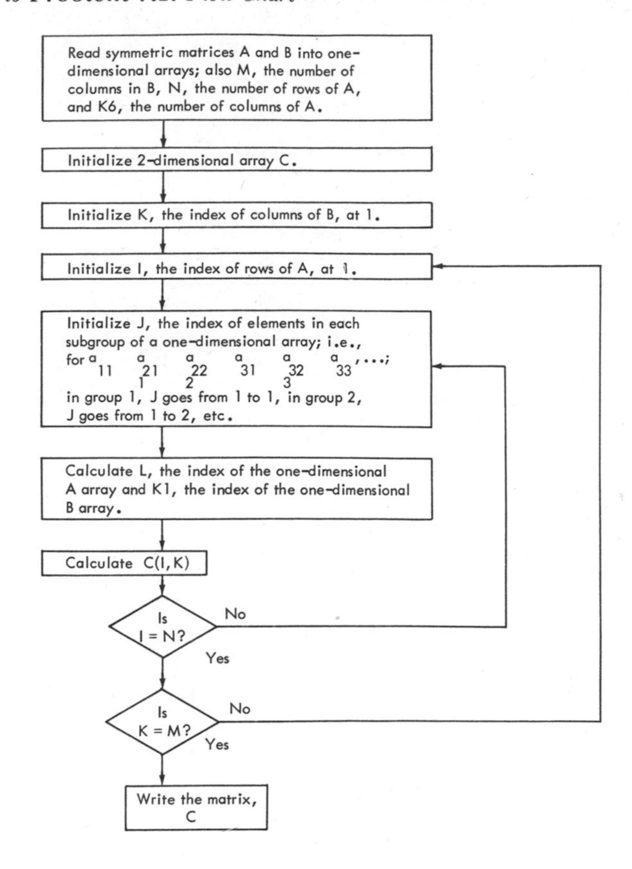
Read symmetric matrices A and B into one-dimensional arrays; also M, the number of columns in B, N, the number of rows of A, and K6, the number of columns of A.
Initialize 2-dimensional array C.
Initialize K, the index of columns of B, at 1.
Initialize I, the index of rows of A, at 1.
Initialize J, the index of elements in each subgroup of a one-dimensional array; i.e., for a11 a21 a22 a31 a32 a33,...; in group 1, J goes from 1 to 1, in group 2, J goes from 1 to 2, etc.
Calculate L, the index of the one-dimensional A array and K1, the index of the one-dimensional B array.
Calculate C(I,K)
Is I = N?
No
Yes
Is K = M?
No
Yes
Write the matrix, C

PROGRAM

```
      DIMENSION A(55),B(55),C(10,10)
 99   READ(5,102) M,N,K6
102   FORMAT(3I2)
      K4 = N*(N-1)/2+N
      K5 = K6*(K6-1)/2 + K6
      READ(5,103) (A(I),I = 1,K4)
      READ(5, 104) (B(I),I = 1,K5)
103   FORMAT (10F6.2)
104   FORMAT (10F6.2)
      DO 10 K = 1,M
      DO 10 I = 1,N
      DO 10 J = K,I
      L = I*(I-1)/2 + J
      K1 = J*(J-1)/2 + K
 10   C(I,K) = C(I,K) + A(L) * B(K1)
      WRITE(6, 101) (C(I,K),I = 1,N),K = 1,N)
```

```
101  FORMAT(10F8.3)
     GO TO 99
     END
```

Answer to **Problem 7.5.** *Flow Chart*

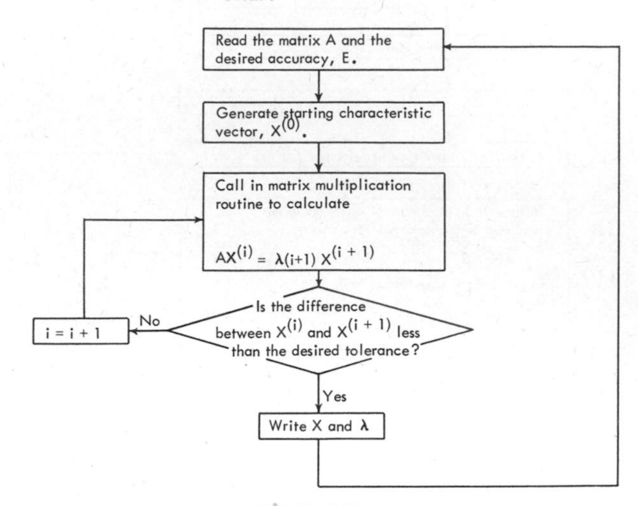

PROGRAM

```
     DIMENSION A(10, 10),X(10)
99   READ(5,27) E,N,(A(I,J),I = 1,N),J = 1,N)
27   FORMAT(F6.4,I3/(10F6.2))
     DO 10 I = 1,N
10   X(I) = 0.
     X(N) = 1.
     DO 40 J = 1,100
     CALL MATMPY(A,X,C,N,N,1)
     DO 20 I = 1,N
20   C(I) = C(I)/C(N)
     DO 60 I = 1,N
60   IF(ABS(C(I)-X(I)).LE.E) GO TO 50
     DO 40 K = 1,N
40   X(K) = C(K)
50   CHAR = C(N)
     WRITE(6,65)
65   FORMAT(20HCHARACTERISTIC VALUE )
     WRITE(6,66) CHAR
66   FORMAT(5XE14.8)
     WRITE(6,67)
67   FORMAT(20HCHARACTERISTIC VECTOR)
     WRITE(6,68)(C(I),I = 1,N)
68   FORMAT(/5XE14.8)
     GO TO 99
     END
```